CONTENTS

About the Authors vii

Preface ix

Part I: Strategies for the AP® Test 1

Preparing for the AP® Calculus Examination 3
What's in This Book 3
What's in the *Calculus for AP®: A Complete Course* Textbook That Will Help You Prepare 4
How to Get the Most Out of Your Calculus Class 4
Setting Up a Review Schedule 5
AP® Information Before the Examination 6

Taking the AP® Calculus Examination 9
Exam Format 9
General AP® Test-Taking Strategies 10
Strategies for the Multiple-Choice Section 10
Strategies for the Free-Response Section 12

AB Diagnostic Test 15

BC Diagnostic Test 43

Part II: A Review of AP® Calculus 69

Chapter 1: Limits and Their Properties 71
Finding and Estimating a Limit 71
Strategies for Solving a Limit Problem 72
Infinite Limits Versus Limits at Infinity (Unbounded Behavior) 73
Continuity 75
Past AP® Free-Response Problems Covered by This Chapter 76
Multiple-Choice Questions 77
Free-Response Question 81
Answers 81

Chapter 2: Differentiation 85
The Derivative 85
Definition of the Derivative of a Function 86
Notations for Derivatives 87
Connection Between Differentiability and Continuity 88
Derivatives: Applications/Rules 89
Differentiation of a Logarithmic Function 92
Logarithmic Differentiation 93
Past AP® Free-Response Problems Covered by This Chapter 94

Multiple-Choice Questions 94
Free-Response Question 98
Answers 98

Chapter 3: Applications of Derivatives 104
Extrema on an Interval 105
Key Theorems 105
Extremum 106
Concavity of a Graph 107
Characteristics of f, f', f'' and Their Relationships 108
Analysis of Curves 109
Applications of Derivatives 111
Indeterminate Forms and L'Hôpital's Rule 112
Past AP® Free-Response Problems Covered by This Chapter 114
Multiple-Choice Questions 114
Free-Response Question 119
Answers 120

Chapter 4: Integration 126
Definition of an Antiderivative 126
Riemann Sums 128
The Trapezoidal Rule 131
Major Theorems of Calculus 132
Mean Value Theorem for Integrals 133
The Second Fundamental Theorem of Calculus 134
Techniques of Integration 135
Change of Variables 136
The General Power Rule for Integration 137
Past AP® Free-Response Problems Covered by This Chapter 139
Multiple-Choice Questions 139
Free-Response Question 143
Answers 143

Chapter 5: Differential Equations 147
Slope Fields 147
Euler's Method 150
Separation of Variables 152
Differential Equations: Growth and Decay 152
Logistic Differential Equations 153
Past AP® Free-Response Problems Covered by This Chapter 155
Multiple-Choice Questions 156
Free-Response Question 161
Answers 161

Chapter 6: Applications of Integration 166
Area of a Region Between Two Curves 167
Integration as an Accumulation Process 169
Volume of a Solid of Revolution—The Disk Method 170
Solids with Known Cross Sections 172
Past AP® Free-Response Problems Covered by This Chapter 174
Multiple-Choice Questions 175
Free-Response Question 180
Answers 181

FAST TRACK TO A 5

Preparing for the AP®
Calculus AB and
Calculus BC Examinations

To Accompany
Calculus for AP®: A Complete Course
1st Edition
by James Stewart and Stephen Kokoska

Lucy Mavrokordatos
Hillcrest High School, Dallas, Texas

Sharon Cade
Mathematics Consultant

Rhea Caldwell
Mathematics Consultant

Tracey Etheredge
Barack Obama Male Leadership Academy, Dallas, Texas

Guy Mauldin
Science Hill High School, Johnson City, Tennessee

Nancy Stephenson
Mathematics Consultant

Jeff Lucia
Providence Day School, Charlotte, North Carolina

CENGAGE

Australia · Brazil · Mexico · Singapore · United Kingdom · United States

CENGAGE

ISBN: 978-1-337-28282-6

Cengage Learning
20 Channel Center Street
Boston, MA 02210
USA

Cengage Learning is a leading provider of customized learning solutions with office locations around the globe, including Singapore, the United Kingdom, Australia, Mexico, Brazil, and Japan. Locate your local office at: **www.cengage.com/global**.

Cengage Learning products are represented in Canada by Nelson Education, Ltd.

To learn more about Cengage Learning Solutions, visit **www.cengage.com**.

Printed in the United States of America
Print Number: 01 Print Year: 2019

Chapter 7: Advanced Integration Techniques 186
Basic Integration Rules, Techniques 186
Integration by Parts 188
Partial Fractions 189
Improper Integrals 191
Past AP® Free-Response Problems Covered by This Chapter 192
Multiple-Choice Questions 193
Free-Response Question 196
Answers 197

Chapter 8: Infinite Series 202
Sequences 202
Series and Convergence 204
Series 204
Tests for Convergence 206
Taylor Polynomials and Approximations 211
Lagrange Error Bound for Taylor Polynomials 212
Power Series 212
Power Series of Elementary Functions 214
Past AP® Free-Response Problems Covered by This Chapter 214
Multiple-Choice Questions 215
Free-Response Question 219
Answers 219

Chapter 9: Parametric Equations, Vectors, and Polar Coordinates 225
Parametric Equations 225
Polar Equations 228
Vector-Valued Functions 232
Past AP® Free-Response Problems Covered by This Chapter 235
Multiple-Choice Questions 236
Free-Response Question 239
Answers 240

Part III: Practice Tests 245
AB Practice Test 1 247
Answers to AB Practice Test 1 258
AB Practice Test 2 276
Answers to AB Practice Test 2 288
BC Practice Test 1 308
Answers to BC Practice Test 1 318
BC Practice Test 2 337
Answers to BC Practice Test 2 350

ABOUT THE AUTHORS

LUCY MAVROKORDATOS has been teaching AP® Calculus and Pre-AP® Pre-Calculus since 1984 and has been teaching at Hillcrest High School in Dallas ISD for the last 13 years. She has taught courses for College Algebra, Pre-Calculus, and Linear Algebra at Richland Community College during the past 8 years. In 2008, she received a teaching fellowship for the Texas Instruments Foundation Innovation in STEM (Science, Technology, Engineering and Mathematics). In 2007, she was awarded the Texas EXES Outstanding Teacher Award, The Lillian B. Rhodes Teaching Award, and Sam's Club Teacher of the Year. In 2006, she won the Outstanding Teaching Award for Service above Self from the Rotary Club of Dallas. In 2005, she was named the Hillcrest High School Teacher of the Year.

SHARON CADE has taught mathematics and has been a department chair in both public and independent schools since 1978. She is currently a Mathematics Consultant in the Pacific Northwest. She began as an AP® reader in 1995 and was also a table leader and question team member. Sharon led day- and week-long institutes beginning in 1999 as an AP® Consultant. In addition, she read grant proposals for the Department of Education in 2000, 2003, and 2012. Sharon was honored as the Oregon State Winner of the Presidential Award for Excellence in Science and Mathematics Teaching. She also received the GTE GIFT (Growth Initiative for Teachers) Award as well as an outstanding teacher designation from the Tandy Technology Scholars, and was named the Oregon Multicultural Education Association Teacher of the Year. In 2008–2009 she was on the Beaverton (Oregon) School District Talented and Gifted Program Project Team. Sharon is now on the board of directors of the Peninsula Senior Activity Center. She continues as a member of the Gonzaga University Board of Regents (since 1999) and is currently Vice-Chair. She is formerly a member of the board of directors of the Boys and Girls Club of Long Beach, Washington.

RHEA CALDWELL taught mathematics in independent schools beginning in 1978 and was chairman of the Mathematics Department of Providence Day School in Charlotte, North Carolina, from 1990. She was recognized in 2002 as the North Carolina Teacher of the Year for Independent Schools by the North Carolina Council of Teachers of Mathematics. She has taught calculus for over 20 years and began as an AP® Calculus reader in 2003. She coached math contest teams as another way to share her passion for mathematics. She retired from full-time teaching in 2014.

TRACEY ETHEREDGE has been teaching mathematics for over 21 years in the Dallas Independent School District and served as an AP® Math Lead Teacher in the DISD Advanced Placement® department for 9 years. She has been teaching AP® Calculus AB for 13 years and AP Calculus BC for 9 years and is currently teaching mathematics at the Barack Obama Male Leadership Academy in Dallas, Texas. She has a BS in mathematics from Jackson State University and an MA in Educational Leadership from Lamar University. She has been a Pre-AP® and AP® math trainer for the National Math and Science Initiative—former AP® Strategies Division. She has also served as a National Math and Science Initiative mentor for AP® Calculus teachers. She has also been a College Board AP® Calculus Reader for the AP® Calculus AB Exam since 2012.

GUY MAULDIN is in his fifty-eighth year of teaching mathematics. The first 17 years were at the college level and then he discovered that high school students were so much more fun. He has graded AP® calculus exams for 24 years while serving in various leadership roles. He has served as a consultant for the College Board since 1986 and he has written materials for various projects. He has received the Presidential Award for Excellence in Mathematics Teaching, the Tandy Champion of the Classroom recognition, Sigma Xi teacher of the year, Siemen's Teaching Award, and TEA Distinguished Classroom Teacher.

NANCY STEPHENSON recently retired from teaching AP® Calculus AB and BC at St. Thomas High School in Houston, Texas. Prior to teaching at St. Thomas, she taught in public school in the Houston area for 40 years. She holds a BS in education from the University of Arkansas at Monticello and an MS in mathematics from the University of Louisiana at Monroe. She is a College Board consultant who has presented at numerous College Board one-day and two-day conferences and has led AP® summer institutes for Rice University, Texas A&M University, The University of Texas at San Antonio, Southern Methodist University, the National Math and Science Initiative, and Fairfax County Public Schools in Fairfax, Virginia. She has been a Reader, Table Leader, and Question Team Member for the AP® Calculus exam for many years. She is also a former member of the AP® Calculus Development Committee. She received the Siemens Award for outstanding teaching of an AP® course in 2001.

JEFF LUCIA has taught mathematics in independent schools since 1978, and for over 30 years has been at Providence Day School in Charlotte, North Carolina. Since 1989, he has worked for the College Board as a reader and table leader for the examination grading in AP® Calculus and AP® Statistics. In 1992, he was a founding member of the board of directors for the North Carolina Association of Advanced Placement® Mathematics Teachers (NCA2PMT), where he continues to serve as membership chairman. He was recognized in 2004 by the North Carolina Council of Teachers of Mathematics as North Carolina Teacher of the Year for Independent Schools.

PREFACE

"Life is good for only two things, discovering mathematics and teaching mathematics."
—Siméon Poisson

Calculus requires you to know past mathematics, to explore new mathematical ideas, and to experiment with techniques. You must glean all of the information present and re-work the visible knowledge in order to find the road map to a deeper mathematical understanding.

We hope that this text will help you find your own personal road map to discovery; that you will reflect on what you've learned in class, combine it with what you will review in this text, and formulate your own concept of mathematics. Teaching and discovering mathematics has been fun all of our lives and we wish for you that joy.

Over the years we have drawn enormous inspiration from our students, so we wish to dedicate this book to all students of mathematics past, present, and future, that they may see the beauty of the subject and use it to better the world.

Lucy Mavrokordatos

Sharon Cade

Rhea Caldwell

Tracey Etheredge

Guy Mauldin

Nancy Stephenson

Jeff Lucia

Part I

Strategies for the AP® Test

PREPARING FOR THE AP® CALCULUS EXAMINATION

Advanced Placement® (AP®) can be exhilarating. Whether you are taking an AP® course at your school or you are working on the AP® curriculum independently, the stage is set for a great intellectual experience.

But sometime in the spring, when the examination begins to loom on a very real horizon, AP® can seem intimidating. It is a normal feeling to be nervous about the test; you are in good company.

The best way to deal with an AP® examination is to master it, not let it master you. You should think of this examination as a way to show off how much calculus you know. Attitude *does* help. But, no matter what type of math student you are, there is still a lot you can do to prepare for the exam. Solid preparation in class combined with the use of this book, which is designed to put you on a fast track of review, is the component to a good performance on the AP® exam. Focused review and practice time will help you master the examination so that you can walk in with confidence and earn a great score.

WHAT'S IN THIS BOOK

This book is keyed to *Calculus for AP®: A Complete Course*, but because it follows the new AP® Calculus AB and BC Curriculum Framework, it is compatible with all textbooks. It is divided into three parts.

Part I offers suggestions for getting yourself ready; at the end of Part I you will find two diagnostic tests, one for AB Calculus and another for BC Calculus. These tests have problems representative of the AP® Calculus examination. Answers to all the problems are provided at the end of the test, with references to the pages in *Calculus for AP®: A Complete Course* where a discussion of the topic can be found.

Part II is made up of nine chapters that cover the topics in the AP® Calculus AB and BC Curriculum Framework. These chapters are not a substitute for your textbook and class discussion; they simply review the AP® Calculus course. At the end of each chapter, you will find 15 multiple-choice questions and 1 free-response question based on the material in that chapter. Again, you will find page references at the end of each answer directing you to the discussion on that particular point in *Calculus for AP®: A Complete Course.*

AP® is a trademark registered by the College Board, which is not affiliated with, and does not endorse, this product.

Part III has four complete AP® Calculus practice examinations: two for AB Calculus and two for BC Calculus. At the end of each test, you will find the answers, explanations, and page references to *Calculus for AP®: A Complete Course* for the multiple-choice and the free-response questions.

WHAT'S IN THE *CALCULUS FOR AP®: A COMPLETE COURSE* TEXTBOOK THAT WILL HELP YOU PREPARE

As you work through the textbook, there are some things that you should do to get the most out of the text.

- As you read the sections,
  - read the Remarks,
  - do the Exploration problems,
  - read the notes on Technology, and
  - take time to read the examples, especially the ones with multiple parts that try to represent various ways to look at similar problems and notice how different their solution methods might be.
- After finishing a section or the chapter, work through
  - the True or False exercises to help you discern small differences in conceptual understanding,
  - the Think about It problems and the Writing about Concepts exercises to help you improve your conceptual understanding, and your ability to explain your thinking,
  - the How Do You See It problems to process the information—to help you compare methods and/or look at concepts,
  - the Review Exercises and the Problem-Solving sections, and
  - the AP® Review Questions to practice your test-taking skills and understanding of the material you just studied.

In calculus, reading the text is an essential part of the learning curve and will, in the end, save you time in understanding and mastering the material. There is more to the study of calculus than just being able to do some mathematics; you must understand the concepts and how they fit together. You will also learn to broaden your thinking as well as think logically if you allow yourself to try to see mathematics in a new way, not just as a set of algorithms.

HOW TO GET THE MOST OUT OF YOUR CALCULUS CLASS

- Know your advanced algebra skills:
  - Linear equations
  - Quadratics (factoring)
  - Functions (parent, transformations, piecewise, odd, even, domain, range)
  - Polynomials (zeros, end behavior)
  - Exponential and logarithmic curves
  - Rational and radical equations
  - Direct, inverse relations
  - Conics (for BC)

- Know your trigonometry:
  - Unit circle (0, 30, 45, 60, and 90 degrees and equivalent radian measures)
  - Symmetry around the unit circle
  - Basic identities
- Know basic sequences and series and when to apply which sequence or series formula.
- Have some knowledge of vectors (for BC).
- Know your calculator:
  - Four functions you should be able to do for the AP® test:
    - Plot the graph of a function in an appropriate window.
    - Find the zeros of a function (solving the equations numerically).
    - Calculate the derivative of a function numerically.
    - Calculate the definite integral numerically.
  - Know how to calculate the value of a function at a specific x: on the graph, 2nd calc, value; on the home screen, $y1$(value).
  - Graph your functions and analyze them as a comparison to the algebra you do. Note: You will not receive credit for a student-drawn graph. This step is to help you develop understanding of the function.

Remember that you have to analyze what the calculator gives you (e.g., how to know when a calculator has a "hole": try $1/(x-2)$ and look for the value at $x = 2$).

Read the text; take risks; ask questions; and look for the connections between the algebraic, numeric, and graphical approaches to similar problems. As much as possible, graph every problem to enhance your understanding of the concepts you are working with.

SETTING UP A REVIEW SCHEDULE

The AP® Calculus courses are concerned with developing a student's understanding of the concepts while providing experiences with its methods and applications. Both the AB and BC courses require a depth of understanding. If you have been doing your homework steadily and keeping up with the course work, you are in good shape. Organize your notes, homework, and handouts from class by topic. For example, have a set of notes on pre-calculus topics (no longer tested on the AP® exam but essential to your success with calculus), limits, derivative rules and applications, integral rules and applications, series and sequences techniques and methods, and major theorems. If you can summarize the main information on a few pages, by topic, you will find reviewing much easier. Refer to these materials and this study guide as you begin to prepare for the exam. Use your textbook to get more detail as needed.

As you begin to prepare, read Part I of this book. You will be much more comfortable going into the test if you understand how the test questions are designed and how best to approach them. Then take the diagnostic test and see where you are right now.

Take out a calendar and set up a schedule for yourself. If you begin studying early, you can chip away at the review chapters in Part II. You'll be surprised at how much material you can cover by studying an hour a day (a few days per week) for a month or so before the test. Analyze the sections of the diagnostic test; if you missed a number of questions in one particular area, allow more time for the chapter covering that area of the course. The practice tests in Part III give you more experience with different kinds of multiple-choice questions and a wide range of free-response questions.

If time is short, at least scan the review chapters and work on the multiple-choice and free-response questions at the end of each review. This will give you an idea of your understanding of that topic. Then take the tests in Part III. However, it will do you no good to take the tests if you don't understand the material. If you read something that is beyond your understanding, go back to the book and reread that section. If you need further help, seek out your teacher or a friend.

If you let time get too short, review your notes and the chapters in this text and practice as many multiple-choice and free-response questions as you can. The more problems you attempt, the better you will get at taking this kind of test. The multiple-choice questions often require deeper thinking than may at first be apparent. The free-response questions require a mastery of numerical, algebraic, and graphical approaches to problem solving, as well as an ability to verbally describe the meaning of the question/solution. You must actively do problems to gain understanding and excel in your performance. Athletes don't perform well just by reading books about their sport or by watching others. They must practice. So you, too, just like an athlete, must practice, practice, and practice if you want to do your best!

AP® INFORMATION BEFORE THE EXAMINATION

IN FEBRUARY

- Make sure that you are *registered* to take the test. Some schools take care of the paperwork and handle the fees for their AP® students, but check with your teacher or the AP® coordinator to make sure that you are registered. This is especially important if you have a documented disability and need test accommodations. If you are studying AP® independently, or if your school does not have an AP® coordinator, call AP® Services at the College Board at (609) 771-7300 or (888) 225-5427 (toll-free in the United States and Canada). You can also email apexams@info.collegeboard.org for the name of the local AP® coordinator, who will help you through the registration process.
- Check on the eligibility of your **calculator**. Go online to http://www.collegeboard.com/student/testing/ap/calculus_ab/calc.html?calcab#list early enough so that if you need a different calculator, you will have time to get one and to become familiar with it.

BY MID-MARCH

- Begin your review process; set a schedule for yourself that you can follow. You should complete the reading of this book, the example problems, and practice tests a week before the test.

WEEK BEFORE

- **Review.** Read through your notes and scan the material in this book, especially the AP® tips. Concentrate on the broad outlines of the course, not the small details. Restudy any concept that you feel needs more attention.
- Begin to gather your materials together for the test.

NIGHT BEFORE

- Put all of your **materials** in one place.
- Relax and get a good night's **rest** (this alone could improve your score because you will be able to think more clearly throughout the test).

THINGS TO HAVE ON TEST DAY

- **Approved graphing calculator** with fresh batteries (you may have a second calculator as a backup, but it must also be a graphing calculator). The calculator must not have a typewriter-style (QWERTY) keyboard, nor can it be a non-graphing scientific calculator or on your phone (http://www.collegeboard.com/student/testing/ap/calculus_ab/calc.html?calcab#list). Calculator memories are *not* cleared for the exam.

AP® Tip

Be sure your calculator is set in **radian mode** (pi radians, or approximately three radians, is half the circle; 3 degrees is an angle just barely above the x-axis).

- #2 pencils (at least two) with good erasers.
- A watch (to monitor your pace, but turn off the alarm if it has one).
- Social Security number (if you choose to include it on the forms).
- The College Board school code.
- Photo identification and the admissions ticket.
- Comfortable clothes and a sweatshirt or sweater in case the room is cold.

Schools may have your admissions ticket at the testing site; a photo identification may not be needed at your own school, but check with your AP® coordinator prior to test day.

THINGS PROHIBITED ON TEST DAY

- **Electronic equipment** such as cell phones, smartphones, smartwatches, laptops, tablets, or computers. See the full list of prohibited items on the College Board's website: https://professionals.collegeboard.org/testing/ap/test-day/bring.

On the day of the examination, it is wise to eat a good breakfast. Studies show that students who eat a hot breakfast before testing get higher scores. Breakfast can give you the energy you need to power you through the test and more. You will spend some time waiting while everyone is seated in the right room for the right test. That's before the test has even begun. With a short break between Section I and Section II, the AP® Calculus exam can last almost 4 hours.

Now go get a 5!

TAKING THE AP®
CALCULUS EXAMINATION

To do well on the AP® Calculus examination, following points are important:

- A student should understand and be able to work with the connections between the graphical, numerical, analytical, and verbal representations of functions.
- A student should be able to use derivatives to solve a variety of problems and understand the meaning of a derivative in terms of rate of change and local linearity.
- A student should use integrals to solve a variety of problems and should understand the meaning of a definite integral in terms of the limit of Riemann sums as well as the net accumulation of change.
- A student also needs to:
    - understand both parts of the Fundamental Theorem of Calculus.
    - communicate mathematics in written sentences.
    - appropriately model a physical situation.
    - use technology correctly and efficiently.
    - determine the reasonableness of solutions and understand them in terms of units of measurement, size, and so on.

It is important to realize that a student who is in AP® Calculus is expected to have studied *all* of the prerequisite material. A student should have a mastery of functions and their properties and an understanding of algebra, graphs, and the language of domain, range, symmetry, periodicity, and so on. The student should also understand trigonometry and have a mastery of the basic values in the unit circle and the basic trigonometric identities.

EXAM FORMAT

The AP® Calculus examination consists of two major sections and each of those has two parts. All sections test proficiency on a variety of topics.

MULTIPLE CHOICE: Section I has two sets of multiple-choice questions. Part A has 30 questions with an allotted time of 60 minutes and does not allow the use of a calculator. Part B has 15 questions and has 45 minutes allotted to it; this set contains some questions for which a graphing calculator would be needed to answer the questions. The multiple-choice section score is based on the number of questions answered correctly; no points will be deducted for incorrect answers and no points are awarded for unanswered questions. Therefore, you should answer all questions even if you have to guess.

AP® is a trademark registered by the College Board, which is not affiliated with, and does not endorse, this product.

FREE RESPONSE: Section II has six free-response questions, and it is broken into two portions. Part A consists of two problems; some parts of some problems may require a graphing calculator and you will be allowed 30 minutes. Part B has four problems and you will be allowed 60 minutes; a calculator is not permitted during this time. Although you may continue working on Part A problems during this 60-minute session, you may no longer use a calculator. Thus, when working on Part A, you must be sure to answer the questions requiring a calculator during that first 30-minute period.

The grade for the examination is equally weighted between the multiple-choice and free-response sections of the exam. You can possibly earn a 5 on the exam even if you miss an entire free-response question. Students taking the BC exam will also receive an AB sub-score grade.

The free-response questions and solutions are published annually after the AP® Reading is completed and can be found for Calculus AB at https://apstudent.collegeboard.org/apcourse/ap-calculus-ab/exam-practice and for Calculus BC at https://apstudent.collegeboard.org/apcourse/ap-calculus-bc/exam-practice.

GENERAL AP® TEST-TAKING STRATEGIES

Strategize the test question. Begin somewhere. Ask "What do I need?" and then "How do I get there?" Start with a clear definition; for example, on the 2003 AB 6 question about continuity, you need to have a clear definition of continuity to answer the question fully.

- Know what the required tools on your calculator are and know how to access and use them:
  - Plot the graph of a function within a viewing window.
  - Find the zeros of a function (numerically solve equations).
  - Numerically calculate the derivative of a function.
  - Numerically calculate the value of a definite integral.
- Know the relationships between f, f', and f''.
- Know your derivative and integral rules.
- Underline key components of the questions.
- Reread the question after you have answered it to be sure that you answered the question asked, that you haven't gone too far, and that you haven't contradicted yourself.
- Treat units carefully.
- Set the calculator to THREE decimal places and properly use the store key for intermediate steps (if you round too soon, your final answer will not be correct to the requisite three decimal places). If you choose to write your answer with more than three decimal places, only the first three places are read as your answer.

STRATEGIES FOR THE MULTIPLE-CHOICE SECTION

READ THE QUESTION CAREFULLY: Pressured for time, many students make the mistake of reading the questions too quickly or merely skimming them. By reading a question carefully, you may already have some idea about the correct answer. Careful reading is especially important in EXCEPT questions. After you solve the problem and have a solution, reread the question to be sure the answer you solved for actually answers the question. For example, you may have solved for where the maximum occurred (the x-value) but the question actually asks for the maximum value of f (the y-value), and thus you need one more step to complete the problem.

ELIMINATE ANY ANSWER YOU KNOW IS WRONG: You can write on the multiple-choice questions in the test book. As you read through the responses, draw a line through any answer you know is wrong. Do as much scratch work as is necessary in the exam book, but be sure to mark your solution choice on the answer sheet in the corresponding oval. In most math questions, it is generally better to NOT read through the possible answers until you have found what you think is the solution. There are times where you may have to look at the choices so that you have an idea of how to start or where you are going but generally they can lead you into incorrect assumptions.

READ ALL OF THE POSSIBLE ANSWERS, THEN CHOOSE THE MOST ACCURATE RESPONSE: AP® examinations are written to test your precise knowledge of a subject. Some of the responses may be partially correct, but there will only be one response that is completely true.

BE CAREFUL OF ABSOLUTE RESPONSES: These answers often include the words *always* or *never.* They could be correct but you should try to think of counterexamples to disprove them.

SKIP TOUGH QUESTIONS: Skip them in the first go-through but be sure that you mark them in the margin so that you can come back to them later if you possibly can. *Make sure you skip those questions on your answer sheet, too.*

THERE IS NO PENALTY FOR GUESSING: Thus, at the end, try to narrow down your choices by eliminating answers which you figure are not correct and make an educated guess. It is to your advantage to answer every question.

ADDITIONAL THOUGHTS

- The exact numerical answer may not be among the choices given. You will have to choose the solution that best approximates the exact numerical value.
- The domain of a function f is assumed to be the set of all real numbers x, where $f(x)$ is a real number, unless specified otherwise.
- f^{-1} or the prefix *arc-* indicates the inverse of a trigonometric function (e.g., $\cos^{-1} x = \arccos x$).

TYPES OF MULTIPLE-CHOICE QUESTIONS

All kinds of topics will be covered in the multiple-choice section; your skills and vocabulary will be tested as well as your ability to do multistep problem solving. Terms like *average value*, *the definition of continuity*, *extremum* (*relative and absolute*), *the definition of a derivative in its two forms*, *differential equations*, *graphical interpretations*, and *slope fields* are just a sampling of terms that identify the kinds of problems you will see. Read through this text and do the practice problems to familiarize yourself with the way the questions are framed.

Multiple-choice questions will be formatted in two basic ways. You will find classic questions where there are just four choices for solutions. This is the most common type of problem; it requires you to read the question and select the most correct answer. Strategies for solving this type of problem include

- reading the question carefully,
- solving the problem and then interpreting your solution to correctly fit the question,
- eliminating known wrong answers, and
- on occasion, testing each solution to see which one is correct.

There will also be problems that could be called list and group where you may be asked "Which of the following is true about *g*?" They will give choices such as I, II, and III and the multiple-choice answers might appear as

(A) I only
(B) II only
(C) I and II only
(D) I, II, and III

This kind of problem requires a clear understanding of some concept or definition. To approach this kind of question,

- eliminate known wrong answers,
- recall necessary theorems or definitions to help you interpret the question, and
- reread the problem to check your solution's accuracy.

STRATEGIES FOR THE FREE-RESPONSE SECTION

- ALL work needs to be shown IN the test booklet.
- Scan all of the questions in the section you are working in. First solve the problems that you think you can do easily. You can mark and come back to the harder ones later. Most questions have multiple entry points. If you cannot answer Part A, proceed to the next part, because Part A is not always the easiest part.
- Show all of your work. Partial credit will be awarded for problems if the correct work is shown even if the answer is not present or is incorrect. Although not required, it can be helpful to the reader if you circle your final answer.
- Cross out incorrect answers with an "X" rather than spending time erasing. Crossed-out or erased work will not be graded. However, don't cross out or erase work unless you have replaced it. Let the reader see what you tried; it may be worth some points.
- Be clear, neat, and organized in your work. If a reader cannot clearly understand your work, you may not receive full credit.
- Some free-response questions have several parts, such as a, b, c, and d. Attempt to solve each part. Even if your answer to "a" is incorrect, you still may be awarded points for the remaining parts of the question if the work is correct for those parts. Remember, the answers may not depend on an earlier response and that is why it is important to try each part. If you work with your incorrect answer (as long as it is reasonably derived) from a previous part, the reader will read with you in a later part (i.e., the reader will check your numerical answer on the basis of your incorrect input).

- Units are important in your answer. Keeping track of your units throughout calculations and performing unit cancellations, where possible, will help guide you to your answer. Points will be deducted for missing or incorrect units in the answer if the question asks that units be given.
- Don't just write equations or numbers in hopes of finding the correct answer. Extraneous or incorrect information could lead to a lower score. Don't make up work that is trivial, but do try the problem and the reader will read with you.
- You do not need to work the questions in order, but be sure the answer is entered in the correct section.
- When you use a table or a graph from one section (part a) in another part of the problem (part c, for example) be sure to refer to it in some way—state your use of it or draw an arrow back to it. If you inadvertently put a response in the wrong part of the problem, again, note it clearly to the reader.
- Show all your work.
  - Clearly label any functions [if the problem uses $g(x)$, don't call it $f(x)$]. If $g(x)$ = some expression, use $g(x)$ in any problem in lieu of writing the expression. This helps to avoid a copy error.
  - Label your sign charts accurately, for example, f' or f'', for the derivative tests. However, these by themselves do not count as a justification. No credit is given for sign charts, but they can help develop your analysis and subsequent answer to the question. Do not use the pronoun "it" in your descriptions or solutions; specify which function or derivative or variable that you are using or the part of the question you are answering.
  - Label all graphs with appropriate notation, including numeric intervals (by 1s or 10s, for example) and the names for the x- and y-axes (like distance and time).
  - Label all tables or other objects that you use to show your work. Show standard mathematic (non-calculator) notation. For example, you must show the integral as $\int_1^3 (x+2)\,dx$, not as fnInt 1 $(x+2, x, 1, 3)$.

REMEMBER: You are not required to simplify your answer. It is best if you leave an answer in an un-simplified form to avoid making careless errors and to save time. For example, $y - 2.3 = -6(x + 5.4)$ would be an appropriate equation of a tangent line; there is no need to simplify it to slope-intercept form.

- Decimals require an accuracy of three decimal places in the solution. So be sure to understand how to carry (store in your calculator) the intermediate steps of a problem until you round to three decimal places at the end of the problem. If you do multiple calculations and each calculation is rounded to three decimal places prior to the next calculation, your final solution will not have the required accuracy. The third digit in the final solution can be rounded or truncated.

SCORING FOR FREE-RESPONSE QUESTIONS

The free-response sections are graded on a scale of 0–9 with a dash (–) given for no work on the page. The chief reader is ultimately responsible for not only working through the solution and alternate solutions for each problem, but also assigning points on a 9-point scale to each problem. This varies from problem to problem based on how many parts are in the problem, as well as the difficulty or complexity of the particular question.

For example, in a problem that asks for units, units are generally assigned 1 point for the whole problem. In other words, if you do units correctly in part a, but incorrectly in part c, you would not be awarded the 1 point for units.

If a problem requires an explanation, or reasoning, it generally earns 1–2 points. In many cases, explanations can be in writing or with mathematical symbols.

In a typical area and volume problem, the integral is often worth 1 point and the answer is worth an additional 1 point. Sometimes the limits of integration are also worth 1 point. Thus, it is important that you at least start working on a problem because often some points can be earned for the setup, even if the solution is not there or is incorrect.

A "bald" answer is seldom awarded a point. A bald answer is one that has no supporting work or documentation, like "yes" or just a number.

DIAGNOSTIC TESTS

AP® CALCULUS AB DIAGNOSTIC TEST
Section I, Part A: Multiple-Choice Questions
Time: 60 minutes
Number of Questions: 30

A calculator may not be used on this part of the examination.

1. If $f(x) = \frac{\ln x}{x}$, what is $f'(x)$?
   (A) $\frac{1 + \ln x}{x}$
   (B) $\frac{1 - \ln x}{x}$
   (C) $\frac{1 + \ln x}{x^2}$
   (D) $\frac{1 - \ln x}{x^2}$

2. How many points of inflection exist for the function $y = \sin 2x$ on the open interval $0 < x < \frac{\pi}{2}$?
   (A) 3
   (B) 2
   (C) 1
   (D) None

3. If $\frac{dy}{dx} = 2xy$, then a possible solution for y is
   (A) $3e^{x^2}$
   (B) $e^{x^2} + 5$
   (C) $x^2 - 4$
   (D) $\ln(x^2 + 1)$

4. What is the equation of the line normal to the curve $y = e^{2x}\ln(x)$ where $x = 1$?
   (A) $y = e^2(x - 1)$
   (B) $y = -e^2(x - 1)$
   (C) $y = e(x - 1)$
   (D) $y = -e^{-2}(x - 1)$

5. The graph of $f(t)$ consists of a semicircle and a line segment as shown to the right. Which of the following represents the value of $\int_2^x f(t)\,dt$, where $x > 4$?
(A) $\pi - (x-4)^2$
(B) $2\pi - \frac{1}{2}(x-4)^2$
(C) $\pi - \frac{1}{2}(x-4)^2$
(D) $\pi + \frac{1}{2}(x-4)^2$

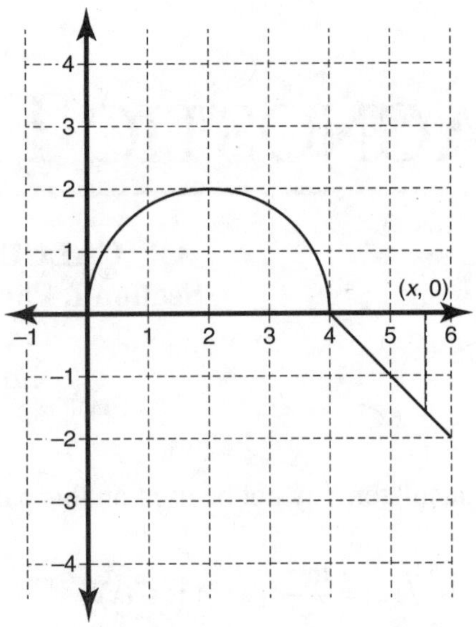

6. What is the value of $\lim_{x\to 0} \frac{\tan x}{x}$?
(A) 0
(B) 1
(C) ∞
(D) $-\infty$

7. For $xy^2 - 3x = y^3$, find y' when $y = -1$.
(A) −2
(B) −1
(C) −½
(D) ½

8. $\int 9xe^{3x^2+1}\,dx$
(A) $\frac{3}{2}x^2e^{x^3+x} + C$
(B) $\frac{9}{2}x^2e^{3x^3+1} + C$
(C) $e^{3x^2+1} + C$
(D) $\frac{3}{2}e^{3x^2+1} + C$

9. Given the piecewise function $f(x) = \begin{cases} 4 - bx^2, & -1 < x \le 2 \\ abx, & 2 < x < 4 \end{cases}$ with a and b as nonzero constants, what are all possible values of b that will make $f(x)$ continuous and differentiable?
(A) Only 1
(B) Only −1
(C) 1 or −1
(D) −1 or −4

10. The position of a particle moving in a line is $s(t) = t^3 - 5t^2 + 2t - 13$. What is the speed of the particle at $t = 2$?
(A) −21
(B) −6
(C) 6
(D) 10

11. Which of the following differential equations has the slope field shown to the right?
 (A) $\frac{dy}{dx} = y - x$
 (B) $\frac{dy}{dx} = 1 + y$
 (C) $\frac{dy}{dx} = x^2$
 (D) $\frac{dy}{dx} = y^2$

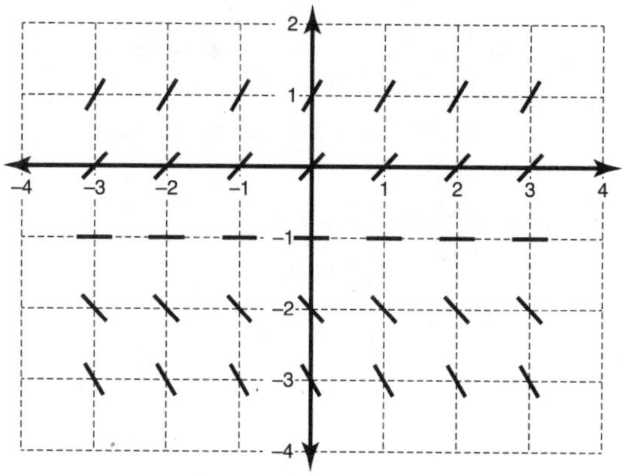

12. $\int_1^6 \sqrt{x+3}\, dx =$
 (A) $-\frac{5}{36}$
 (B) 1
 (C) $\frac{58}{5}$
 (D) $\frac{38}{3}$

13. The derivative of $f(x)$ is given by $f'(x) = \frac{3x^2(x-2)(x+5)^{1/3}}{(x-6)}$. In which of the following open intervals is $f(x)$ decreasing?
 (A) $(-\infty, -5) \cup (2, 6)$
 (B) $(-5, 0) \cup (2, 6)$
 (C) $(-5, 0) \cup (0, 2)$
 (D) $(0, 2)$ only

14. The sum of two positive numbers is 5. What is the value of the larger number if the product of the smaller number and the cube of the larger is a maximum?
 (A) 5
 (B) $\frac{15}{4}$
 (C) $\frac{5}{4}$
 (D) 1

15. If $f(x) = \ln x$ and $\frac{f'(x)}{-[f(x)]^2} = g'(x)$, which of the following could be $g(x)$?
 (A) $-\frac{1}{2}\ln|\ln x|$
 (B) $-\frac{1}{4}(\ln x)^2$
 (C) $\frac{1}{\ln x}$
 (D) $\frac{-1}{\ln x}$

16. For $f(x) = \frac{2x-4}{x^2-x-2}$, which of the following is true?
 I. $f(x)$ has no relative extrema.
 II. There are vertical asymptotes at $x = 2$ and $x = -1$.
 III. There is a horizontal asymptote at $y = 0$.
 (A) I only
 (B) II only
 (C) III only
 (D) I and III only

17. Let $F(x) = \int_1^x \cos(\pi t^2)\, dt$. What is the value of $F'(2)$?
 (A) -4π
 (B) -1
 (C) 0
 (D) 1

18. The line $y = ax + k$ is tangent to the circle $x^2 + (y - 4)^2 = 20$ at the point (4, 6). What is the value of $(a + k)$?
(A) −14
(B) −12
(C) 12
(D) 14

19. If $\ln y = x^2 \ln x$, what is $\frac{dy}{dx}$ in terms of x and y?
(A) $xy(2 \ln x + 1)$
(B) $y(2x \ln x + 1)$
(C) $y\left(2x + \frac{1}{x}\right)$
(D) $y(2 \ln x + x)$

20. If the derivative of a function is given $f'(x) = \frac{x-6}{e^x}$, then in which open interval is the function both increasing and concave up?
(A) $(-\infty, 5)$
(B) $(-\infty, 6)$
(C) $(5, 6)$
(D) $(6, 7)$

21. A particle moves along the y-axis so that its position at time t is given by $y(t) = -3t^4 + 18t^2$, for $t \geq 0$. What is the value of the velocity when the acceleration is 0?
(A) −24
(B) −18
(C) 15
(D) 24

22. Which of the following expressions represents the average value of $f(x) = \sqrt{2x-1}$ in [1, 3]?
(A) $\frac{\sqrt{2(3)-1} - \sqrt{2(1)-1}}{2}$
(B) $\int_1^3 \sqrt{2x-1}\, dx$
(C) $\frac{1}{3}\int_1^3 \sqrt{2x-1}\, dx$
(D) $\frac{1}{2}\int_1^3 \sqrt{2x-1}\, dx$

23. If $f(x) = \sin x$, $g(x) = \cos(2x)$, and $h(x) = f(g(x))$, what is $h'\left(\frac{\pi}{4}\right)$?
(A) −2
(B) $-\sqrt{2}$
(C) $\sqrt{2}$
(D) 2

24. A young girl, 5 feet tall, is walking away from a lamppost which is 12 feet tall. She walks at a constant rate of 2 feet per second and notices that, as she moves away from the lamppost, the length of her shadow is increasing. How fast is the length of her shadow increasing in feet per second when she is 20 feet from the post?
(A) $\frac{7}{10}$ ft/sec
(B) $\frac{10}{7}$ ft/sec
(C) 2 ft/sec
(D) $\frac{34}{7}$ ft/sec

25. If $f(x) = 3x^3 + 5x$ and $g(x) = f^{-1}(x)$, what is $g'(8)$?
(A) $\frac{1}{14}$
(B) $\frac{1}{11}$
(C) $\frac{1}{8}$
(D) 11

26. Find $\int \frac{x^3 - x^2 + 1}{x}\, dx$.
(A) $\frac{x^3}{3} - \frac{x^2}{2} + \ln x + C$
(B) $\frac{x^3}{3} - \frac{x^2}{2} - \frac{1}{x^2} + C$
(C) $\frac{x^3}{3} - \frac{x^2}{2} + \frac{1}{x^2} + C$
(D) $\frac{x^3}{3} - \frac{x^2}{2} + \ln|x| + C$

Use this graph of $f(x)$ and $g(x)$ for problems 27 and 28.

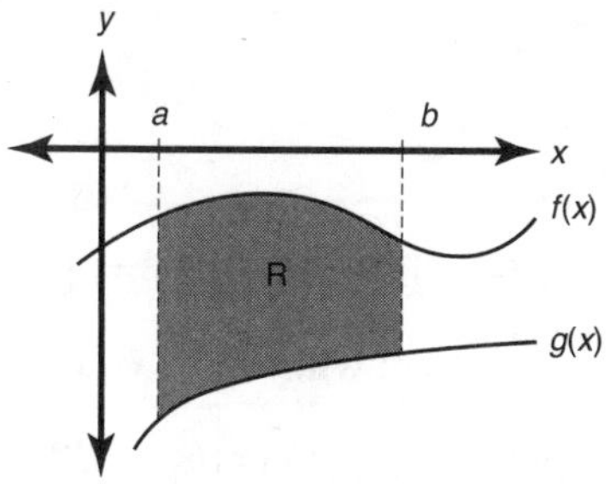

27. The graphs of $f(x)$ and $g(x)$ are shown in the figure above. If R is the region bounded by $f(x)$, $g(x)$, $x = a$, and $x = b$, which of the following represents the area of region R?

I. $\int_a^b [f(x) - g(x)]\,dx$

II. $\int_b^a [f(x) - g(x)]\,dx$

III. $\int_b^a [g(x) - f(x)]\,dx$

(A) I only
(B) II only
(C) III only
(D) I and III only

28. The graphs of $f(x)$ and $g(x)$ are shown in the figure on the left. If R is the region bounded by $f(x)$, $g(x)$, $x = a$, and $x = b$, which of the following represents the volume when R is rotated about the line $y = 1$?

(A) $\pi\int_a^b (f(x)-g(x))^2\,dx$

(B) $\pi\int_a^b (f(x)+1)^2 - (g(x)+1)^2\,dx$

(C) $\pi\int_a^b (1+g(x))^2 - (1+f(x))^2\,dx$

(D) $\pi\int_a^b (1-g(x))^2 - (1+f(x))^2\,dx$

29. Find $\frac{dy}{dx}$ if the relationship between x and y is implicitly defined by $x^2 + xy + y^3 = 2x + y$.

(A) $\frac{dy}{dx} = \frac{2-2x-y}{x+3y^2-1}$

(B) $\frac{dy}{dx} = \frac{2-2x}{x+3y^2-1}$

(C) $\frac{dy}{dx} = \frac{2-2x-y-3y^2}{x-1}$

(D) $\frac{dy}{dx} = \frac{2-2x+y}{x+3y^2-1}$

30. Find the point on the graph of $y=\sqrt{x}$ which is closest to the point (1, 0).

(A) (1, 1)

(B) $\left(\frac{1}{2}, \frac{1}{\sqrt{2}}\right)$

(C) $\left(\frac{1}{3}, \frac{1}{\sqrt{3}}\right)$

(D) $\left(\frac{1}{4}, \frac{1}{2}\right)$

Section I, Part B: Multiple-Choice Questions
Time: 45 minutes
Number of Questions: 15

A calculator may be used on this part of the examination.

31. If $k > 1$, the area under the curve $y = kx^2$ from $x = 0$ to $x = k$ is
    (A) $\frac{1}{3}k^4$
    (B) $\frac{1}{3}k^3$
    (C) $\frac{1}{4}k^4$
    (D) $\frac{1}{3}k^3 - k$

Use the following information for problems 32 and 33.

The rate of natural gas sales for the year 2013 at a certain gas company is given by $P(t) = t^2 - 400t + 160000$, where $P(t)$ is measured in gallons per day and t is the number of days in 2013 (from day 0 to day 365).

32. To the nearest gallon, what is the total number of gallons of natural gas sales at this company for the 31 days (day 0 to day 31) of January 2013?
    (A) 4,777,730
    (B) 4,617,930
    (C) 154,120
    (D) 148,965

33. To the nearest gallon, what is the average rate of natural gas sales at this company for the 31 days (day 0 to day 31) of January 2013?
    (A) 4,777,730
    (B) 4,617,930
    (C) 154,120
    (D) 148,965

34. If $f(-x) = -f(x)$ and $f(2) = 3$ and $f'(2) = \frac{1}{5}$, then what is the equation of the tangent line to $f(x)$ at $x = -2$?
    (A) $y - 3 = \frac{1}{5}(x - 2)$
    (B) $y + 3 = \frac{1}{5}(x - 2)$
    (C) $y - 3 = -\frac{1}{5}(x + 2)$
    (D) $y + 3 = \frac{1}{5}(x + 2)$

35. A solid is generated by revolving the region bounded by the x-axis, the line $x = 5$, and the function $y = \ln x$ around the x-axis. The volume of the solid is
    (A) 4.047
    (B) 4.857
    (C) 15.259
    (D) 88.706

36. A continuous function $g(t)$ is defined in the closed interval [0, 6] with values given in the table below. Using a midpoint Riemann sum with three subintervals of equal length, the approximate value of $\int_0^6 g(t)\,dt$ is

t	$g(t)$
0	4
1	7
2	8
3	12
4	15
5	22
6	26

    (A) 68
    (B) 82
    (C) 89
    (D) 94

37. A particle, initially at rest, moves in a line so that its acceleration is $a(t)=\dfrac{10}{t+1}$ for $t \geq 0$. What is the velocity of the particle at time $t = 4$?
(A) −0.4
(B) 2
(C) 10
(D) 16.094

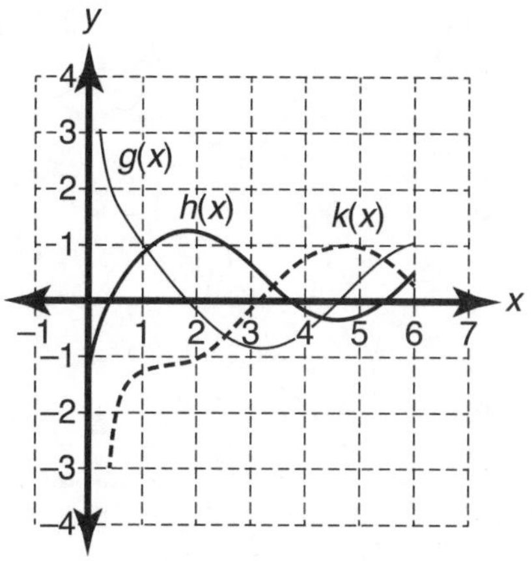

38. Three functions $g(x)$, $h(x)$, and $k(x)$ as graphed above represent a function, $f(x)$, and its first and second derivatives, $f'(x)$ and $f''(x)$, but not necessarily in this order. Using $g(x)$, $h(x)$ and $k(x)$, which ordered triple represents $(f(x), f'(x), f''(x))$?
(A) $[g(x), h(x), k(x)]$
(B) $[k(x), h(x), g(x)]$
(C) $[g(x), k(x), h(x)]$
(D) $[h(x), g(x), k(x)]$

39. $\int \cos(7t+3)\,dt =$
(A) $7\sin(7t+3)+C$
(B) $\sin(7t+3)+C$
(C) $\dfrac{1}{7}\sin(7t+3)+C$
(D) $-7\sin(7t+3)+C$

40. If $\int_3^{10} 4f(x)\,dx = 20$ and $\int_7^{10} 3f(x)\,dx = -12$, then $\int_3^{7} 11f(x)\,dx =$
(A) 11
(B) 32
(C) 57
(D) 99

41. Which value of x best approximates the value that satisfies the conclusion of the Mean Value Theorem for the function $f(x)=x^{\frac{2}{3}}+1$ on the interval $1 \leq x \leq 8$?
(A) 1.158
(B) 1.555
(C) 3.657
(D) 3.764

42. What is $g'(0)$ if $g(x)=\dfrac{x-f(x)}{3-x^2}$, $f(0) = 1$, and $f'(0) = -1$?
(A) 0
(B) $\dfrac{2}{3}$
(C) $\dfrac{5}{9}$
(D) $\dfrac{7}{9}$

43. For $f(x) = \sec 2x$ and $g(x) = \tan x$, at what value of x on the interval $\left(-\dfrac{\pi}{4}, \dfrac{\pi}{4}\right)$ do the graphs of f and g have tangent lines that are parallel?
(A) −1.8393
(B) −1.2111
(C) −1.073
(D) 0.2216

44. For $f(x) = ax^2 + bx^3$, what is the ordered pair (a, b) if the point $(-1, 2)$ is an extrema of $f(x)$?
(A) (4, 6)
(B) (6, 4)
(C) $\left(\frac{-2}{5}, \frac{-8}{5}\right)$
(D) $\left(\frac{6}{5}, \frac{4}{5}\right)$

45. Find the volume of the solid whose base is bounded in the xy-plane by the graphs $f(x) = \sqrt[3]{x+1}$ and $g(x) = \frac{x}{3} - \frac{1}{3}$, and whose cross sections taken perpendicular to the y-axis are isosceles right triangles with one leg of the right triangle in the xy-plane.
(A) 2.914
(B) 5.829
(C) 6.750
(D) 10.414

Section II
Free-Response Questions
Time: 1 hour and 30 minutes
Number of Problems: 6

Part A
Time: 30 minutes
Number of Problems: 2

You may use a calculator for any problem in this section.

1. Point P moves at a constant rate along the semicircle centered at O from M to N. The radius of the semicircle is 10 centimeters, and it takes 30 seconds for P to move from M to N. $\angle POM$ has measure x radians, $\angle OPM$ has measure y radians, and $MP = s$ centimeters as indicated in the figure. Note that triangle MOP is always an isosceles triangle.

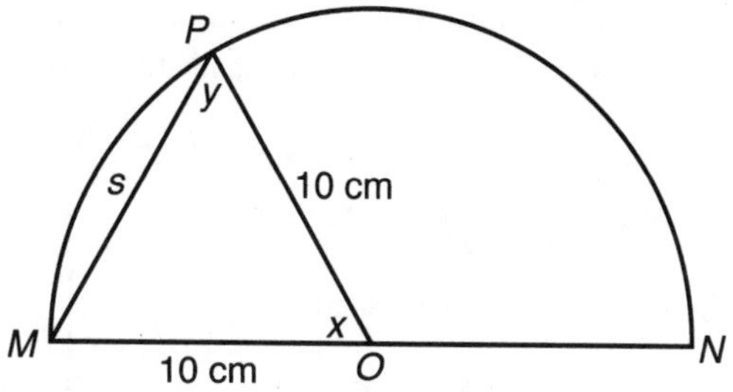

   (a) What is the rate of change, in radians per second, of x with respect to time?

   (b) What is the rate of change, in radians per second, of y with respect to time?

   (c) s and x are related by the Law of Cosines; that is, $s^2 = 10^2 + 10^2 - 2 \cdot 10 \cdot 10 \cdot \cos x$. What is the rate of change of s with respect to time when $x = \pi/2$ radians? Indicate units of measure.

   (d) Let A be the area of ΔOMP. Show that A is largest when $x = \pi/2$ radians.

2. A car is traveling along a straight road with values of its continuous velocity function, in feet per second, given in the table below.

t	$v(t)$
0	90
10	75
20	80
30	100
40	90
50	85
60	80

   (a) Estimate the instantaneous acceleration of the car at $t = 20$ seconds. Show the computation used to arrive at your answer and include appropriate units.

   (b) What is the average acceleration of the car during the time interval $t = 50$ seconds to $t = 60$ seconds? Include appropriate units.

   (c) Use a trapezoidal approximation with $n = 6$ to estimate the value of $\int_0^{60} v(t)\,dt$.

(d) Using appropriate units, explain the meaning of $\int_0^{60} v(t)\,dt$.

Section II
Part B
Time: 60 minutes
Number of Problems: 4

You may not use a calculator for any problem in this section. During the timed portion for Section II, Part B, you may continue to work on the problems in Section II, Part A without the use of a calculator.

3. Let R and S be the regions bounded by the graphs of $f(x) = -\ln x$, $g(x) = 2\cos x$, $x = 1$, and $x = 3$. The point of intersection is (P, Q).

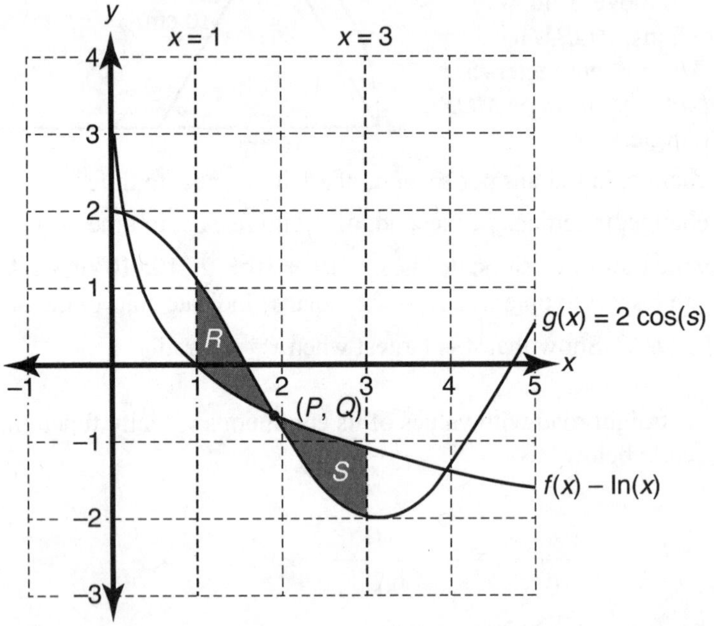

(a) Set up, but do not evaluate, an integral expression in terms of a single independent variable that represents the sum of the areas of region R and region S.

(b) Set up, but do not evaluate, an integral expression in terms of a single independent variable that represents the volume of the solid generated when region S is rotated about the line $y = 2$.

(c) The base of a solid is region R, and each plane cross section of the solid perpendicular to the x-axis is a square whose side is the vertical distance between $f(x)$ and $g(x)$. Set up, but do not evaluate, an integral expression in terms of a single independent variable that represents the volume of the solid.

4. Consider the differential equation $\frac{dy}{dx} = \frac{x^2}{y}$ for $y > 0$.

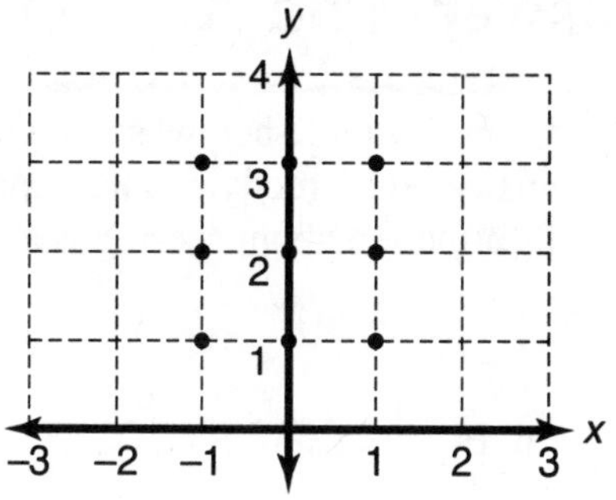

(a) On the axes provided, sketch a slope field for the given differential equation at the nine points indicated. Draw a function through the point (0, 2) on your slope field that represents an approximate solution to the given differential equation with initial condition $y(0) = 2$.

(b) If $y(0) = 2$, then find the particular solution $y(x)$ to the given differential equation.

(c) Use the function determined in (b) to find $\left.\frac{dy}{dx}\right|_{x=1}$

5. Consider the curve defined by $x^2 - \sin y = y + 4$.

(a) Show that $\frac{dy}{dx} = \frac{2x}{1 + \cos y}$.

(b) Find the equation for each tangent line to the curve where $y = 0$.

(c) Find $\frac{d^2y}{dx^2}$ in terms of x and y only.

(d) For all points on the curve at which $y = \pi/2$, is the curve concave up or concave down? Explain your answer.

6. Let R be the region bounded by the graphs of $y = \sqrt{x}$ and $y = \frac{x}{4}$.

(a) Find the area of region R.

(b) There is a line $x = k$ that divides the region R into two sections of equal area. Write an integral expression that could be used to find the value of k. Do not evaluate the integral.

(c) Write an integral expression that could be used to find the volume of the solid region formed when region R is revolved about the line $y = -1$. Do not evaluate the integral.

(d) If the region R is the base of a solid with cross sections *parallel* to the x-axis being equilateral triangles, find the volume of the solid region.

Answers and Answer Explanations

Using the table below, score your test. Determine how many questions you answered correctly and how many you answered incorrectly. Additional information about scoring is at the end of the diagnostic test.

1. D	2. D	3. A	4. D	5. C
6. B	7. C	8. D	9. B	10. C
11. B	12. D	13. A	14. B	15. C
16. D	17. D	18. C	19. A	20. D
21. D	22. D	23. A	24. B	25. A
26. D	27. D	28. D	29. A	30. B
31. A	32. A	33. C	34. D	35. C
36. B	37. D	38. D	39. C	40. D
41. D	42. B	43. D	44. B	45. D

1. ANSWER: (D) $f'(x)=\dfrac{\frac{1}{x}(x)-(\ln x)}{x^2}=\dfrac{1-\ln x}{x^2}$.
   (*Calculus for AP*®, pages 207–210; EU 2.1;LO 2.1C; EK 2.1C2,C3; MPAC 1,3)

2. ANSWER: (D) Since $y' = 2\cos 2x$, then $y''=-4\sin 2x = 0$. Therefore, $2x = 0 + k\pi$, and $x=\dfrac{\pi}{2}+\dfrac{k\pi}{2}$. There are no points of inflection in the open interval $\left(0,\dfrac{\pi}{2}\right)$.
   (*Calculus for AP*®, pages 324; EU 2.2; LO 2.2A; EK 2.2A1; MPAC 1,3,4)

3. ANSWER: (A) Separating variables and integrating, we get $\int\dfrac{dy}{y} = \int 2x\,dx$.
   Thus, $\ln|y| = x^2+C$. Therefore, $y=e^{x^2+C}=Ce^{x^2}$; hence $y=3e^{x^2}$ is one solution.
   (*Calculus for AP*®, pages 618-624; EU 3.5; LO 3.5A; EK 3.5A2; MPAC 3)

4. ANSWER: (D) Differentiating, we get $y'=2e^{2x}\ln(x)+\dfrac{1}{x}e^{2x}$, and the slope of the tangent line at $x=1$ is e^2. Since the normal line is perpendicular to the curve at the point of tangency, the slope of the normal line is $\dfrac{-1}{e^2}$ or $-e^{-2}$.

The point of tangency is (1, 0), and e therefore the equation of the normal line is $y = -e^{-2}(x - 1)$.
(*Calculus for AP*®, pages 196–197; EU 2.3; LO 2.3B; EK2.3B1; MPAC 3)

5. ANSWER: (C) $\int_2^x f(t)\,dt$ represents the area under $f(t)$ from 2 to x. The region from 2 to 4 is a quarter circle of radius 2 whose area is π. The region from 4 to x is an isosceles right triangle with base and height $(x - 4)$, so its area is $\frac{1}{2}(x-4)^2$. Since the triangular region is below the x-axis, the net signed area is $\pi - \frac{1}{2}(x-4)^2$.
(*Calculus for AP*®, pages 422–423; EU 3.3; LO 3.3A; EK 3.3A3; MPAC 4)

6. ANSWER: (B) $\lim_{x\to 0}\frac{\tan x}{x} = \lim_{x\to 0}\frac{\sin x}{x\cos x} = \lim_{x\to 0}\frac{\sin x}{x}\cdot\frac{1}{\cos x} = 1(1) = 1$.
(*Calculus for AP*®, pages 105–113; EU 1.1; LO 1.1C; EK 1.1C2; MPAC 1,3)

7. ANSWER: (C) By implicit differentiation, we get $y^2 + 2xy\,y' - 3 = 3y^2y'$. When $y = -1$, then $x = ½$ and $y' = -½$.
(*Calculus for AP*®, pages 240–245; EU 2.1; LO 2.1C; EK 2.1C5; MPAC 1,3)

8. ANSWER: (D) Integrate by substitution with $u = 3x^2 + 1$ and $du = 6x\,dx$. Then $\int 9xe^{3x^2+1}\,dx = \frac{9}{6}\int e^u\,du = \frac{3}{2}e^{3x^2+1} + C$
(*Calculus for AP*®, pages 457–461; EU 3.3; LO 3.3B; EK 3.3B5; MPAC 1,3)

9. ANSWER: (B) For $f(2)$: $4 - 4b = 2ab$. For $f'(2)$: $-4b = ab$. Solving the system, $a = -4$ and $b = -1$.
(*Calculus for AP*®, pages 182–184; EU 2.2; LO 2.2B; EK 2.2B2; MPAC 2,4)

10. ANSWER: (C) The velocity function is $v(t) = 3t^2 - 10t + 2$. Speed is the magnitude of velocity. $|v(2)| = |12 - 20 + 2| = 6$.
(*Calculus for AP*®, pages 171; EU 2.3; LO 2.3C; EK 2.3C1; MPAC 2)

11. ANSWER: (B) The easiest way to recognize which of the differential equations has the pictured slope field is to see that all the points at which $y = -1$ have slope 0 and all the points at which $y = 0$ have slope 1. This suggests that the slope (dy/dx) is 1 more than y. Thus, (B) is the only choice for which that is true.
(*Calculus for AP*®, pages 606–611; EU 2.3; LO 2.3F; EK 2.3F1; MPAC 2,4,5)

$$\int_1^6 \sqrt{x+3}\,dx = \frac{2}{3}(x+3)^{\frac{3}{2}}\Big|_1^6 = \frac{2}{3}(27-8) = \frac{38}{3}.$$

12. ANSWER: (D)
(*Calculus for AP®*, pages 436–440; EU 3.3; LO 3.3B; EK 3.3B2; MPAC 1,3)

13. ANSWER: (A) Use an interval chart to analyze the signs of the factors of $f(x)$.

	$x < -5$	$-5 < x < 0$	$0 < x < 2$	$2 < x < 6$	$6 < x < \infty$
$f'(x)$	Negative	Positive	Positive	Negative	Positive
$f(x)$	*Decreasing*	Increasing	Increasing	*Decreasing*	Increasing

(*Calculus for AP®*, pages 316–333; EU 2.2; LO 2.2A; EK 2.2A1; MPAC 2,3,4)

14. ANSWER: (B) Let the larger number be x and the smaller number $= 5 - x$. Then, $f(x) = x^3(5-x) = 5x^3 - x^4$, $f'(x) = 15x^2 - 4x^3 = x^2(15-4x) = 0$, and $x = 0$ (which is not positive) or $x = \frac{15}{4}$. The only possible positive choice for x is $x = \frac{15}{4}$. (Also, $x \neq 5$ as $5 - x$ would be 0.) Check the value of the function at the endpoints of the interval as well as the critical point determined by the first derivative.

$f(0) = f(5) = 0$, and $f\left(\frac{15}{4}\right) = \left(\frac{15}{4}\right)^3\left(5 - \frac{15}{4}\right) > 0$. Therefore, a relative maximum occurs at $x = \frac{15}{4}$.
(*Calculus for AP®*, pages 365–372; EU 2.3; LO 2.3C; EK 2.3C3; MPAC 2,3,5)

15. ANSWER: (C) $f'(x) = \frac{1}{x}$ and $g'(x) = \frac{-1}{x(\ln x)^2}$. Then $g(x) = \int \frac{-1}{x(\ln x)^2}dx$

and, by using substitution where $u = \ln x$, $du = \frac{1}{x}dx$, and

$$g(x) = \int \frac{-1}{(u)^2}du = \frac{1}{u} + C = \frac{1}{\ln x} + C.$$

(*Calculus for AP®*, pages 457–461; EU 3.3; LO 3.3B; EK 3.3B5; MPAC 1,3)

16. ANSWER: (D) Rewrite the function: $f(x)=\dfrac{2(x-2)}{(x-2)(x+1)}=\dfrac{2}{(x+1)}$.

Therefore, there is a hole at $x = 2$ and a vertical asymptote only at $x = -1$, making statement II false. There is a horizontal asymptote, $y = 0$, because $\lim\limits_{x\to\infty} f(x)=0$, and thus statement III is true. Statement I is true because the first derivative, $f'(x)=\dfrac{-2}{(x+1)^2}$, does not equal 0 nor is it undefined except at the vertical asymptote. Therefore, I and III are true.
(*Calculus for AP*®, pages 100–102, 293–300; EU 1.1; LO 1.1D; EK 1.1D1; MPAC 1,2)

17. ANSWER: (D) By the Second Fundamental Theorem of Calculus, $F'(x) = f(x) = \cos(\pi x^2)$. Therefore, $F'(2) = \cos(4\pi) = 1$.
(*Calculus for AP*®, pages 436–440; EU 3.3; LO 3.3B; EK 3.3B1; MPAC 5)

18. ANSWER: (C) Since $2x + 2(y - 4)y' = 0$, then $y'\big|_{(4,6)} = \dfrac{-4}{6-4} = -2 = a$, which is the slope of the tangent line. Substituting in the linear function, $k = 14$ and $(a + k) = 12$.
(*Calculus for AP*®, pages 165–167; EU 2.3; LO 2.3B; EK 2.3B1; MPAC 1,3)

19. ANSWER: (A) By differentiation, $\dfrac{1}{y}\left(\dfrac{dy}{dx}\right) = 2x\ln x + x^2\left(\dfrac{1}{x}\right)$. Simplifying, $\dfrac{dy}{dx}=y(2x\ln x+x)$ or $\dfrac{dy}{dx}=xy(2\ln x+1)$.
(*Calculus for AP*®, pages 240–245; EU 2.1; LO 2.1C; EK 2.1C5; MPAC 2,5)

20. ANSWER: (D) $f'(x)=\dfrac{x-6}{e^x}$, then $f''(x)=\dfrac{e^x-e^x(x-6)}{e^{2x}}=\dfrac{7-x}{e^x}$.
This is shown in the following interval chart.

	$x < 6$	$6 < x < 7$	$x > 7$
$f'(x)$	Negative	Positive	Positive
$f''(x)$	Positive	Positive	Negative
$f(x)$	Decreasing / concave up	*Increasing /concave up*	Increasing / concave down

(*Calculus for AP*®, pages 350–362; EU 2.2; LO 2.2A; EK 2.2A1,2,3; MPAC 2,4)

21. ANSWER: (D) $v(t) = -12t^3 + 36t$ and $a(t) = -36t^2 + 36 = 0$. Then, $t = 1$ and $v(1) = 24$.
(*Calculus for AP*®, pages 261–263; EU 2.3; LO 2.3C; EK2.3C1; MPAC 2,3)

22. ANSWER: (D) The average value of a function is given by
$f_{avg}=\frac{1}{b-a}\int_a^b f(x)\,dx$, so $f_{avg}=\frac{1}{3-1}\int_1^3\sqrt{2x-1}\,dx$; therefore
$f_{avg}=\frac{1}{2}\int_1^3\sqrt{2x-1}\,dx.$
(*Calculus for AP*®, pages 490–494; EU 3.4; LO 3.4B; EK 3.4B1; MPAC 2)

23. ANSWER: (A) By the Chain Rule: $h'(x) = \cos[\cos(2x)] \cdot (-2\sin 2x)$, and
$h'\left(\frac{\pi}{4}\right)=\cos\left[\cos\left(\frac{\pi}{2}\right)\right]\cdot\left(-2\sin\frac{\pi}{2}\right)$. Thus, $h'\left(\frac{\pi}{4}\right)=\cos(0)\cdot[-2(1)]=$
$1(-2)=-2.$
(*Calculus for AP*®, pages 227–233; EU 2.1; LO 2.1C; EK 2.1C4; MPAC 1,2,3)

24. ANSWER: (B) Using similar triangles, with the length of the shadow = *y*:
$\frac{5}{12}=\frac{y}{x+y}\Rightarrow 5x=7y$ and $5\frac{dx}{dt}=7\frac{dy}{dt}$. Finally, $\frac{dy}{dt}=\frac{10}{7}$ feet/sec.

(Notice that $\frac{dy}{dt}$ is independent of the distance from the pole.)

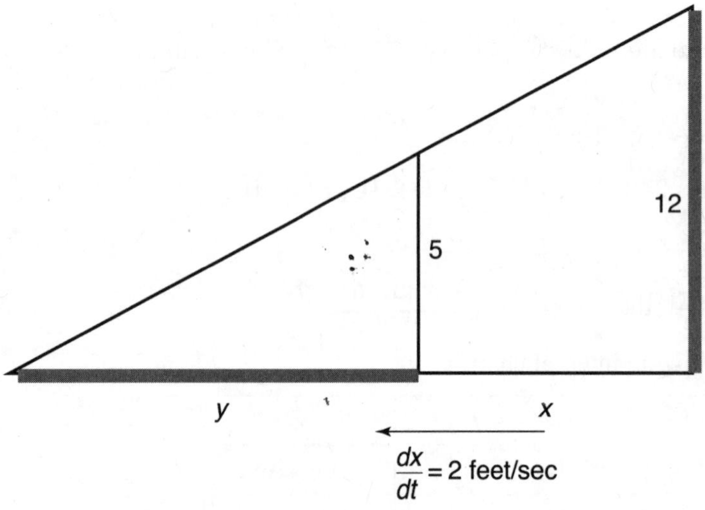

(*Calculus for AP*®, pages 274–279; EU 2.3; LO 2.3C; EK 2.3C2; MPAC 2,3)

25. ANSWER: (A) If $g(x)=f^{-1}(x)$, then $g'(b)=\frac{1}{f'(a)}$ where the point (a, b) is on the graph of $f(x)$. Since $f(1) = 8$ and $f'(1) = 14$, then $g'(8)=\frac{1}{14}$.
(*Calculus for AP*®, pages 247–248; EU 2.1; LO 2.1C; EK 2.1C2; MPAC 2)

26. ANSWER: (D) $\int \frac{x^3 - x^2 + 1}{x} dx = \int \left[x^2 - x + \frac{1}{x} \right] dx = \frac{x^3}{3} - \frac{x^2}{2} + \ln|x| + C.$
(*Calculus for AP*®, pages 457–465; EU 3.3; LO 3.3B; EK 3.3B5 MPAC 2,5)

27. ANSWER: (D) Since $f(x) > g(x)$, then the area of region R is correctly stated in case I: $\int_a^b \left[f(x) - g(x) \right] dx$. The statement in case III:

$\int_b^a \left[g(x) - f(x) \right] dx$ becomes $-\left(\int_a^b \left[g(x) - f(x) \right] dx \right)$ when the endpoints of the interval are exchanged, and then becomes $\int_a^b \left[f(x) - g(x) \right] dx$ by distributing the negative sign.
(*Calculus for AP*®, pages 477–486; EU 3.4; LO 3.4D; EK 3.4D1; MPAC 2)

28. ANSWER: (D) $V = \int \pi r_o^2 - \pi r_i^2 \, dx$ and $r = 1 - y$, then
$V = \int \pi \left(1 - g(x)\right)^2 - \pi \left(1 - f(x)\right)^2 dx.$
(*Calculus for AP*®, pages 525–528; EU 3.4; LO 3.4D; EK 3.4D2; MPAC 2)

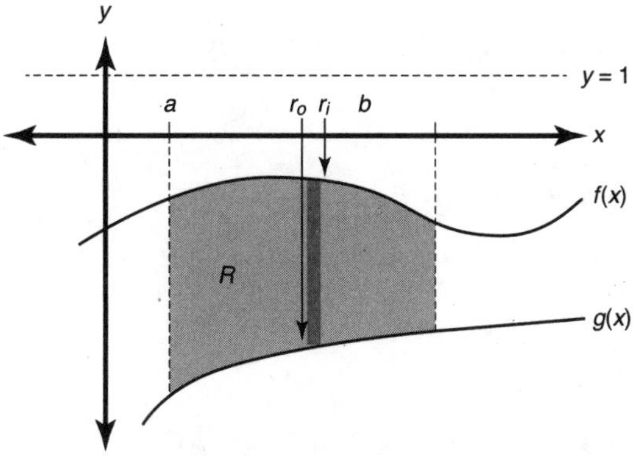

29. ANSWER: (A) Take the derivative of each side with respect to x.
$2x + x\frac{dy}{dx} + y + 3y^2\frac{dy}{dx} = 2 + \frac{dy}{dx}$. Solve for $\frac{dy}{dx}$ to get $\frac{dy}{dx} = \frac{2 - 2x - y}{x + 3y^2 - 1}$.
(*Calculus for AP*®, pages 240–245; EU 2.12.2; LO 2.1C5; EK 2.1C5; MPAC 2,3)

30. ANSWER: (B) The point on the curve is $\left(x, \sqrt{x}\right)$, so the distance from this point to (1, 0) is $D = \sqrt{(x-1)^2 + \left(\sqrt{x} - 0\right)^2}$ and $\frac{dD}{dx} = \frac{2(x-1)+1}{\sqrt{(x-1)^2 + x}}$. This derivative is 0 only when $x = \frac{1}{2}$. Consequently, the closest point to (1, 0) is

$\left(\frac{1}{2}, \frac{1}{\sqrt{2}}\right)$. By context one can tell that this is not the point with the greatest distance. There is no such point.
(*Calculus for AP*®, pages 365–372; EU 2.32; LO 2.3C1C,2.2A,2.3A; EK 2.3C2; MPAC 2,33,4)

31. ANSWER: (A) $A = \int_0^k kx^2\,dx = \frac{1}{3}kx^3 \Big|_0^k = \frac{1}{3}k^4$.
(*Calculus for AP*®, pages 477–486; EU 3.4; LO 3.4D; EK 3.4D1; MPAC 2,3)

32. ANSWER: (A) Total gallons: $\int_0^{31} (t^2 - 400t + 160{,}000)\,dt \approx 4{,}777{,}730$ gallons.
(*Calculus for AP*®, pages 450–454; EU 3.4; LO 3.4E; EK 3.4E1; MPAC 2,5)

33. ANSWER: (C) The average rate of natural gas sales is equal to the average value of the rate of natural gas sales function. This is
$\frac{1}{31-0}\int_0^{31} P(t)\,dt = 154{,}120$ gallons.
(*Calculus for AP*®, pages 490–494; EU 3.4; LO 3.4B; EK 3.4B1; MPAC 2,5)

34. ANSWER: (D) $f(x)$ is an odd function with symmetry about the origin. Therefore, $f(-2) = -3$ and $f'(-2) = \frac{1}{5}$, and the tangent line is given by
$y + 3 = \frac{1}{5}(x + 2)$.
(*Calculus for AP*®, pages 165–167; EU 2.3; LO 2.3B; EK 2.3B1; MPAC 25)

35. ANSWER: (C) The volume, using the method of disks, is
$V = \pi \int_1^5 [\ln x]^2\,dx = 15.259$.
(*Calculus for AP*®, pages 522–525; EU 3.4; LO 3.4D; EK 3.4D2; MPAC 1,3)

36. ANSWER: (B) The three subintervals of t are (0,2), (2,4), and (4,6). The midpoints of these are t = 1, 3, and 5. Therefore,
$\int_0^6 g(t)\,dt \approx 2(7 + 12 + 22) = 82$.
(*Calculus for AP*®, pages 395–410; EU 3.2; LO 3.2B; EK 3.2B2; MPAC 2,3)

37. ANSWER: (D) $v(t) = \int a(t)\,dt = \int \frac{10}{t+1}\,dt = 10\ln(t+1) + C$. With initial condition $v(0) = 0$, $C = 0$, and $v(t) = 10\ln(t+1)$. Finally, $v(4) = 10\ln 5 \approx 16.094$.
(*Calculus for AP*®, pages 388–389; EU 2.3,3.3,3.4; LO 2.3C,3.3B,3.4A; EK 2.3C1,3.3B2,3.4A2; MPAC 2,3,4)

38. ANSWER: (D) Near $x = 2$, $h(x)$ appears to have a maximum and $g(x)$ has a zero. Near $x = 3$, there seems to be a change in concavity for $h(x)$ and a zero for $k(x)$. Therefore, $f(x) = h(x)$, $f'(x) = g(x)$, and $f''(x) = k(x)$. Thus, the ordered pair is $[h(x),\ g(x),\ k(x)]$.
(*Calculus for AP*®, pages 316–327; EU 2.2; LO 2.2A; EK 2.2A3; MPAC 4,5)

39. ANSWER: (C) Integrate by substitution. Let $u = 7t + 3$ and $du = 7\,dt$.

$$\int \cos(7t+3)\,dt = \frac{1}{7}\int 7\cos(7t+3)\,dt$$

$$= \frac{1}{7}\int \cos u\,du = \frac{1}{7}\sin u + C = \frac{1}{7}\sin(7t+3) + C.$$

(*Calculus for AP*®, pages 557–561; EU 3.3; LO 3.3B; EK 3.3B5; MPAC 3)

40. ANSWER: (D) $\int_3^{10} f(x)\,dx = 5$ and $\int_7^{10} f(x)\,dx = -4$. Since

$\int_3^7 f(x)\,dx + \int_7^{10} f(x)\,dx = \int_3^{10} f(x)\,dx$, we get

$\int_3^7 f(x)\,dx = 9$ and $\int_7^{10} 11 f(x)\,dx = 99$.

(*Calculus for AP*®, page 425; EU 3.2; LO 3.2C; EK 3.2C2; MPAC 2)

41. ANSWER: (D) $f'(x) = \frac{2}{3}x^{\frac{1}{3}} = \frac{f(8) - f(1)}{8-1} = \frac{3}{7}$ and $x^{\frac{1}{3}} = \frac{14}{9}$, so $x = 3.764$.

(*Calculus for AP*®, pages 308–311; EU 2.4; LO 2.4A; EK 2.4A1; MPAC 2,3)

42. ANSWER: (B) $g'(x) = \dfrac{(1 - f'(x))(3 - x^2) - (-2x)(x - f(x))}{(3 - x^2)^2}$ and

$g'(0) = \dfrac{(1+1)(3) - 0}{9} = \dfrac{2}{3}$.

(*Calculus for AP*®, pages 207–210; EU 2.1; LO 2.1C; EK 2.1C3; MPAC 2,3,5)

43. ANSWER: (D) Graph $f'(x) = 2\sec 2x \tan 2x$ and $g'(x) = \sec^2 x$. The x-value of the point of intersection is 0.2216.
(*Calculus for AP*®, pages 165–167, 216–220; EU 2.3; LO 2.3B; EK 2.3B1; MPAC 2,3)

44. ANSWER: (B) $f(-1) = 2 = a - b$, $f'(-1) = 0 = -2a + 3b$. Solving the simultaneous equations, then $(a, b) = (6, 4)$.
(*Calculus for AP*®, pages 293–300; EU 2.2; LO 2.2A; EK 2.2A1; MPAC 2,3)

45. ANSWER: (D) The base, s, of the isosceles right triangle is $g(x) - f(x)$ and the area of each cross section is $\frac{1}{2}s^2$. Solving for x in both functions, the curve is $x = y^3 - 1$ and the line is $x = 3y + 1$. The curves intersect at the points $(-2, -1)$ and $(7, 2)$. Thus, the volume is given by

$$\frac{1}{2}\int_{-1}^{2}\left[(3y+1)-\left(y^3-1\right)\right]^2 dy \approx 10.414.$$

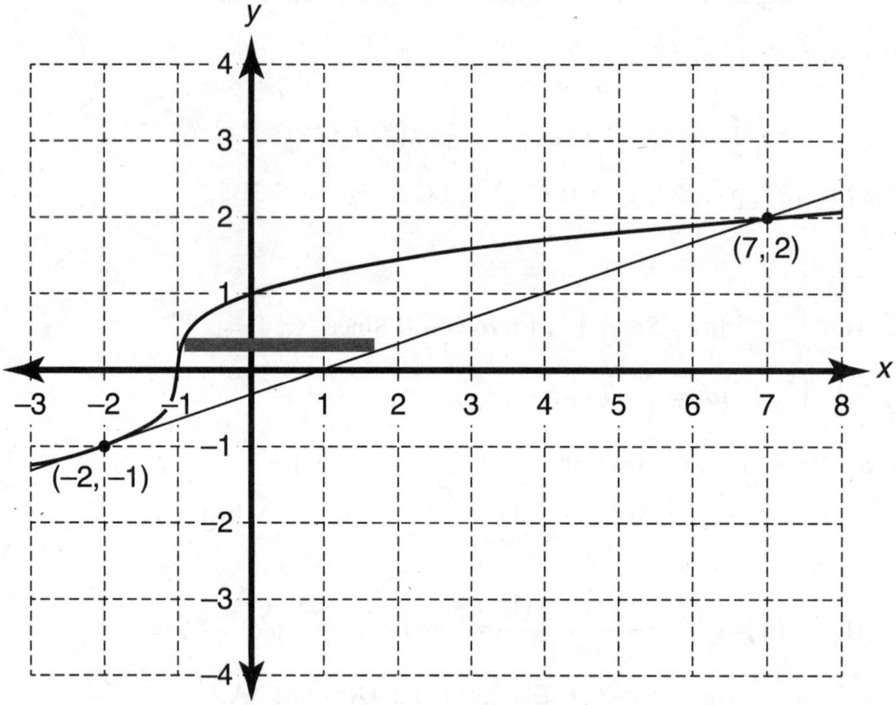

(*Calculus for AP®*, pages 518–522; EU 3.4; LO 3.4D; EK 3.4D2; MP AC 2,3)

FREE-RESPONSE QUESTIONS

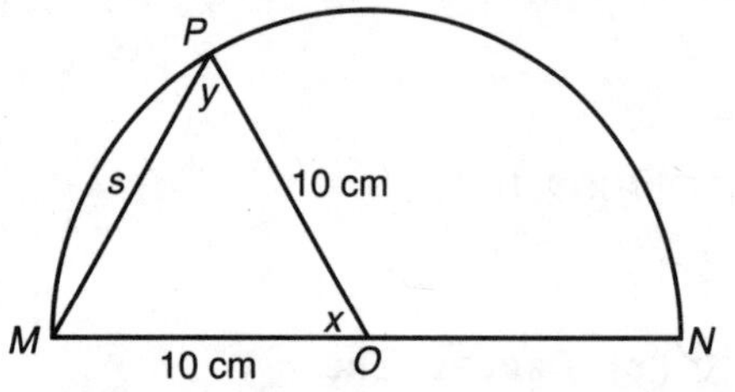

1. Point P moves at a constant rate along semicircle centered at O from M to N. The radius of the semicircle is 10 centimeters, and it takes 30 seconds for P to move from M to N. $\angle POM$ has measure x radians, $\angle OPM$ has measure y radians, and $MP = s$ centimeters as indicated in the figure.
   (a) What is the rate of change, in radians per second, of x with respect to time?
   (b) What is the rate of change, in radians per second, of y with respect to time?
   (c) s and x are related by the Law of Cosines; that is, $s^2 = 10^2 + 10^2 - 2\cdot 10\cdot 10\cdot \cos x$. What is the rate of change of s with respect to time when $x = \pi/2$ radians? Indicate units of measure.
   (d) Let A be the area of ΔOMP. Show that A is largest when $x = \pi/2$ radians.

	Solution	Possible points
(a)	$\frac{dx}{dt}=\frac{\pi}{30}\approx 0.105$ rad/sec	1: answer
(b)	Because ΔOMP is isosceles, $x+2y=180°=$ π radians. $y=\frac{\pi}{2}-\frac{1}{2}x$ $\frac{dy}{dt}=-\frac{1}{2}\frac{dx}{dt}$ $\frac{dy}{dt}=-\frac{\pi}{60}\approx -0.052$ rad/sec	2: $\begin{cases}1: \text{correct } y(x) \text{ equation}\\ 1: dy/dt \text{ and answer}\end{cases}$
(c)	$s^2=200-200\cos x$ $2s\frac{ds}{dt}=200\sin x\frac{dx}{dt}$ At $x=\frac{\pi}{2}$, $s=10\sqrt{2}$, so $20\sqrt{2}\frac{ds}{dt}=200\sin\left(\frac{\pi}{2}\right)\cdot\frac{\pi}{30}$ $\frac{ds}{dt}=\frac{\pi}{3\sqrt{2}}$ At $x=\frac{\pi}{2}$, length of s is increasing at $\frac{\pi}{3\sqrt{2}}\approx 0.740$ centimeters per second.	3: $\begin{cases}1: \text{correct derivative}\\ 1: \text{correct value of } s \text{ at } t=\pi/2\\ 1: \text{answer with units}\end{cases}$
(d)	$A=\frac{1}{2}\cdot 10\cdot 10\cdot\sin x=50\sin x.$ Thus, $\frac{dA}{dx}=50\cos x$ or $\frac{dA}{dt}=5-\cos x\frac{dx}{dt}$. At $x=\frac{\pi}{2}$, $\frac{dA}{dx}=0$ or $\frac{dA}{dt}=0$. $\frac{dA}{dx}$: 0 | + + + | π/2 | − − − | π The sign test indicates that dA/dx changes from positive to negative at $t=\pi/2$. Noting that $A(0)=A(n)=0$, the maximum value of A occurs when $x=\pi/2$.	3: $\begin{cases}1: \text{correct } A(x) \text{ equation}\\ 1: \text{correct derivative}\\ 1: \text{answer with reason}\end{cases}$

1. (a), (b), (c) (*Calculus for AP®*, pages 274–279; EU 3.3; LO 3.3C; EK 3.3C2; MPAC 2,3,4,6)

1. (d) (*Calculus for AP®*, pages 365–372; EU 2.3; LO 2.3C; EK 2.3C3; MPAC 2,3,6)
2. A car is traveling along a straight road with values of its continuous velocity function, in feet per second, given in the table below.
3.

t	$v(t)$
0	90
10	75
20	80
30	100
40	90
50	85
60	80

(a) Estimate the instantaneous acceleration of the car at $t = 20$ seconds. Show the computation used to arrive at your answer and include appropriate units.

(b) What is the average acceleration of the car during the time interval $t = 50$ seconds to $t = 60$ seconds? Include appropriate units.

(c) Use a trapezoidal approximation with $n = 6$ to estimate the value of $\int_0^{60} v(t)\,dt$.

(d) Using appropriate units, explain the meaning of $\int_0^{60} v(t)\,dt$.

	Solution	Possible points
(a)	$\frac{80-75}{20-10}=\frac{1}{2}$ ft/sec^2 OR $\frac{100-75}{30-10}=1.25$ ft/sec^2 OR $\frac{100-80}{30-20}=2$ ft/sec^2	$2:\begin{cases}1:\text{method}\\1:\text{answer}\end{cases}$
(b)	$\frac{1}{60-50}\int_{50}^{60} a(t)dt=\frac{1}{10}(v(60)-v(50))=$ $\frac{1}{10}(80-85)=-0.5$ ft/sec^2	$2:\begin{cases}1:\text{method}\\1:\text{answer}\end{cases}$
(c)	$\int_0^{60} v(t)\,dt \approx \frac{60-0}{2\cdot 6}[90+2\cdot 75+2\cdot 80+$ $2\cdot 100+2\cdot 90+2\cdot 85+80]=5150$	$3:\begin{cases}1:\text{coefficient}\\1:\text{trapezoid multipliers}\\1:\text{answer}\end{cases}$
(d)	The car traveled approximately 5,150 feet from $t = 0$ to $t = 60$ seconds.	1: answer
	Units	1: correct units in both (a) and (b)

2. (a) (*Calculus for AP®*, page 168; EU 2.1; LO 2.1B; EK 2.1B1; MPAC 2,3,4)
2. (b) (*Calculus for AP®*, pages 490–494; EU 3.4; LO 3.4B; EK 3.4B1; MPAC 2.3)
2. (c) (*Calculus for AP®*, pages 400–401; EU 3.2; LO 3.2B; EK 3.2B2; MPAC 2,3,4)
2. (d) (*Calculus for AP®*, pages 450–454; EU 3.4; LO 3.4C; EK 3.4C1; MPAC 2,6)

3. Let R and S be the regions bounded by the graphs of $f(x) = -\ln x$, $g(x) = 2\cos x$, $x = 1$, and $x = 3$. The point of intersection is (P, Q).

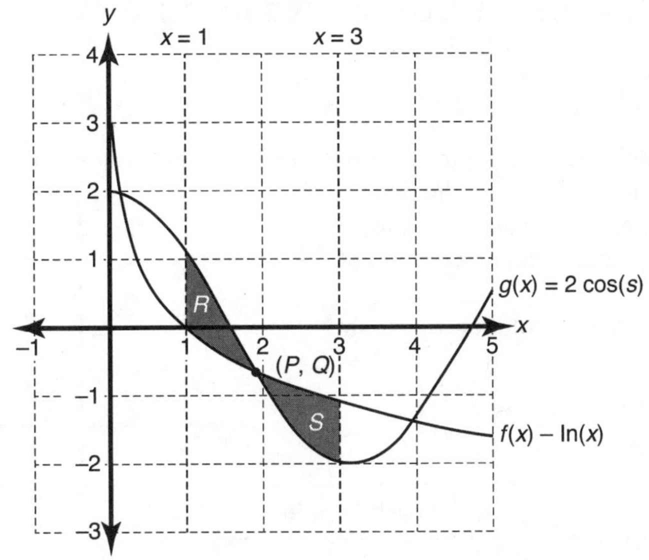

(a) Set up, but do not evaluate, an integral expression in terms of a single independent variable that represents the sum of the areas of region R and region S.

(b) Set up, but do not evaluate, an integral expression in terms of a single independent variable that represents the volume of the solid generated when region S is rotated about the line $y = 2$.

(c) The base of a solid is region R, and each plane cross section of the solid perpendicular to the x-axis is a square whose side is the vertical distance between $f(x)$ and $g(x)$. Set up, but do not evaluate, an integral expression in terms of a single independent variable that represents the volume of the solid.

	Solution	**Possible points**
(a)	$\text{Area} = \int_1^P \left(2\cos x - (-\ln x)\right)dx + \int_P^3 \left(-\ln x - 2\cos x\right)dx$	3: {1: intervals; 2: integrands; <−1> reversal; <−1> error with constant
(b)	$\text{Volume} = \pi \int_P^3 \left[\left(2 - 2\cos x\right)^2 - \left(2 - (-\ln x)\right)^2\right]dx$	3: {1: interval; 2: integrand; <−1>reversal; <−1> error with constant; <−1>omits 2 in one radius
(c)	$\text{Volume} = \int_1^P \left(2\cos x - (-\ln x)\right)^2 dx$	3: {1: interval; 2: integrand; <−1> error on area of cross section; <−1> error on *difference* of functions

3. (a), (b) (*Calculus for AP®*, pages 477–486, 525–528; EU 3.4; LO 3.4D; EK 3.4D1, 3.4D2; MPAC 4)
3. (c) (*Calculus for AP®*, pages 518–522; EU 3.4; LO 3.4d; EK 3.4D2; MPAC 3,4)

4. Consider the differential equation $\frac{dy}{dx} = \frac{x^2}{y}$ for $y > 0$.

(a) On the axes provided, sketch a slope field for the given differential equation at the nine points indicated. Draw a function through the point (0, 2) on your slope field that represents an approximate solution to the given differential equation with initial condition $y(0) = 2$.

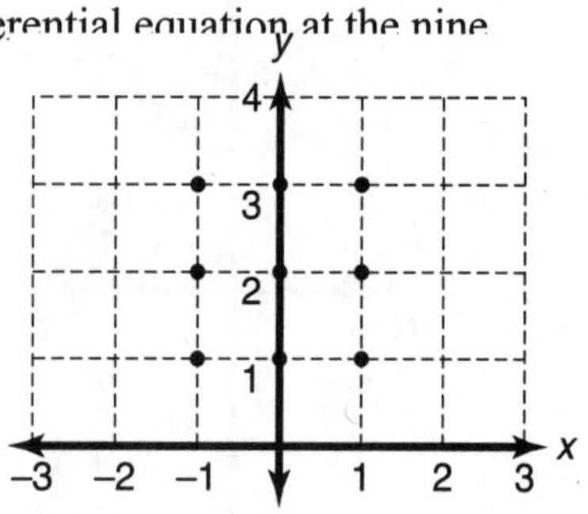

(b) If $y(0) = 2$, then find the particular solution $y(x)$ to the given differential equation.

(c) Use the function determined in (b) to find $\left.\frac{dy}{dx}\right|_{x=1}$

	Solution	Possible points
(a)	The values of dy/dx at the points indicated are given in the table. <table><tr><td>y \ x</td><td>–1</td><td>0</td><td>1</td></tr><tr><td>3</td><td>1/3</td><td>0</td><td>1/3</td></tr><tr><td>2</td><td>1/2</td><td>0</td><td>1/2</td></tr><tr><td>1</td><td>1</td><td>0</td><td>1</td></tr></table> 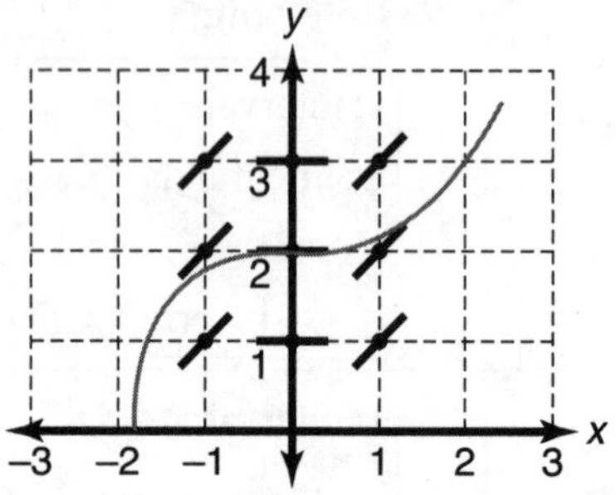	$3: \begin{cases} 1: \text{correct slopes for } x = 0 \\ \quad <-1> \text{ for first error} \\ 2: \text{correct slopes for } x = -1 \text{ and } 1 \\ \quad <-1> \text{ for each of first two errors} \end{cases}$
(b)	$\int y\,dy = \int x^2\,dx$, so $\frac{1}{2}y^2 = \frac{1}{3}x^3 + C$. Using the initial condition (0, 2), $\frac{1}{2}(2)^2 = \frac{1}{3}(0)^3 + C$, so $C = 2$. Therefore, $\frac{1}{2}y^2 = \frac{1}{3}x^3 + 2 \Rightarrow y = \pm\sqrt{\frac{2}{3}x^3 + 4}$. Since $y > 0$, disregard the negative solution. Therefore, $y(x) = \sqrt{\frac{2}{3}x^3 + 4}$. With $x > -1.818$	$5: \begin{cases} 1: \text{separation of variables} \\ 2: \text{correct antiderivatives} \\ 1: \text{includes constant of integration} \\ 1: \text{solves correctly for constant} \end{cases}$

(c)	$y(1)=\sqrt{\frac{14}{3}}$. (Note that the point $\left(1,\sqrt{\frac{14}{3}}\right)$ should be roughly visible on the slope field.) $\left.\frac{dy}{dx}\right\|_{x=1}=\frac{1^2}{\sqrt{\frac{14}{3}}}=\sqrt{\frac{3}{14}}$.	1: answer

4. (a) (*Calculus for AP*®, pages 606–611; EU 2.3; LO 2.3F; EK 2.3F1; MPAC 4,5)
4. (b), (c) (*Calculus for AP*®, pages 618–624; 227–233; EU 2.3; LO 2.3E; EK 2.3E1, 2.3E2; MPAC 2,3,5)

5. Consider the curve defined by $x^2 - \sin y = y + 4$.
   (a) Show that $\frac{dy}{dx}=\frac{2x}{1+\cos y}$.
   (b) Find the equation for each tangent line to the curve where $y = 0$.
   (c) Find $\frac{d^2y}{dx^2}$ in terms of x and y only.
   (d) For all points on the curve at which $y = \pi/2$, is the curve concave up or concave down? Explain your answer.

	Solution	Possible points
(a)	$2x - \cos y\frac{dy}{dx}=\frac{dy}{dx}$ $\frac{dy}{dx}=\frac{2x}{1+\cos y}$	$2:\begin{cases}1:\text{correct implicit derivative}\\1:\text{correct } dy/dx\end{cases}$
(b)	$y=0 \Rightarrow x^2=4 \Rightarrow x=\pm 2$ $\left.\frac{dy}{dx}\right\|_{(2,0)}=\frac{4}{1+1}=2$ The tangent line is $y-0=2(x-2) \Rightarrow y=2x-4$. $\left.\frac{dy}{dx}\right\|_{(-2,0)}=\frac{-4}{1+1}=-2$ The tangent line is $y-0=2(x-2) \Rightarrow y=2x-4$.	$3:\begin{cases}1:\text{solutions for } x\\2:\text{equations of tangent lines}\end{cases}$

(c)	$\frac{d^2y}{dx^2}=\frac{d}{dx}\left[\frac{dy}{dx}\right]$ $=\frac{(1+\cos y)\cdot 2-2x(-\sin y)\frac{dy}{dx}}{(1+\cos y)^2}$ $=\frac{2+2\cos y+2x\sin y\cdot\frac{2x}{1+\cos y}}{(1+\cos y)^2}$	$2:\begin{cases}1:\text{correct execution of quotient rule}\\1:\text{substitution for } dy/dx\end{cases}$
(d)	$\left.\frac{d^2y}{dx^2}\right\vert_{y=\frac{\pi}{2}}=\frac{2+4x^2}{1}\Rightarrow 2+4x^2>0.$ The curve is concave up for all values of x for which $y=\pi/2$.	$2:\begin{cases}1:\text{evaluation of } \frac{d^2y}{dx^2} \text{ at } y=\frac{\pi}{2}\\1:\text{answer}\end{cases}$

5. (a), (b), (c) (*Calculus for AP*®, pages 240–245, 165–167; EU 2.1,2.3; LO 2,1C,2.3B,2.1D; EK 2.1C5,2.3B1,2.1D2; MPAC 1,2,3,5)
5. (d) (*Calculus for AP*®, pages 322–324; EU 2.2; LO 2.2A; EK 2.2A1; MPAC 1,2,3)

6. Let R be the region bounded by the graphs of $y=\sqrt{x}$ and $y=\frac{x}{4}$.
   (a) Find the area of region R.
   (b) There is a line $x=k$ which divides the region R into two sections of equal area. Write an integral expression that could be used to find the value of k. Do not evaluate the integral.
   (c) Write an integral expression that could be used to find the volume of the solid region formed when region R is revolved about the line $y=-1$. Do not evaluate the integral.
   (d) If the region R is the base of a solid with cross sections *parallel* to the x-axis being equilateral triangles, find the volume of the solid region.

	Solution	Possible points
(a)	$A=\int_0^{16}\left(\sqrt{x}-\frac{x}{4}\right)dx$ $=\left.\left(\frac{2}{3}x^{\frac{3}{2}}-\frac{x^2}{8}\right)\right\vert_{x=0}^{x=16}$ $=\frac{32}{3}$	$3:\begin{cases}1:\text{integrand}\\1:\text{limits}\\1:\text{answer}\end{cases}$
(b)	$\int_0^k\left(\sqrt{x}-\frac{x}{4}\right)dx=16$	$2:\begin{cases}1:\text{correct limits}\\1:\text{equation}\end{cases}$

(c)	$V=\pi\int_0^{16}\left[\left(\sqrt{x}+1\right)^2-\left(\frac{x}{4}+1\right)^2\right]dx$	2: integrand as difference of squares and consistent limits
(d)	$V=\int_0^4\frac{\sqrt{3}}{4}\left(4y-y^2\right)^2\,dy$	2: $\begin{cases}1: \text{integrand}\\1: \text{limits}\end{cases}$

6. (a), (b) (*Calculus for AP*®, pages 477–486; EU 3.4; LO 3.4D; EK 3.4D1; MPAC 4)
6. (c) (*Calculus for AP*®, pages 525–528; EU 3.4; LO 3.4D; EK 3.4D2; MPAC 4)
6. (d) (*Calculus for AP*®, pages 518–522; EU 3.4; LO 3.4D; EK 3.4D2; MPAC 4)

CALCULUS AB AND BC SCORING CHART

SECTION I: MULTIPLE-CHOICE QUESTIONS

________ ×1.2 = ________
correct (out of 45) — do not round (out of 45)

SECTION II: FREE-RESPONSE QUESTIONS

Question 1	Score out of 9 points =	________
Question 2	Score out of 9 points =	________
Question 3	Score out of 9 points =	________
Question 4	Score out of 9 points =	________
Question 5	Score out of 9 points =	________
Question 6	Score out of 9 points =	________
	Sum for Section II =	________ (out of 54)

Composite Score

Section I total	=
Section II total	=
Composite score	= ________ (out of 108)

Grade Conversion Chart*

Composite score range	AP® exam grade
68–108	5
52–67	4
39–51	3
27–38	2
0–26	1

***Note:** The ranges listed above are only approximate. Each year the ranges for the actual AP® exam are somewhat different. The cutoffs are established after the exams are given to over 200,000 students and are based on the difficulty level of the exam each year.

AP® CALCULUS BC DIAGNOSTIC TEST
Section I, Part A: Multiple-Choice Questions
Time: 60 minutes
Number of Questions: 30

A calculator may not be used on this part of the examination.

*Asterisks indicate those topics covered on the BC exam.

1. If $f(x) = x^3e^{2x}$, then $f'(x) =$
   (A) $6x^2e^{2x}$
   (B) $x^3e^{2x} + 3x^2e^{2x}$
   (C) $\frac{1}{2}x^3e^{2x} + 3x^2e^{2x}$
   (D) $2x^3e^{2x} + 3x^2e^{2x}$

*2. Which of the following gives the length of the path described by the parametric equations $x = e^{3t}$ and $y = \sin(2t)$ from $t = 0$ to $t = \frac{\pi}{2}$?
   (A) $\int_0^{\pi/2} \sqrt{9e^{6t} + 4\cos^2(2t)}\, dt$
   (B) $\int_0^{\pi/2} \left(9e^{6t} + 4\cos^2(2t)\right) dt$
   (C) $\int_0^{\pi/2} \sqrt{e^{6t} + \sin^2(2t)}\, dt$
   (D) $\int_0^{\pi/2} \sqrt{3e^{3t} + 2\cos(2t)}\, dt$

3. Which of the following is the solution to the differential equation $\frac{dy}{dx} = 2x(y+5)$ with the initial condition $y(1) = -2$?
   (A) $y = -\sqrt{2x^2 + 2}$
   (B) $y = 3e^{x^2-1}$
   (C) $y = 3e^{x^2-5}$
   (D) $y = 3e^{x^2-1} - 5$

4. $\int x^2 \sec^2\left(x^3\right) dx =$
   (A) $\sec(x^3) + C$
   (B) $\tan(x^3) + C$
   (C) $\frac{1}{3}\sec^3\left(x^3\right) + C$
   (D) $\frac{1}{3}\tan\left(x^3\right) + C$

AP® is a trademark registered by the College Board, which is not affiliated with, and does not endorse, this product.

5. The graph of f' consists of a semicircle and a line segment as shown to the right. If $f(-2) = 5$, then $f(6) =$
(A) $2\pi - 6$.
(B) $2\pi - 1$.
(C) $2\pi + 6$.
(D) $2\pi + 11$.

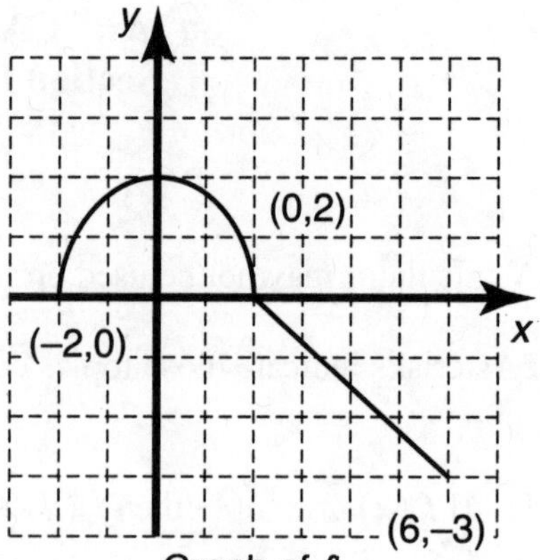

Graph of f'

6. What is the value of $\lim_{x \to 0} \frac{e^{5x} - 1}{e^x + x - 1}$?
(A) 0
(B) $\frac{1}{2}$
(C) $\frac{5}{2}$
(D) Nonexistent

7. If $f(x) = \cos(3x)$, then $f'\left(\frac{\pi}{18}\right) =$
(A) $-\frac{3\sqrt{3}}{2}$.
(B) $-\frac{3}{2}$.
(C) $\frac{3}{2}$.
(D) $\frac{3\sqrt{3}}{2}$.

*8. What is the sum of the series $1 - \frac{1}{3!} + \frac{1}{5!} - \frac{1}{7!} + \cdots + \frac{(-1)^n}{(2n+1)!} + \cdots$?
(A) sin 1
(B) cos 1
(C) e
(D) The series diverges

9. $\frac{d}{dx}\int_0^{x^3} \tan(t+1)\,dt =$
(A) $\tan(x^3 + 1)$.
(B) $\sec^2(x^3 + 1)$.
(C) $3x^2 \tan(x^3 + 1)$.
(D) $3x^2 \sec^2(x^3 + 1)$.

10. What are all values of x for which the function f is increasing if f is defined to be $f(x) = x^3 - 3x^2 - 24x + 5$?
(A) $x > 1$
(B) $-2 < x < 4$
(C) $x < -4$ or $x > 2$
(D) $x < -2$ or $x > 4$

*11. $\int x\cos(2x)dx + \cos(2x) + C$
(A) $x \sin(2x) + \cos(2x) + C$
(B) $\frac{x}{2}\sin(2x) + \frac{1}{4}\cos(2x) + C$
(C) $-2x\sin(2x) + \cos(2x) + C$
(D) $2x \sin(2x) + 4 \cos(2x) + C$

12. $\int_1^3 \frac{x}{x^2 + 4}dx =$
(A) arctan 13 − arctan 5
(B) ln 13 − ln 5
(C) $e^{13} - e^5$
(D) $\frac{1}{2}(\ln 13 - \ln 5)$

*13. If $f(x) = x^2\cos(2x)$, which of the following is the Taylor series for f about $x = 0$?

(A) $1-\frac{4x^2}{2!}+\frac{16x^4}{4!}-\frac{64x^6}{6!}+\cdots$

(B) $x^2+2x^3+\frac{4x^4}{2!}+\frac{8x^5}{3!}+\cdots$

(C) $x^2-\frac{4x^4}{2!}+\frac{16x^6}{4!}-\frac{64x^8}{6!}+\cdots$

(D) $2x^3-\frac{8x^5}{3!}+\frac{32x^7}{5!}-\frac{128x^9}{7!}+\cdots$

14. Using the substitution $u = x^3 + 1$, $\int_0^2 x^2\left(x^3+1\right)^4 dx$ is equal to which of the following?

(A) $\int_0^2 u^4 du$

(B) $\frac{1}{3}\int_0^2 u^4 du$

(C) $\frac{1}{3}\int_1^9 u^4 du$

(D) $3\int_1^9 u^4 du$

15. If the line $y = 3x + 8$ is tangent to the function $f(x) = kx^3$, then $k =$

(A) $\frac{1}{16}$.

(B) $\frac{1}{4}$.

(C) $\frac{1}{3}$.

(D) 3.

*16. What is the slope of the line tangent to the graph of the polar curve $r = 2 + 3\sin\theta$ at $\theta = 0$?

(A) $-\frac{3}{2}$

(B) $-\frac{2}{3}$

(C) $\frac{2}{3}$

(D) 3

17. Let $f(x) = \begin{cases} ax^2+9 \text{ for } x \le 2 \\ cx-3 \text{ for } x > 2 \end{cases}$.

If f is differentiable for all x, then $a + c =$

(A) −15.

(B) $-7\frac{1}{2}$

(C) $7\frac{1}{2}$.

(D) 15.

*18. What are all values of x for which the series $\sum_{N=1}^{\infty}\frac{(x-5)^n}{n3^n}$ converges?

(A) $4 < x < 6$

(B) $2 < x < 8$

(C) $2 \le x < 8$

(D) All real numbers

19. $\lim_{h\to 0}\frac{\cos\left(\frac{5\pi}{6}+h\right)-\cos\frac{5\pi}{6}}{h} =$

(A) $-\frac{\sqrt{3}}{2}$

(B) $-\frac{1}{2}$

(C) $\frac{1}{2}$

(D) $\frac{\sqrt{3}}{2}$

*20. $\int_0^{\infty} e^{-4x}\,dx =$

(A) $-\frac{1}{4}$

(B) $\frac{1}{4}$

(C) 4

(D) Divergent

21. A particle moves along the x-axis so that its velocity at time t is given by $v(t) = 3t^2 - 6t$. If the position of the particle at time $t = 1$ is 5, what is the position of the particle at time $t = 2$?

(A) −2

(B) 0

(C) 3

(D) 6

*22. $\int \frac{x+17}{x^2+x-2}dx =$

(A) $\frac{5}{(x+2)^2} - \frac{6}{(x-1)^2} + C$

(B) $\ln|x^2 + x - 2| + C$

(C) $5\ln|x - 1| - 6\ln|x + 2| + C$

(D) $6\ln|x - 1| - 5\ln|x + 2| + C$

23. If $y^2 = xy - 6$, then at the point (5,2), $\frac{dy}{dx} =$

(A) −2

(B) $\frac{2}{9}$

(C) $\frac{2}{5}$

(D) 4

24.

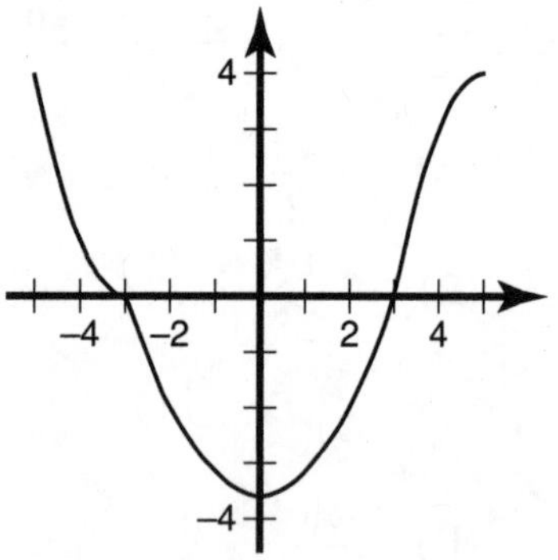

Graph of f′

The graph of f', the derivative of the function f, is shown above. Which of the following statements must be true?

I. The graph of f has a relative minimum at $x = 0$.

II. The graph of f has an inflection point at $x = 0$.

III. The graph of f is decreasing for $-3 < x < 3$.

(A) I only

(B) III only

(C) I and III only

(D) II and III only

25. Let R be the region bounded by the graphs of $y = x^2$ and $y = 3x$. A solid has the region R as its base. Each cross section perpendicular to the x-axis is a rectangle whose height is five times the length of the base. Which of the following gives the volume of the solid?

(A) $\int_0^3 (3x - x^2)\,dx$

(B) $\int_0^3 5(3x - x^2)\,dx$

(C) $\int_0^3 5(3x - x^2)^2\,dx$

(D) $\pi\int_0^3 5(3x - x^2)^2\,dx$

*26. The number of bears in a national park is modeled by the function P that satisfies the logistic differential equation $\frac{dP}{dt} = 3P\left(1 - \frac{P}{2000}\right)$, where t is the time in years and $P(0) = 250$. What is $\lim_{t\to\infty} P(t)$?

(A) 250

(B) 1000

(C) 2000

(D) 6000

27. $\frac{d}{dx}[\arctan(5x)] =$

(A) $\frac{1}{\sqrt{1-25x^2}}$

(B) $\frac{5}{\sqrt{1-25x^2}}$

(C) $\frac{1}{1+25x^2}$

(D) $\frac{5}{1+25x^2}$

28. If $f''(x) = (x + 3)(x - 1)^2(x - 4)$, then the graph of f has inflection points when $x =$

(A) 1 only

(B) −3 and 4 only

(C) −3, 1, and 4 only

(D) −3, 0, 1, and 4 only

*29. Which of the following series is absolutely convergent?

(A) $\sum_{n=0}^{\infty} \frac{(-1)^n}{\sqrt{n}}$

(B) $\sum_{n=0}^{\infty} \frac{(-1)^n}{n}$

(C) $\sum_{n=0}^{\infty} \frac{(-1)^n}{n^3}$

(D) $\sum_{n=0}^{\infty} \left(\frac{-e}{\cos 5}\right)^n$

30. Let f be a differentiable function such that $f(2) = 5, f(7) = 2, f'(5) = -4$, and $f'(7) = -3$. The function g is differentiable and $g(x) = f^{-1}(x)$ for all x. What is the value of $g'(2)$?

(A) -3

(B) $-\frac{1}{3}$

(C) $-\frac{1}{4}$

(D) $\frac{1}{3}$

Section I, Part B: Multiple-Choice Questions
Time: 45 minutes
Number of Questions: 15

A calculator may be used on this part of the examination.

31. A water tank has the shape of a cone with a radius at the top of 4 meters and a height of 8 meters. If water is filling the tank at a rate of $5\frac{\text{m}^3}{\text{min}}$, what is the rate at which the water level is rising when the water is 3 meters deep?
$\left(\text{Volume of a cone } = \frac{1}{3}\pi r^2 h.\right)$
(A) $\frac{5}{\pi}\frac{\text{meters}}{\text{minute}}$
(B) $\frac{5}{3\pi}\frac{\text{meters}}{\text{minute}}$
(C) $\frac{45\pi}{4}\frac{\text{meters}}{\text{minute}}$
(D) $\frac{20}{9\pi}\frac{\text{meters}}{\text{minute}}$

32. A particle travels along a straight line with a velocity of $v(t) = \cos(t^2) - t$ meters per second. What is the total distance, in meters, traveled by the particle from $t = 0$ to $t = 2$ seconds?
(A) 0.769
(B) 1.539
(C) 2.434
(D) 2.757

*33. The fourth-degree Taylor polynomial for $f(x)$ is given by $4 - 9(x-5)^2 - 10(x-5)^3 + 2(x-5)^4$. What is the value of $f'''(5)$?
(A) −60
(B) −10
(C) 2
(D) 48

34. If $\int_1^5 (2f(x)+3)\,dx = 20$, what is the value of $\int_1^5 f(x)\,dx$?
(A) 4
(B) 8.5
(C) 11.5
(D) 16

35.

X	$f(x)$	$f'(x)$	$f''(x)$
5	2	−3	4

Use the values given in the table above and the fact that $h(x) = (f(x))^4$ to find the value of $h'(5)$.
(A) −108
(B) −96
(C) 32
(D) 128

*36. The area bounded by the polar curve $r = 2\theta + \sin\theta$ from $\theta = 0$ to $\theta = \pi$ is
(A) 5.935
(B) 11.870
(C) 27.739
(D) 55.479

37. The first derivative of the function f is given by $f'(x) = \cos(e^x)$ for $0 \le x \le 2$. At which of the following values of x does the graph of f have a local minimum?
(A) 0.452
(B) 1.550
(C) 1.445
(D) 1.838

38.

X	1	2	3	4	5
$f(x)$	8	10	15	17	20

The function f is continuous and differentiable on the closed interval [1, 5]. The table above gives selected values of f on this interval. Which of the following statements could be false?

(A) There exists c, $1 < c < 5$, for which $f(c) = 12$.
(B) There exists c, $1 < c < 5$, for which $f(c) = 3$.
(C) f is increasing for $1 \le x \le 5$.
(D) f has an absolute minimum value on $1 \le x \le 5$.

*39. Given the series $\sum_{n=1}^{\infty} \frac{3n+5}{4n^3 - n^2 + 5}$, the limit comparison test can be used to show that the given series converges by comparing the given series to which of the following?

(A) $\sum_{n=1}^{\infty} \frac{1}{n}$

(B) $\sum_{n=1}^{\infty} \frac{1}{n^2}$

(C) $\sum_{n=1}^{\infty} \frac{1}{n^3}$

(D) $\sum_{n=1}^{\infty} \frac{1}{n^4}$

40.

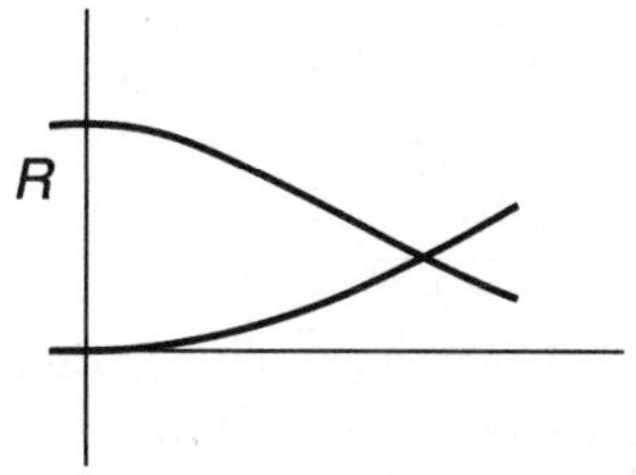

Let R be the region in the first quadrant bounded by the graphs of $f(x) = 1 + e^{-x^2}$ and $g(x) = 1 - \cos x$ as shown in the figure above. Which of the following is the area of R?

(A) 1.866
(B) 3.572
(C) 5.862
(D) 11.222

41. Oil is leaking out of a tank at a rate of $5e^{-0.3t}$ liters per minute, where t is the number of minutes since the tank began to leak. If the tank contained 700 liters of oil when the pump started to leak, how many liters of oil are in the tank at $t = 45$ minutes?

(A) 16.667
(B) 666.706
(C) 683.333
(D) 716.667

*42. If $\lim_{c \to \infty} \int_1^c \frac{dx}{x^p} = 3$, which of the following must be true?

(A) $\sum_{n=1}^{\infty} \frac{1}{n^p}$ diverges.

(B) $\sum_{n=1}^{\infty} \frac{1}{n^p}$ converges.

(C) $\sum_{n=1}^{\infty} \frac{1}{n^p} = 3$.

(D) $\sum_{n=1}^{\infty} \frac{1}{n^{p+1}}$ diverges.

43.

X	3	7	9	12
$f(x)$	12	15	20	24

The values of a continuous function f for selected values of x are given in the table above. What is the value of the right Riemann sum approximation for $\int_3^{12} f(x)\,dx$ using three subintervals and values from the table?

(A) 138
(B) 155
(C) 172
(D) 216

44. What is the average rate of change of the function $f(x) = \sin x$ on the interval [1,4]?

(A) −0.533
(B) 0.042
(C) 0.398
(D) 1.194

*45. A particle moves in the xy-plane so that its velocity vector has components $x'(t) = \ln(t + 4)$ and $y'(t) = \sin(t^2)$. What is the slope of the line tangent to the curve at the point where $t = 3$?

(A) −41.580
(B) −0.024
(C) 0.212
(D) 4.722

Section II
Free-Response Questions
Time: 1 hour and 30 minutes
Number of Problems: 6

Part A
Time: 30 minutes
Number of Problems: 2

You may use a calculator for any problem in this section.

1. The rate at which water is being pumped into a tank is modeled by the function $E(t) = 270\sin^2\left(\frac{t}{4}\right)$, where $E(t)$ is measured in gallons per hour and t is measured in hours, $0 < t < 12$. During the same time interval, water is being removed from the tank at a rate modeled by $R(t) = 80\sqrt{t}\sin^2\left(\frac{t}{8}\right)$. There are 200 gallons of water in the tank at time $t = 0$.
   (a) Find $E'(10)$. Using appropriate units, explain the meaning of your answer in the context of this problem.
   (b) How many gallons of water were pumped into the tank during the 12-hour time interval?
   (c) Is the amount of water in the tank increasing or decreasing at time $t = 10$ hours? Give a reason for your answer.
   (d) At what time t, $0 \le t \le 12$, is the amount of water in the tank at a maximum? Justify your answer.

2. A particle moving along a curve in the xy-plane has position $\langle x(t),\ y(t) \rangle$ at time t with $\frac{dx}{dt} = \sin(t^2)$ and $y(t) = \cos(e^t)$. At time $t = 2$, the object is at the position $(-1,5)$.
   (a) Write the equation of the tangent line to the curve at the point where $t = 2$.
   (b) For what value of t, $0 < t < 1$, does the tangent line to the curve have a slope of 4? Find the acceleration vector at this time.
   (c) Find the speed of the particle at $t = 2$.
   (d) Find the x-coordinate of the position of the particle at time $t = 3$.

Section II
Part B
Time: 60 minutes
Number of Problems: 4

You may not use a calculator for any problem in this section. During the timed portion for Section II, Part B, you may continue to work on the problems in Section II, Part A without the use of a calculator.

3.

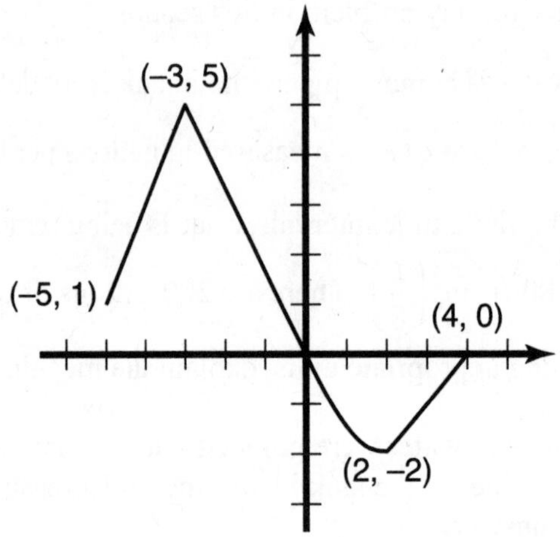

Let f be the continuous function defined on $[-5,5]$ whose graph, consisting of three line segments and a quarter circle is shown above. Let g be the function given by $g(x) = \int_{-3}^{x} f(t)\,dt$.

(a) Find the values of $g(-5)$ and $g(5)$.

(b) For $-5 < x < 5$, find all values of x for which the graph of g has a relative maximum. Justify your answer.

(c) For $-5 < x < 5$, find all values of x for which the graph of g has a point of inflection. Explain your reasoning.

(d) The function h is defined by $h(x) = \dfrac{f(x)}{5x}$. Find $h'(-4)$.

4.

t (minutes)	0	3	5	9	12
$P(t)$ (degrees Celsius)	68	60	55	49	42

The temperature of coffee in a cup at time t is modeled by a strictly decreasing twice-differentiable function P, where $P(t)$ is measured in degrees Celsius and t is measured in minutes. Values of $P(t)$ at selected values of time are shown in the table above.

(a) Is there a time t, $0 \le t \le 12$, at which $P(t) = 57°C$? Give a reason for your answer.

(b) Use the data in the table to estimate $P'(10)$. Show the computations that lead to your answer. Using correct units, interpret the meaning of your answer in the context of the problem.

(c) Use the data in the table to evaluate $\int_3^9 P'(t)\,dt$. Using correct units, interpret the meaning of $\int_3^9 P'(t)\,dt$ in the context of the problem.

(d) Use a right Riemann sum with the four subintervals indicated by the data in the table to approximate $\frac{1}{12}\int_0^{12} P(t)\,dt$. Using correct units, explain the meaning of $\frac{1}{12}\int_0^{12} P(t)\,dt$ in the context of the problem.

5. The rate of change of the population of wolves in a national forest is modeled by the differential equation $\frac{dW}{dt}=\frac{1}{2}(500-W)$, where t is the time in years and $W(t)$is the number of wolves. At time $t = 0$, there are 100 wolves in the forest. $W(t)$ is the solution to the differential equation with initial condition $W(0) = 100$.

(a) Is the number of wolves growing faster when there are 200 wolves or when there are 300 wolves? Explain your reasoning.

(b) Find $\frac{d^2W}{dt^2}$ in terms of W. Use your answer to determine whether the graph of W is concave up or concave down when there are 400 wolves in the forest.

(c) Use separation of variables to find $y = W(t)$, the particular solution to the differential equation with initial condition $W(0) = 100$.

6. The function is defined by $f(x)=\frac{1}{1+x^2}$. The Maclaurin series for f is given by $1-x^2+x^4-x^6+\cdots+(-1)^n x^{2n}+\cdots$ which converges to $f(x)$ for $-1<x<1$.

(a) Find the first three nonzero terms and the general term for the Maclaurin series for $f'(x)$.

(b) Use your results from part (a) to find the sum of the infinite series

$$-\frac{2}{3}+\frac{4}{3^2}-\frac{6}{3^5}+\cdots+\frac{(-1)^n(2n)}{3^{2n-1}}+\cdots$$

(c) Find the first three nonzero terms and the general term for the Maclaurin series representing $\int_0^x f(t)\,dt$.

(d) Use your answer to part (c) to approximate the value of $\int_0^{1/3} f(t)\,dt$ so that the Alternating Series Error Bound for your approximation is less than $\frac{1}{1000}$. Justify your answer.

Answers and Answer Explanations

Using the table below, score your test. Determine how many questions you answered correctly and how many you answered incorrectly. Additional information about scoring is at the end of the diagnostic test.

1. D	*2. A	3. D	4.D	5.B
6. C	7. B	*8. A	9. C	10. D
*11. B	12. D	*13. C	14. C	15. A
*16. C	17. D	*18. C	19. B	*20. B
21. C	*22. D	23. A	24. D	25. C
*26. C	27. D	28. B	*29. C	30. B
31. D	32. C	*33. A	34. A	35. B
*36. C	37. B	38. C	*39. B	40. A
41. C	*42. B	43. C	44. A	*45. C

1. ANSWER: (D) Using the Product Rule and the Chain Rule, we get $f'(x) = 2x^3e^{2x} + 3x^2e^{2x}$.
(*Calculus for AP*®, pages 207–210, 227–233; EU 2.1; LO 2.1C; EK 2.1C3; MPAC 3)

*2. ANSWER: (A) Use the formula for the arc length of parametric functions and substitute $x'(t) = 3e^{3t}$ and $y'(t) = 2\cos(2t)$ into the formula.
(*Calculus for AP*®, pages 777–782; EU 3.4; LO 3.4C; EK 3.4C1; MPAC 3)

3. ANSWER: (D) Separating variables, we get $\int \frac{dy}{y+5} = \int 2x\,dx$.

Integrating gives $\ln|y + 5| = x^2 + C$. Using the initial condition, we find that $C = -1 + \ln 3$ and $\ln|y + 5| = x^2 - 1 + \ln 3$. Thus, $|y+5| = 3e^{2-1}$. Solving for y gives us a solution of $y = 3e^{x^2-1} - 5$.
(*Calculus for AP*®, pages 618–624; EU 3.5; LO 3.5A; EK 3.5A2; MPAC 3)

4. ANSWER: (D) Use substitution with $u = x^3$ and $du = 3x^2dx$. Then
$\int \frac{1}{3}\sec^2 u\,du = \frac{1}{3}\tan u + C = \frac{1}{3}\tan(x^3) + C.$
(*Calculus for AP*®, pages 457–461; EU 3.1; LO 3.1A; EK 3.1A2; MPAC 3)

5. ANSWER: (B) Using the First Fundamental Theorem of Calculus gives $f(6) = f(-2) + \int_{-2}^{6} f'(x)dx$. Substituting the given value of $f(-2)$ and using the signed areas of the semicircle and triangle, we have $f(6) = 5 + 2\pi - 6 = 2\pi - 1$.
(*Calculus for AP®*, pages 436–440; EU 3.3; LO 3.3; EK 3.3A3; MPAC 1,2,4)

6. ANSWER: (C) Using L'Hopital's Rule gives
$\lim_{x\to 0} \frac{e^{5x}-1}{e^x + x - 1} = \lim_{x\to 0} \frac{5e^{5x}}{e^x + 1} = \frac{5}{1+1} = \frac{5}{2}$.
(*Calculus for AP®*, pages 337–343; EU 1.1; LO 1.1C; EK 1.1C3; MPAC 1,2,3)

7. ANSWER: (B) Using the Chain Rule, $f'(x) = -3\sin\frac{\pi}{6} = -3\left(\frac{1}{2}\right) = -\frac{3}{2}$.
(*Calculus for AP®*, pages 227–233; EU 2.1; LO 2.1C; EK 2.1C4; MPAC 3)

*8. ANSWER: (A) Since $\sin x = x - \frac{x^3}{3!} + \frac{x^5}{5!} - \frac{x^7}{7!} + \cdots + \frac{(-1)^n x^3}{n!} + \cdots$ we can substitute $x = 1$ to get $1 - \frac{1}{3!} + \frac{1}{5!} - \frac{1}{7!} + \cdots + \frac{(-1)^n}{(2n+1)!} + \cdots = \sin 1$.
(*Calculus for AP®*, pages 728–737; EU 4.2; LO 4.2B; EK 4.2B5; MPAC 3)

9. ANSWER: (C) Using the Second Fundamental Theorem,
$\frac{d}{dx}\int_0^{x^3} \tan(t+1)dt = \frac{d}{dx}\left[x^3\right] \cdot \tan\left(x^3+1\right) = 3x^2 \tan(x^3+1)$.
(*Calculus for AP®*, pages 436–440; EU 3.3; LO 3.3A; EK 3.3A2; MPAC 1,2,3)

10. ANSWER: (D) $f'(x) = 3x^2 - 6x - 24 = 3(x-4)(x+2)$. $f'(x)$ is positive for $x < -2$ or $x > 4$ so the graph of f is increasing there.
(*Calculus for AP®*, pages 292–300; EU 2.2; LO 2.2A; EK 2.2A1; MPAC 2,3)

*11. ANSWER: (B) Integrate by parts with $u = x$, $du = dx$, $dv = \cos(2x)dx$, and $v = \frac{1}{2}\sin(2x)$. Then
$\int x\cos(2x)dx = \frac{1}{2}x\sin(2x) - \int\frac{1}{2}\sin(2x)dx = \frac{1}{2}x\sin(2x) + \frac{1}{4}\cos(2x) + C$.
(*Calculus for AP®*, pages 544–548; EU 3.3; LO 3.3B(a); EK 3.3B5; MPAC 3)

12. ANSWER: (D) Use substitution with $u = x^2 + 4$ and $du = 2xdx$. Then
$\int_1^3 \frac{x}{x^2+4}dx = \frac{1}{2}\ln(x^2+4)\Big|_1^3 = \frac{1}{2}(\ln 13 - \ln 15)$.

(*Calculus for AP*®, pages 457–461; EU 3.3; LO 3.3B(b); EK 3.3B2; MPAC 3)

*13. ANSWER: (C) Using the fact that $\cos x = 1 - \frac{x^2}{2!} + \frac{x^4}{4!} - \frac{x^6}{6!} + \cdots$, substitute $2x$ in place of x and then multiply by x^2 to get $x^2 - \frac{4x^4}{2!} + \frac{16x^6}{4!} - \frac{64x^8}{6!} + \cdots$.
(*Calculus for AP*®, pages 728–737; EU 2.1; LO 2.1C; EK 2.1C4; MPAC 2 and 3)

14. ANSWER: (C) Since $u = x^3 + 1$, we have $du = 3x^2dx$. When $x = 0$, $u = 1$, and when $x = 2$, $u = 9$. Therefore, $\int_0^2 x^2(x^3+1)^4\,dx = \frac{1}{3}\int_1^9 u^4\,du$.
(*Calculus for AP*®, pages 436–465; EU 3.3; LO 3.3B(b); EK 3.3B5; MPAC 3)

15. ANSWER: (A) Differentiating gives us $y' = 3$ and $f'(x) = 3kx^2$.
Setting the slopes equal gives $3 = 3\,kx^2$ so that $k = \frac{1}{x^2}$. Since the function and the line intersect at the point of tangency, we also have $3x + 8 = kx^3$. Solving the system of equations gives us $x = -4$ so that
$k = \frac{1}{x^2} = \frac{1}{(-4)^2} = \frac{1}{16}$.
(*Calculus for AP*®, pages 165–167; EU 2.3; LO 2.3B; EK 2.3B2; MPAC 1,2,3)

*16. ANSWER: (C) Using the slope formula for polar equations,
$$\frac{dy}{dx} = \frac{(2+3\sin\theta)(\cos\theta)+(3\cos\theta)(\sin\theta)}{-(2+3\sin\theta)(\sin\theta)+(3\cos\theta)(\cos\theta)}.$$
When $\theta = 0$, $\frac{dy}{dx} = \frac{(2+3(0))(1)+(3(1))(0)}{-(2+3(0))(0)+(3(1))(1)} = \frac{2+0}{0+3} = \frac{2}{3}$.
(*Calculus for AP*®, pages 803–810; EU 2.1; LO 2.1C; EK 2.1C7; MPAC 3)

17. ANSWER: (D) Differentiating the piecewise function, we have $f'(x) = 2ax$ for $x < 2$ and $f'(x) = c$ for $x > 2$. For f to be differentiable, f must also be continuous so $\lim_{x\to 2}(ax^2+9) = \lim_{x\to 2^+}(cx-3)$ and $\lim_{x\to 2^-}(2ax) = \lim_{x\to 2^+}(c)$.
Evaluating these limits gives the system of equations $4a + 9 = 2c - 3$ and $4a = c$. Solving the system of equations, we have $a = 3$ and $c = 12$, so $a + c = 15$.
(*Calculus for AP*®, pages 182–184; EU 2.2; LO 2.2B; EK 2.2B2; MPAC 2,3)

*18. ANSWER: (C) Using the Ratio Test,
$\lim_{n\to\infty}\left|\frac{a_{n+1}}{a_n}\right| = \lim_{n\to\infty}\left|\frac{(x-5)^{n+1}}{(n+1)3^{n+1}} \cdot \frac{n3^n}{(x-5)^n}\right| = \frac{|x-5|}{3}$. Solving for the x-values that

make $\frac{|x-5|}{3} < 1$, we have $2 < x < 8$. The endpoint analysis shows that at $x = 8$, the resulting series is $\sum_{n=1}^{\infty} \frac{1}{n}$, which diverges because it is the harmonic series. At $x = 2$, the resulting series is $\sum_{n=1}^{\infty} \frac{(-1)^n}{n}$, which converges by the alternating series test.

Therefore, the series converges for $2 \le x < 8$.

(*Calculus for AP*®, pages 715–717; EU 4.2; LO 4.2C; EK 4.2C2; MPAC 1,2,3)

19. ANSWER: (B) By the definition of the derivative, this is $f'\left(\frac{5\pi}{6}\right)$, where $f(x) = \cos x$. $f'(x) = -\sin x$ so $f'\left(\frac{5\pi}{6}\right) = -\sin\left(\frac{5\pi}{6}\right) = -\frac{1}{2}$.
(*Calculus for AP*®, pages 169–171; EU 2.1; LO 2.1A; EK 2.1A2; MPAC 3)

*20. ANSWER: (B) Since this is an improper integral, we must rewrite it using limits:

$$\int_0^{\infty} e^{-4x}dx = \lim_{c\to\infty}\int_0^c e^{-4x}dx = -\frac{1}{4}\lim_{c\to\infty} e^{-4x}\Big|_o^c = -\frac{1}{4}\lim_{c\to\infty}\frac{1}{e^{4x}}\Big|_0^c = -\frac{1}{4}\lim_{c\to\infty}\left(\frac{1}{e^{4c}}-1\right) = \frac{1}{4}.$$

(*Calculus for AP*®, pages 586–594; EU 3.2; LO 3.2D; EK 3.2D1,3.3D2; MPAC 2,3)

21. ANSWER: (C) Since $v(t) = x'(t)$, by the First Fundamental Theorem, we have

$$x(2) = x(1) + \int_1^2 x'(t)dt = 5 + \int_1^2 (3t^2 - 6t)dt = 5 + (t^3 - 3t^2)\Big|_1^2 = 5 + (8-12) - (1-3) = 3.$$

(*Calculus for AP*®, pages 437–440; EU 3.4; LO 3.4C; EK 3.4C1; MPAC 1,2,3)

*22. ANSWER: (D) Partial fraction decomposition gives
$\frac{x+17}{(x+2)(x-1)} = \frac{A}{x+2} + \frac{B}{x-1}$ where $A = -5$ and $B = 6$. Then

$$\int \frac{x+17}{(x+2)(x-1)}dx = \int\left(\frac{6}{x-1} - \frac{5}{x+2}\right)dx = 6\ln|x-1| - 5\ln|x+2| + C.$$

(*Calculus for AP*®, pages 569–572; EU 3.3; LO 3.3B; EK 3.3B5; MPAC 3)

23. ANSWER: (A) Using implicit differentiation, we have
$2y\frac{dy}{dx} = x\frac{dy}{dx} + y$ so $\frac{dy}{dx} = \frac{y}{2y-x}$. Substituting $x = 2$ and $y = 2$ results in

$\frac{dy}{dx} = \frac{2}{4-5} = -2.$

(*Calculus for AP*®, pages 240–245; EU 2.1; LO 2.1C; EK 2.1C5; MPAC 3)

24. ANSWER: (D) Since f' does not change sign at $x = 0$, f does not have a relative maximum at $x = 0$, so I is false. Since f' changes from decreasing to increasing at $x = 0$, f has an inflection point at $x = 0$, so II is true. Since $f' < 0$ for $-3 < x < 2$, f is increasing there so III is true.
(*Calculus for AP*®, pages 293–300, 324; EU 2.2; LO 2.2A; EK 2.2A1; MPAC 2,3)

25. ANSWER: (C) The graphs of $y = x^2$ and $y = 3x$ intersect at $x = 0$ and $x = 3$. Each cross section is a rectangle with base of $3x - x^2$ and height of $5(3x - x^2)$, the area of each cross section is $A(x) = 5(3x - x^2)^2$ so the volume is found by $V = \int_0^3 5(3x - x^2)^2\,dx$.
(*Calculus for AP*®, pages 518–522; EU 3.4; LO 3.4D; EK 3.4D2; MPAC 2,3)

*26. ANSWER: (C) In logistic growth, the population grows at a rate of $\frac{dy}{dt} = ky\left(1 - \frac{y}{L}\right)$, where L is the limiting number. In this equation, $L = 2000$.
(*Calculus for AP*®, pages 630–634; EU 3.5; LO 3.5B; EK 3.5B2; MPAC 1,2)

27. ANSWER: (D) Using the Chain Rule
$$\frac{d}{dx}[\arctan(5x)] = 5\left(\frac{1}{1 + (5x)^2}\right) = \frac{5}{1 + 25x^2}.$$
(*Calculus for AP*®, pages 227–233, 245–246; EU 3.5; LO 3.5A; EK 3.5A1; MPAC 2,3)

28. ANSWER: (B) $f''(x)$ changes from positive to negative or vice versa at $x = -3$ and $x = 4$ so the graph of f has an inflection point at $x = -3$ and $x = 4$. The graph of f does not change signs at $x = 0$ or $x = 1$ so the graph of f does not have an inflection point at $x = 0$ or $x = 1$.
(*Calculus for AP*®, page 324; EU 2.2; LO 2.2A; EK 2.2A1; MPAC 2,3)

*29. ANSWER: (C) $\sum_{n=0}^{\infty} \frac{(-1)^n}{n^3}$ converges by the alternating series test, and

$\sum_{n=0}^{\infty} \left|\frac{(-1)^n}{n^3}\right| = \sum_{n=0}^{\infty} \frac{1}{n^3}$ converges by the p-series test, so this series is absolutely convergent.
(*Calculus for AP*®, pages 699–701; EU 4.1; LO 4.1A; EK 4.1A4; MPAC 1,2,3)

$$g'(2) = (f^{-1})'(2) = \frac{1}{f'(f^{-1}(2))} = \frac{1}{f'(7)} = \frac{1}{-3} = -\frac{1}{3}.$$

30. ANSWER: (B)
(*Calculus for AP*®, pages 247–248; EU 2.1; LO 2.1C; EK 2.1C2; MPAC 3)

31. ANSWER: (D) Since
$$f=\frac{h}{2}, V=\frac{1}{3}\pi r^2 h=\frac{1}{3}\pi\left(\frac{h}{2}\right)^2(h)=\frac{1}{12}\pi h^3,\text{ so }\frac{dV}{dt}=\frac{1}{14}\pi h^2\frac{dh}{dt}.$$
Substituting $h = 8$ and $\frac{dh}{dt}=5$, we get $5=\frac{9\pi}{4}\frac{dh}{dt}$ so $\frac{dh}{dt}=\frac{20}{9\pi}$.
(*Calculus for AP*®, pages 274–279; EU 2.3; LO 2.3C; EK 2.3C2; MPAC 2,3)

32. ANSWER: (C) Total distance = $\int_0^2\left|\cos(t^2)-t\right|dt = 2.434$
(*Calculus for AP*®, page 452; EU 3.4; LO 3.4C; EK 3.4C1; MPAC 2, 3)

*33. ANSWER: (A) Using the Taylor polynomial formula, we have
$\frac{f'''(5)}{3!}(x-5)^3=-10(x-5)^3$ so $f'''(5)=(-10)(3!)=-60$.
(*Calculus for AP*®, pages 728–737; EU 4.2; LO 4.2A; EK 4.2A1; MPAC 2,3,5)

34. ANSWER: (A)
$$\begin{aligned}\int_1^5(2f(x)+3)dx &= 2\int_1^5 f(x)dx+\int_1^5 3dx\\ &= 2\int_1^5 f(x)dx+3x\Big|_1^5\\ &= 2\int_1^5 f(x)dx+15-3\\ &= 2\int_1^5 f(x)dx+12.\end{aligned}$$
Solving $2\int_1^5 f(x)dx+12=20$ gives $\int_1^5 f(x)\,dx=4$
(*Calculus for AP*®, pages 423–425; EU 3.2; LO 3.2C; EK 3.2C2; MPAC 2,3)

35. ANSWER: (B) Using the Chain Rule,
$h'(x)=4(f(x))^3(h'(x))$, so $h'(5)=4(f(5))^3(h'(5))=4(2)^3(-3)=-96$.
(*Calculus for AP*®, pages 227–233; EU 2.1; LO 2.1C; EK 2.1C4; MPAC 2,3,5)

*36. ANSWER: (C) Area $=\frac{1}{2}\int_0^{\pi}(2\theta+\sin\theta)^2\,d\theta=27.739$.
(*Calculus for AP*®, pages 803–810; EU 3.4; LO 3.4D; EK 3.4D1; MPAC 3,4)

37. ANSWER: (B) f' changes from negative to positive at 1.550, so the relative minimum of the graph of f occurs at $x = 1.550$.
(*Calculus for AP*®, pages 293–300; EU 2.2; LO 2.2A; EK 2.2A1; MPAC 2,3)

38. ANSWER: (C) Answer A is true by the Intermediate Value Theorem since 12 lies between $f(2) = 10$ and $f(3) = 15$. Answer B is true by the Mean Value Theorem since $\frac{f(5)-f(1)}{5-1} = \frac{20-8}{4} = 3$. Answer D is true by the Extreme Value Theorem since f is continuous on a closed interval. Answer C could be true but is not necessarily true.
(*Calculus for AP*®, pages 295, 308–311, 141–142; EU 1.2; LO 1.2B; EK 1.2B1; MPAC 1,2,4)

*39. ANSWER: (B) Using the limit comparison test and comparing to $\sum_{n=1}^{\infty} \frac{1}{n^2}$, which converges by the p-series test, results in $\lim_{n\to\infty}\left(\frac{3n+5}{4n^3-n^2+7}\cdot\frac{n^2}{1}\right) = \lim_{n\to\infty}\left(\frac{3n^3+5n^2}{4n^3-n^2+7}\right) = \frac{3}{4}$. Since $\frac{3}{4}$ is finite and positive, the given series also converges by the limit comparison test.
(*Calculus for AP*®, pages 688–689; EU 4.1; LO 4.1A; EK 4.1A6; MPAC 1,2,3)

40. ANSWER: (A) The graphs of $f(x)$ and $g(x)$ intersect at $x = 1.6389...$
The area is found by Area $= \int_0^{1.6389...} \left(f(x) - g(x)\right) dx = 1.866$.
(*Calculus for AP*®, pages 477–484; EU 3.4; LO 3.4D; EK 3.4D1; MPAC 2,3)

41. ANSWER: (C) Amount of oil $= 700 - \int_0^{45} \left(5e^{-0.3t}\right) dt = 683.333$ liters.
(*Calculus for AP*®, pages 436–440; EU 3.4; LO 3.4E; EK 3.4E1; MPAC 2,3,4)

*42. ANSWER: (B) Since the given integral equals 3, $\int_1^{\infty} \frac{1}{x^p} dx = 3$ and the improper integral converges. Since the improper integral converges, the corresponding series $\sum_{n=0}^{\infty} \frac{1}{n^p}$ also converges by the integral test.
(*Calculus for AP*®, pages 675–678; EU 4.1; LO 4.1A; EK 4.1A6; MPAC 1,2,3,4)

43. ANSWER: (C) Using the three subintervals [3,7], [7,9], and [9,12], the right Riemann sum is (4)(15) + (2)(20) + (3)(24) = 172.
(*Calculus for AP*®, pages 395–410, 418–420; EU 3.2; LO 3.2B; EK 3.2B2; MPAC 2,3,4)

44. ANSWER: (A)
Average rate of change $= \frac{f(4)-f(1)}{4-1} = \frac{\sin 4 - \sin 1}{3} = -0.533$.
(*Calculus for AP*®, page 171; EU 2.1; LO 2.1A; EK 2.1A1; MPAC 3)

*45. ANSWER: (C) Slope $= \dfrac{y'(9)}{x'(9)} = \dfrac{\sin 9}{\ln 7} = 0.212$.

(*Calculus for AP®*, pages 769–782; EU 2.1; LO 2.1C; EK 2.1C7; MPAC 3)

FREE-RESPONSE QUESTIONS

1. The rate at which water is being pumped into a tank is modeled by the function $E(t) = 270\sin^2\left(\dfrac{t}{4}\right)$, where $E(t)$ is measured in gallons per hour and t is measured in hours, $0 \le t \le 12$. During the same time interval, water is being removed from the tank at a rate modeled by $R(t) = 80\sqrt{t}\sin^2\left(\dfrac{t}{8}\right)$. There are 200 gallons of water in the tank at time $t = 0$.

   (a) Find $E'(10)$. Using appropriate units, explain the meaning of your answer in the context of this problem.
   (b) How many gallons of water were pumped into the tank during the 12-hour time interval?
   (c) Is the amount of water in the tank increasing or decreasing at time $t = 10$ hours? Give a reason for your answer.
   (d) At what time t, $0 \le t \le 12$, is the amount of water in the tank at a maximum? Justify your answer.

	Solution	Possible points
(a)	$E'(10) = -64.727$ When $t = 10$ hours, the rate at which water is being pumped into the tank is decreasing at a rate of $64.727 \dfrac{\text{gallons}}{\text{hour}^2}$.	$2: \begin{cases} 1: E'(10) \\ 2: \text{explanation with units} \end{cases}$
(b)	$\int_0^{12} E(t)\,dt = 1695.442$ gallons	$2: \begin{cases} 1: \text{integral} \\ 1: \text{answer} \end{cases}$
(c)	$E(10) - R(10) = -131.123$ Since $E(10) < R(10)$, the amount of water in the tank is decreasing at $t = 10$ hours.	$2: \begin{cases} 1: \text{considers } E(10) \text{ and } R(10) \\ 1: \text{answer and reason} \end{cases}$
(d)	The amount of water in the tank at time, $0 \le t \le 12$, is $200 + \int_0^t (E(x) - R(x))\,dx$. $E(t) - R(t) = 0 \Rightarrow t = 8.678028$ t | Amount of Water in the Tank 0 | 200 8.678028 | 1088.491 12 | 579.718 The amount of water in the tank is a maximum at time $t = 8.678$ hours.	$3: \begin{cases} 1: \text{considers } E(t) - R(t) = 0 \\ 1: \text{answer} \\ 1: \text{justification} \end{cases}$

1. (a) (*Calculus for AP®*, pages 163–167; EU 2.1; LO 2.1B; EK 2.1B1; MPAC 3,6)
1. (b) (*Calculus for AP®*, pages 436–440; EU 3.4; LO 3.4A; EK 3.4A2; MPAC 2,3)
1. (c) (*Calculus for AP®*, pages 293–300; EU 2.1; LO 2.1B; EK 2.1B1; MPAC 3,6)
1. (d) (*Calculus for AP®*, pages 292–300; EU 3.4; LO 3.4AEK 3.4A2; MPAC 2,3)

2. A particle moving along a curve in the *xy*-plane has position $\langle x(t),\ y(t)\rangle$ at time *t* with $\frac{dx}{dt} = \sin(t^2)$ and $y(t) = \cos(e^t)$. At time $t = 2$, the object is at the position $(-1,5)$.
   (a) Write the equation of the tangent line to the curve at the point where $t = 2$.
   (b) For what value of *t*, $0 < t < 1$, does the tangent line to the curve have a slope of 4? Find the acceleration vector at this time.
   (c) Find the speed of the particle at $t = 2$.
   (d) Find the *x*-coordinate of the position of the particle at time $t = 3$.

	Solution	**Possible points**
(a)	Slope $= \frac{\cos(e^2)}{\sin 4} = -0.592$ The tangent line equation is $y - 5 = -0.592(x + 1)$	$2: \begin{cases} 1: \text{slope} \\ 1: \text{equation} \end{cases}$
(b)	$\frac{\cos(e^t)}{\sin(t^2)} = 4$ when $t = 0.260078$ $a(0.260078) = \langle 0.519, -1.249\rangle$ (or $\langle 0.518, -1.248\rangle$)	$3: \begin{cases} 1: \text{ slope in terms of } t \\ 1: \text{ value of } t \\ 1: \text{ acceleration vector} \end{cases}$
(c)	Speed $= \sqrt{(\sin 4)^2 + \left(\cos\left(e^2\right)\right)^2} = 0880$ (or 0.879)	1:speed
(d)	$x(3) = x(2) + \int_2^3 x'(t)dt$ $= -1 + \int_2^3 \sin(t^2)dt$ $= -1.031$	$3: \begin{cases} 1: \text{integral} \\ 1: \text{handles initial condition} \\ 1: \text{answer} \end{cases}$

2. (a), (b) (*Calculus for AP®*, pages 769–782; EU 2.3; LO 2.3B; EK 2.3B1; MPAC 1,3)
2. (c) (*Calculus for AP®*, pages 769–782; EU 2.3 LO 2.3C; EK 2.3C4; MPAC 2,3)
2. (d) (*Calculus for AP®*, pages 436–440; EU 3.4; LO 3.4A; EK 3.4A2; MPAC 2,3)

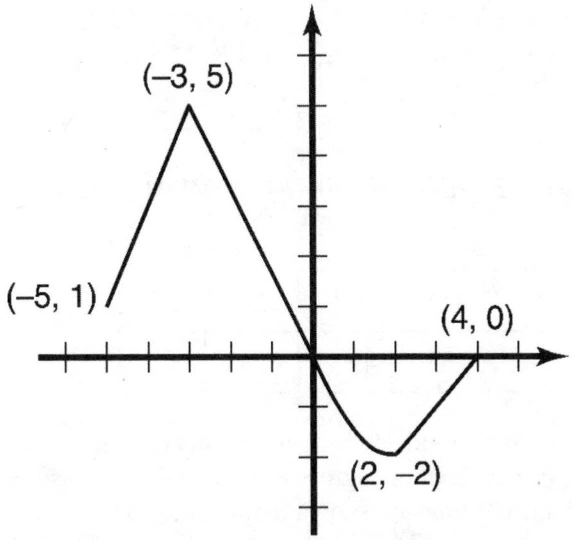

3. Let f be the continuous function defined on $[-5,5]$ whose graph, consisting of three line segments and a quarter circle is shown above. Let g be the function given by $g(x)=\int_{-3}^{x} f(t)\,dt$.

   (a) Find the values of $g(-5)$ and $g(5)$.
   (b) For $-5 < x < 5$, find all values of x for which the graph of g has a relative maximum. Justify your answer.
   (c) For $-5 < x < 5$, find all values of x for which the graph of g has a point of inflection. Explain your reasoning.
   (d) The function h is defined by $h(x)=\dfrac{f(x)}{5x}$. Find $h'(-4)$

	Solution	Possible points
(a)	$g(-5)=\int_{-3}^{-5} f(t)\,dt=-\frac{1}{2}(2)(1+5)=-6$ $g(5)=\int_{-3}^{5} f(t)\,dt=\frac{1}{2}(3)(5)-\pi-\frac{1}{2}(2)(2)=\frac{11}{2}-\pi$	$2:\begin{cases}1: g(-5)\\1: g(5)\end{cases}$
(b)	g has a relative maximum at $x = 0$ because $g'(x)=f(x)$ changes from positive to negative there.	$2:\begin{cases}1: x\text{-value}\\1: \text{justification}\end{cases}$
(c)	g has a point of inflection at $x = -3$ because $g'(x)=f(x)$ changes from increasing to decreasing there and at $x = 2$ because $g'(x)=f(x)$ changes from decreasing to increasing there.	$2:\begin{cases}1: x\text{-value}\\1: \text{explanation}\end{cases}$
(d)	$h'(x)=\dfrac{5xf'(x)-5f(x)}{(5x^2)}$ $h'(-4)=\dfrac{5(-4)f'(-4)-5f(-4)}{(5(-4))^2}$ $=\dfrac{-20(2)-5(3)}{(-20)^2}$ $=\dfrac{-40-15}{400}=-\dfrac{55}{400}=-\dfrac{11}{80}$	$3:\begin{cases}2: h'(x)\\1: \text{answer}\end{cases}$

3. (a) (*Calculus for AP*®, pages 422–423; EU 3.3; LO 3.3A; EK 3.3A3; MPAC 2,3,4)
3. (b) (*Calculus for AP*®, page 199–200; EU 2.2,3.3; LO 2.2A,3.3A; EK 2.2A1,3.3A2; MPAC 2,3,4)
3. (c) (*Calculus for AP*®, pages 316–327; EU 2.2,3.3; LO 2.2A,3.3A; EK 2.2A1,3.3A2; MPAC 2,3,4)
3. (d) (*Calculus for AP*®, pages 207–210; EU 2.1; LO 2.1C; EK 2.1C3; MPAC 2,3,4)

4.

t (minutes)	0	3	5	9	12
$P(t)$ (degrees Celsius)	68	60	55	49	42

The temperature of coffee in a cup at time t is modeled by a strictly decreasing twice-differentiable function C, where $P(t)$ is measured in degrees Celsius and t is measured in minutes. Values of $P(t)$ at selected values of time are shown in the table above.

(a) Is there a time t, $0 \le t \le 12$, at which $P(t) = 57°C$? Give a reason for your answer.

(b) Use the data in the table to estimate $P'(10)$. Show the computations that lead to your answer. Using correct units, interpret the meaning of your answer in the context of the problem.

(c) Use the data in the table to evaluate $\int_3^9 P'(t)dt$. Using correct units, interpret the meaning of $\int_3^9 P'(t)dt$ in the context of the problem.

(d) Use a right Riemann sum with the four subintervals indicated by the data in the table to approximate $\frac{1}{12}\int_0^{12} P'(t)dt$. Using correct units, explain the meaning of $\frac{1}{12}\int_0^{12} P'(t)dt$ in the context of the problem.

	Solution	Possible points
(a)	P is differentiable $\Rightarrow$ P is continuous. $P(5) = 55 < 57 < 60 = P(3)$. Therefore, by the Intermediate Value Theorem, there is a time t, $3 < t < 5$, such that $P(t) = 57$.	$2: \begin{cases} 1: P(5) < 57 < P(3) \\ 2: \text{conclusion using Intermediate Value Theorem} \end{cases}$
(b)	$P'(10) \approx \frac{P(12) - P(9)}{12 - 9} = \frac{42 - 49}{3} = -\frac{7}{3}$ The temperature of the coffee is decreasing at a rate of approximately $\frac{7}{3}$ °C per minute at time $t = 10$ minutes.	$2: \begin{cases} 1: \text{estimate} \\ 1: \text{interpretation with units} \end{cases}$
(c)	$\int_3^9 P'(t)dt = P(9) - P(3) = 40 - 55 = -6$ The coffee has cooled by 6°C over the interval from $t = 3$ minutes to $t = 9$ minutes.	$2: \begin{cases} 1: \text{value} \\ 1: \text{interpretation with units} \end{cases}$

(d)	$\frac{1}{12}\int_0^{12} P(t)dt \approx \frac{1}{12}(3P(3)+2P(5)+4P(9)+3P(12))$ $=\frac{1}{12}(3\cdot 60+2\cdot 55+4\cdot 49+3\cdot 42)$ $=\frac{1}{12}(612)=51°\text{C}$ $\frac{1}{12}\int_0^{12} P(t)dt$ is the average temperature of the coffee, in degrees Celsius, over the time interval $0 \le t \le 12$ minutes.	$2:\begin{cases}1:\text{right Riemann sum}\\1:\text{approximation}\end{cases}$

4. (a) (*Calculus for AP®*, pages 141–142; EU 1.2; LO 1.2B; EK 1.2B1; MPAC 1,2,3,6)
4. (b) (*Calculus for AP®*, page 171; EU 2.1; LO 2.1B; EK 2.1B1; MPAC 1,2,3,6)
4. (c) (*Calculus for AP®*, pages 436–440; EU 3.3; LO 3.3B(b); EK 3.3B2; MPAC 1,2,3,6)
4. (d) (*Calculus for AP®*, pages 395–410, 418–420, 490–494; EU 3.2; LO 3.2B; EK 3.2B2; MPAC 1,2,3,5)

5. The rate of change of the population of wolves in a national forest is modeled by the differential equation $\frac{dW}{dt}=\frac{1}{2}(500-W)$, where t is the time in years and $W(t)$ is the number of wolves. At time $t = 0$, there are 100 wolves in the forest. $W(t)$ is the solution to the differential equation with initial condition $W(0) = 100$.
   (a) Is the number of wolves growing faster when there are 200 wolves or when there are 300 wolves? Explain your reasoning.
   (b) Find $\frac{d^2W}{dt^2}$ in terms of W. Use your answer to determine whether the graph of W is concave up or concave down when there are 400 wolves in the forest.
   (c) Use separation of variables to find $y = W(t)$, the particular solution to the differential equation with initial condition $W(0) = 100$.

	Solution	Possible points
(a)	$\left.\frac{dW}{dt}\right\|_{W=200}=\frac{1}{2}(500-200)=150\frac{\text{wolves}}{\text{year}}$ $\left.\frac{dW}{dt}\right\|_{W=300}=\frac{1}{2}(500-300)=100\frac{\text{wolves}}{\text{year}}$ Because $\left.\frac{dW}{dt}\right\|_{W=200} > \left.\frac{dW}{dt}\right\|_{W=300}$ The number of wolves is growing faster when $W = 200$ wolves.	$2:\begin{cases}1:\text{uses }\frac{dW}{dt}\\1:\text{answer with reason}\end{cases}$

(b)	$\frac{d^2W}{dt^2} = -\frac{1}{2}\frac{dW}{dt}$ $= -\frac{1}{2}\left(\frac{1}{2}(500 - W)\right)$ $= -125 + \frac{1}{4}W$ When $W = 400$, $\frac{d^2W}{dt^2} = -125 + \frac{1}{4}(400) = -25$ Since $\frac{d^2W}{dt^2} < 0$ when $W = 400$, the graph of W is concave down.	$2: \begin{cases} 1: \frac{d^2W}{dt^2} \text{ in terms of } t \\ 1: \text{answer with reason} \end{cases}$
(c)	$\int \frac{dW}{500 - W} = \int \frac{1}{2} dt$ $-\ln\lvert 500 - W \rvert = \frac{1}{2}t + C$ Because $100 \le W < 500$, $\lvert 500 - W \rvert = 500 - W$ $-\ln\lvert 500 - 100 \rvert = \frac{1}{2}(0) + C \Rightarrow -\ln\ 400 = C$ $500 - W = 400e^{-\frac{1}{2}t}$ $W = 500 - 400e^{-\frac{1}{2}t}, t \ge 0$	$5: \begin{cases} 1: \text{separation of variables} \\ 1: \text{antiderivatives} \\ 1: \text{constant of integration} \\ 1: \text{uses initial condition} \\ 1: \text{solves for } W \end{cases}$

5. (a) (*Calculus for AP®*, pages 167–168; EU 2.3; LO 2.3D; EK 2.3D1; MPAC 1,2,3,5,6)
5. (b) (*Calculus for AP®*, pages 240–245; EU 2.2,2.3; LO 2.2A,2.3D; EK 2.2A1, 2.3D1; MPAC 1,2,3,5,6)
5. (c) (*Calculus for AP®*, pages 618–624; EU 3.5; LO 3.5A; EK 3.5A2; MPAC 2,3)

6. The function f is defined by $f(x) = \frac{1}{1+x^2}$. The Maclaurin series for f is given by $1 - x^2 + x^4 - x^6 + \cdots + (-1)^n x^{2n} + \cdots$ which converges to $f(x)$ for $-1 < x < 1$.

   (a) Find the first three nonzero terms and the general term for the Maclaurin series for $f'(x)$.

   (b) Use your results from part (a) to find the sum of the infinite series $-\frac{2}{3} + \frac{4}{3^2} - \frac{6}{3^5} + \cdots + \frac{(-1)^n(2n)}{3^{2n-1}} + \cdots$.

   (c) Find the first three nonzero terms and the general term for the Maclaurin series representing $\int_0^x f(t)\,dt$.

   (d) Use your answer to part (c) to approximate the value of $\int_0^{1/3} f(t)\,dt$ so that the Alternating Series Error Bound for your approximation is less than $\frac{1}{1000}$. Justify your answer.

	Solution	Possible points
(a)	$f'(x) = -2x + 4x^3 - 6x^5 + \cdots + (-1)^n 2nx^{2n-1} + \cdots$	$2: \begin{cases} 1: \text{first three terms} \\ 1: \text{general term} \end{cases}$
(b)	The given series is the Maclaurin series for $f'(x)$ with $x = \frac{1}{3}$. $f'(x) = -(1+x^2)^{-2}(2x) = -\frac{2x}{\left(1+x^2\right)^2}$ The sum of the series is $f'\left(\frac{1}{3}\right) = -\frac{2\left(\frac{1}{3}\right)}{\left(1+\frac{1}{9}\right)^2} = -\frac{\frac{2}{3}}{\left(\frac{10}{9}\right)^2} = -\frac{27}{50}$	$2: \begin{cases} 1: f'(x) \\ 1: f'\left(\frac{1}{3}\right) \end{cases}$
(c)	$\int_0^x \frac{1}{1+t^2}\,dt = x - \frac{x^3}{3} + \frac{x^5}{5} - \cdots + \frac{(-1)^n x^{2n+1}}{2n+1} + \cdots$	$2: \begin{cases} 1: \text{ first three terms} \\ 1: \text{ general term} \end{cases}$
(d)	$\int_0^{1/3} f(t)\,dt \approx \frac{1}{3} - \frac{\frac{1}{27}}{3} = \frac{1}{3} - \frac{1}{81} = \frac{26}{81}$ Since the terms of the series alternate, decrease in absolute value, and have a limit of 0, $\left\lvert \int_0^{1/3} f(t)\,dt - \frac{26}{81} \right\rvert < \frac{1}{5(243)} < \frac{1}{1000}$ By the Alternating Series Error Bound.	$3: \begin{cases} 1: \text{approximation} \\ 1: \text{absolute value of} \\ \quad \text{3rd term} < \frac{1}{1000} \\ 1: \text{justification} \end{cases}$

6. (a), (b), (c) (*Calculus for AP*®, pages 721–724; EU 4.2; LO 4.2B; EK 4.2B5; MPAC 1,2,3)
6. (d) (*Calculus for AP*®, pages 695–697; EU 4.2; LO 4.2A; EK 4.2A5; MPAC 1,2,3)

CALCULUS AB AND BC SCORING CHART

SECTION I: MULTIPLE-CHOICE QUESTIONS

______ × 1.8 = ______

# correct	do not round
(out of 45)	(out of 45)

SECTION II: FREE-RESPONSE QUESTIONS

Question 1	Score out of 9 points =	______
Question 2	Score out of 9 points =	______
Question 3	Score out of 9 points =	______
Question 4	Score out of 9 points =	______
Question 5	Score out of 9 points =	______
Question 6	Score out of 9 points =	______
	Sum for Section II =	______
		(out of 54)

Composite Score

Section I total =
Section II total =
Composite score = ______ (out of 108)

Composite score range	AP® exam grade
68–108	5
52–67	4
39–51	3
27–38	2
0–26	1

***Note:** The ranges listed above are only approximate. Each year the ranges for the actual AP® exam are somewhat different. The cutoffs are established after the exams are given to over 200,000 students and are based on the difficulty level of the exam each year.

Part II

A Review of AP® Calculus

1

LIMITS AND THEIR PROPERTIES

The concept of limits is fundamental to the study of calculus. The limit process is used in two classic ways: to find a rate of change (the slope at a point on a curve) and to find the area of a plane region bounded by the graphs of functions. Understanding and mastering limits are critical first steps in the successful study of calculus. You want to be able to understand the limit concept by exploring it graphically and numerically and to evaluate it graphically, algebraically, and numerically.

Objectives

- Understand limits, including asymptotic and unbounded behavior.
- Calculate limits using algebra.
- Estimate limits from graphs and data.
- Understand one-sided limits.
- Understand continuity in terms of limits.

FINDING AND ESTIMATING A LIMIT

(*Calculus for AP®*, pages 92–97)

The informal definition of the limit of a function is the value that the dependent variable (usually y) approaches as the independent variable (x) approaches some fixed value or infinity. The formal definition of a limit can be found in *Calculus for AP®* on page 147. (*Note:* The formal definition is not an AP® required topic.)

GRAPHICAL METHOD FOR ESTIMATING A LIMIT

After graphing, visually identify the y-value as x approaches a value c.

The graph below illustrates the concept of limits, the relationship both to the function and to the value at some c, *if it exists.*

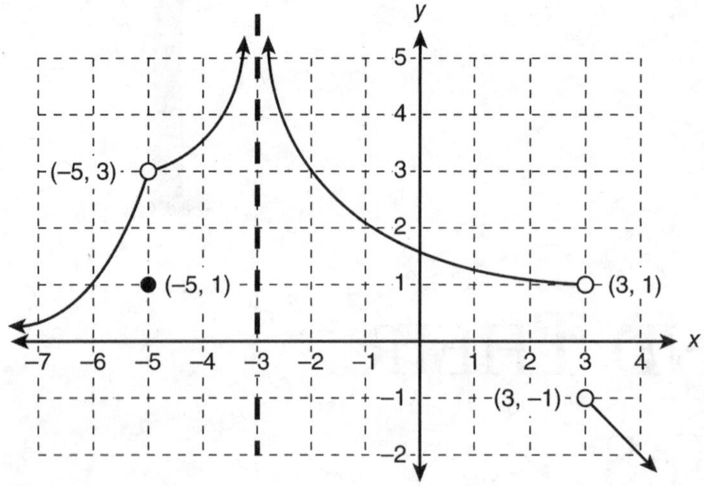

For example,

1. The limit of $f(x)$ as x approaches −5 is 3.

   Note that, although the limit is 3, the actual value at −5 is 1; in other words, the limit is unrelated to the actual y-value.
2. The limit of $f(x)$ as x approaches −3 is positive infinity. The limit does not exist, and there is a vertical asymptote.
3. The limit of $f(x)$ as x approaches 3 does not exist. There is a discontinuity at $x = 3$, and the right-hand and left-hand limits are not equal.

NUMERICAL METHOD FOR ESTIMATING A LIMIT

Numerically implies using numbers, or a table of values, to identify what the value y approaches as numbers approach a given x-value. For example, use the table on your calculator with the table set up at 1/10 as the Δ for x, and see what the y-value nears as the x-value moves from 2 to 1 (2, 1.9, 1.8,. . .) for the function $y = \frac{1}{x-1}$.

In order for the limit to exist, both limits, as x approaches from the right side of c and from the left side of c, must exist and must be equal. Note that the limit is independent of the y-value.

STRATEGIES FOR SOLVING A LIMIT PROBLEM

(*Calculus for AP®*, pages 105–113)

There are various methods for solving a limit problem. However, strategically, the four steps below, followed in order, allow the most efficient use of techniques.

Step 1: Always begin with direct substitution.

Step 2: Try to simplify or cancel.

Step 3: Try to rationalize the denominator or numerator.
Step 4: Finally, try using your calculator to interpret the data. To do this,
1. enter your function in $y =$,
2. go to your table setup to fix your x, and
3. go to the table and evaluate the y-values as the x-values get closer to your c *from both the left and the right.*

AP® Tip

The first three steps of this approach will enable you to solve the problem efficiently, and possibly without a calculator, and could therefore be useful on the non-calculator section of the AP® exam.

INFINITE LIMITS VERSUS LIMITS AT INFINITY (UNBOUNDED BEHAVIOR)

(*Calculus for AP®*, pages 97–102, 117–128)

INFINITE LIMITS: Infinite limits occur when y approaches infinity as x approaches a number. Visually, the graph approaches a VERTICAL ASYMPTOTE (see figure below).

LIMITS AT INFINITY: Limits at infinity occur when y approaches a number as x approaches infinity. Visually, the graph approaches a HORIZONTAL ASYMPTOTE.

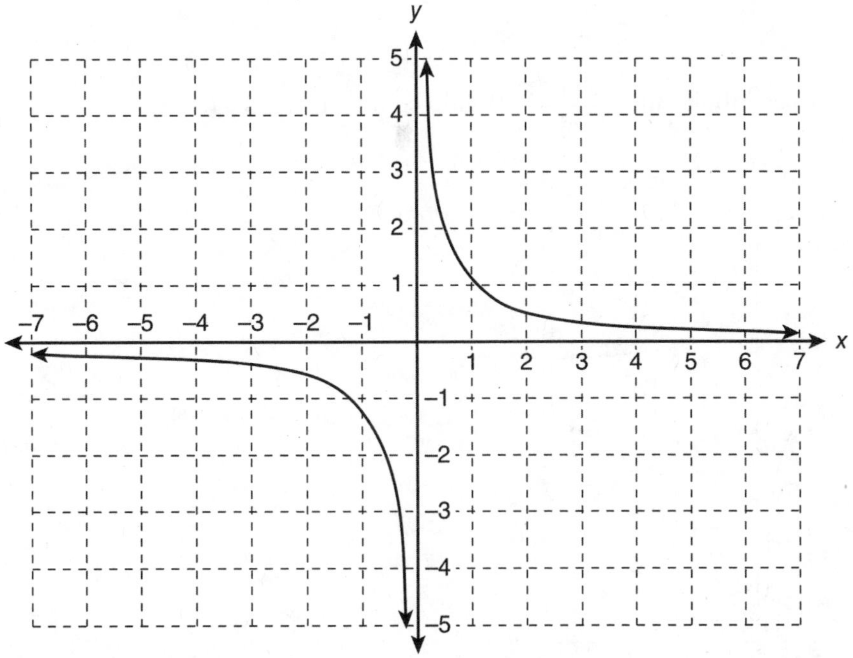

In the figure above, the y-axis is the vertical asymptote. As the x-values approach 0, the y-values approach ± infinity. The x-axis is the horizontal asymptote because the y-values approach a specific number, 0 in this case, as the x-values approach ± infinity.

In a rational function (a function divided by a function),

- a hole occurs if a variable factor in the numerator can cancel with that same factor in the denominator. For example, $y = (x - 3)(x + 2)/(x - 3)$ would be a line with a hole at $x = 3$.
- a vertical asymptote occurs when a factor remains in the denominator. For example, $y = \dfrac{1}{(x-2)}$ would have a vertical asymptote at $x = 2$.
- a horizontal asymptote occurs when, as x goes to infinity, the power of the numerator is ≤ the power of the denominator. For example, as x approaches infinity for $\dfrac{x-2}{x^2}$ (see figure below), there is a horizontal asymptote at $y = 0$.

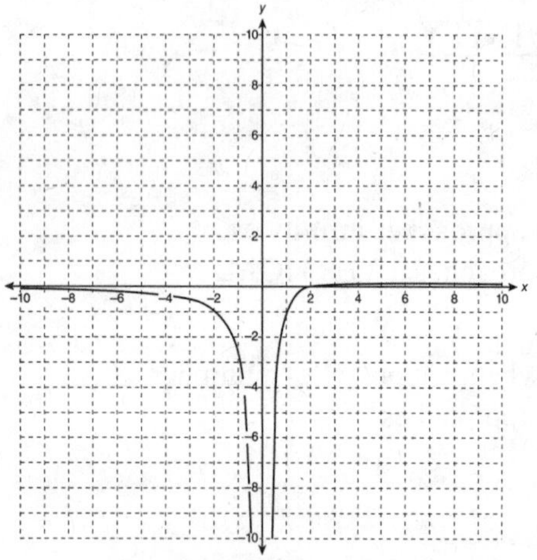

- or, as x approaches infinity for $\dfrac{3x^2 + 5x}{x^2}$ (figure below), there is a horizontal asymptote at $y = 3$.

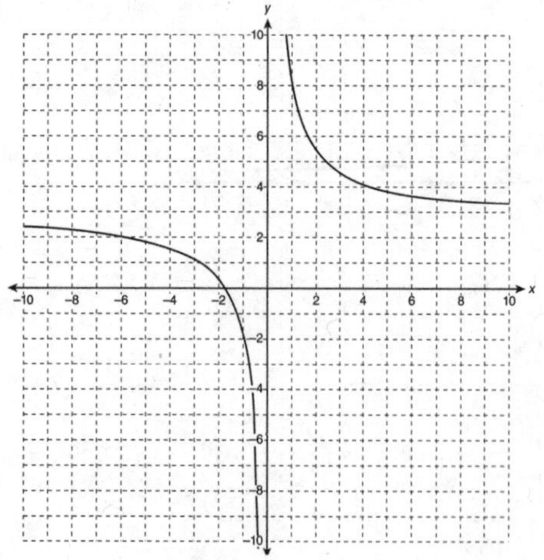

CONTINUITY

(*Calculus for AP®*, pages 131–142)

DEFINITION OF CONTINUITY: A function f is continuous at c if the following three conditions exist:

1) $f(c)$ is defined,
2) $\lim_{x \to c} f(x)$ exists, and
3) $\lim_{x \to c} f(x) = f(c)$.

In other words, a function is continuous if the graph has no interruptions, or you can draw the graph without lifting your pencil.

Following are examples of discontinuities due to the failure of the above-mentioned conditions:

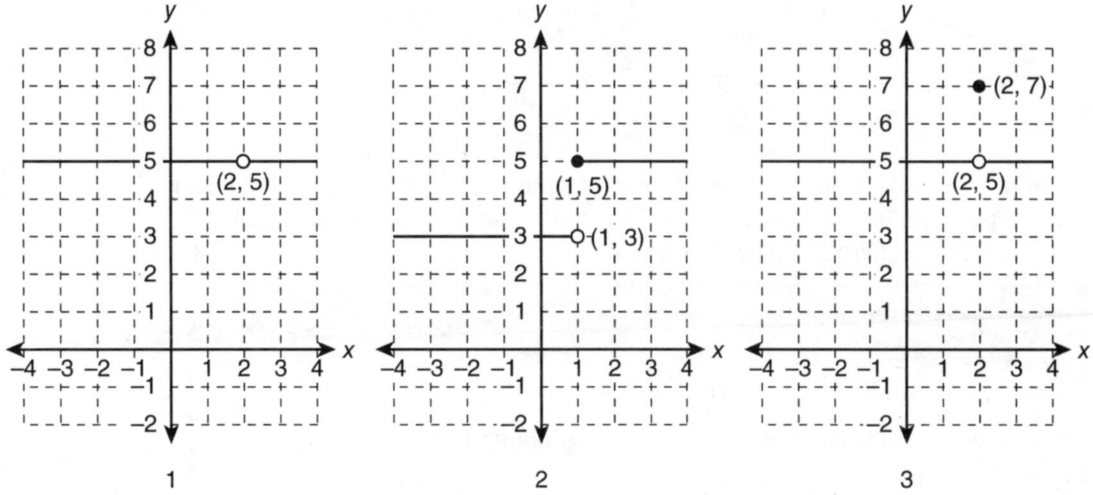

1) $f(c)$ is not defined.
2) $\lim_{x \to 1} f(x)$ does not exist (limits from right and left are not the same).
3) $\lim_{x \to 2} f(x) \neq f(2)$ [limit exists but is not the same as $f(2)$].

> **AP® Tip**
>
> Continuity is a critical concept to know for the AP® exam. For the 2003 test problem 6, for example, students were required to show all components of this definition.

KEY THEOREM: The *Intermediate Value Theorem* is an existence theorem. It states that if a function f is continuous on a closed interval $[a, b]$ and if there is some y-value (called k) between $f(a)$ and $f(b)$, then there has to be at least one x-value between a and b (called c) such that $f(c)$ is equal to k. *Note:* This is an existence theorem. It guarantees that such a number exists, but does not provide a method for finding that number.

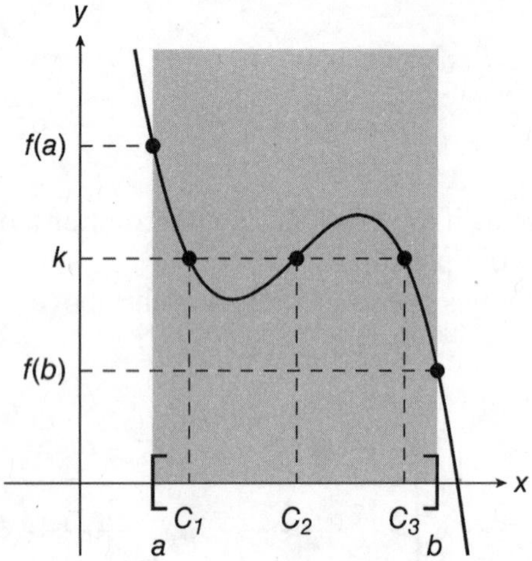

The Intermediate Value Theorem allows us to know that, if $f(a)$ is negative and $f(b)$ is positive, or vice versa, and the function is continuous, then there has to be a zero, or x-intercept, between a and b.

AP® Tip

TWO SPECIAL TRIGONOMETRIC LIMITS

You will want to know these two special trigonometric limits for the AP® exam. They are

$$\lim_{x\to 0}\frac{\sin x}{x}=1 \qquad \lim_{x\to 0}\frac{1-\cos x}{x}=0$$

PAST AP® FREE-RESPONSE PROBLEMS COVERED BY THIS CHAPTER

Note: These and other questions can be found at apcentral.com.
2003 AB 6a
2006 BC 3c
2008 AB 6d
2011 AB 6a
2012 AB 4c

MULTIPLE-CHOICE QUESTIONS

A calculator may not be used on the following questions.

1. Evaluate the limit, if it exists: $\lim\limits_{x \to 2} \dfrac{x^2 + x - 6}{2 - x}$.

   (A) 5
   (B) 3
   (C) −5
   (D) The limit does not exist.

2. Evaluate the limit, if it exists: $\lim\limits_{x \to 9} \dfrac{\sqrt{x-5} - 2}{x - 9}$.

   (A) $\dfrac{1}{4}$
   (B) $-\dfrac{1}{4}$
   (C) 0
   (D) The limit does not exist.

3. Evaluate the limit, if it exists: $\lim\limits_{x \to 2} \dfrac{\frac{1}{x} - \frac{1}{2}}{x - 2}$.

   (A) $\dfrac{1}{4}$
   (B) $-\dfrac{1}{4}$
   (C) 1
   (D) The limit does not exist.

4. Evaluate the limit, if it exists: $\lim\limits_{x \to 1} \dfrac{\tan^{-1} x}{\sin^{-1} x + 1}$.

   (A) $\dfrac{1}{4}$
   (B) $\dfrac{1}{2}$
   (C) $\dfrac{\pi}{2}$
   (D) $\dfrac{\pi}{2\pi + 4}$

5. Estimate the limit, if it exists: $\lim_{x \to 3} f(x)$ where $f(x)$ is represented by the given graph:

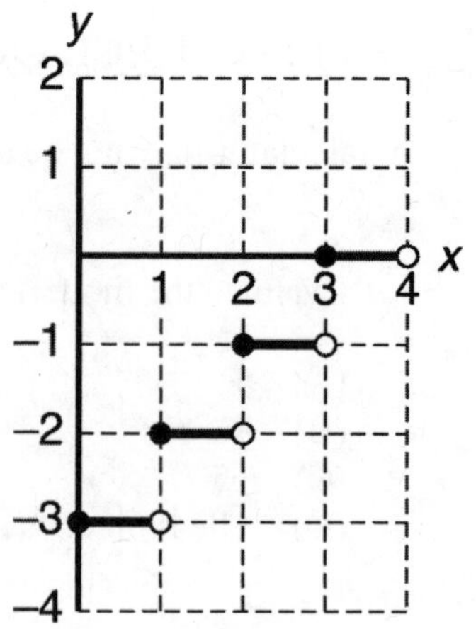

(A) 0
(B) −1
(C) 1
(D) The limit does not exist.

6. Given the function $f(x)=\begin{cases}\sin 2x, & x \le \pi \\ 2x+k, & x > \pi\end{cases}$ what value of k will make this piecewise function continuous?
(A) -2π
(B) $-\pi$
(C) π
(D) 2π

7. Find the limit, if it exists: $\lim_{x \to 0} x\left(e^x + \frac{1}{x}\right)$.
(A) 0
(B) 1
(C) 2
(D) The limit does not exist.

8. Identify the vertical asymptotes for $f(x)=\frac{x^2+3x-4}{x^2+x-2}$.
(A) $x=-2, x=1$
(B) $x=-2$
(C) $x=1$
(D) $x=-2, x=1$

9. If $p(x)$ is a continuous function on the closed interval [1, 3], with $p(1) \le K \le p(3)$ and c is in the closed interval [1, 3], then which of the following statements must be true?
(A) $p(c)=\frac{p(3)+p(1)}{2}$
(B) $p(c)=\frac{p(3)-p(1)}{2}$
(C) There is at least one value c such that $p(c)=K$.
(D) There is only one value c such that $p(c)=K$.

10. How many vertical asymptotes exist for the function $f(x) = \dfrac{1}{2\sin^2 x - \sin x - 1}$ in the open interval $0 < x < 2\pi$?

(A) 0
(B) 1
(C) 2
(D) 3

x	1	2	3	4
$f(x)$	4	2	3	1
$g(x)$	2	3	1	4

11. Selected values for continuous functions $f(x)$ and $g(x)$ are given in the table above. $\lim\limits_{x\to 3} \dfrac{f(g(x))}{g(f(x))} =$

(A) $\dfrac{1}{4}$
(B) $\dfrac{1}{3}$
(C) 3
(D) 4

12. $\lim\limits_{x\to\infty} \dfrac{\sin x}{e^x + \cos x} =$

(A) -1
(B) 0
(C) $\dfrac{1}{e}$
(D) 1

13. For what value of k is the function $f(x) = \begin{cases} \dfrac{2x^2 + 5x - 3}{x^2 - 9}, & x \neq -3 \\ k, & x = -3 \end{cases}$ continuous at $x = -3$?

(A) $-\dfrac{7}{6}$
(B) 0
(C) $\dfrac{5}{6}$
(D) $\dfrac{7}{6}$

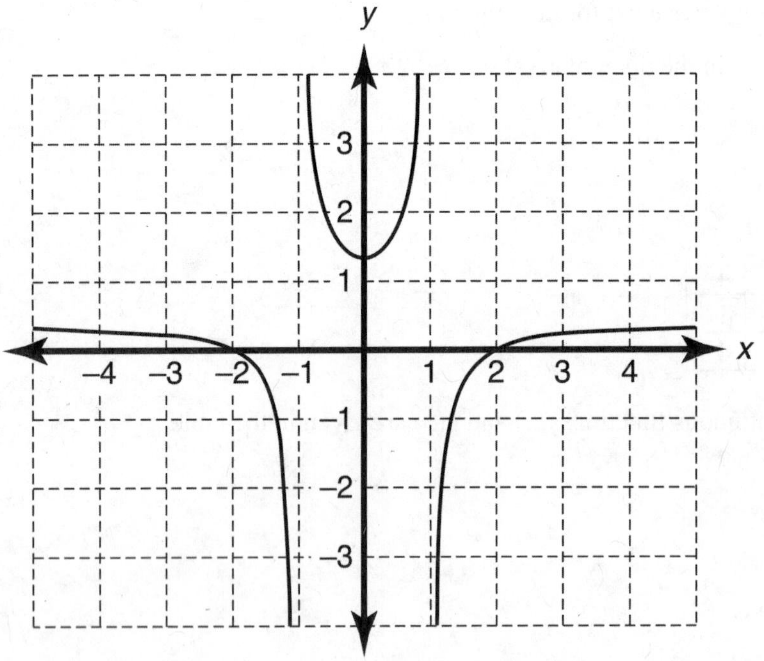

14. The function $g(x)$ is shown in the graph above and is of the form $g(x)=\dfrac{x^2+a}{bx^2-3}$. Which of the following could be the values of the constants a and b?
(A) $a=-2, b=-1$
(B) $a=-2, b=-3$
(C) $a=-4, b=3$
(D) $a=-4, b=-3$

15. Which of the following statements is true?
(A) $\lim_{x\to 3} \log_3 x = 2$
(B) $\lim_{x\to 0^+} \log_3 x$ does not exist.
(C) $\lim_{x\to -\infty} e^x$ does not exist.
(D) $\lim_{x\to 1} e^{x-1} = 0$

FREE-RESPONSE QUESTION

A calculator may not be used for this question.

1. Use the graphs of $f(x)$ and $g(x)$ given below to answer the following questions:

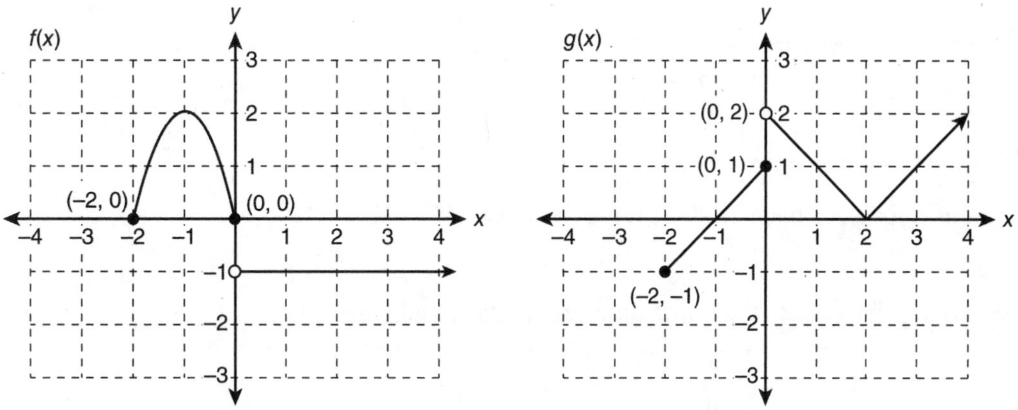

(a) Is $f[g(x)]$ continuous at $x = 0$? Explain why or why not.
(b) Is $g[f(x)]$ continuous at $x = 0$? Explain why or why not.
(c) What is $\lim_{x\to\infty} f[g(x)]$? Explain your reasoning.

(d) If $h(x)=\begin{cases} f(x)+g(x), & -2\le x\le 0 \\ k+g(x)f(x), & x>0 \end{cases}$, what is k so that $h(x)$ is continuous at $x = 0$?

Answers

MULTIPLE-CHOICE QUESTIONS

1. ANSWER: (C) Simplify the function by factoring as follows: $\lim_{x\to 2}\frac{(x-2)(x+3)}{-(x-2)} = \lim_{x\to 2}[-(x+3)] = -5$. (*Calculus for AP®*, pages 105–113; EU 1.1; LO 1.1C; EK 1.1C2; MPAC 2,3)

2. ANSWER: (A) Rationalize the numerator and simplify as follows:

$$\lim_{x\to 9}\left(\frac{\sqrt{x-5}-2}{x-9}\right)\left(\frac{\sqrt{x-5}+2}{\sqrt{x-5}+2}\right) = \lim_{x\to 9}\frac{(x-5)-4}{(x-9)(\sqrt{x-5}+2)}$$
$$= \lim_{x\to 9}\frac{x-9}{(x-9)\left(\sqrt{x-5}+2\right)}$$
$$= \lim_{x\to 9}\frac{1}{\sqrt{x-5}+2} = \frac{1}{4}.$$

(*Calculus for AP®*, pages 105–113; EU 1.1; LO 1.1C; EK 1.1C2; MPAC 2,3)

3. ANSWER: (B) Multiply the numerator and denominator by the common denominator of all the fractions represented and simplify as follows:

$$\lim_{x\to 2}\frac{\left(\frac{1}{x}-\frac{1}{2}\right)(2x)}{(x-2)(2x)}=\lim_{x\to 2}\frac{2-x}{(x-2)2x}$$
$$=\lim_{x\to 2}\frac{-1(x-2)}{(x-2)2x}$$
$$=\lim_{x\to 2}\left(-\frac{1}{2x}\right)=-\frac{1}{4}.$$

(*Calculus for AP*®, pages 105–113; EU 1.1; LO 1.1C; EK 1.1C2; MPAC 2,3)

4. ANSWER: (D) Evaluate the limit numerically (direct substitution):

$$\lim_{x\to 1}\frac{\tan^{-1}x}{\sin^{-1}x+1}=\frac{\frac{\pi}{4}}{\frac{\pi}{2}+1}=\frac{\frac{\pi}{4}}{\frac{\pi+2}{2}}=\frac{\pi}{4}\left(\frac{2}{\pi+2}\right)=\frac{\pi}{2\pi+4}.$$

(*Calculus for AP*®, pages 105–113; EU 1.1; LO 1.1C; EK 1.1C1; MPAC 2,3)

5. ANSWER: (D) $\lim_{x\to 3^-}f(x)=-1$ and $\lim_{x\to 3^+}f(x)=0$. Therefore, $\lim_{x\to 3}f(x)$ does not exist. (*Calculus for AP*®, pages 111–112; EU 1.1; LO 1.1B; EK 1.1B1; MPAC 2,4)

6. ANSWER: (A) For this piecewise function, $\lim_{x\to \pi^+}f(x)=2\pi+k$ and $\lim_{x\to \pi^-}f(x)=0$. Therefore, $2\pi+k=0$, and $k=-2\pi$. (*Calculus for AP*®, pages 131–142; EU 1.1; LO 1.1A; EK 1.1A2,1.1A3; MPAC 2,3)

7. ANSWER: (B) Rewriting $\lim_{x\to 0}x\left(e^x+\frac{1}{x}\right)$, we get $\lim_{x\to 0}(xe^x+1)=0(e^0)+1=0+1=1$. (*Calculus for AP*®, pages 105–113; EU 1.1; LO 1.1C; EK 1.1C1,1.1C2; MPAC 2,3)

8. ANSWER: (B) Simplify the function by canceling the common factor. Thus, $f(x)=\frac{(x+4)(x-1)}{(x+2)(x-1)}$ becomes $f(x)=\frac{(x+4)}{(x+2)}$, $x\neq 1$. Since $\lim_{x\to -2^-}f(x)=-\infty$ and $\lim_{x\to -2^+}f(x)=+\infty$, this indicates a vertical asymptote at $x=-2$. The $\lim_{x\to 1}f(x)=\frac{5}{3}$ indicates that there is no vertical asymptote at $x=1$. (There is a hole in the graph at $x=1$.) Thus, there is only one vertical asymptote that is located at $x=-2$. (*Calculus for AP*®, pages 100–102; EU 1.1; LO 1.1C; EK 1.1C2; MPAC 2,3)

9. ANSWER: (C) This statement illustrates the Intermediate Value Theorem. (*Calculus for AP*®, page 141; EU 1.2; LO 1.2; EK 1.2B1; MPAC 2)

10. ANSWER: (D) By factoring,
$f(x)=\dfrac{1}{2\sin^2 x-\sin x-1}=\dfrac{1}{(2\sin x+1)(\sin x-1)}$. The factors in the denominator equal 0 for the x-values of $\dfrac{7\pi}{6}$, $\dfrac{11\pi}{6}$, and $\dfrac{\pi}{2}$ in the interval. Therefore, there are three vertical asymptotes for the function in the open interval. (*Calculus for AP*®, pages 100–102; EU 1.1; LO 1.1D; EK 1.1D1; MPAC 2,3)

11. ANSWER: (D) $\lim\limits_{x\to 3}\dfrac{f(g(x))}{g(f(x))}\Rightarrow \lim\limits_{x\to 3}\dfrac{f(g(3))}{g(f(3))}\Rightarrow \lim\limits_{x\to 3}\dfrac{f(1)}{g(3)}\Rightarrow \dfrac{4}{1}=4$ (*Calculus for AP*®, page 139; EU 1.1; LO 1.1C; EK 1.1C1; MPAC 2,3,4)

12. ANSWER: (B) The values for $\sin x$ and $\cos x$ are continuous and vary from -1 to 1 inclusive. However, the value for e^x approaches infinity, as x approaches infinity. Therefore, $\lim\limits_{x\to\infty}\dfrac{\sin x}{e^x+\cos x}=0$. (*Calculus for AP*®, pages 117–128; EU 1.1; LO 1.1C; EK 1.1C2; MPAC 2,3)

13. ANSWER: (D) Factoring:
$\left\{\dfrac{2x^2+5x-3}{x^2-9}\Rightarrow\dfrac{(2x-1)(x+3)}{(x-3)(x+3)}\Rightarrow\dfrac{(2x-1)}{(x-3)}, x\neq -3\right.$. The common factor of $(x + 3)$ indicates that there is a removable discontinuity at $x = -3$, which is removable by replacing k with the value of $\lim\limits_{x\to -3}\dfrac{2x-1}{x-3}=\dfrac{-7}{-6}=\dfrac{7}{6}=k$.
(*Calculus for AP*®, pages 131–142; EU 1.2; LO 1.2A; EK 1.2A1; MPAC 2,5)

14. ANSWER: (C) There are roots at $x = \pm 2$. Therefore, $a = -4$. Since there are vertical asymptotes at $x = \pm 1$, the denominator bx^2-3 must have factors of $(x + 1)$ and $(x - 1)$, thus $b = 3$. (*Calculus for AP*®, pages 100–102; EU 1.2; LO 1.2A; EK 1.2A3; MPAC 4)

15. ANSWER: (B) The correct limit for (A) is 1, for (C) is 0, and for (D) is 1. Students are encouraged to check these limits with their graphing calculators. (*Calculus for AP*®, pages 105–113; EU 1.1; LO 1.1A; EK 1.1A2; MPAC 2)

FREE-RESPONSE QUESTION

	Solution	Possible points
(a)	$\lim_{x\to 0^-} f[g(x)] = \lim_{x\to 0^-} f\left[g(0^-)\right] = f(1) = -1.$ $\lim_{x\to 0^+} f[g(x)] = \lim_{x\to 0^+} f\left[g(0^+)\right] = f(2) = -1.$ $f[g(X)]$ is defined. The $\lim_{x\to 0} f[g(x)] = -1$ since the values from the right and the left are the same. Since $f(g(0))$ is equal to -1, the limit exists and $\lim_{x\to 0} f[g(x)] = f[g(0)] = -1$. Yes, $f[g(x)]$ is continuous at $x = 0$.	$2: \begin{cases} 1\text{: using left- and right-hand limits} \\ 1\text{: answer "yes" with explanation} \end{cases}$
(b)	$\lim_{x\to 0^-} g[f(x)] = \lim_{x\to 0^-} g\left[f(0^-)\right] = g(0) = 2.$ $\lim_{x\to 0^+} g[f(x)] = \lim_{x\to 0^+} g\left[f(0^+)\right] = g(-1) = 0.$ Therefore, $\lim_{x\to 0} g[f(x)]$ does not exist since the limits from the left and right are not the same. No, $g\left[f(x)\right]$ is not continuous at $x = 0$.	$2: \begin{cases} 1\text{: using left- and right-hand limits} \\ 1\text{: answer "no" with explanation} \end{cases}$
(c)	Since $\lim_{x\to\infty} g(x) = \infty$ and $\lim_{x\to\infty} f(x) = 1$, then $\lim_{x\to\infty} f[g(x)] = -1.$	$2: \begin{cases} 1\text{: value of each limit} \\ 1\text{: answer} \end{cases}$
(d)	$\lim_{x\to 0^-} f(x) + g(x) = \lim_{x\to 0^-} f(x) + \lim_{x\to 0^-} g(x) = 0 + 1 = 1$ and $h(0) = f(0) + g(0) = 0 + 1 = +1.$ $\lim_{x\to 0^-} [k + f(x)g(x)] = k + \left(\lim_{x\to 0^+} f(x)\right)\left(\lim_{x\to 0^+} g(x)\right) =$ $k + (-1)(2) = k - 1.$ Therefore, $k - 2 = 1$ and $k = 3$.	$3: \begin{cases} 1\text{: left-hand limit} \\ 1\text{: right-hand limit} \\ 1\text{: answer} \end{cases}$

(a), (b) (*Calculus for AP*®, pages 131–142; EU 1.2,1.1; LO 1.2A,1.1C; EK 1.2A1,1.1C1; MPAC 2,4)

(c) (*Calculus for AP*®, page 139; EU 1.1; LO 1.1C; EK 1.1C1; MPAC 2)

(d) (*Calculus for AP*®, pages 111–112, 131–142; EU 1.1; LO 1.1C; EK 1.1C1,1.1C2; MPAC 2,3,4)

2

DIFFERENTIATION

Differentiation is one of the fundamental operations in calculus. It is the process of finding the derivative of a function. A derivative can be interpreted geometrically as the slope of a curve and physically as a rate of change. The derivative has applications throughout the business and science worlds, including evaluating fluctuations of change or maxima and minima.

Objectives

- Learn the concept of the derivative—numerically (from tables), graphically, and analytically—and be able to use the limit definition.
- Understand instantaneous versus average rate of change.
- Learn to find and use tangent lines to a curve at a given point.
- Understand speed, velocity, and acceleration.
- Understand related rates.
- Be able to apply differentiation rules.
- Be able to optimize functions and find optimum solutions to situations.

THE DERIVATIVE

(*Calculus for AP®*, pages 163–167)

Derivatives can be defined as the instantaneous rate of change or as the limit of the difference quotient. The slope formula is a *difference quotient* (this is a term used on the AP® exam). The limit, if it exists, of the values of the slopes of secant lines as they approach the tangent line is the slope of the curve at that point.

AP® is a trademark registered by the College Board, which is not affiliated with, and does not endorse, this product.

The derivative of a function is the rate of change of that function. For example, the rate of change (or physically, the slope) of the position function is velocity because it is the change in distance (vertical axis) over the change in time (horizontal axis). The rate of change of the velocity function is acceleration because it represents the change in velocity (vertical axis) over the change in time (horizontal axis).

In the equation $y = f(x)$, the derivative at point x is equal to the slope of the tangent line at the point $(x, f(x))$.

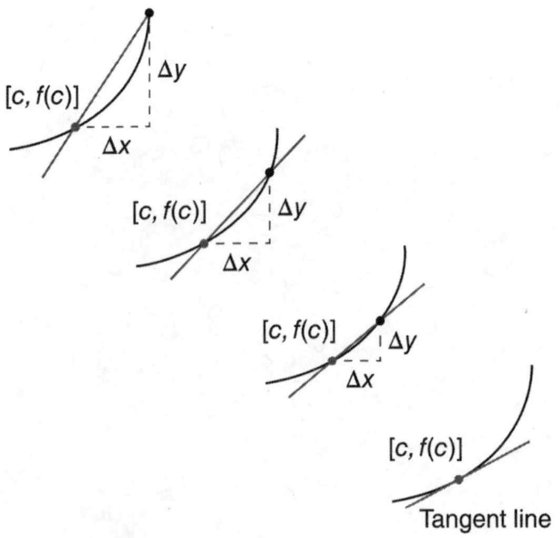

AP® Tip

Use $y - y_1 = m(x - x_1)$ when you need to find an equation of the line. And remember, you do NOT have to simplify on any of the free-response AP® test questions. Simplifying may lead to making a mistake and getting the question wrong.

DEFINITION OF THE DERIVATIVE OF A FUNCTION

(*Calculus for AP®*, pages 169–171)

The derivative of f at a point x is given by

$$f'(x) = \lim_{\Delta x \to 0} \frac{f(x + \Delta x) - f(x)}{\Delta x}$$

provided the limit exists.

AP® Tip

This form is called a *difference quotient*, a term used in AP® exams.

This means that by finding the limit of the slopes of secant lines as the differences between the x-values go to zero, you will solve for the slope formula of the function. The above definition is really just the familiar slope formula of $m = \frac{\Delta y}{\Delta x}$, or $\frac{(y_2 - y_1)}{(x_2 - x_1)}$, where $f(x + \Delta x)$ is y_2, so $f(x)$ is y_1 and Δx is $(x_2 - x_1)$.

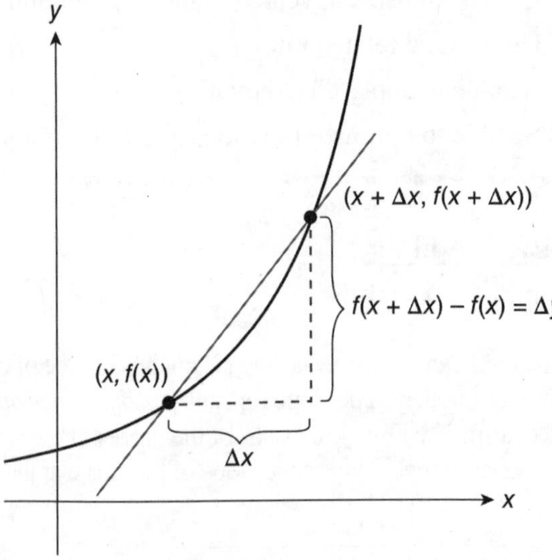

ALTERNATIVE FORM OF THE DERIVATIVE

(*Calculus for AP*®, page 183)

$$f'(c) = \lim_{x \to c} \frac{f(x) - f(c)}{x - c}$$

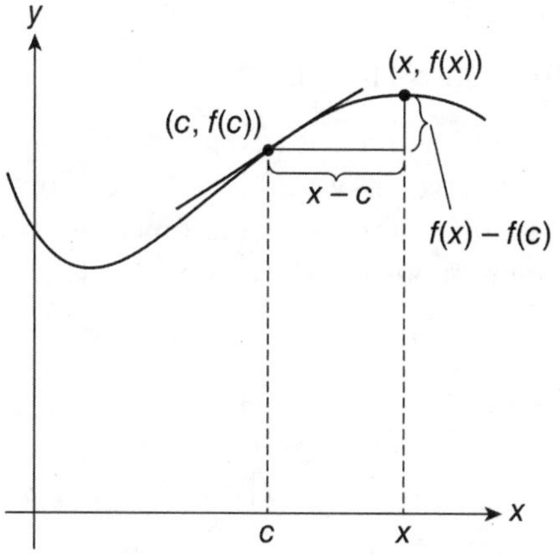

This essentially means the same as the preceding equation but uses different notation; for example, the second ordered pair is $(x, f(x))$, and we find the slopes of the secant lines as x gets closer to c (*rather than the differences of the x's going to zero*). The definition of the derivative finds the slope at any value x, whereas the alternative form of the derivative finds a specific value of x, called c. The general point $(x, f(x))$ is moving toward $(c, f(c))$.

NOTATIONS FOR DERIVATIVES

(*Calculus for AP*®, page 181)

$$f'(x), \frac{dy}{dx}, \quad y', \frac{d}{dx}[f(x)]$$

You can find more forms as well as higher derivative notations in *Calculus for AP*® on page 185.

$f'(x)$ is read as "the first derivative of f."

dy/dx is read as "the derivative of y with respect to x."

y' is read as "the first derivative of y."

$\frac{d}{dx}[f(x)]$ is read as "the first derivative of $f(x)$ with respect to x."

For example, $d/dx\,(x^4)$ means "find the first derivative of x^4 with respect to x."

AP® Tip

On the AP® exam, you should be able to recognize the various notations for first derivative (and subsequent derivatives). For example, $\frac{d^2y}{dx^2}$ is the second derivative of y with respect to x, but the notation is sometimes mistaken for the first derivative squared, which would look like $\left(\frac{dy}{dx}\right)^2$.

CONNECTION BETWEEN DIFFERENTIABILITY AND CONTINUITY

(*Calculus for AP®*, pages 182–184)

DIFFERENTIABILITY

If a function is differentiable at $x = c$, it is also continuous at $x = c$. The converse, however, is not true: Continuity does not imply differentiability. For example, the following functions, $y = c - (x - a)^{2/3}$ and $y = c + (x - a)^{1/3}$, are continuous but not differentiable at $x = a$.

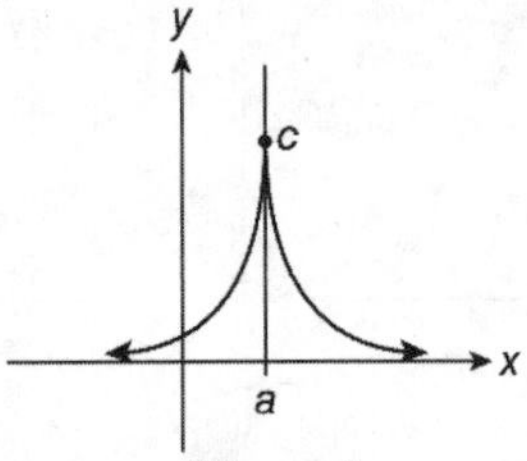

Figure 1

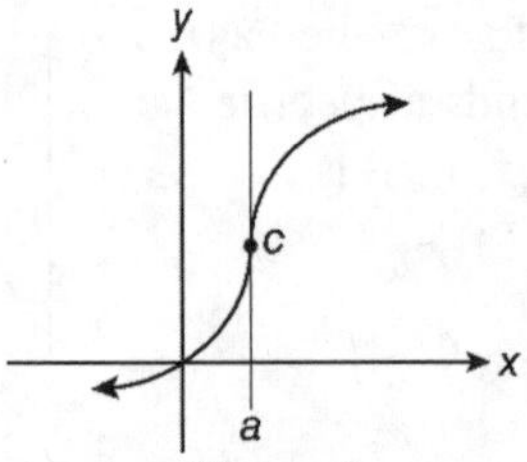

Figure 2

A function is not differentiable at a point if one of the following is true:

- It is discontinuous (a function that is not continuous at a point cannot be differentiable at that point).
- A sharp turn occurs (as in Figure 1 or in an absolute value function).
- There is a vertical tangent line (as in Figure 2).

AP® Tips

- You need to know how to find the derivative using the limit process and to be able to recognize the difference quotient in its limit form.
- You need to know how to apply the Constant Rule, the Power Rule, the Product Rule, the Quotient Rule, and the Chain Rule.
- You must understand the relationship between position, velocity, and acceleration (Hint: Speed is the absolute value of the velocity.), and the difference between the average rate of change over an interval and the instantaneous rate of change at a point.
- Generally accepted notation when relating position to velocity and acceleration is

  $s(t)$ = position
  $v(t) = s'(t)$ = velocity
  $a(t) = s''(t) = v'(t)$ = acceleration
- Be prepared to see other variables used instead of $f(x)$. If the exam uses $g(x)$, $h(x)$, and so on, you must use like derivative forms: $g'(x)$, $h''(x)$, and so on; points are not allotted if you do not use the given labels.
- Be sure to answer the question that is asked. If the question asks where the function is increasing, do not answer that the first derivative is positive on the interval, although that is the analysis that leads to the conclusion asked for and you want to be sure to state your reasoning.
- Be sure to distinguish between distance traveled and displacement.

DERIVATIVES: APPLICATIONS/RULES

UNDERSTANDING THE CONCEPT OF SPEED

(*Calculus for AP®*, pages 508–511)

It is important to understand the difference between speed and velocity. Speed is the absolute value of the velocity. Velocity denotes the direction as well as the speed.

If velocity is positive and acceleration is positive (or velocity is increasing), then speed is increasing. For example, if a runner is moving to the right on a horizontal line, and the wind is behind her, she is running faster in the positive direction; therefore, speed is increasing. Or, if a ball is thrown into the air [velocity is positive (directional), but acceleration is negative (gravitational pull)], speed is decreasing. Think about a quadratic graph that opens downward as you move from left to right. The slope (velocity) goes from a large positive number (a steep slope) to a smaller positive number and finally to zero (at the peak) and then has a small negative slope moving to a larger (steeper) negative slope. When the ball drops from its peak, the velocity is negative (directional) and acceleration is also negative (gravitational pull); therefore, speed is increasing. Also, think of this last case in this way: If velocity is negative but increasing, which means that its derivative (acceleration) is positive (it is moving from -3 to -2), then its speed (absolute value of velocity) is decreasing. Simply put, if velocity and acceleration are working in the same direction (have the same sign), then speed is increasing (speeding up). If velocity and acceleration are working in opposite directions (have opposite signs), then speed is decreasing (slowing down).

AP® Tips

- Know that the value of the derivative at a point is the same as the slope of the tangent line at that point.
- Know that the instantaneous rate of change is the same as the derivative at that time (point) and is the limit of the average rate of change. This is similar to the concept of the limit of the slope of the secant lines versus the actual slope of the tangent line at a given point.
- Know how to use graphs and tables to approximate the rate of change. If the AP® exam instructions are to use the table of values, then be sure to use the values in the table exactly as given. (Do not try to use the regression capabilities on your calculator; it is never necessary.)
- Know that if the velocity and acceleration have the same sign (both are positive or negative), then the speed is increasing. If the velocity and acceleration are opposite in sign (i.e., one is positive and one is negative), then the speed is decreasing.

DIFFERENTIATION RULES

(*Calculus for AP*®, pages 193–256)

It is important to know these rules and to recognize which ones to use.
Remember to simplify the problem before applying any of these rules.

BASIC DIFFERENTIATION RULES: Let u and v be differentiable functions of x.

Constant Rule $\frac{d}{dx}(c)=0$

Constant Multiple Rule $\frac{d}{dx}(cu)=cu'$

Sum or Difference Rule $\frac{d}{dx}(u\pm v)=u'\pm v'$

Product Rule $\frac{d}{dx}(uv)=uv'+vu'$

Quotient Rule $\frac{d}{dx}\left[\frac{u}{v}\right]=\frac{vu'-uv'}{v^2}$

Simple Power Rule $\frac{d}{dx}\left[x^n\right]=nx^{n-1}$ $\frac{d}{dx}(x)=1$

General Power Rule $\frac{d}{dx}\left[u^n\right]=nu^{n-1}u'$

Chain Rule $\frac{d}{dx}[f(u)]=f'(u)u'$

Trigonometric Functions

$\frac{d}{dx}(\sin u)=(\cos u)u'$ $\frac{d}{dx}(\csc u)=(\csc u\cot u)u'$

$\frac{d}{dx}(\cos u)=-(\sin u)u'$ $\frac{d}{dx}(\sec u)=(\sec u\tan u)u'$

$\frac{d}{dx}(\tan u)=(\sec^2 u)u'$ $\frac{d}{dx}(\cot u)=-(\csc^2 u)u'$

Logarithmic Function $\frac{d}{dx}(\ln x)=\frac{1}{x}, x>0$ $\frac{d}{dx}(\ln u)=\frac{1}{u}\frac{du}{dx}=\frac{u'}{u}, u>0$

Derivative of an Inverse Function If f has an inverse function g, then g is differentiable at any x for which $f'(g(x))\neq 0$, and $g'(x)=\frac{1}{f'(g(x))}$

(*Note: Calculus for AP*® on pages 247–248 for further work on inverse functions and their derivatives.)

Exponential Function $\frac{d}{dx}e^x=e^x$ and $\frac{d}{dx}(e^u)=e^u\frac{du}{dx}=e^u u'$

Inverse Trigonometric Functions

$$\frac{d}{dx}(\text{arc}\sin u)=\frac{u'}{\sqrt{1-u^2}} \qquad \frac{d}{dx}(\text{arc}\cot u)=\frac{-u'}{1+u^2}$$

$$\frac{d}{dx}(\text{arc}\cos u)=\frac{-u'}{\sqrt{1-u^2}} \qquad \frac{d}{dx}(\text{arc}\sec u)=\frac{u'}{|u|\sqrt{u^2-1}}$$

$$\frac{d}{dx}(\text{arc}\tan u)=\frac{u'}{1+u^2} \qquad \frac{d}{dx}(\text{arc}\csc u)=\frac{-u'}{|u|\sqrt{u^2-1}}$$

AP® Tips

- Be sure to analyze the exam problem before starting it. Look for clues as to which formula to use.
  1. Is it really a Quotient Rule problem, or is it just a constant in the denominator that can be factored out?
  2. Can I simplify first, for example, factor out an x in all terms and cancel?
  3. Would it be easier to recognize $(\sin x)/(\cos x)$ as $\tan x$ or to use the Quotient Rule?
- Know the difference between the implicit form of a function, where both variables are on the same side and it may be difficult to solve for one or the other variables (e.g., $x - 2xy = 4$), and the explicit form of a function, which can be written in terms of one of the variables (e.g., $y = 2x - 3$ or $x = y^2$).

GUIDELINES FOR IMPLICIT DIFFERENTIATION

(*Calculus for AP®*, pages 240–245)

When it is difficult to solve an equation in terms of y (e.g., $x^2 - 2y + 4y = 2$), use the following steps to solve it implicitly:

1. Differentiate both sides of the equation with respect to x.

$$2x-6y^2\frac{dy}{dx}+4\frac{dy}{dx}=0$$

2. Collect all terms involving dy/dx on one side of the equation and move all other terms to the other side of the equation. The idea is to isolate dy/dx on one side or the other.

$$-6y^2\frac{dy}{dx}+4\frac{dy}{dx}=-2x$$

3. Factor dy/dx out of the left side of the equation.

$$\frac{dy}{dx}(-6y^2+4)=-2x$$

4. Solve for dy/dx by dividing both sides of the equation by the factor that does not contain dy/dx.

$$\frac{dy}{dx}(-6y^2+4)=-2x$$

RELATED RATES

(*Calculus for AP®*, pages 274–279)

When working related-rate problems, instead of finding a derivative of an equation y with respect to the variable x, you are finding the derivative of equations with respect to a "hidden" variable t. This means that the variables are tied together in their relationship with time. For example, a ladder resting against a building has a horizontal distance from the building, a vertical height up the side of the house, and a set length of the ladder. The velocity at which the base is moved away from the building (dx/dt, x is the horizontal distance as a function of time) affects the speed of the vertical movement (dy/dt, y is the vertical distance as a function of time). Another example is to determine how the rate of the radius of a balloon changes when its volume changes at a given rate.

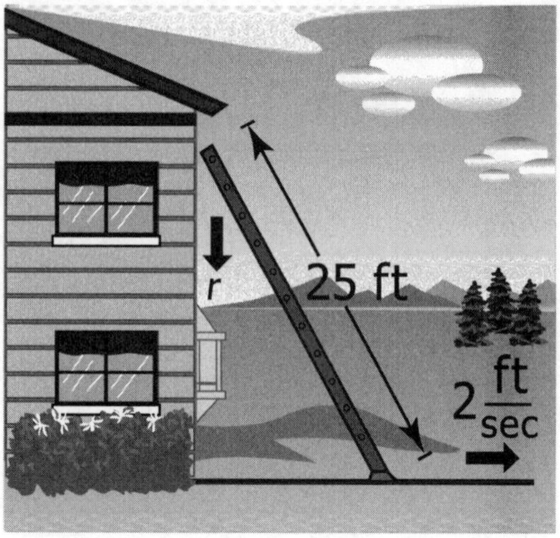

DIFFERENTIATION OF A LOGARITHMIC FUNCTION

(*Calculus for AP®*, pages 252–255)

Use this rule for differentiating a logarithmic function.

$$\frac{d}{dx}(\ln u)=\frac{1}{u}\frac{du}{dx}=\frac{u'}{u},\quad u>0$$

For example, $\frac{d}{dx}\left[\ln(x^2+1)\right]=\frac{u'}{u}=\frac{2x}{x^2+1},\ u>0.$

The key to a complex logarithmic function is to apply the properties of logarithms first. For example, if

$$f(x)=\ln\frac{x(x^2+1)^2}{\sqrt{2x^3-1}},$$

you can apply the properties of logarithms to change its form to

$$f(x)=\ln x+2\ln(x^2+1)-\frac{1}{2}\ln(2x^3-1)$$

and then apply the rules for differentiation to each part.

When you apply this rule, you must also watch for the use of the Product Rule, Chain Rule, and so on. See the examples in *Calculus for AP®* on page 254.

LOGARITHMIC DIFFERENTIATION

(*Calculus for AP®*, pages 255–257)

This is a process by which you can differentiate a complex function using logarithms. It is a technique where you take the log of both sides, differentiate the equation, and then solve for y'.

Let

$$y = \frac{2x(x-2)^2}{\sqrt{x^2+1}}.$$

If you were to apply the general differentiation rules, you would need the Quotient Rule, the Product Rule, and the Chain Rule to simplify it. However, if you took the log of both sides, it would become

$$\ln y = \ln \frac{2x(x-2)^2}{\sqrt{x^2+1}}.$$

which can be simplified to

$\ln y = \ln 2x + 2 \ln (x-2) - ½ \ln (x^2+1)$.

You could then apply the differentiation of log rules to each side to get

$$\frac{y'}{y} = \frac{2}{2x} + 2\left(\frac{1}{x-2}\right) - \frac{1}{2}\left(\frac{2x}{x^2+1}\right),$$

which simplifies to

$$\frac{1}{x} + \left(\frac{2}{x-2}\right) - \left(\frac{x}{x^2+1}\right).$$

Since that is still equal to $\frac{y'}{y}$, multiply both sides by y to solve for y' (substitute the actual y into this form so that you can simplify in terms of x).

$$y' = \frac{2x(x-2)^2}{\sqrt{x^2+1}}\left[\frac{2x^3+3x-2}{x(x-2)(x^2+1)}\right].$$

Then this can then be simplified to

$$y' = \frac{2(x-2)(2x^3+3x-2)}{(x^2+1)^{3/2}},$$

and the answer should stay in factored form so that you can solve for critical numbers and analyze the curve.

PAST AP® FREE-RESPONSE PROBLEMS COVERED BY THIS CHAPTER

Note: These and other questions can be found at apcentral.com.

1998	AB 4a,b; 6	**2010**	AB 1b; 2a
1999	AB 1a,b; 6	**2011**	AB 1a; 2a; 3a; 5a; 6b BC 1a,b; 3c
2000	AB 5	**2012**	AB 1a; 4a,b; 6c BC 2c; 4a
2001	AB 5a; 6a	**2013**	AB 1a,c; 2a,c,d; 3a,d; 4d
2002	AB 5	**2014**	AB 1a,b,d; 3c,d; 4a,d; 5c
2003	AB 2a,b; 3a,b; 5a; 6c		
2004	AB 1d; 3a; 4a,b		
2006	AB 6		
2007	AB 3d; 5a,b		
2008	AB 3a,b; 6a		
2009	AB 1a,c; 5a		

MULTIPLE-CHOICE QUESTIONS

Calculators may not be used for the following questions.

1. What does the limit statement $\lim_{x \to 1} \frac{\ln(x+1) - \ln 2}{x - 1}$ represent?

   (A) 0
   (B) $\frac{d}{dx}[\ln(x+1)]$
   (C) $f'(1)$, if $f(x) = \ln(x + 1)$
   (D) 1

2. Find the derivative of the function $y = \frac{4}{x^3}$.

   (A) $-\frac{12}{x^2}$
   (B) $\frac{12}{x^2}$
   (C) $\frac{12}{x^4}$
   (D) $-\frac{12}{x^4}$

3. Find $\frac{dy}{dx}$ if $3xy = 4x + y^2$.

(A) $\frac{4-3y}{2y-3x}$

(B) $\frac{3x-4}{2x}$

(C) $\frac{3y-x}{2}$

(D) $\frac{3y-4}{2y-3x}$

4. Find $\frac{dy}{dx}$ for $e^{x+y} = y$.

(A) $\frac{e^{x+y}}{(1-e^{x+y})}$

(B) $\frac{e^{x+y}}{(1+e^{x+y})}$

(C) $\frac{e^{x+y}}{(e^{x+y}-1)}$

(D) e^{x+y}

5. If the nth derivative of y is denoted as $y^{(n)}$ and $y = -\sin x$, then $y^{(7)}$ is same as

(A) y

(B) $\frac{dy}{dx}$

(C) $\frac{d^2y}{dx^2}$

(D) $\frac{d^3y}{dx^3}$

6. Find the second derivative of $f(x)$ if $f(x) = (2x + 3)^4$.

(A) $4\,(2x + 3)^3$
(B) $8\,(2x + 3)^3$
(C) $24\,(2x + 3)^2$
(D) $48\,(2x + 3)^2$

Calculators may be used for the following questions.

7. Find $\frac{dy}{dx}$ for $y = 4\sin^2(3x)$.
   (A) $8\sin(3x)$
   (B) $8\sin(3x)\cos(3x)$
   (C) $12\sin(3x)\cos(3x)$
   (D) $24\sin(3x)\cos(3x)$

8. In right triangle ΔABC, point A is moving along a leg of the right triangle toward point C at a rate of $\frac{1}{2}$ cm/sec and point B is moving toward point C at a rate of $\frac{1}{3}$ cm/sec along a line containing the other leg of the right triangle, as illustrated in the triangle shown below.
   What is the rate of change in the area of ΔABC, with respect to time, at the instant when $AC = 15$ cm and $BC = 20$ cm?

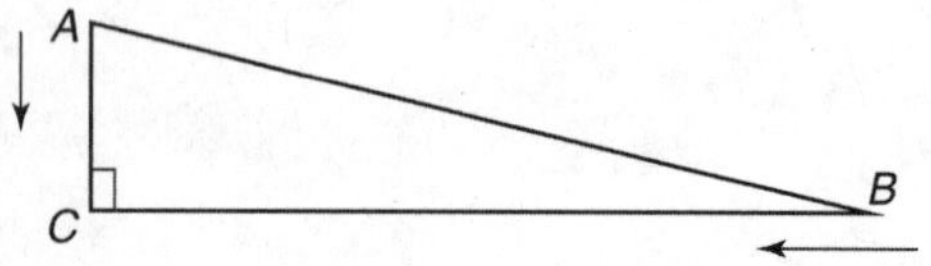

   (A) $-0.0833\ \text{cm}^2/\text{sec}$
   (B) $-0.4167\ \text{cm}^2/\text{sec}$
   (C) $-0.8333\ \text{cm}^2/\text{sec}$
   (D) $-7.5\ \text{cm}^2/\text{sec}$

9. If $\ln y = (\ln x)^2 + 2$, find $\frac{dy}{dx}$ in terms of x and y.
   (A) $y\left[2\ln(x) + \frac{1}{x}\right]$
   (B) $y\left[\left(\frac{2}{x}\right)\ln(x)\right]$
   (C) $\left(\frac{2}{x}\right)\ln(x)$
   (D) $y\left[\frac{2(\ln x)}{x} + 2\right]$

10. If $f(2) = -3$, $f'(2) = \frac{3}{4}$, and $g(x) = f^{-1}(x)$, what is the equation of the tangent line to $g(x)$ at $x = -3$?
   (A) $y - 2 = \frac{-3}{4}(x + 3)$
   (B) $y - 2 = \frac{-4}{3}(x + 3)$
   (C) $y + 2 = \frac{4}{3}(x - 3)$
   (D) $y - 2 = \frac{4}{3}(x + 3)$

11. For what positive value of x does the tangent line to the curve $y = \ln(1-x)$ intersect the y-axis at the point (0, 2)?

(A) 0.382
(B) 0.547
(C) 0.667
(D) 0.778

A calculator may not be used for the following questions.

12. For what values of a and c is the piecewise function

$$f(x)=\begin{cases} ax^2+\sin x, & x \le \pi \\ 2x-c, & x>\pi \end{cases}$$ differentiable?

(A) $a=\frac{3\pi}{2}$ and $c=\frac{\pi}{2}$

(B) $a=\frac{3}{2\pi}$ and $c=\frac{7\pi}{2}$

(C) $a=\frac{3}{2\pi}$ and $c=-\frac{\pi}{2}$

(D) $a=\frac{3}{2\pi}$ and $c=\frac{\pi}{2}$

13. If $y=\tan^{-1}(x^2+3x)$, then $\frac{dy}{dx}=$

(A) $\frac{1}{1+(x^2+3x)^2}$

(B) $\frac{1}{x^2+3x+1}$

(C) $\frac{2x+3}{1+(x^2+3x)^2}$

(D) $\frac{2x+3}{(x^2+3x)^2}$

x	$f(x)$	$g(x)$	$f'(x)$	$g'(x)$
1	3	1	–2	4
2	5	3	1	–4
3	2	1	–2	1
4	4	–3	2	–1

14. Selected function and derivative values for the differentiable functions $f(x)$ and $g(x)$ are given in the table above. If $p(x) = x f(x) - g(3x-2)$, then $p'(2) =$
(A) 11
(B) 10
(C) 8
(D) 6

15. When the height of a cylinder is 12 cm and the radius is 4 cm, the circumference of the cylinder is increasing at a rate of $\frac{\pi}{4}$ cm/ min, and the height of the cylinder is increasing four times faster than the radius. How fast is the volume of the cylinder changing?

(A) $\frac{\pi}{2}$ cm^3/min
(B) 4π cm^3/min
(C) 12π cm^3/min
(D) 20π cm^3/min

FREE-RESPONSE QUESTION

A calculator may be used for this question.

1. An isosceles triangle is inscribed in a semicircle, as shown in the diagram, and it continues to be inscribed as the semicircle changes size. The area of the semicircle is increasing at the rate of 1 cm^2/sec when the radius of the semicircle is 3 cm.

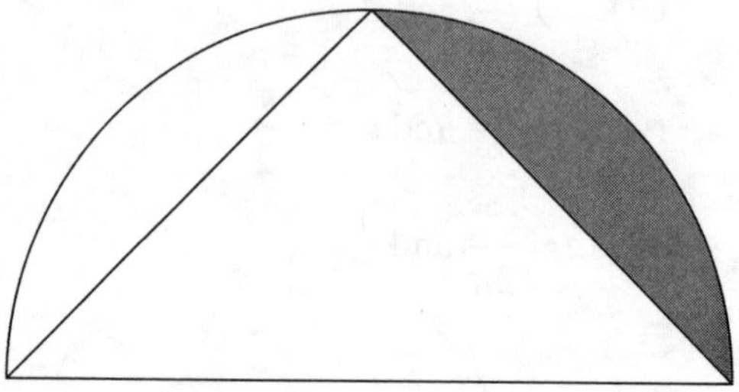

(a) How fast is the radius of the semicircle increasing when the radius is 3 cm? Include units in your answer.
(b) How fast is the perimeter of the semicircle increasing when the radius is 3 cm? Include units in your answer.
(c) How fast is the area of the isosceles triangle increasing when the radius is 3 cm? Include units in your answer.
(d) How fast is the shaded region increasing when the radius is 3 cm? Include units in your answer.

Answers

MULTIPLE-CHOICE QUESTIONS

1. ANSWER: (C) The given limit represents the alternative form of the definition of a derivative:

$$f'(c) = \lim_{x \to c} \frac{f(x) - f(c)}{x - c}.$$

If the function is defined as $f(x) = \ln(x+1)$, then substituting in $c = 1$ gives $\lim_{x \to c} \frac{\ln(x+1) - \ln 2}{x - 1}$ (*Calculus for AP*®, page 183; EU 2.1; LO 2.1A; EK 2.1A3; MPAC 1,2,5)

2. ANSWER: (D) To find the derivative, change the form of the function: $y = \frac{4}{x^3}$ to $y = 4x - 3$. Now find the derivative using the Power Rule and Constant Multiple Rule: $\frac{dy}{dx} = 4(-3)x^{-3-1} = -12x^{-4} = -\frac{12}{x^4}$.

(*Calculus for AP®*, pages 193–199; EU 2.1; LO 2.1C; EK 2.1C2; MPAC 2,3)

3. ANSWER: (D) To find the derivative, differentiate both sides of the equation implicitly with respect to x.

$$\frac{d}{dx}(3xy) = \frac{d}{dx}(4x + y^2)$$

$$3\left(y + x\frac{dy}{dx}\right) = 4 + 2y\frac{dy}{dx}$$

$$3y + 3x\frac{dy}{dx} = 4 + 2y\frac{dy}{dx}$$

Now isolate the terms containing $\frac{dy}{dx}$ and then factor out the common factor.

$$3x\frac{dy}{dx} - 2y\frac{dy}{dx} = 4 - 3y$$

$$\frac{dy}{dx}(3x - 2y) = 4 - 3y$$

Now solve for $\frac{dy}{dx} \cdot \frac{dy}{dx} = \frac{4-3y}{3x-2y} = \frac{-1(3y-4)}{-1(2y-3x)} = \frac{3y-4}{2y-3x}$. Note that the form for the answer could have been $\frac{4-3y}{3x-2y}$. Be sure to watch for factoring out negative values on multiple-choice questions. (*Calculus for AP®*, pages 240–245; EU 2.1; LO 2.1C; EK 2.1C5; MPAC 2,3)

4. ANSWER: (A) Begin by differentiating both sides of the equation with respect to x.

$$\frac{d}{dx}\left(e^{x+y}\right) = \frac{d}{dx}(y)$$

$$e^{x+y}\left(1 + \frac{dy}{dx}\right) = \frac{dy}{dx}$$

$$e^{x+y} + e^{x+y}\frac{dy}{dx} = \frac{dy}{dx}$$

$$e^{x+y} = \frac{dy}{dx} - e^{x+y}\frac{dy}{dx} = \left(1 - e^{x+y}\right)\frac{dy}{dx}$$

Solve for $\frac{dy}{dx} \cdot \frac{dy}{dx} = \frac{e^{x+y}}{\left(1 - e^{x+y}\right)}$. (*Calculus for AP®*, pages 202, 240–245; EU 2.1; LO 2.1C; EK 2.1C5; MPAC 2,3)

5. ANSWER: (D) To find the seventh derivative, differentiate until a pattern is observed.

$y = -\sin x$

$\frac{dy}{dx} = -\cos x$

$\frac{d^2y}{dx^2} = \sin x$

$\frac{d^3y}{dx^3} = \cos x$

$y^{(4)} = \sin x$

Because the fourth derivative is the same as the original function, the seventh derivative is the same as the third derivative. (*Calculus for AP*®, pages 216–220; EU 2.1; LO 2.1D; EK 2.1D1; MPAC 2,3,5)

6. ANSWER: (D) To find the first derivative, differentiate using the Chain Rule as follows: $\frac{dy}{dx} = 4(2x+3)^3(2) = 8(2x+3)^3$. Now differentiate again to find the second derivative: $\frac{d^2y}{dx^2} = 8(3)(2x+3)^2(2) = 48(2x+3)^2$. (*Calculus for AP*®, pages 227–233; EU 2.1; LO 2.1C; EK 2.1C4; MPAC 2,3)

7. ANSWER: (D) Differentiating $y = 4\sin^2(3x)$ with respect to x results in

$\frac{dy}{dx} = 4\frac{d}{dx}[\sin(3x)]^2$.

Using the Chain Rule,

$\frac{dy}{dx} = (4)2[\sin(3x)]\cos(3x)(3)$.

Simplifying yields, $\frac{dy}{dx} = 24\sin(3x)\cos(3x)$. (*Calculus for AP*®, pages 227–233; EU 2.1; LO 2.1C; EK 2.1C4; MPAC 2,3)

8. ANSWER: (D)

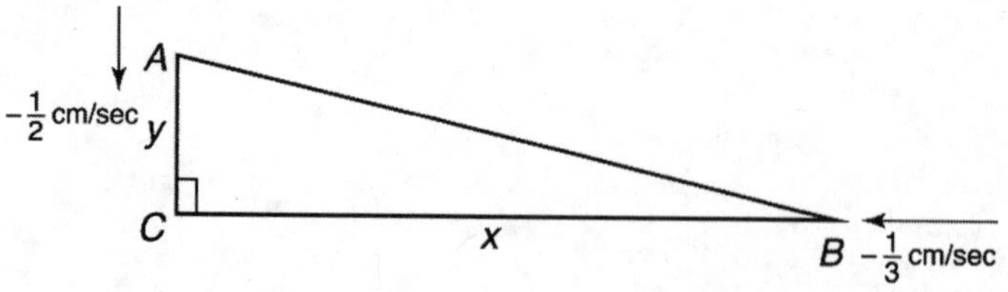

Let $AC = y$ and $BC = x$. The area of $\Delta ABC = K = \frac{1}{2}xy$. Taking the derivative,

$$\frac{dK}{dt} = \frac{1}{2}\left[\frac{dx}{dt}(y) + \frac{dy}{dt}(x)\right].$$

By substitution,

$$\frac{dK}{dt} = \frac{1}{2}\left[\left(-\frac{1}{3}\right)15 + \left(-\frac{1}{2}\right)20\right] = \frac{1}{2}(-5-10) = -7.5 \text{ cm}^2/\text{sec}.$$

(*Calculus for AP®*, pages 274–279; EU 2.3; LO 2.3C; EK 2.3C2; MPAC 2,3,4)

9. ANSWER: (B) Differentiating both sides,

$\frac{1}{y}\left(\frac{dy}{dx}\right) = 2\ln(x)\left(\frac{1}{x}\right) = \frac{2}{x}(\ln x)$. Solving for $\frac{dy}{dx}$, $\frac{dy}{dx} = y\left[\left(\frac{2}{x}\right)\ln(x)\right]$.
(*Calculus for AP®*, pages 240–245; EU 2.1; LO 2.1C; EK 2.1C4; MPAC 2,3,5)

10. ANSWER: (D) Since $g(x) = f^{-1}(x)$ and $g'(x) = \frac{1}{f'[g(x)]}$,

$g'(-3) = \frac{1}{f'[g(-3)]} = \frac{1}{f'(2)} = \frac{4}{3}$. With $g(-3) = 2$, the equation of the tangent line to $g(x)$ is $y - 2 = \frac{4}{3}(x+3)$. (*Calculus for AP®*, pages 247–248; EU 2.1; LO 2.1C; EK 2.1C6; MPAC 2,3,5)

11. ANSWER: (D) $y' = \frac{-1}{1-x}$. The tangent line has equation

$\ln(1-x) - 2 = \frac{-1}{1-x}(x-0) \Rightarrow x = 0.778$. (*Calculus for AP®*, pages 252–255; EU 2.3; LO 2.3B; EK 2.3B1; MPAC 2,3)

12. ANSWER: (D) $\lim_{x\to\pi^-} f(x) = \lim_{x\to\pi^+} f(x) \Rightarrow a\pi^2 + 0 = 2\pi - c.$

$$f'(x) = \begin{cases} 2ax + \cos x, & x \le \pi \\ 2, & x > \pi \end{cases}, \Rightarrow \lim_{x\to\pi} = f'(x) = \lim_{x\to\pi^+} f'(x) \Rightarrow 2a\pi - 1 = 2.$$

Solving for a, $2a\pi = 3 \Rightarrow a = \frac{3}{2\pi}$, and by substitution,

$$c = 2\pi - \frac{3}{2\pi}(\pi^2) \Rightarrow c = \frac{\pi}{2}.$$

(*Calculus for AP®*, pages 131–142, 182–184; EU 2.3; LO 2.3A; EK 2.3A2; MPAC 2,3)

13. ANSWER: (C) If $y = \tan^{-1} u$, where $u = f(x)$, then using the Chain Rule,

$$\frac{dy}{dx} = \frac{1}{1+u^2}\frac{du}{dx} \Rightarrow \frac{1}{1+\left(x^2+3x\right)^2}(2x+3) \Rightarrow \frac{2x+3}{1+\left(x^2+3x\right)^2}.$$

(*Calculus for AP*®, pages 245–246; EU 2.1; LO 2.1C; EK 2.1C6; MPAC 2,3)

14. ANSWER: (B) For $p(x) = xf(x) - g(3x-2) \Rightarrow p'(x) = f(x) + xf'(x) - g'(3x - 2) \cdot 3$. Then $p'(2) = f(2) + 2 \cdot f'(2) - g'(4)(3)$ becomes $p'(2) = 5 + 2(1) - (-1)(3) = 10$.

(*Calculus for AP*®, pages 207–210, 227–233; EU 2.1 LO 2.1C; EK 2.1C3,2.1C4; MPAC 2,3,4)

15. ANSWER: (D) $C = 2\pi r \Rightarrow \frac{dC}{dt} = 2\pi\frac{dr}{dt}$.

Since $\frac{dC}{dt} = \frac{\pi}{4}, \frac{dr}{dt} = \frac{1}{8}$ cm/min,

$$\Rightarrow \frac{dh}{dt} = 4 \cdot \frac{1}{8} = \frac{1}{2} \text{ cm/min.}$$

$$V = \pi r^2 h \Rightarrow \frac{dV}{dt} = 2\pi r h\frac{dr}{dt} + \pi r^2\frac{dh}{dt}$$

$$\Rightarrow \left.\frac{dV}{dt}\right|_{\substack{r=4\\h=12}} = 2\pi(4)(12)\frac{1}{8} + \pi(4)^2\left(\frac{1}{2}\right) \Rightarrow 20\pi \text{ cm}^3\text{/min.}$$

(*Calculus for AP*®, pages 274–279; EU 2.3; LO 2.3C; EK 2.3C2; MPAC 2,3)

FREE-RESPONSE QUESTION

Solution		Possible points
(a)	$A=\frac{\pi}{2}r^2$ $\frac{dA}{dt}=\pi r\frac{dr}{dt}$ $1=3\pi\frac{dr}{dt}\Rightarrow\frac{dr}{dt}=\frac{1}{3\pi}\approx 0.106$ cm/sec	$2:\begin{cases}1: & \frac{dA}{dt}\\1: & \text{answer}\end{cases}$
(b)	$p=\pi r+2r$ $\frac{dp}{dt}=(\pi+2)\frac{dr}{dt}=\frac{\pi+2}{3\pi}\approx 0.546$ cm/sec	$2:\begin{cases}1: & \frac{dp}{dt}\\1: & \text{answer}\end{cases}$
(c)	$A=\frac{1}{2}\text{base}\times\text{height}=\frac{1}{2}(2r)r=r^2$ $\frac{dA}{dt}=2r\frac{dr}{dt}=\frac{6}{3\pi}=\frac{2}{\pi}\approx 0.637\ \text{cm}^2/\text{sec}$	$2:\begin{cases}1: & \frac{dA}{dt}\\1: & \text{answer}\end{cases}$
(d)	A = area of $\frac{1}{4}$ of the circle minus the area of $\frac{1}{2}$ of the triangle. $A=\frac{1}{4}\pi r^2-\frac{1}{2}r^2$ $\frac{dA}{dt}=\left(\frac{\pi}{2}r-r\right)\frac{dr}{dt}=\frac{\frac{3\pi}{2}-3}{3\pi}=\frac{3\pi-6}{6\pi}\approx 0.182\ \text{cm}^2/\text{sec}$	$2:\begin{cases}1: & \frac{dA}{dt}\\1: & \text{answer}\end{cases}$
		1 : {units for a, b, c, and d

(a), (b), (c), and (d) (*Calculus for AP*®, pages 274–279; EU 2.3; LO 2.3C; EK 2.3C2; MPAC 2,3,4,5)

3

APPLICATIONS OF DERIVATIVES

Curve sketching is one of the major applications of derivatives. The derivative can be used to find the extrema of a function, where the function increases and decreases, and where it is concave up and down. These components enable us to accurately graph almost any function. In addition, we can solve business problems and approximate solutions to various types of problems using Newton's method and differentials (although those are not AP® topics). We can also apply the concept of maxima and minima to answer real-world questions. Derivatives can also be utilized in determining limits that appear to be indeterminate.

Objectives

- Understand maxima and minima (global/absolute, local/relative).
- Understand points of inflection.
- Learn the characteristics of the graphs of f, f', and f'' and their relationships to each other.
- Be able to analyze curves using the above information as well as the following concepts: increasing/decreasing, concave up/down, and monotonicity (a function is strictly monotonic if it is either increasing on the entire interval or decreasing on the entire interval).
- Be able to apply L'Hôpital's Rule.
- Understand and be able to apply the Mean Value Theorem, Rolle's Theorem, the Intermediate Value Theorem, and the Extreme Value Theorem.
- Be able to solve optimization problems.
- Be able to use approximation techniques to solve problems.

EXTREMA ON AN INTERVAL

(*Calculus for AP*®, pages 292–301)

Extrema of a function are defined as the maximum or minimum values on a given interval. It is the y-value of the high point or low point of the graph and helps us to determine answers in the business world such as maximum profit or minimum cost. Relative extrema occur only at critical numbers. A critical number is a number c, defined on the function, where $f'(c)$ is either zero or does not exist, and c must be in the domain of the function.

KEY THEOREMS

THE EXTREME VALUE THEOREM

(*Calculus for AP*®, page 295)

If f is continuous on a closed interval $[a, b]$, then f has both a minimum and a maximum on the interval.

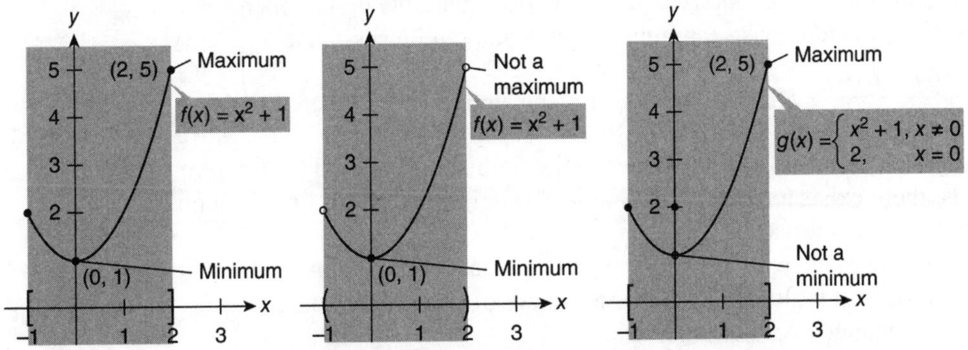

AP® Tip

It is important to distinguish between an extremum on an open interval (normally just called a relative or local maximum or minimum on an interval) and the absolute maximum or minimum on an interval. The absolute maximum or minimum requires you to check the endpoints of the interval to see if the y-values are greater than or less than the extrema found within the interval. There can also be an absolute maximum or minimum if the point is a relative maximum or minimum and is the ONLY critical point.

ROLLE'S THEOREM

(*Calculus for AP*®, pages 306–308)

If f is continuous on a closed interval $[a, b]$, differentiable on the open interval (a, b), and if the y-values at a and b are equal $[f(a) = f(b)]$, then there has to be at least one number c between a and b, such that $f'(c) = 0$, or in other words, there is a horizontal tangent line at c. (See graph on the right.)

The conditions in this theorem guarantee the existence of an extreme value in the interior of a closed interval.

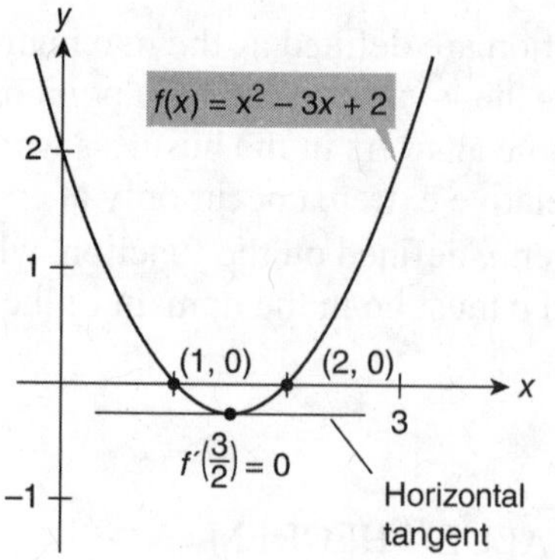

THE MEAN VALUE THEOREM

(*Calculus for AP*®, pages 308–311)

If f is continuous on a closed interval $[a, b]$ and differentiable on the open interval (a, b), then there exists a number c between a and b such that

$f'(c) = \dfrac{f(b) - f(a)}{b - a}$. This means that, at c, the slope of the tangent line is equal to the slope of the secant line between the points $(a, f(a))$ and $(b, f(b))$. In other words, there exists a tangent line that is parallel to the secant line through the endpoints of the interval.

In terms of rate of change, this means that there has to be a point on the open interval (a, b) at which the instantaneous rate of change is equal to the average rate of change over that interval.

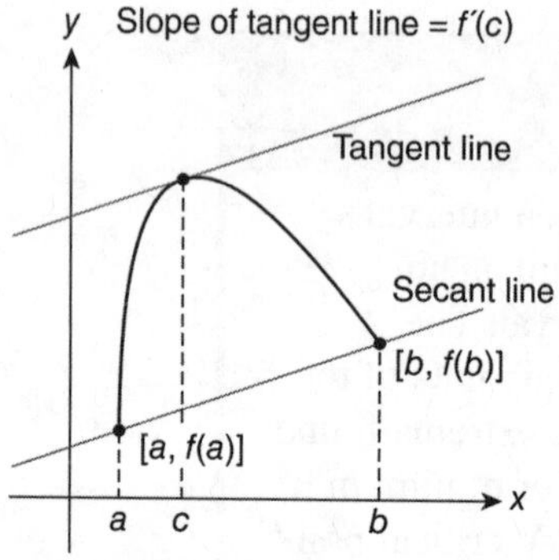

EXTREMUM

There are three ways to determine a relative extremum.

- The first is the f test where one checks the y-values locally. In other words, is the value of $f(c)$, at some point $x = c$, the highest (or lowest) y-value in that local area? Note that this test only works for closed intervals.
- The second is the first derivative test. We determine the critical numbers of f (where the first derivative is 0 or undefined, but the x-value is in the domain) and do an interval test to see if the value of the first derivative is

positive or negative in those intervals, which means the function is increasing (f' is positive) or decreasing (f' is negative) in that interval. If the function changes from increasing to decreasing at the critical number, then that is where a relative maximum occurs; if the function changes from decreasing to increasing, then a relative minimum occurs at that critical number. If it does not change direction at the critical number, then it is neither a relative maximum nor a relative minimum. This must be stated in terms of the derivative. Students must say f' changes from positive to negative for a maximum and vice versa for a minimum. Using f changes from increasing to decreasing is not sufficient.

- The third is the second derivative test. This is not an interval test but a test based on concavity. If a function is concave up (U-shaped), then there will be a relative minimum at the critical number of f; if it is concave down (upside down U), then there will be a relative maximum at that critical number. Thus, if the critical number found for the first derivative test is plugged into the second derivative and the value is positive, then the function is concave up, and there is a relative minimum at c. If the value of the second derivative is negative when the critical number is substituted in the second derivative, then the function is concave down and there is a relative maximum at the point. WARNING: Students frequently claim a relative maximum or relative minimum by discussing only the second derivative and failing to state that the first derivative is zero at that point.

  Note: Generally you use the first or second derivative tests to determine extrema (although using the f test is what you are doing when testing for absolute extrema). Students often depend solely on the first derivative test, but there are times (like when you've already solved for or been given the second derivative) when the second derivative test is more efficient to use or when the first derivative test doesn't work. You should be aware of and able to use all three tests.

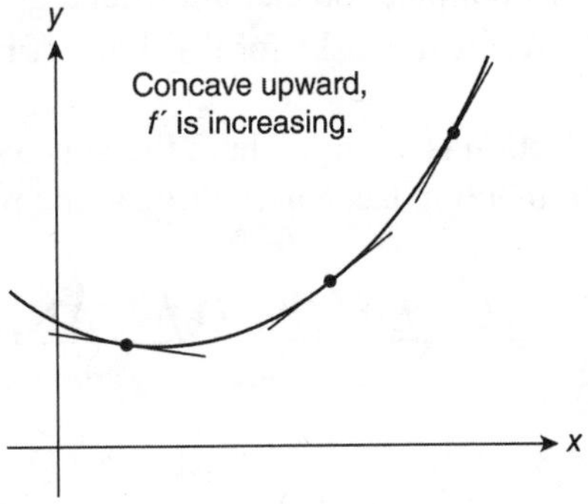

CONCAVITY OF A GRAPH

(*Calculus for AP®*, pages 322–324)

The graph of a function is concave upward on the interval if f' is increasing on the interval. Visualizing this, you see a U-shaped curve where the slopes of the tangent lines are getting increasingly larger (from a very negative slope to a very positive slope). The function f is concave downward on the interval if f' is decreasing (e.g., in the diagram above right, the third degree equation from -4 to 1 has a very large positive slope at -4, and it becomes negative to the right of -1 and increases its negative steepness until 1; thus the slope's value is decreasing). For a function to be concave down, in whatever interval is being considered, the values of the slope will decrease as the x-values increase. Another way to visualize this is to think that a function is concave up if the tangent lines lie below the curve, and the function is concave down if the tangent lines lie above the curve.

In the figure to the right, the heavy line graph is our function; the thin line graph is the first derivative, and the dotted line graph is the second derivative. Note that, on the interval from $-\infty$ to -1, the function f is increasing; the f' values (the thin line graph) are positive; from -1 to 3.6 the function is decreasing and the f' values are negative, and to the right of $x = 3.6$, the f' values are again positive and the function f is increasing. Connecting this concept with the second derivative graph (the dotted line graph), you will notice that when the dotted values are negative (to the left of about $x = 1.2$), the original function is concave down and when the dotted values are positive (above the x-axis), the original function is concave up. To further analyze the graphs, when the f' graph is decreasing, the f'' graph's values are negative, and the function is concave down. Likewise, when the graph of f' is increasing, the graph of f'' is positive and the graph of f is concave up. (*Note:* It is essential that you can interpret a graph from the values and slopes of f' as the AP® exam asks for this kind of interpretation; see the next section.)

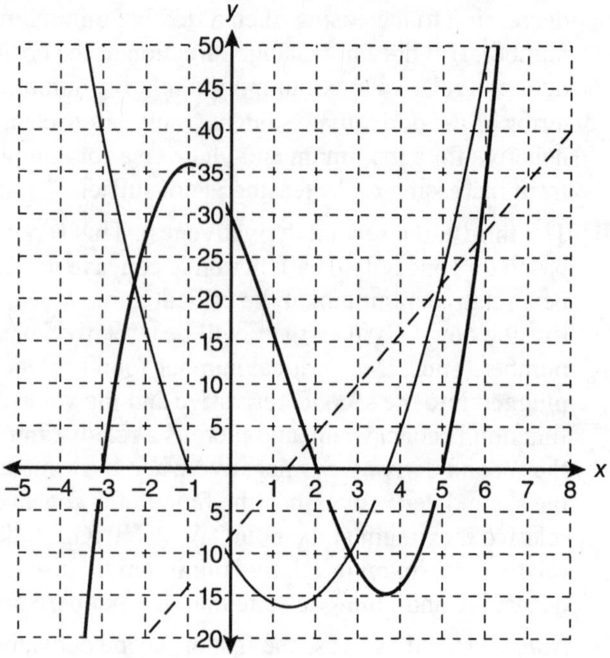

A point of inflection is a point where the concavity changes. It is not necessary that the function has a derivative at the point of concavity.

CHARACTERISTICS OF f, f', AND f'', AND THEIR RELATIONSHIPS

(*Calculus for AP®*, pages 316–327)

In order to analyze the function f, we want to graph it over various intervals to understand the behavior of its values.

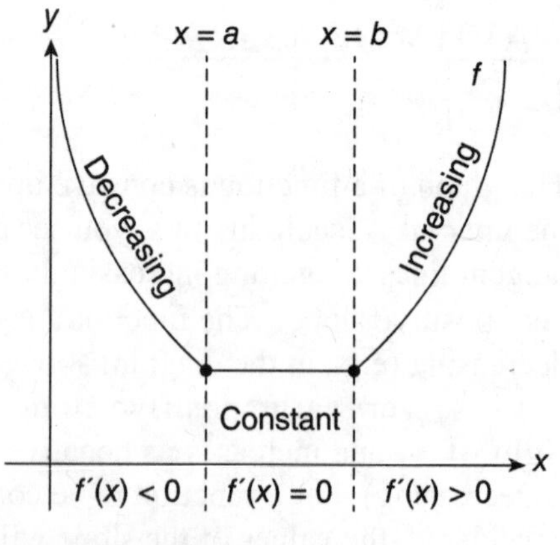

The function f' allows us to determine over which intervals the function is increasing or decreasing. Find the zeros and undefined x-values of the first derivative function and check the intervals between those critical numbers (the zeros of f' are where the slope of f is zero, or the function has a horizontal tangent line). When f' is positive, the slope of function f is positive and therefore function f is increasing; this means that if $x_1 < x_2$, then $f(x_1) < f(x_2)$. When f' is negative, the slope of function f is negative or function f is moving downward from left to right or, in other words, the function is decreasing.

The function f'' allows you to determine over which intervals the first derivative function is increasing or decreasing in the same way as the f' relates to the original function. But the second derivative also allows you to determine the concavity of the original function. If the second derivative is negative, that means the f' is decreasing (envision a parabola opening downward) and that means that the slope values are getting smaller (from a potentially very large positive slope to a smaller positive slope to a negative slope), thus forming a shape that is considered concave down. If the second derivative is positive, that means that f' is increasing (envision a parabola opening upward), which means that the slope values are getting larger (from a potentially very negative value to a very large positive slope).

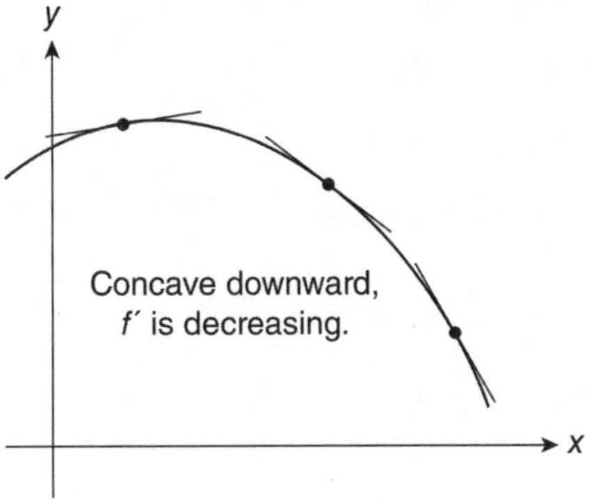

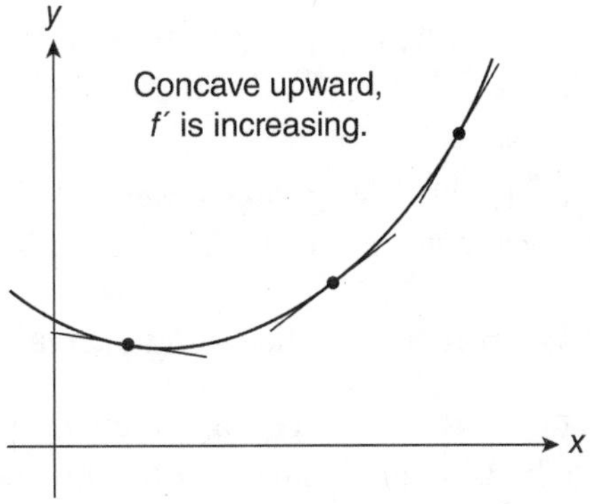

Although f' and f'' are used to tell you something about f, remember that they also tell you something about each other. For example, if f'' is positive, then the function f is concave up; but we also know that f' is increasing (the relationship between a function (f') and its derivative (f''). If f' is decreasing, that would tell us that f'' is negative, which would then lead to the conclusion that f is concave down.

ANALYSIS OF CURVES

(*Calculus for AP*®, pages 350–362)

Given the function $f(x)$ and its derivatives $f'(x)$ and $f''(x)$, let's review what we know about curves.

DOMAIN: What the x-values can be. Look for problems in the denominator or under the square root and watch for piecewise functions.

RANGE: What the y-values are. Find at end after graphing: look for minimum and maximum y-values, discontinuities, and horizontal tangent lines.

X-VALUES OF DISCONTINUITY: Where the function is undefined, holes, piecewise.

X-VALUES OF NONDIFFERENTIABILITY: Sharp turns, vertical tangent lines, points of discontinuity, and vertical tangents.

X-AND *Y*-INTERCEPTS: x-intercept when $y = 0$, y-intercept when $x = 0$.

SYMMETRY: After you make the following substitution(s), if symmetry exists, then the simplified answer would equal the original $f(x)$.

X-axis Substitute $-y$ for y

Y-axis Substitute $-x$ for x

Origin Substitute $-y$ for y and $-x$ for x

VERTICAL ASYMPTOTES

(infinite limits)

$\lim_{x\to c} f(x) = \infty$

where denominator = 0 (and the numeration is not zero)

HORIZONTAL ASYMPTOTES

(limits at infinity)

$\lim_{x\to\infty} f(x) = L$

apply rules of functions to determine

SLANT ASYMPTOTES: When the power in the numerator is greater by 1 than the power in the denominator, use long division to solve for the slant asymptote.

CRITICAL NUMBERS

Where f' is 0 or undefined and the x-value is in the domain

Increasing Intervals/Decreasing Intervals

Test the intervals around the critical numbers and undefined points of the function: if $f' > 0$, then the function is increasing; if $f' < 0$, then the function is decreasing.

RELATIVE EXTREMA: The critical numbers occur where f changes from increasing to decreasing (relative maximum) or from decreasing to increasing (relative minimum)

or where $f(x)$ has the greatest local value (relative maximum) or least local value (relative minimum)

or where f'' of the critical number is negative (relative maximum occurs when the function is concave down) or is positive (relative minimum occurs when the function is concave up).

CONCAVITY

Examine the sign of the second derivative to determine intervals of concavity.

if $f'' > 0$, then f is concave up on that interval; if $f'' < 0$, then f is concave down on that interval.

INFLECTION POINTS

Where concavity changes at a defined point of the function.

WARNING: A common mistake is that students show that the second derivative is zero and do not show that the second derivative changes signs at this point.

Note: **Inflection may change at one of the undefined values used to test, but that value cannot be an inflection POINT since it is not in the domain (it is not a part of the graph).**

APPLICATIONS OF DERIVATIVES

(*Calculus for AP®*, pages 365–372)

Optimization problems are those that require you to determine such things as the greatest profit, least cost, minimum distance, greatest volume, and so on. To determine the solution you must

- identify all given quantities and quantities that need to be determined,
- write both primary and secondary equations that describe the problem and what quantities need to be maximized or minimized,
- determine a feasible domain, and
- solve the problem for the maximum or minimum value by using the calculus techniques of derivatives.

AP® Tip

When finding a maximum of anything, take its derivative. For example, if you want the maximum slope of a curve, you need to use the second derivative (as the first derivative of the first derivative) to determine the critical numbers to interpret where the maximum slope values occur. The x-value of the function tells you where the event occurs; the y-value of the function is generally the answer to the question. However, always reread the question so that you answer it correctly.

As an example, find the maximum slope of the function $f(x) = 3x^3 - 2x^2 + 5x$. Normally, to find a maximum you would just take the first derivative of the function. However, in this case, since the goal is to find the maximum slope, you would want to take the derivative of the function in order to get an expression for the slope and then take the derivative of that to find where the maximum slope will occur. Thus, you must take the second derivative of the original function, which is the first derivative of the slope function, and set it equal to zero to find the critical numbers of f'. To find the slope, after you determine which critical number, if any, leads to a maximum point, substitute that x-value back into the f' equation to solve for the maximum slope. This would also be similar to solving for a maximum velocity given a position equation.

There are many applications of derivatives. They include curve analysis, finding the extrema of a given problem, finding rates of change, and solving for the slope of the tangent line at a given point (see Chapter 3). The AP® exam often asks for a further application of the concept. For example, instead of just asking for the slope of the tangent line, the question might ask for the equation of the tangent line; and you would then apply the values of the first derivative and the point to the point-slope equation of a line to solve for the solution required.

NEWTON'S METHOD is a technique for approximating the real zeros of a function. It is a topic that is useful to understand, but it is not tested on the AP® exam.

DIFFERENTIALS can be talked about in terms of local linearity, a reform topic in calculus terminology. It essentially gives you a method by which to solve for an approximate value of $f(x_2)$ if you know $f(x_1)$ and the difference between x_1 and x_2. In other words, $f(x + \Delta x) \cong f(x) + dy \cong f(x) + f'(x)\,dx$. This is really just saying that Δy, which is the actual difference of the y-values $f(x + \Delta x) - f(x)$, is approximated by this mathematical idea called a differential, *dy*. The differential, *dy*, gives a linear approximation which is the same as the tangent line approximation. Tangent line approximations are frequently tested on the AP® exam and one can determine whether the tangent line approximation is an over approximation or an under approximation by using the second derivative test for concavity. (The concept is demonstrated extremely well by Example 1 in *Calculus for AP®* on page 283.) This concept is not generally tested on the AP® exam, although the concept of local linearity can be. Chapter 8 on slope fields and Euler's Method will address this.

INDETERMINATE FORMS AND L'HÔPITAL'S RULE

(*Calculus for AP®*, pages 337–343)

When you solve a limit problem, the answers can be determinate or indeterminate. A numerical answer is determinate if the answers are in the form

$$\infty + \infty = \infty$$

$$-\infty - \infty = -\infty$$

$$0^{\infty} = 0$$

$$0^{-\infty} = \frac{1}{0^{\infty}} = \infty$$

However, other answers are of a form we call indeterminate, which means that we cannot determine the true solution from that answer. Indeterminate forms include $\frac{0}{0}, \frac{\infty}{\infty}, \infty - \infty, 0 \cdot \infty, 1^{\infty}, 0^0, \infty^0$.

0/0 and $\frac{\infty}{\infty}$ are the only two of the seven cases that are tested. Often these indeterminate forms occur with problems that have variable bases or variable exponents. They are called indeterminate because the answer cannot be determined by the result of direct substitution.

For example, $\lim_{x \to 0} x\left(\frac{1}{x}\right) = 1$, $\lim_{x \to 0} x\left(\frac{2}{x}\right) = 2$, $\lim_{x \to \infty} x\left(\frac{1}{e^x}\right) = 0$, and $\lim_{x \to \infty} e^x\left(\frac{1}{x}\right) = \infty$.

But if you used direct substitution, they would all be equal to $0 * \infty$ that is an indeterminate value; we cannot determine the value of the limit by direct substitution.

Previously, when we encountered these forms, we attempted to rewrite the expression by using various algebraic techniques such as dividing by the denominator or by the term with the highest power in the denominator. However, algebraic manipulation does not always work and this is especially true when the problem is a mixture of algebraic and transcendental functions such as $\lim_{x\to 0}\frac{e^{2x}-1}{x}$.

However, L'Hôpital proved that if

- f and g are functions that are differentiable (except perhaps at c) in an open interval (a, b) containing c,
- $g'(x) \neq 0$ for all x in (a, b) except possibly at c itself and
- the limit of the quotient $\frac{f(x)}{g(x)}$, as x approaches some c, produces the indeterminate form of $\frac{0}{0}$ or the indeterminate form of $\frac{\pm\infty}{\pm\infty}$,
- then $\lim_{x\to c}\frac{f(x)}{g(x)} = \lim_{x\to c}\frac{f'(x)}{g'(x)}$ provided that the limit on the right exists or is infinite. You do not know that the equation is true until you know that the second limit exists. (*Note:* Be sure not to apply the quotient rule here; just take the derivative of f divided by the derivative of g.)

L'Hôpital's Rule can also be applied to one-sided limits. L'Hôpital's Rule works only for limits where direct substitution yields the form $\frac{0}{0}$ or the form $\frac{\pm\infty}{\pm\infty}$; it does not work for the other indeterminate forms mentioned previously unless you can rewrite the form to fit $\frac{0}{0}$ or $\frac{\pm\infty}{\pm\infty}$.

For example, $\lim_{x\to 0}\frac{e^{2x}-1}{x}$ by direct substitution is $\frac{e^0-1}{0}=\frac{0}{0}$. Therefore, you can apply L'Hôpital's Rule by taking the derivatives of the numerator and of the denominator $\frac{\frac{d}{dx}\left(e^{2x}-1\right)}{\frac{d}{dx}x}$.

$\lim_{x\to 0}\frac{e^{2x}-1}{x} = \lim_{x\to 0}\frac{2e^{2x}}{1}$, and now by direct substitution, it becomes equal $\frac{2}{1}$ or 2.

L'Hôpital's Rule may be applied more than once. If the second limit is of the form $\frac{0}{0}$ or $\frac{\pm\infty}{\pm\infty}$, then apply the rule again. As long as the limit has the correct form, you can continue to apply L'Hôpital's Rule.

Reading Examples 6–10 in *Calculus for AP®* on pages 343–347, or similar examples of applying L'Hôpital's Rule in another text will illustrate the methods by which you change an indeterminate form that is not $\frac{0}{0}$ or $\frac{\pm\infty}{\pm\infty}$ to become one of those forms so that you can apply L'Hôpital's Rule.

PAST AP® FREE-RESPONSE PROBLEMS COVERED BY THIS CHAPTER

Note: These and other questions can be found at apcentral.com.
1999 BC 1
2000 AB 2a,b; 3
2001 AB 4
2003 AB 4a,b,c
2004 AB 1b; 3b; 4c; 5b,d
2005 AB 3a,d; 4a,b,d; 5
2006 AB 3b; 4a; BC 3b
2007 AB 2b,c; 3a,b,c; 4a; 5d; 6; BC 4a,b
2008 AB 2a,c; 4b,c,d; 6b,c; BC 5a,b
2009 AB 2b; 3d; 5d; 6a,c
2010 AB 2d; 3b,c; 5b; 6a,b
2011 AB 4b,c,d; 5b
2012 AB 3b,c,d; 5b
2013 AB 3b; 4a
2014 AB 3b; 4b; 5a,b

MULTIPLE-CHOICE QUESTIONS

A calculator may not be used on the following questions.

1. Let ***M*** represent the absolute maximum of $f(x)$ in an interval.
Let ***R*** represent a root of $f(x)$ in the given interval.
Let ***m*** represent the absolute minimum of $f(x)$ in the interval.
If $f(x) = x^3 - 3x^2$, then which of the following is true over the closed interval $-3 \le x \le 1$?
(A) *M* and ***R*** occur at a critical point and ***m*** occurs at an endpoint.
(B) *M* and ***m*** occur at critical points.
(C) *M*, ***m***, and ***R*** occur at endpoints of the given interval.
(D) *M* occurs at an endpoint, whereas ***m*** and ***R*** occur at a critical point.

2. What value of *c* in the open interval (0, 4) satisfies the Mean Value Theorem for $f(x)=\sqrt{3x+4}$?
(A) 0
(B) $\frac{3}{5}$
(C) $\frac{5}{3}$
(D) 2

3. If $f'(x)=\dfrac{x^2(x+1)}{(x-1)^{\frac{1}{3}}}$, then on which interval(s) is the continuous function $f(x)$ increasing?
   (A) $(-\infty,-1)\cup(1,\infty)$
   (B) $(-\infty,0)\cup(1,\infty)$
   (C) $(-\infty,-1)\cup(0,\infty)$
   (D) $(1,\infty)$

4. The points of inflection for $f(x)$ are at $x=p_1$ and $x=p_2$. Which of the following is (are) true?
   I. The points of inflection for $f(x-a)$ are at $x=p_1+a$ and $x=p_2+a$.
   II. The points of inflection for $bf(x)$ are at $x=bp_1$ and $x=bp_2$.
   III. The points of inflection for $f(cx)$ are at $\frac{P_1}{c}$ and $x=\frac{P_2}{c}$.

   (A) I only
   (B) II only
   (C) I and II only
   (D) I and III only

5. $\lim\limits_{x\to 0}\dfrac{\sin 4x}{x^2+8x}=$
   (A) 0.
   (B) $\frac{1}{2}$.
   (C) 1.
   (D) ∞.

6. The graph of $f'(x)$ is given below for $x\in[-3,3]$. On which interval(s) is the function $f(x)$ both increasing and concave up?

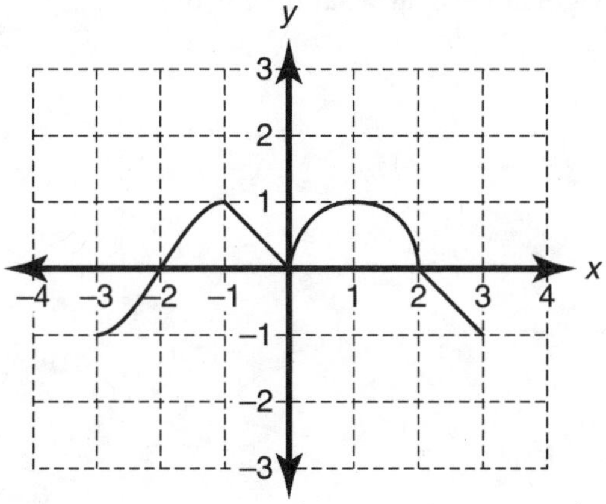

   (A) $(-2,2)$
   (B) $(-2,0)\cup(0,2)$
   (C) $(-3,-2)$
   (D) $(-2,-1)\cup(0,1)$

7. A farmer has 100 yards of fencing to form two identical rectangular pens and a third pen that is twice as long as the other two pens, as shown in the diagram below. All three pens have the same width, x. Which value of y produces the maximum total fenced area?

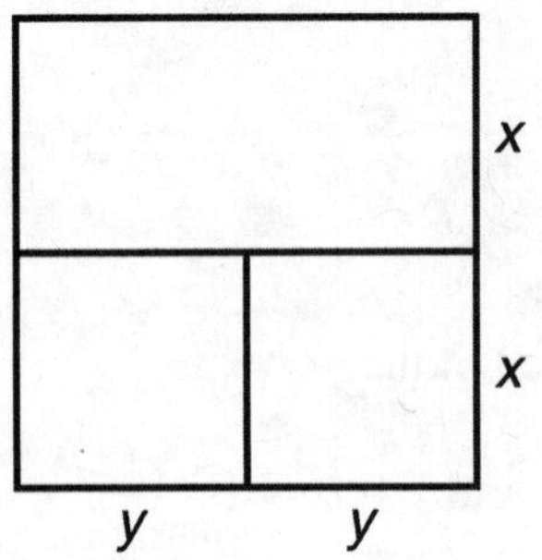

(A) $\frac{25}{2}$
(B) 10
(C) $\frac{100}{11}$
(D) $\frac{25}{3}$

8. For the function $f(x) = 12x^5 - 5x^4$, how many of the inflection points of the function are also extrema?
(A) 3
(B) 2
(C) 1
(D) None

9. The position of an object moving along a straight line for $t \geq 0$ is given by $s_1(t) = t^3 + 2$, and the position of a second object moving along the same line is given by $s_2(t) = t^2$. If both objects begin at $t = 0$, at what time is the distance between the objects a minimum?
(A) 2
(B) $\frac{50}{27}$
(C) $\frac{2}{3}$
(D) 0

10. Given the following conditions for $f(x)$, which graph best illustrates $f(x)$?

$f(x)$: The domain of the function is the real numbers, but $x \neq 1$;

$\lim_{x\to-\infty} f(x) = -1$; $\lim_{x\to1^-} f(x) = \infty$; $\lim_{x\to1^+} f(x) = -\infty$

$f'(x) > 0$ for all x where $x \neq 1$, and $f'(x)$ does not exist at $x = 1$.

$f''(x) > 0$ for $x < 1$, $f''(x) < 0$ for $x > 1$, and $f''(x)$ does not exist at $x = 1$.

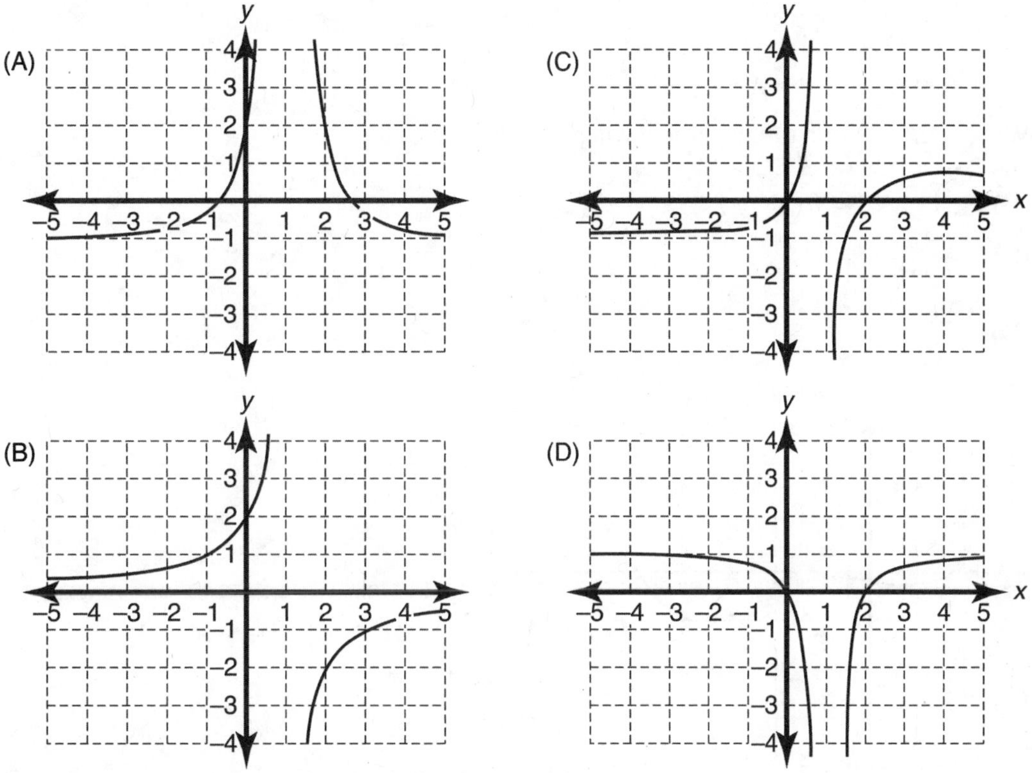

A calculator may be used for the following question.

11. Let $f(x)$ be a function such that $f'(x) = \ln x \cdot \cos x + \dfrac{\sin x}{x}$. In the interval $0 < x < 3$, the graph of $f(x)$ has a point of inflection nearest $x =$

(A) 0.352.
(B) 1.101.
(C) 2.128.
(D) 2.259.

A calculator may not be used on the following questions.

Questions 12 and 13 refer to the following information:

For time $0 \le t \le 10$, a particle moves along the x-axis with position given by $x(t) = t^3 - 7t^2 + 8t + 5$.

12. During what time intervals is the speed of the particle increasing?
    (A) $4 < t \leq 10$ only
    (B) $0 \leq t < \frac{2}{3}$ and $\frac{7}{3} < t < 4$
    (C) $0 \leq t < \frac{2}{3}$ and $4 < t \leq 10$
    (D) $\frac{2}{3} < t < \frac{7}{3}$ and $4 < t \leq 10$

13. What is the position of the particle when it is farthest to the left?
    (A) -14
    (B) -11
    (C) $-\frac{47}{27}$
    (D) $\frac{203}{27}$

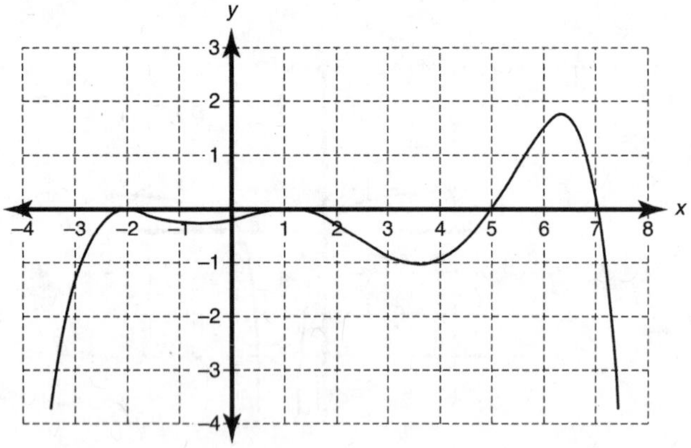

14. Based on the graph of $g''(x)$ pictured above, how many points of inflection exist for the twice differentiable function $g(x)$ on the interval $-4 < x < 8$?
    (A) 4
    (B) 3
    (C) 2
    (D) 1

15. A rectangle is drawn in the first quadrant so that it has two adjacent sides on the coordinate axes and one vertex on the curve $y = -\ln(x)$. Find the x coordinate of the vertex for which the area of the rectangle is a maximum.

(A) $\dfrac{1}{2}$

(B) $-\ln\left(\dfrac{1}{2}\right)$

(C) $\dfrac{1}{e}$

(D) e

FREE-RESPONSE QUESTION

This question does not require the use of a calculator.

1. The function $f(x)$ is defined as $f(x) = -2(x + 2)(x - 1)^2$ on the open interval $(-3, 3)$ as illustrated in the graph shown.
   (a) Determine the coordinates of the relative extrema of $f(x)$ in the open interval $(-3, 3)$.
   (b) Let $g(x)$ be defined as $g(x) = |f(x)|$ in the open interval $(-3, 3)$. Determine the coordinate(s) of the relative maxima of $g(x)$ in the open interval. Explain your reasoning.
   (c) For what values of x is $g'(x)$ not defined? Explain your reasoning.
   (d) Find all values of x for which $g(x)$ is concave down. Explain your reasoning.

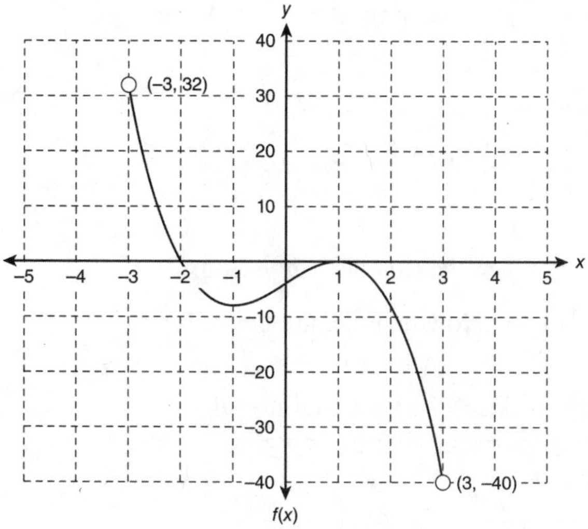

Answers

MULTIPLE-CHOICE QUESTIONS

1. ANSWER: (A) Setting $f(x) = x^3 - 3x^2 = x^2(x - 3) = 0$ gives the roots $x = 0$ and $x = 3$, but only $x = 0$ is in the interval.

   Setting $f'(x) = 3x^2 - 6x = 3x(x - 2) = 0$ gives the critical points $x = 0$ and $x = 2$, but only $x = 0$ is in the interval.

Left endpoint	Critical number	Right endpoint
$f(-3) = -54$	$f(0) = 0$	$f(1) = -4$
	Root	
Absolute minimum	Absolute maximum	

   (*Calculus for AP*®, pages 292–293; EU 2.2; LO 2.2A; EK 2.2A2,2.2A3; MPAC 1,2,3)

2. ANSWER: (C) The Mean Value Theorem states that $f'(c) = \dfrac{f(b) - f(a)}{b - a}$

   for some c in the open interval $a < c < b$. Since

   $$f'(x) = \overbrace{\frac{3}{2\sqrt{3c+4}}}^{\text{derivative formula}} = \overbrace{\frac{f(4)-f(0)}{4-0}}^{mvt} = \frac{4-2}{4-0} = \frac{1}{2},$$ solving $\sqrt{3c+4=3}$ we

   get $c = \dfrac{5}{3}$, which is in the interval (0, 4).

   (*Calculus for AP*®, pages 308–311; EU 2.4; LO 2.4A; EK 2.4A1; MPAC 1,2,3)

3. ANSWER: (A) The function is increasing when the first derivative is greater than zero. Setting $f'(x) = \dfrac{x^2(x+1)}{(x-1)^{\frac{1}{3}}}$, $f'(x)$ is zero when the numerator is zero; thus $(x + 1)x^2 = 0$. Then $x = 0$ or -1. Also, $f'(x)$ is undefined at $x = 1$.

Interval	$-\infty < x < -1$	$-1 < x < 0$	$0 < x < 1$	$1 < x < \infty$
Sign of $f'(x)$	$f'(-2) > 0$	$f'(-\frac{1}{2}) < 0$	$f'(\frac{1}{2}) < 0$	$f'(2) > 0$
Conclusion on $f(x)$	Increasing	Decreasing	Decreasing	Increasing

   (*Calculus for AP*®, pages 316–327; EU 2.2; LO 2.2A; EK 2.2A1; MPAC 2,3)

4. ANSWER: (D) Case I: True. For $f(x-a)$ the graph is shifted horizontally a units, and therefore the points of inflection are also shifted a units and are at $x = p_1 + a$ and $x = p_2 + a$. [Example: $f(x) = x^4 + 4x^3$ has inflection points at $x = 0$ and -2, and $f(x-1) = (x-1)^4 + 4(x-1)^3$ has inflection points at $x = 1$ and -1.]

   Case II: False. For $bf(x)$, the graph is dilated vertically by a factor of b. The function values of the inflection points are multiplied by b, but the x-coordinates stay the same.

   Case III: True. For $f(cx)$, the graph is dilated horizontally by a factor of c. Thus the function values of the points of inflection stay the same, but the x-coordinates are at $x = p_1/c$ and $x = p_2/c$. [Example: $f(x) = x^4 + 4x^3$ has inflection points at $x = 0$ and -2, and $f(2x) = (2x)^4 + 4(2x)^3 = 16x^4 + 32x^3$ has inflection points at $x = 0$ and -1.] (*Calculus for AP®*, pages 322–324; EU 2.2; LO 2.2A; EK 2.2A1; MPAC 2)

5. ANSWER: (B) Using L'Hôpital's Rule for the quotient indeterminate form

$$\frac{0}{0}, \lim_{x\to 0}\frac{\sin 4x}{x^2+8x} = \lim_{x\to 0}\frac{\frac{d}{dx}(\sin 4x)}{\frac{d}{dx}\left(x^2+8x\right)} = \lim_{x\to 0}\frac{4\cos 4x}{2x+8} = \frac{4\times 1}{0+8} = \frac{1}{2}.$$

   (*Calculus for AP®*, pages 337–343; EU 1.1;LO 1.1C; EK 1.1C3; MPAC 2,3)

6. ANSWER: (D)

Interval	$-3<x<-2$	$-2<x<-1$	$-1<x<0$	$0<x<1$	$1<x<2$	$2<x<3$
Sign of $f'(x)$	Negative	Positive	Positive	Positive	Positive	Negative
Sign of $f''(x)$	Positive	Positive	Negative	Positive	Negative	Negative
Characteristic of graph	Decreasing Concave up	Increasing Concave up	Increasing Concave down	Increasing Concave up	Increasing Concave down	Decreasing Concave down

   (*Calculus for AP®*, pages 316–327; EU 2.2; LO 2.2A. EK 2.2A1; MPAC 2,4)

7. ANSWER: (D) Since $5x + 6y = 100$, then $y = \frac{100-5x}{6}$. The area is

$$A = 2x(2y) = 4x\left(\frac{100-5x}{6}\right) = \frac{200}{3}x - \frac{10}{3}x^2.$$

   With $A'(x) = \frac{200}{3} - \frac{20x}{3} = 0$, $x = 10$ and $y = \frac{25}{3}$.

   $A''(x) = -\frac{20}{3} < 0$ for all x. Therefore, $y = \frac{25}{3}$ and $x = 10$ yield a maximum area. (*Calculus for AP®*, pages 365–372; EU 2.3; LO 2.3C; EK 2.3C3; MPAC 2,3,4)

8. ANSWER: (D) $f'(x) = 60x^4 - 20x^3 = 20x^3(3x - 1) = 0$. Since extrema exist where $f'(x)$ changes sign, the extrema for $f(x)$ occur at $x = \frac{1}{3}$ or $x = 0$. $f''(x) = 240x^3 - 60x^2 = 60x^2(4x - 1) = 0$. The only inflection point occurs at $x = \frac{1}{4}$, where $f''(x)$ changes from negative to positive. $x = 0$ is not a point of inflection. Therefore, there are no inflection points that are also extrema. (*Calculus for AP®*, pages 316–327; EU 2.2; LO 2.2A; EK 2.2A1; MPAC 2,3)

9. ANSWER: (C) Let $D(t) = s_1(t) - s_2(t)$, the distance between the functions at time t. Then $D(t) = t^3 - t^2 + 2$ and $D'(t) = 3t^2 - 2t = t(3t - 2) = 0$, so $t = 0$ or $t = \frac{2}{3}$ are the critical points. Plugging $t = 0$ and $t = \frac{2}{3}$ into $D(t)$, $D(0) = 2$ and $D\left(\frac{2}{3}\right) = \frac{50}{27} < 2$. Therefore, $D\left(\frac{2}{3}\right) = \frac{50}{27}$ is the minimum distance between the objects. (*Calculus for AP®*, pages 365–372; EU 2.3; LO 2.3C; EK 2.3C3; MP AC 2,3,4)

10. ANSWER: (C)

Interval	$-\infty < x < 1$	$x = 1$	$1 < x < \infty$
Sign of $f'(x)$	Positive	Not defined	Positive
Sign of $f''(x)$	Positive	Not defined	Negative
Conclusion on $f(x)$	Increasing Concave up	Vertical asymptote	Increasing Concave down

From the limit statements, we can deduce that there is a horizontal asymptote $y = 1$ as x approaches positive infinity, and another horizontal asymptote $y = -1$ as x approaches negative infinity. (Roots and y-intercept are not uniquely determined from the given information.) (*Calculus for AP®*, pages 350–362; EU 1.1,2.2; LO 1.1D,2.2A; EK 1.1D1,2.2A1; MPAC 2,4)

11. ANSWER: (B) $f(x)$ has an inflection point when $f''(x)$ changes sign or, equivalently, when $f'(x)$ has a relative maximum or minimum. Using a calculator, graph $f'(x)$ and/or $f''(x)$. $f''(x) = 0$, and $f'(x)$ has a relative maximum, when $x = 1.101$. (*Calculus for AP®*, pages 322–324; EU 2.2; LO 2.2A; EK 2.2A1; MPAC 2,3)

12. ANSWER: (D) $v(t) = 3t^2 - 14t + 8 = (3t-2)(t-4)$. $v(t) = 0$ at $t = \frac{2}{3}$ and $t = 4$. $a(t) = 6t - 14$. $a(t) = 0$ at $t = \frac{7}{3}$. The speed of the particle is increasing when $v(t)$ and $a(t)$ have the same sign, which, according to the sign table below, occurs on the intervals $\frac{2}{3} < t < \frac{7}{3}$ and $4 < t \leq 10$.

t	$0 < t < \frac{2}{3}$	$\frac{2}{3} < t < \frac{7}{3}$	$\frac{7}{3} < t < 4$	$4 < t \leq 10$
$v(t)$	Positive	Negative	Negative	Positive
$a(t)$	Negative	Negative	Positive	Positive

(*Calculus for AP*®, pages 508–511; EU 2.3; LO 2.3C; EK 2.3C1; MPAC 2,3)

13. ANSWER: (B) The minimum position occurs at either a critical point or an endpoint. From the sign table in Question 12, there is a relative minimum when $t = 4$, $x(0) = 5$, $x(4) = -11$, and $x(10) = 385$. The least of these, -11, is the minimum position. (*Calculus for AP*®, pages 292–293; EK 2.3C1; MPAC 2,3)

14. ANSWER: (C) Points of inflection for $g(x)$ exist where $g''(x)$ changes sign or is undefined. Thus, there are only two points of inflection, at $x = 5$ and $x = 7$. (*Calculus for AP*®, pages 322–324; EU 2.2; LO 2.2A0.; EK 2.2A1,2.2A3; MPAC 2,4)

15. ANSWER: (C) The area of the rectangle is given by $A(x) = x(-\ln(x))$.

$$A'(x) = -\ln(x) + \frac{x}{-x} = -\ln(x) - 1 = 0 \Rightarrow x = e^{-1}.$$

$$A''(x) = \frac{-1}{x} \Rightarrow A''(e^{-1}) < 0$$ and $A(x)$ is concave down. Thus, the rectangle has maximum area when $x = e^{-1}$.

(*Calculus for AP*®, pages 365–372; EU 2.3; LO 2.3C; EK 2.3C3; MPAC 2,3,4)

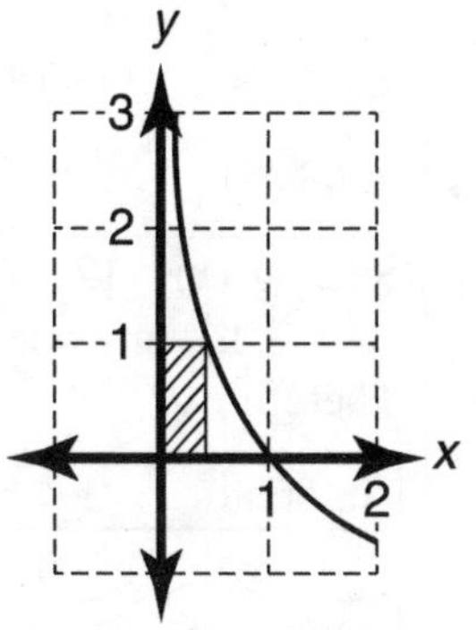

FREE-RESPONSE QUESTION

<table>
<tr><th></th><th>Solution</th><th>Possible points</th></tr>
<tr><td>(a)</td><td>
Given: $f(-3) = 32$ and $f(3) = -40$
$f(x) = -2(x+2)(x-1)^2 = -2x^3 + 6x - 4$
$f'(x) = -6x^2 + 6 = -6(x^2 - 1) = 0$, so $x = \pm 1$.
<table>
<tr><td></td><td>$-3 < x < -1$</td><td>$-1 < x < 1$</td><td>$1 < x < 3$</td></tr>
<tr><td>$f'(x)$</td><td>Positive</td><td>Negative</td><td>Positive</td></tr>
<tr><td>$f(x)$</td><td>Decreasing</td><td>Increasing</td><td>Decreasing</td></tr>
</table>
$f(1) = 0$; $f(-1) = -8$
Therefore in the open interval $(-3, 3)$, the relative maximum for $f(x)$ occurs at the point $(1, 0)$ and the relative minimum for $f(x)$ occurs at the point $(-1, -8)$.
</td><td>
$3: \begin{cases} 1: f'(x) \\ 1: x = \pm 1 \\ 1: \text{answer and reason} \end{cases}$
</td></tr>
<tr><td>(b)</td><td>
For $g(x) = |f(x)|$, the relative maximum will occur at the point $(-1, 8)$. All values of the new function $g(x)$ are made positive with the application of the absolute value to $f(x)$, and the relative minimum of $f(x)$ becomes a relative maximum for $g(x)$.
</td><td>
$2: \begin{cases} 1: \text{reasoning} \\ 1: (-1, 8) \end{cases}$
</td></tr>
<tr><td>(c)</td><td>
Since $g(x) = \begin{cases} -2x^3 + 6x - 4, & x < -2 \\ 2x^3 - 6x + 4, & x > -2 \end{cases}$
then $g(x) = \begin{cases} -6x^2 + 6, & x < -2 \\ 6x^2 - 6, & x > -2. \end{cases}$
$g'(x)$ is not defined at $x = -2$ because $\lim_{x \to -2^-} g'(x) = -18$ and $\lim_{x \to -2^+} g'(x) = 18$. A sharp turn occurs at $x = -2$ on the graph.
</td><td>
$2: \begin{cases} 1: x = -2 \\ 1: \text{reason} \end{cases}$
</td></tr>
<tr><td>(d)</td><td>
Since $g''(x) = 12x = 0$ at $x = 0$ and $g''(x)$ is not defined at $x = -2$, the inflection points occur at $x = 0$ and $x = -2$. Therefore
<table>
<tr><td>Interval</td><td>$-3 < x < -2$</td><td>$-2 < x < 0$</td><td>$0 < x < 3$</td></tr>
<tr><td></td><td>$g''(x) = -12x$</td><td>$g''(x) = 12x$</td><td>$g''(x) = 12x$</td></tr>
<tr><td>Sign of $g''(x)$</td><td>Positive</td><td>Negative</td><td>Positive</td></tr>
<tr><td>$g''(x)$</td><td>Concave up</td><td>Concave down</td><td>Concave up</td></tr>
</table>
and $g(x)$ is concave down in the open interval $(-2, 0)$.
</td><td>
$2: \begin{cases} 1: f'(x) = 0 \\ 1: \text{interval and reason} \end{cases}$
</td></tr>
</table>

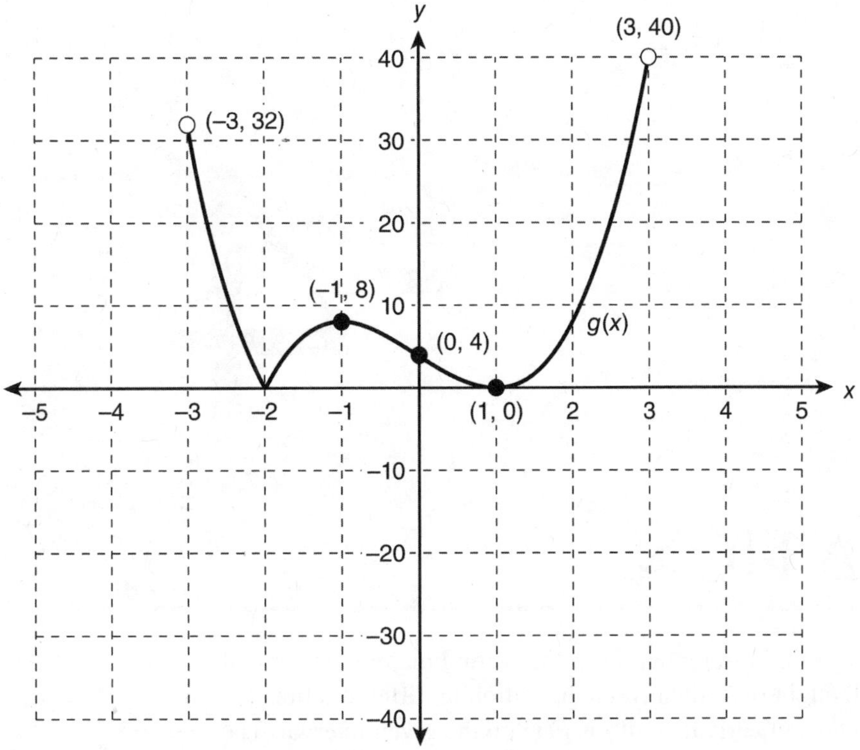

(a), (b) *Calculus for AP*®, pages 293–300; EU 2.2; LO 2.2A; EK 2.2A1; MPAC 2,4)
(c) (*Calculus for AP*®, pages 111–112, 293–300; EU 2.2; LO 2.2A; EK 2.2A1; MPAC 2,4)
(d) (*Calculus for AP*®, pages 322–324; EU 2.2; LO 2.2A; EK 2.2A1; MPAC 2,4)

4

INTEGRATION

Integration, also called antidifferentiation, is the second major operation of calculus. It can be thought of as the inverse operation to differentiation. Given $F'(x) = f(x)$, then the antiderivative of f is $F(x)$ on the given interval. The notation used for antidifferentiation, or integration, is $\int$. Integration is a method that can be used to find areas of regions, as an accumulator of rates of change, to solve for arc lengths (BC only topic), and to find volumes of solids of revolution and the volumes of solids with known cross sections (see Chapter 7). These are the major applications for the AP® exam.

Objectives

- Learn the definition of an antiderivative.
- Understand the concept of a Riemann sum and its relationship to integration.
- Understand when and how to use the fundamental theorems of calculus.
- Be able to use techniques of integration.
- Be able to make numerical approximations of definite integrals.
- Understand the concept of net change.

DEFINITION OF AN ANTIDERIVATIVE

(*Calculus for AP®*, pages 386–388)

If $F'(x) = f(x)$ for all x in an interval, then the function F is an antiderivative of f on that interval.

AP® is a trademark registered by the College Board, which is not affiliated with, and does not endorse, this product.

There is a general antiderivative, $G(x)$, such that $G(x) = F(x) + C$, where C is a constant. If you have a function with a constant attached, the derivative of that constant is zero; thus the antiderivative of $2x$ could be x^2, or $x^2 + 5$, or $x^2 - 2$, or, in general, $x^2 + C$.

A differential equation in x and y is just an equation that involves x, y, and the derivatives of y with respect to x. For example, $y' = 5x^2 - 2y''$ and $y' = -2x$ are differential equations.

You can solve a differential equation for a general or specific solution. If you solve $y' = -2x$ for a general solution, you will get a family of functions as a solution: $y = -x^2 + C$, which is a set of functions transformed vertically along the y-axis. To solve for a specific solution you would need an initial condition of some sort.

INITIAL CONDITIONS AND PARTICULAR SOLUTIONS

(*Calculus for AP®*, pages 388–389)

If you know the value of $y = F(x)$ for one value of x, known as the initial condition, you can then solve the general equation for a particular solution:

$$y = \int f(x)dx = F(x) + C$$

where $f(x)$ is the integrand, dx designates the variable of integration, C is the constant of integration. The term *indefinite integral* is a synonym for antiderivative.

The section below shows the relationship between the differentiation rules and the integration formulas.

$$\frac{d}{dx}[C]=0 \qquad \int 0dx = C$$

$$\frac{d}{dx}[kx]=k \qquad \int kdx = kx + C$$

$$\frac{d}{dx}[kf(x)]=kf'(x) \qquad \int kf(x)dx = k\int f(x)dx$$

$$\frac{d}{dx}[f(x) \pm g(x)]=f'(x) \pm g'(x) \qquad \int [f(x) \pm g(x)]dx = \int f(x)dx \pm \int g(x)dx$$

$$\frac{d}{dx}[x^n] = nx^{n-1} \qquad \int x^n\,dx = \frac{x^{n+1}}{n+1} + C, \quad n \neq -1$$

$$\frac{d}{dx}[\sin x] = \cos x \qquad \int \cos x dx = \sin x + C$$

$$\frac{d}{dx}[\cos x] = -\sin x \qquad \int \sin x dx = -\cos x + C$$

$$\frac{d}{dx}[\tan x]=\sec^2 x \qquad \int \sec^2 x dx = \tan x + C$$

$$\frac{d}{dx}[\sec x]=\sec x \tan x \qquad \int \sec x \tan x dx = \sec x + C$$

$\frac{d}{dx}[\cot x] = -\csc^2 x$ $\qquad$ $\int \csc^2 x\,dx = -\cot x + C$

$\frac{d}{dx}[\csc x] = -\csc x \cot x$ $\qquad$ $\int \csc x \cot x\,dx = -\csc x + C$

$\frac{d}{dx}[\arcsin u] = \frac{u'}{\sqrt{1-u^2}}$ $\qquad$ $\int \frac{du}{\sqrt{a^2-u^2}} = \arcsin\frac{u}{a} + C$

$\frac{d}{dx}[\arccos u] = \frac{-u'}{\sqrt{1-u^2}}$ $\qquad$ $\int \frac{-du}{\sqrt{a^2-u^2}} = \arccos\frac{u}{a} + C$*

$\frac{d}{dx}[\arctan u] = \frac{u'}{1+u^2}$ $\qquad$ $\int \frac{du}{\sqrt{a^2-u^2}} = \frac{1}{a}\arctan\frac{u}{a} + C$

$\frac{d}{dx}[\operatorname{arccot} u] = \frac{-u'}{1+u^2}$ $\qquad$ $\int \frac{-du}{a^2+u^2} = \frac{1}{a}\operatorname{arccot}\frac{u}{a} + C$*

$\frac{d}{dx}[\operatorname{arcsec} u] = \frac{u'}{|u|\sqrt{u^2-1}}$ $\qquad$ $\int \frac{du}{u\sqrt{u^2-a^2}} = \frac{1}{a}\operatorname{arcsec}\frac{|u|}{a} + C$

$\frac{d}{dx}[\operatorname{arccsc} u] = \frac{u'}{|u|\sqrt{u^2-1}}$ $\qquad$ $\int \frac{-du}{u\sqrt{u^2-a^2}} = \frac{1}{a}\operatorname{arccsc}\frac{|u|}{a} + C$*

*Not needed for AP® exam.

AP® Tips

- Just as for differentiation, a key to integration is to rewrite or simplify the integrand first.
- The easiest way to check your integration answer is to take its derivative and see if it returns you to the original integrand.
- You may need to use the two formulas for vertical motion problems: $s(t) = -16t^2 + v_0t + s_0$ if the problem is in feet, and $s(t) = -4.9t^2 + v_0t + s_0$ if the problem is in meters.

RIEMANN SUMS

(*Calculus for AP®*, pages 395–410, 418–420)

Let f be a function defined on a closed interval $[a, b]$ and Δ is the partition of the interval given by $a = x_0 < x_1 < x_2 \cdots < x_{n-1} < x_n = b$ where Δx_i is the width of the ith subinterval (i.e., Δx_1 is the width of the interval between x_0 and x_1). If c_i is any point in the ith subinterval, then the sum

$$\sum_{i=1}^{n} f(c_i)\Delta x_i x_{i-1} \le c_i \le x_i$$

is called a Riemann sum of f for the partition Δ.

This is the very general way of thinking about approximating the area under a curve by finding the area of representative rectangles that either extend above the graph, below the graph, or a combination of both. The widths of the intervals do not need to be equal for a general Riemann sum. However, it is more common to use the left-hand or right-hand endpoints, or the midpoints of each interval, rather than the generic c_i-value within the interval. It is also generally easier to use intervals of a set width. The calculations are much simpler if the Δx_i is constant over the interval from a to b. However, the exam may give you a table or an algebraic formula where the intervals are not of equal width. You must then work with the information given, remembering the fundamental idea of adding the areas of the rectangles no matter what their widths or heights.

The *left endpoint* method takes the height from the left side of the interval times the width of the subinterval. The *midpoint* method averages the endpoints of the subinterval to find the x whose y-value will be used for the height. The *right endpoint* method takes the height from the right side of the interval.

Remember that if the entire interval is from a to b, then a is equivalent to x_0 and b to x_n; a or x_0 would be the value of the left endpoint, $(x_0 + x_1)/2$ would be the value of the midpoint, and x_1 would be the value of the right endpoint of the first interval.

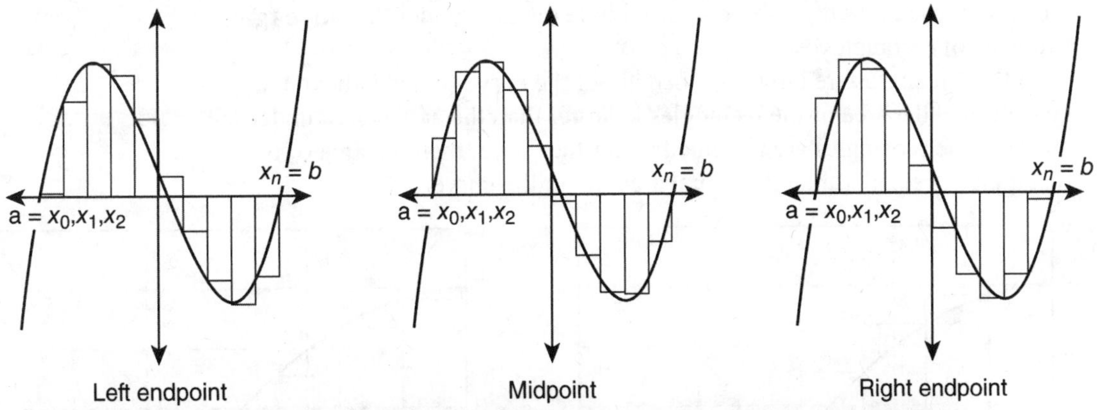

AP® Tips

- When the exam asks for a Riemann sum, it is not requiring that you use the very general definition; but you can use the left-hand endpoint, the right-hand endpoint, or the midpoint method to calculate an approximate value for a definite integral. The exam may require a specific method for you to use, or may keep the question general enough for you to select.
- Don't confuse upper and lower sums with left and right endpoint methods. Upper sums refer to circumscribed rectangles (those that extend above the curve), while lower sums involve inscribed rectangles (those that lie inside the curve).

USING RIEMANN SUMS TO DETERMINE THE AREA OF A REGION IN A PLANE

If f is a continuous and nonnegative function on the interval from a to b (in other words, f is above the y-axis), then the area of the region bounded by the graph of the function f, the x-axis, and the vertical lines $x = a$ and $x = b$, is

$$\text{Area} = \lim_{n\to\infty}\sum_{i=1}^{n} f(c_i)\Delta x_i = \int_a^b f(x)dx$$

a definite integral, where $x_{i-1} < c_i < x_i$ and $\Delta x = \dfrac{b-a}{n}$.

The first step to solving a Riemann sum problem is to determine (although the exam may specify) how many rectangles you want to use (the more rectangles, the smaller the width, the better the approximation for the area under the curve). Then determine the Δx by dividing $(b - a)$, the length of the interval, by the number of rectangles, n. This breaks the area into subintervals of equal width. Find the $f(x)$ value (or the height of the rectangle) for each left-hand, right-hand, or midpoint value of the rectangle. Multiply that height at each x by the established Δx (width) to determine the area of each rectangle; then add those areas together to approximate the area under the curve (given a finite set of rectangles).

If the rectangles are circumscribed about the curve (extend above the curve), then the area of the rectangles is larger than the actual area under the curve; if the rectangles are inscribed under the curve, then the area of the rectangles is smaller than the actual area under the curve.

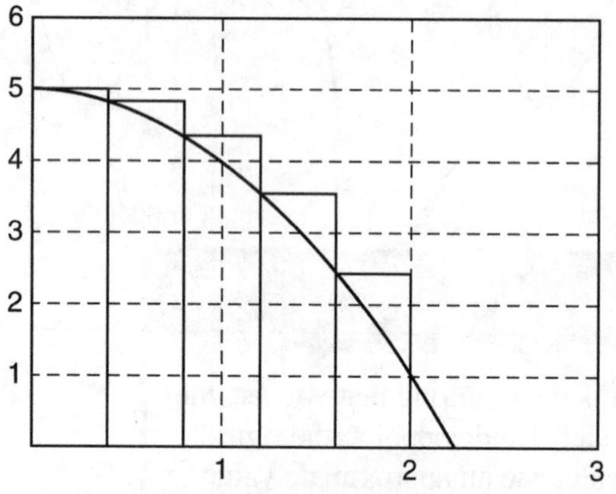

Circumscribed rectangles

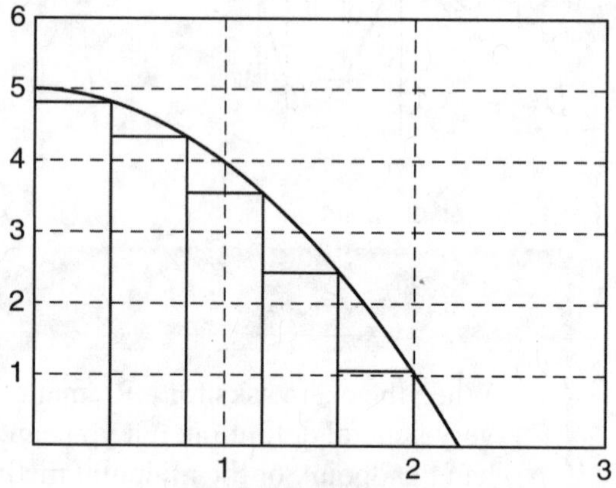

Inscribed rectangles

However, by taking the *limit* of the sums of these areas as n approaches ∞, where n is the number of rectangles, and the width of the rectangles approaches 0, the value becomes the actual area under the curve.

Sometimes, you may be asked to find the area under the graph by using inscribed (or circumscribed) rectangles and you must use both left and right endpoints. That will happen when the function is not strictly increasing or strictly decreasing, like a parabola for example.

THE TRAPEZOIDAL RULE

(*Calculus for AP®*, pages 400–401)

Another way to approximate an integral is to use a numerical integration technique called the Trapezoidal Rule. When a function does not have a relatively elementary antiderivative (see section THE FUNDAMENTAL THEOREM OF CALCULUS), we need another method to evaluate the definite integral. In the beginning, we estimated integrals by taking the areas of rectangles. The more rectangles we used, the better the approximation became. If, instead of using rectangles, we use trapezoids (where the slanted edge would better approximate the curvature), then we could have an even better approximation of the area under the curve, and we could use fewer regions as well.

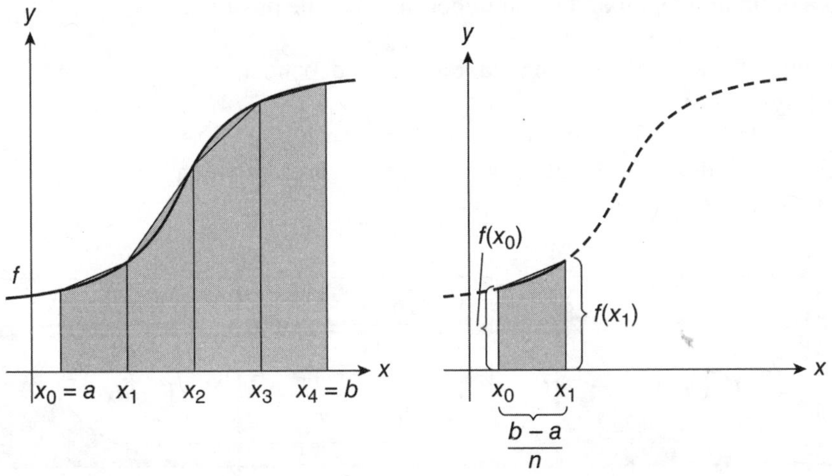

The area of a trapezoid is (½) (height) ($b_1 + b_2$). In this problem, the bases are the y-values [$f(x)$'s] and the height is the length of the interval divided by the number of trapezoids chosen.

$$\text{Thus } \int_a^b f(x)\,dx \approx \frac{b-a}{2n}\left[f(x_0)+2f(x_1)+2f(x_2)+\cdots+2f(x_{n-1})+f(x_n)\right]$$

where $x_0 = a$ is the left endpoint and $x_n = b$ is the right endpoint of the interval. The $f(x)$'s represent the lengths of the sides of the trapezoid, the $(b - a)/n$ represents the height of each trapezoid, and the divided by two is taking the average of those heights. There are 2 $f(x_1)$'s and 2 $f(x_2)$'s and so on, because you use those heights for two trapezoids, while the y-values of the endpoints are only used in the first and last trapezoids.

AP® Tip

The AP® exam often will specify a set number of intervals and give you a table of values to utilize in the use of the Trapezoidal Rule. See 2005 Free Response #3b or 2008 Free Response #2b for examples of the expectations.

MAJOR THEOREMS OF CALCULUS

THE FUNDAMENTAL THEOREM OF CALCULUS

(*Calculus for AP*®, pages 436–440)

If a function f is continuous on the closed interval $[a, b]$ and F is an antiderivative of f on the interval, then $\int_a^b f(x)\,dx = F(b) - F(a)$.

This becomes the shorthand method to evaluating integrals, rather than the limit of the Riemann sum method. If a function is continuous on a closed interval, then it is integrable on the same interval.

$\int_a^b f(x)\,dx$ is called a definite integral and is a number that may be positive, negative, or zero. This number can represent an area, but that is dependent upon whether $f(x)$ is always positive.

If you integrate $f(x) = x^3$ from -2 to 2, the result is 0. However, if you integrate it from 0 to 2, the result is 4; and that does represent the area between the curve and the x-axis from $x = 0$ and $x = 2$.

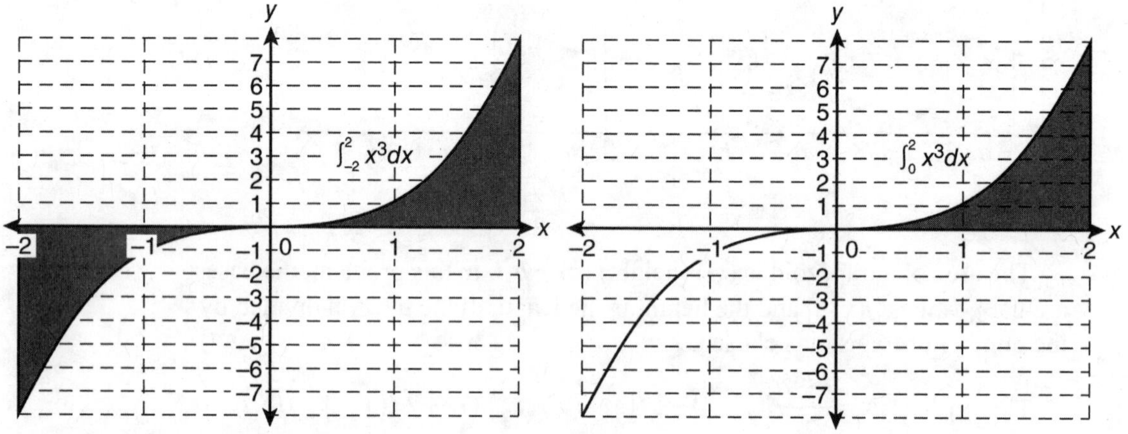

Essentially what is occurring is that the integral from $x = -2$ to $x = 0$ is -4 and from $x = 0$ to $x = 2$ is $+4$; remember the integral is a number. So, over the entire interval, the integral equals 0. If the curve is always above the x-axis, then the integral represents the area under the curve. To find the area between the graph of $y = x^3$ and the x axis from $x = -2$ and $x = 2$, you can find the area from $x = 0$ to $x = 2$, which is $+4$, and then use the fact that the graph is symmetric around the origin to get the total area to equal 8.

The constant of integration C is not necessary because of the Fundamental Theorem of Calculus, $F(b) - F(a)$, subtracts off that value.

$$\int_a^b f(x)\,dx = \left[F(x) + C\right]_a^b = \left[F(b) + C\right] - \left[F(a) + C\right] = F(b) - F(a)$$

AP® Tips

- Understand the difference between simply finding an integral, which is a number (positive, negative, or zero), and finding the area under the curve, which will always be a positive number.
- Know how to graph an absolute value function so that, when you find the area under the curve (it is all above the x-axis), you know to split it into two or more integrals, splitting the intervals used for integration at the function's zeros (see Example 6, *Calculus for AP®* on page 483).

MEAN VALUE THEOREM FOR INTEGRALS

(*Calculus for AP®*, pages 492)

If f is continuous on the closed interval $[a, b]$, then there exists a number c in that interval such that $\int_a^b f(x)\,dx = f(c)(b-a)$.

This means that, for any curve, somewhere "between" the inscribed rectangle and the circumscribed rectangle, there is a rectangle whose area exactly represents the area of the region under the curve. Thus $f(c)$ represents the height of the rectangle and $(b - a)$ represents the width of the rectangle, which is also the distance between the left and right endpoints of the curve.

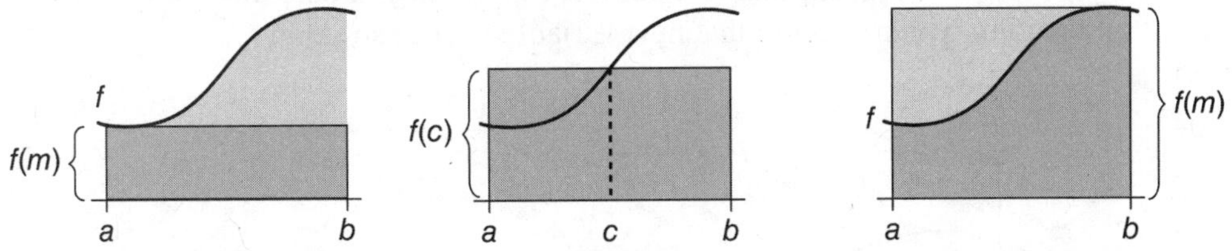

Inscribed rectangle | Mean value rectangle | Circumscribed rectangle

The average value of a function is the height $f(c)$. This is the area of the curve $\int_a^b f(x)\,dx$ divided by its width $(b - a)$.

It is often written as $\frac{1}{b-a}\int_a^b f(x)\,dx$, but we generally think of it as

$\frac{\int_a^b f(x)\,dx}{b-a}$. It can be written or asked for in various ways.

AP® Tips

- On the exam you are sometimes asked for the average value, the $f(c)$, but you could be asked where it occurs, the c-value in the interval from a to b. Remember to always reread the problem to determine the actual response required.
- On the exam, the question may not ask for the term *average value*; for example, a velocity problem might ask for average velocity. Depending on what function is given, position or velocity, you have to use different formulas to find average velocity. So the average velocity from $t = a$ to $t = b$ may be found by $v_{av} = \dfrac{s(b) - s(a)}{b - a}$ if the position function is given or $v_{av} = \dfrac{1}{b - a}\int_a^b v(t)\,dt$ if the velocity function is given.

THE SECOND FUNDAMENTAL THEOREM OF CALCULUS

(*Calculus for AP*®, pages 436–440)

Let $\dfrac{d}{dx}\left[\int_a^x f(t)\,dt\right] = f(x)$, which states that if you integrate a function, $f(t)$, from $t = a$ to an unknown $t = x$, rather than to a number $t = b$, and you take the derivative of that function with respect to that new variable x, your solution will be $f(x)$.

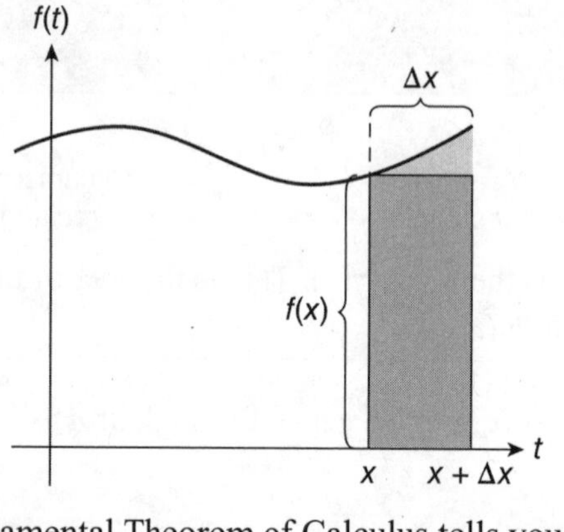

The Second Fundamental Theorem of Calculus tells you that if a function is continuous, then it has an antiderivative. It also helps to represent an interpretation of an integral as an accumulation function. (See Example 6, *Calculus for AP*® on page 450.)

The Second Fundamental Theorem of Calculus also can be applied with the Chain Rule: $\dfrac{d}{dx}\left[\int_a^{u(x)} f(t)\,dt\right] = f\left[u(x)\right]\cdot u'(x)$. In other words, when you take the integral of the composite function $f[u(x)]$ and then its derivative, you must remember to tag along the derivative of what's inside $[u'(x)]$. It also can show a representation of the inverse relationship between derivatives and integrals.

AP® Tip

The interpretation of an integral as an accumulation function (net change) is one of the reform calculus concepts. An example of this is if you have a function that represents the rate of consumption of a beverage, then the integral of that function is the amount of beverage consumed over whatever time interval you choose. (See AP® Free-Response Questions: 2013 AB 1, 2011 AB 5, and 2009 AB 2, available at apcentral.com. Also see pages 450–454 in *Calculus for AP®*.)

TECHNIQUES OF INTEGRATION

(*Calculus for AP®*, pages 457–465)

The basic rules for integration are the Power Rule and the trigonometric rules. But as functions become more complex, other rules must be applied. It is important to begin to recognize patterns as well as to understand when it is necessary to use a technique called change of variables. When you take the derivative of a composite function like $(3x^2 - 4)^3$, it is necessary to think about the inside as u, and when you use the Power Rule, you then have to multiply by the derivative of what's inside as well; in other words, new terms "appear."

The derivative $\frac{d}{dx}(3x^2 - 4)^3 = 3(3x^2 - 4)^2(6x)$, where $6x$ is the derivative of what's inside

Similarly, when you integrate a composite function, it is important that the derivative is already there so that it can "disappear" when you do the opposite operation of integration.

$$\int 3(3x^2 - 4)^2(6x)\,dx = (3x^2 - 4)^3 + C$$

Formally, this is written as $\int f(g(x))g'(x)dx = F(x) + C$, or if $u = g(x)$ then it would be written as $\int f(u)\,du = F(u) + C$.

AP® Tips

- It is essential that you understand the differences in types of problems. Example 3 in *Calculus for AP®* on page 460 helps; but you also need to recognize that if there is some *u* to a power, then there must be a *du* around prior to evaluating the integral.
- Also remember that when integrating, you can introduce a constant as long as you do it in such a way that the problem remains the same; you *cannot* introduce a variable (like multiplying and dividing by *x*).
- If the power in the numerator of a rational function is equal to or higher than the power in the denominator, then you will want to use long division to simplify the integrand prior to integrating.
- Be sure to pay attention to the form of *du*/*u*, which would imply the use of the Log Rule to integrate versus the form of $u^n\, du$, where *n* is a negative number other than 1 and thus the general Power Rule is used. For example, $\int \frac{3x^2+1}{x^3+x}\,dx$ is in the form $\int \frac{du}{u}$, so you would use the Log Rule, but $\int \frac{3x^2+1}{\left(x^3+x\right)^2}\,dx$ would use the general Power Rule where you could write it as $\int \left(3x^2+1\right)\left(x^3+x\right)^{-2}\,dx$, so it is in the form of $\int u^n\,du$.
- Often integrating an e^u takes a rewrite of the problem; see Example 4 in *Calculus for AP®* on page 461 for good models of correct formatting of the problem.

CHANGE OF VARIABLES

(*Calculus for AP®*, pages 457–461, 463–465)

This is a method by which you can integrate. One use is as mentioned earlier in this chapter where you let the inner function be *u* and you find *du* in the problem so that you can integrate it. However, it has a more important use in a problem where there is an additional "variable" that is not the derivative of what's inside.

For example: For the integral $\int x\sqrt{2x-1}\,dx$, $2x-1$ is the inner function and 2 is its derivative, but there is also an *x* in the integrand. Therefore, you should use *u*-substitution.

Let $u = 2x - 1$, then $du = 2\,dx$; rearranging this yields $dx = \frac{du}{2}$.

You must also solve for *x*: $x = \frac{u+1}{2}$.

Then substitute: $\int x\sqrt{2x-1}\,dx = \int \frac{u+1}{2}\sqrt{u}\,\frac{du}{2}$, which can be simplified (by multiplying through by $\sqrt{u}$) to $\int \frac{u^{3/2}+u^{1/2}}{4}du$. The ¼ can be factored out and you can integrate each remaining term.

Thus, $\int \frac{u^{3/2}+u^{1/2}}{4}du = 1/4\left(2/5\,u^{5/2} + 2/3\,u^{3/2}\right) + C$. Now, to finish the problem, substitute back in the appropriate x term:
$\frac{1}{10}(2x-1)^{5/2} + \frac{1}{6}(2x-1)^{3/2} + C.$

Note: Be aware that if there had been a constant, the problem could be done more directly via the Chain Rule. To compute $\int 4\sqrt{2x-1}\,dx$, factor out a 2 out of the integral, leaving a 2 inside, which is the derivative of the inner function, $2x-1$.

Change of variables is also a technique used to put a problem in the form of du/u and subsequently use the Log Rule of integration.

THE GENERAL POWER RULE FOR INTEGRATION

(*Calculus for AP®*, pages 463–465)

$\int [g(x)]^n g'(x)\,dx = \frac{[g(x)]^{n+1}}{n+1} + C, n \neq -1$ or if $u = g(x)$, then

$\int u^n du = \frac{u^{n+1}}{n+1} + C, n \neq -1.$

If it is a definite integral, you do not need to substitute the x variable back in as long as you have made the correct adjustments to the lower and upper bounds of the integrand. For example, $\int_1^5 \frac{x}{\sqrt{2x-1}}dx$ could use the u-substitution of $u = 2x-1$. Therefore, the lower limit of 1 would substitute in for x and $u = 2(1) - 1$ and is thus also 1; the upper limit of 5 would become $2(5) - 1 = 9$. (*Note:* $u = 2x - 1$ which becomes $x = (u + 1)/2$ and $du = 2\,dx$, which becomes $dx = \frac{du}{2}$.) The problem would then look like $\int_1^9 \frac{u+1}{2}u^{-1/2}\frac{du}{2}$, which simplifies to $\frac{1}{4}\int_1^9 u^{1/2} + u^{-1/2}\,du.$

This problem is a good example for which you can choose a different u-substitution. Let $u = \sqrt{2x-1}$, then $x = \frac{u^2+1}{2}$ and $dx = u\,du$.

Thus, to do the definite integral, the lower bound would be $u = \sqrt{2(1)-1} = 1$ and the upper bound would be $u = \sqrt{2(5)-1} = 3$; and the integral would be $\int_1^3 \frac{1}{u}\left(\frac{u^2+1}{2}\right)u\,du$, which simplifies to $\frac{1}{2}\int_1^3 (u^2+1)\,du.$

You should try both of these substitutions to see that they have the same result.

EVEN AND ODD FUNCTIONS

Another way to view an integration problem is to determine its symmetry. If the function $y = f(x)$ is even (thus symmetrical over the y-axis), then $\int_{-a}^{a} f(x)\,dx = 2\int_{0}^{a} f(x)\,dx.$

If the function $y = f(x)$ is odd (thus symmetrical around the origin), then $\int_{-a}^{a} f(x)\,dx = 0.$

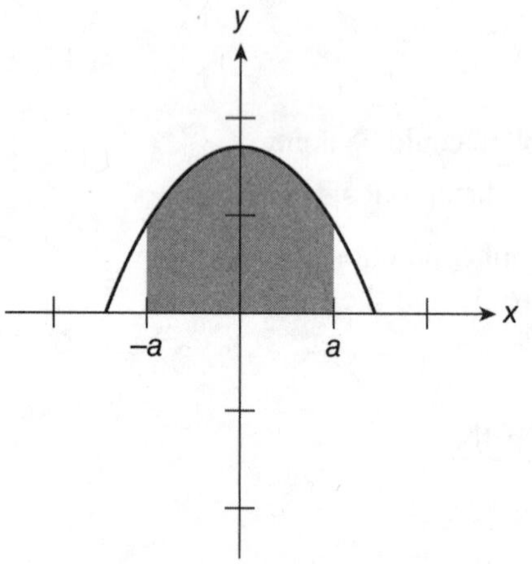

even

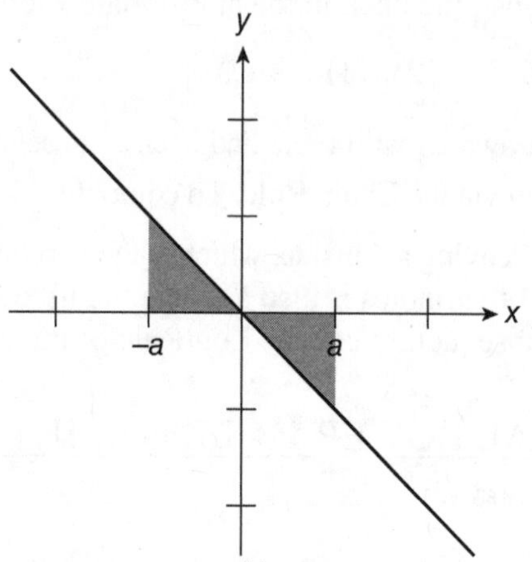

odd

AP® Tips

- You need to understand the Trapezoidal Sum, and you should be able to use it without a calculator program. You need to be able to use it with subintervals of equal or unequal widths. For example, given the following table

x	2	4	7	9	13	17
$f(x)$	1	3	8	10	16	20

Use the Trapezoidal Sum to approximate the area under the curve from $x = 2$ to $x = 13$, using 4 subintervals. We notice that the subintervals do not have equal widths. We need to calculate the areas of 4 different trapezoids as follows:

$T = (1/2)\cdot 2\cdot(1+3) + (1/2)\cdot 3\cdot\,(3+8) + (1/2)\cdot 2\cdot\,(8+10) + (1/2)\cdot 4\cdot\,(10+16)$

You do not have to simplify this expression in order to receive full credit on the AP® exam. Notice that we did not use all the points given on the table!

- Although Simpson's Rule is an important concept for calculus, it is not tested on the AP® exam.
- Bases other than e are rarely tested on the AP® exam.
- Hyperbolic functions are not tested on the AP® exam.
- The key to inverse trigonometric integration formulas is to recognize them and then apply the appropriate one to the problem.

PAST AP® FREE-RESPONSE PROBLEMS COVERED BY THIS CHAPTER

Note: These and other questions can be found at apcentral.com.

1998 AB 3
1999 AB 1c,d; 3; 5
2000 AB 2c
2001 AB 2a,b; 3; 5b
2002 AB 2; 3; 4; 6
2003 AB 2c,d; 3c,d; 4d; 6b
2004 AB 1a,c; 3d; 5a,c
2005 AB 2; 3b; 4c
2006 AB 2; 4b,c; BC 3d
2007 AB 5c
2008 AB 2b
2009 AB 2a,c,d; 5b,c; 6b; BC 4a,b
2010 AB 1a,c,d; 2b,c; 3a,d
2011 AB 1b; 2b,c,d; 6c
2012 AB 1b,c,d; 4d; 6a; BC 2a; 4b
2013 AB 1d; 2b; 3c; 4c
2014 AB 1c; 4c; 5d

MULTIPLE-CHOICE QUESTIONS

A calculator may not be used for the following questions.

1. $\int(\sec^2 x - 2)dx =$
   (A) $\tan x + C$
   (B) $\tan x - 2x + C$
   (C) $\dfrac{\tan^3 x}{3} - x + C$
   (D) $\dfrac{\sec^3 x}{3} - 2x + C$

2. Find $\int_0^2 3x^2 f\left(x^3\right)dx$ if $\int_0^8 f(t)\,dt = k$.
   (A) k^3
   (B) $9k$
   (C) $3k$
   (D) k

3. If $F(x) = \int_0^{x^2} \sqrt{t+5}$, what is $F'(2)$?
   (A) $\sqrt{7}$
   (B) 3
   (C) 12
   (D) 18

4. What is the average value of $f(x) = (\sin x)\, 4^{\cos x}$ for the closed interval $0 \le x \le \frac{\pi}{2}$?

(A) $\frac{3}{\ln 4}$

(B) $\frac{6}{\pi \ln 4}$

(C) $\frac{4}{\ln 4}$

(D) $\frac{8}{\pi \ln 4}$

5. The graph of $f(x)$ consists of line segments and quarter circles as shown in the graph to the right. What is the value of $\int_{-3}^{4} f(x)\,dx$?

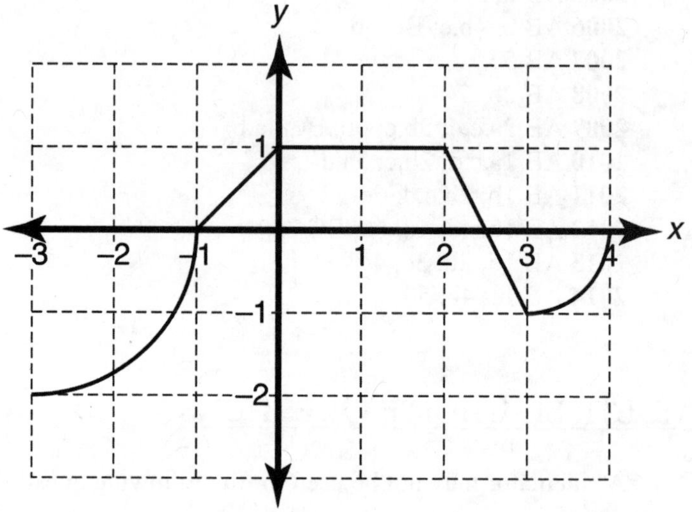

(A) $\frac{10-5\pi}{4}$

(B) $\frac{10+5\pi}{4}$

(C) $\frac{12+5\pi}{4}$

(D) $\frac{12-5\pi}{4}$

A calculator may be used for the following questions.

6. Let R be the region between the function $f(x) = x^3 + 6x^2 + 10x + 4$, the x-axis, and the lines $x = 0$ and $x = 4$. Using the Trapezoidal Sum, compute the area when there are four equal subdivisions.
(A) 196
(B) 288
(C) 296
(D) 396

7. What is $f(x)$ if $f'(x) = \frac{x}{x^2 - 1}$ and $f(2) = 0$?

(A) $f(x) = \frac{1}{2}\ln\left|x^2 - 1\right| - \ln 3$

(B) $f(x) = \frac{1}{2}\ln\left|x^2 - 1\right| - \ln\sqrt{3}$

(C) $f(x) = \frac{1}{2}\ln\left|x^2 - 1\right| + \ln\sqrt{3}$

(D) $f(x) = \frac{1}{2}\ln|x| - \frac{1}{2}x$

8. What is the average value of $f(x) = 2\ln x?$ on the closed interval $1 \le x \le 3$?
(A) 2.592
(B) 2.000
(C) 1.296
(D) 1.952

9. Evaluate: $\int_{-1}^{0} \frac{x^2}{\sqrt[5]{2x^3+1}}dx.$

(A) $\frac{4}{15}$
(B) $\frac{5}{12}$
(C) 0
(D) The function is not integrable on the interval $-1 \le x \le 0$.

10. If $\int_1^3 f(x)dx = k$ and $\int_1^7 f(x)dx = -4$, what is the value of $\int_7^3 (x + f(x))\,dx$?
(A) $k - 4$
(B) $16 - k$
(C) $-16 - k$
(D) $-16 + k$

x	−4	−3	−2	−1	0	1	2	3	4
$f(x)$	0.48	1.25	1.07	0.53	0.27	1.04	3.56	2.18	2

11. Selected values for the continuous function $f(x)$ are given in the table above. Using three left-hand rectangles of equal width, an approximation for $\int_{-3}^{3} f(x)dx$ is
(A) 9.90.
(B) 7.72.
(C) 5.64.
(D) 4.90.

12. Initially a water tank contains 100ft^3. Water begins to drain from the tank at the rate of $\frac{30e^{\frac{t}{3}}}{1+e^{\frac{t}{3}}}$ cubic feet per hour. How many cubic feet of water will remain in the tank after 3 hours?
(A) 39.768
(B) 44.190
(C) 55.810
(D) 60.232

A calculator may not be used on the following questions.

13. If $R(x)$ is an even function and $S(x)$ is an odd function where $\int_{-a}^{0} R(x)\,dx = 5$ and $\int_{0}^{a} S(x)\,dx = -3$, find the value of $\int_{-a}^{a} \left[2(S(x)) - R(x) + 3\right] dx$.
(A) $-10 + 3a$
(B) $-10 + 6a$
(C) $10 + 6a$
(D) $-6 + 6a$

14. $\int \frac{9x}{\sqrt{1-81x^4}}\,dx =$
(A) $\left(1-9x^2\right)^{\frac{1}{2}} + C$
(B) $\frac{1}{2}\left(1-9x^2\right)^{\frac{3}{2}} + C$
(C) $\sin^{-1}(9x^2) + C$
(D) $\frac{1}{2}\sin^{-1}\left(9x^2\right) + C$

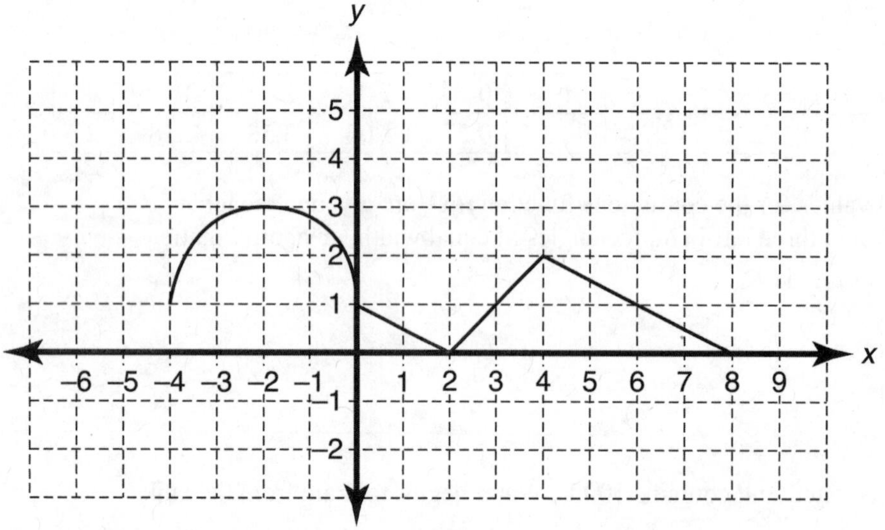

15. The graph of $f(x)$ shown above consists of three line segments and one semicircle. Let $g(x) = \int_{-2}^{x} f(t)\,dt$. Which of the following statements must be false?
(A) $g(4) = \int_{-2}^{4} f(t)\,dt = \pi + 5$
(B) $g(-4) = \int_{-2}^{-4} f(t)\,dt = -\pi - 2$
(C) $g'(6) = 1$
(D) $g(x)$ has a relative maximum at $x = 4$

FREE-RESPONSE QUESTION

This question requires the use of a calculator.

1. The acceleration of a particle is given as $a(t) = 3e^t - t^4\ \text{cm/sec}^2$ on the closed interval [0, 3] as illustrated on the graph shown.
   (a) Find the velocity of the particle at any time *t* if $v(0) = 6$ cm/sec.
   (b) Find the position of the particle at any time *t* if $x(0) = -5$ cm.
   (c) At $t = 6.5$, is the speed of the particle increasing or decreasing? Explain your reasoning.
   (d) On the closed interval [0, 3], what is the velocity of the particle when its acceleration is at a maximum? Explain your reasoning.

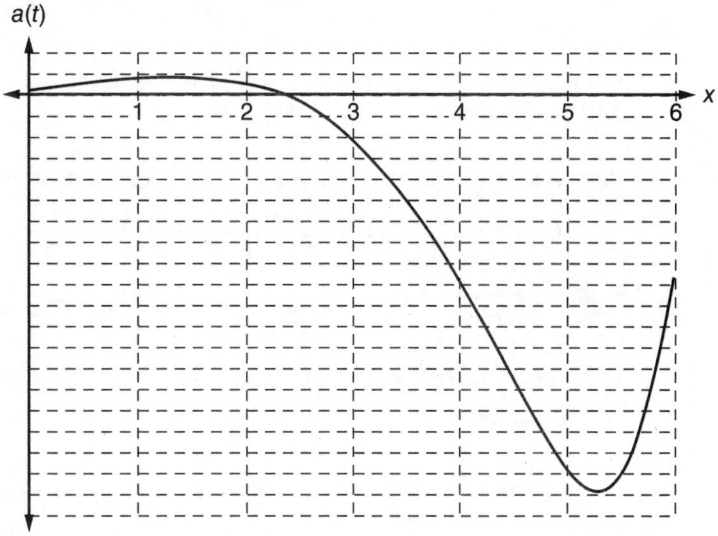

Answers

MULTIPLE-CHOICE QUESTIONS

1. ANSWER: (B) $\int \sec^2 x - 2\,dx = \tan x - 2x + C.$
   (*Calculus for AP*®, pages 388–389; LO 3.1A,3.3B; EK 3.1A1,3.1A2,3.3B3; MPAC 2,3)

2. ANSWER: (D) By substitution, $u = x^3$, $du = 3x^2dx$, and $\int_0^2 3x^2 f(x^3)\,dx$ becomes $\int_0^8 f(u)\,du$, which equals *k*.
   (*Calculus for AP*®, pages 463–465; EU 3.2,3.5; LO 3.2C,3.3B; EK 3.2C2,3.3B5; MPAC 2,3,5)

3. ANSWER: (C) By the Second Fundamental Theorem of Calculus,
   $$\frac{d}{dx}\left[\int_a^{g(x)} f(t)\,dt\right] = f(g(x)) \cdot g'(x)$$
   So, $F'(x) = 2x\sqrt{x^2+5}$ and $F'(2) = 4\sqrt{9} = 12.$
   (*Calculus for AP*®, pages 436–437; EU 3.3; LO 3.3A; EK 3.3A2; MPAC 2,3,5)

4. ANSWER: (B) If f is integrable on a closed interval $[a, b]$, then the average value of f on the interval is $\frac{1}{b-a}\int_a^b f(x)\,dx$. Using the substitution $u = \cos x$ and $du = -\sin x\, dx$,

$$\frac{1}{\frac{\pi}{2}-0}\int_0^{\frac{\pi}{2}}(\sin x)4^{\cos x}\,dx = -\frac{2}{\pi}\int_1^0 4^u\,du = -\frac{2}{\pi\ln 4}\left(4^0-4^1\right) = \frac{-2(-3)}{\pi\ln 4} = \frac{6}{\pi\ln 4}.$$

(*Calculus for AP*®, pages 490–494; EU 3.4; LO 3.4B; EK 3.4B1; MPAC 2,3)

5. ANSWER: (A) Evaluating each region by a geometric formula,

$$\int_{-3}^{4} f(x)\,dx = -\frac{1}{4}\pi(2)^2 + \frac{1}{2}(1)(1) + 2(1) + \frac{1}{2}(1)\left(\frac{1}{2}\right) - \frac{1}{2}(1)\left(\frac{1}{2}\right) - \frac{1}{4}\pi(1)^2$$

$$= \frac{5}{2} - \frac{5\pi}{4} = \frac{10-5\pi}{4}.$$

(*Calculus for AP*®, pages 422–423; EU 3.2; LO 3.2C; EK 3.2C1; MPAC 2,3,4)

6. ANSWER: (C) $\frac{1}{2}\left[\frac{4-0}{4}\right]\left[f(0)+2f(1)+2f(2)+2f(3)+f(4)\right] = 296.$

(*Calculus for AP*®, pages 400–401; EU 3.2; LO 3.2B; EK 3.2B2; MPAC 2,3)

7. ANSWER: (B) $\ln|x^2-1| + C = \ln|2^2-1| + C = 0$ By substitution, $u = x^2-1$ and $du = 2x\,dx$, $\frac{1}{2}\int\frac{2x}{x^2-1}\,dx = \frac{1}{2}\int\frac{1}{u}\,du = \frac{1}{2}\ln u + C$. Therefore,

$C = \frac{1}{2}\ln 3 = \ln\sqrt{3}$ and $f(x) = \frac{1}{2}\ln|x^2-1| - \ln\sqrt{3}$.

(*Calculus for AP*®, pages 457–461; EU 3.3,3.5; LO 3.3B,3.5a; EK 3.3B5,3.5A1; MPAC 2,3,5)

8. ANSWER: (C) If f is a continuous function on a closed interval $[a, b]$, the average value is given by $\frac{1}{3-1}\int_1^3 2\ln x\,dx = \frac{1}{2}(2.592) = 1.296.$

(*Calculus for AP*®, pages 490–494; EU 3.4; LO 3.4B; EK 3.4B1; MPAC 2,3)

9. ANSWER: (D) The function is undefined where $\sqrt[5]{2x^3+1} = 0$, or $x = \left(-\frac{1}{2}\right)^{\frac{1}{3}}$.

Since $-1 < \left(-\frac{1}{2}\right)^{\frac{1}{3}} < 0$, then the function is notintegrable on this interval.

(*Calculus for AP*®, pages 386–388; EU 3.2; LO 3.2C; EK 3.2C3; MPAC 2)

10. ANSWER: (D) $\int_7^3 (x + f(x))\,dx = -\int_3^7 (x + f(x))\,dx = -\int_3^7 x\,dx - \int_3^7 f(x)\,dx$

$$-\int_3^7 x\,dx = -\frac{x^2}{2}\bigg|_3^7 = \left(\frac{49}{2} - \frac{9}{2}\right) = -20$$

$$\int_3^7 f(x)\,dx = \left(\int_1^7 f(x)\,dx - \int_1^3 f(x)\,dx\right) = -4 - k.$$

Therefore, $-\int_3^7 x\,dx - \int_3^7 f(x)\,dx = -20 - (-4 - k) = -16 + k.$

(*Calculus for AP*®, pages 423–425; EU 3.2; LO 3.2C; EK 3.2C1,3.2C2; MPAC 2)

11. ANSWER: (C)

$$\int_{-3}^3 f(x)\,dx \approx 2\left[f(-3) + f(-1) + f(1)\right] = 2(1.25 + 0.53 + 1.04) = 2(2.82) = 5.64$$

(*Calculus for AP*®, pages 395–410, 418–420; EU 3.2; LO 3.2B; EK 3.2B2; MPAC 2,3,4)

12. ANSWER: (B) $100 - \int_0^3 \frac{30e^{t/3}}{1 + e^{t/3}}\,dt \approx 100 - 55.810 \approx 44.190$ cubic feet left in the tank.

(*Calculus for AP*®, pages 436–440; EU 3.4; LO 3.4A; EK 3.4A2; MPAC 2,3)

13. ANSWER: (B)

$$\int_{-a}^a [2(S(x)) - R(x) + 3]dx = 2(0) - 2(5) + 3x\bigg|_{-a}^a = -10 + 6a$$

(*Calculus for AP*®, page 465; EU 3.2; LO 3.2C; EK 3.2C2; MPAC 2,3,5)

14. ANSWER: (D) Let $u = 9x^2$ and $du = 18xdx$, then

$$\int \frac{9x}{\sqrt{1 - 81x^4}}\,dx \Rightarrow \frac{1}{2}\int \frac{du}{\sqrt{1 - u^2}} = \frac{1}{2}\sin^{-1} u + C = \frac{1}{2}\sin^{-1}\left(9x^2\right) + C$$

(*Calculus for AP*®, pages 457–461; EU 3.3; LO 3.3B; EK 3.3B5; MPAC 2,3)

15. ANSWER: (D) $g(x)$ has a relative maximum when $g'(x)$ changes from positive to negative. Since $g'(x) = f(x)$ is positive on the left and right of 4, there is no relative maximum at $x = 4$.

(*Calculus for AP*®, pages 437–440, 499; EU 3.2,3.3; LO 3.2C,3.3A; EK 3.2C1,3.3A2; MPAC 2,3,4)

FREE-RESPONSE QUESTION

	Solution	Possible points
(a)	Given: $a(t) = 3e^t - t^4$; $v(0) = 6$ cm/sec $v(t) = \int (3e^t - t^4)\,dt = 3e^t - \frac{t^5}{5} + C$ $v(0) = 6$ which equals $3 - 0 + C$; therefore, $C = 3$. Then, $v(t) = 3e^t - \frac{t^5}{5} + 3$ cm/sec.	$2: \begin{cases} 1: \text{integrand} \\ 1: \text{answer} \end{cases}$
(b)	Since $x(t) = \int (3e^t - \frac{t^5}{5} + 3)\,dt = 3e^t - \frac{t^6}{30} + 3t + C$ and $x(0) = -5 = 3 - 0 + 0 + C$; therefore, $C = 8$. Then $x(t) = 3e^t - \frac{t^6}{30} + 3t - 8$ cm.	$2: \begin{cases} 1: \text{integrand} \\ 1: \text{answer} \end{cases}$
(c)	The speed of the particle is increasing when $a(t)$ and $v(t)$ have the same signs, and decreasing when $a(t)$ and $v(t)$ have opposite signs. Since $a(6.5) =$ 210.362 cm/sec^2 and $v(6.5) = -322.156$ cm/sec, the speed of the particle at $t = 6.5$ sec is decreasing.	$3: \begin{cases} 1: a(6.5) \\ 1: v(6.5) \\ 1: \text{reasoning} \end{cases}$
(d)	$a'(t) = 0$ at $t = 1.496$ $v(1.496) = 14.892$ cm/sec or $t = 5.279$ but only 1.496 is in our interval [0, 3] For $0 < t < 1.496$, $a'(t) > 0$, and for $1.496 < t < 3$, $a'(t) < 0$. Therefore, $a(t)$ changes from increasing to decreasing at $t = 1.496$, so a maximum acceleration occurs at $t = 1.496$ and its velocity at $t = 1.496$ is 14.892 cm/sec	$2: \begin{cases} 1: \text{answer} \\ 1: \text{reasoning} \end{cases}$

(a), (b)(*Calculus for AP®*, pages 388–389; EU 3.4,3.3; LO 3.4A,3.3B; EK 3.4A2,3.3B2; MPAC 2,3,4)
(c), (d)(*Calculus for AP®*, pages 292–300, 508–511; EU 3.4; LO 3.4C; EK 3.4C1; MPAC 2,3)

5

DIFFERENTIAL EQUATIONS

A differential equation is an equation that has terms that include the function and its derivatives, like $xy' + y = 0$. A function $y = f(x)$ is a solution of a differential equation if y and its derivatives are replaced by $f(x)$ and its derivatives to satisfy the equation. The solution is called the general solution, but a particular solution can result if initial conditions are given.

Differential equations can be approached in a multitude of ways: graphically interpreted via slope fields, numerically approximated through Euler's Method, and algebraically solved through separation of variables.

Objectives

- Understand slope fields (sketch and find a particular solution).
- Understand and solve separable differential equations:
  - direct variations [$y' = ky$; $y' = ky(L - y)$]
  - exponential growth and decay ($y = Ce^{kt}$); growth $k > 0$, decay $k < 0$
  - use of initial conditions
- Understand and solve logistic differential equations (BC topic only).
- Approximate solutions to differential equations using Euler's Method (BC topic only).

SLOPE FIELDS

(*Calculus for AP*®, pages 606–611)

A slope field is a graphical picture of a derivative that projects the curve within that picture. It is sometimes seen as a unifying bridge between implicit differentiation and differential equations. Given a differential equation of the form $y' = F(x, y)$, one can draw line segments (local linearity) at each point (x, y) in the xy-plane where F is defined representing the slope (y') at the selected points.

For example, let $y' = 2x$. To graph the slope field, choose a set of points. On the blank graph to the right, draw a short line segment at each point representing the slope value. For example, at $x = 0$ you would have a vertical set of horizontal line segments. Once you have drawn your slope field, compare it to the graph below the blank grid.

X	Y	$y' = 2x$
–2	–2	–4
–2	–1	–4
–2	0	–4
–2	1	–4
–2	2	–4
–1	–2	–2
–1	–1	–2
–1	0	–2
–1	1	–2
–1	2	–2
0	–2	0
0	–1	0
0	0	0
0	1	0
0	2	0
1	–2	2
1	–1	2
1	0	2
1	1	2
1	2	2
2	–2	4
2	–1	4
2	0	4
2	1	4
2	2	4

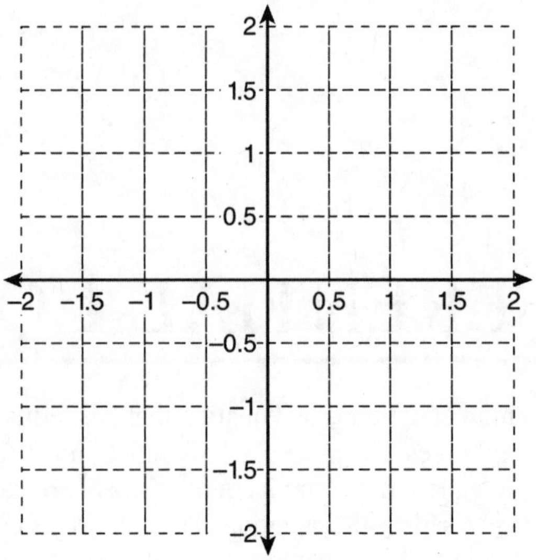

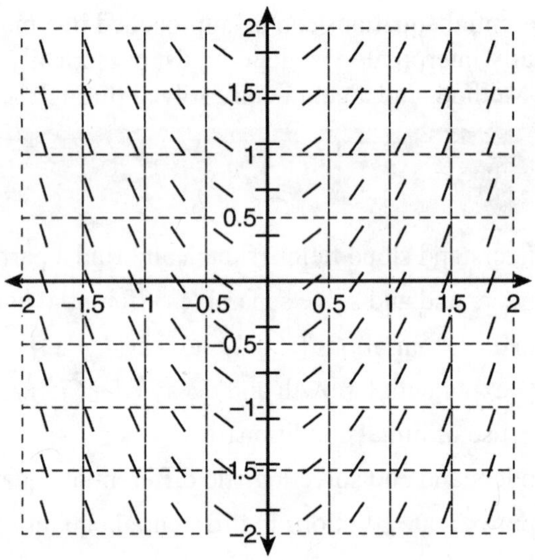

Now that you have drawn the slope field, attempt to "connect the dots" (or line segments in this case) to form a curve; use $(0, y)$ as an initial condition for each of your curves. You should "see" a set of parabolas opening up (actually $y = x^2 + C$). Explore a few more of these on your own [e.g., $y' = 1/x$ (Do you see $y = \ln x + C$?) or try $y' = 1$ (Do you see $y = x + C$?)].

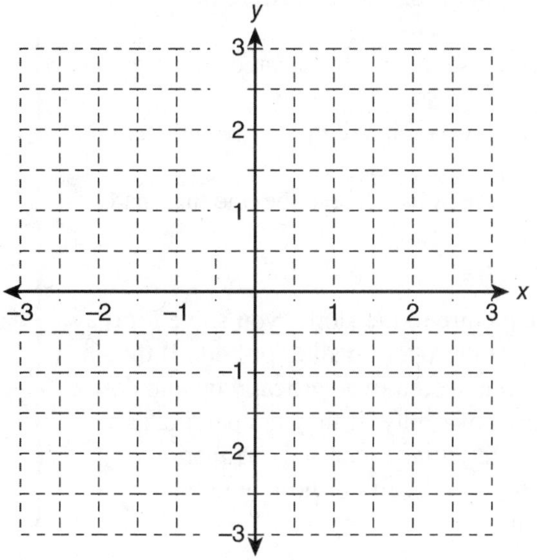

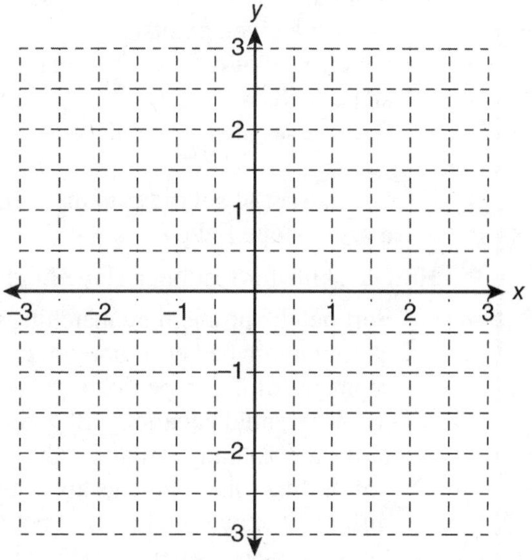

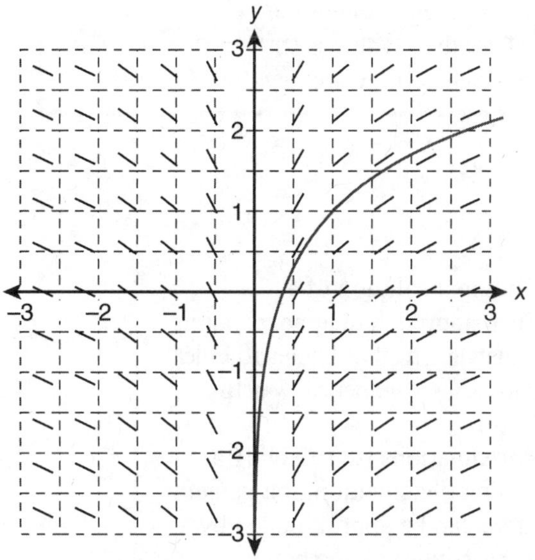

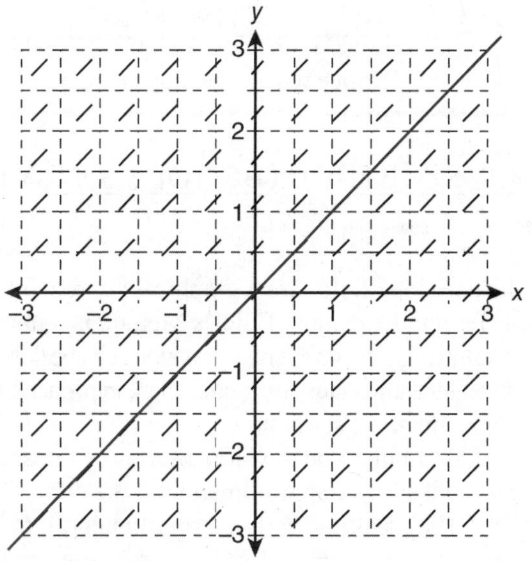

To see that this also works for a general differential equation involving both x's and y's (implicit differentiation), try $y' = -x/y$ (Do you see a circle, $c = x^2 + y^2$?). Then explore this on your calculator (the TI-83+ has a program "app" that can be downloaded from the TI site; the TI-86, TI-89, and TI Inspire have built-in programs). It will help you to "see" the curves. Although the AP® exam will require that you draw the slope field by hand, exploring it on your calculator should help familiarize you with the concept.

AP® is a trademark registered by the College Board, which is not affiliated with, and does not endorse, this product.

AP® Tips

- Required slope field skills:
  - Verify whether or not a given function is a solution to a differential equation.
  - Manually construct a portion of a slope field for a given differential equation, using the given points.
  - Given a set of differential equations, choose the one associated with a given slope field.
  - Given a set of slope fields, choose the one associated with a given differential equation.
  - Given a set of solutions to differential equations, choose the one that matches a given slope field.
- How-to skills for reading a slope field:
  - Sort out the problem by matching the picture to the slopes you solve for (pay attention to whether or not you need just the x- or y-values or both. If the line segments of the slope fields are parallel as you move vertically up and down, the differential equation will be in terms of x only. If they are parallel as you move horizontally left and right, the differential equation is a function of y only). If the line segments are not parallel vertically or horizontally, the differential equation involves both x and y.
  - Look for places where the slope is 0.
  - Look at the slopes along the x-axis (where the y-value is 0).
  - Look at the slopes along the y-axis (where the x-value is 0).
  - Notice where the slopes are positive and where they are negative.

EULER'S METHOD (BC TOPIC ONLY)

(*Calculus for AP®*, pages 611–615)

Just as slope fields are a graphical approach to finding a solution of a differential equation, Euler's Method is a numerical approach to approximating a solution. Few differential equations can be solved analytically; thus Leonhard Euler, an eighteenth-century mathematician, introduced a fairly simple numerical way to approximate the solution.

Essentially, you develop a series of linear approximations (thus having a piecewise linear approximation to the curve) by using the equation of a tangent line. The idea that, within a small interval, the curve can be approximated by a line segment is called local linearity; the smaller the x-interval, the better the approximation.

Given $y'=F(x, y)$ and a point (x_0, y_0), we can find an approximate solution that passes through the given point with a slope of $F(x_0, y_0)$ at that point.

Theoretically we need to

1. begin at a starting point (x_0, y_0).
2. determine a small step h (this will be the amount we add to the previous x-value to get to the next x-value).
3. then let $x_1 = x_0 + h$; thus $y_1 = y_0 + hF(x_0, y_0)$, which is just $y + h\,(\Delta x)$.

   Iterate:

   $$x_2 = x_1 + h, \qquad y_2 = y_1 + hF(x_1, y_1),$$
   $$\vdots \qquad\qquad \vdots$$
   $$x_n = x_{n-1} + h, \qquad y_n = y_{n-1} + hF(x_{n-1} + y_{n-1}).$$

4. graph the new point (x_n, y_n) and connect it to the prior point. Continue this over the interval chosen to complete the approximate solution.

Another way to look at this is to say $y_{new} = y_{old} + \Delta xm$ (where Δx is a change in x and m is a slope); from above, $y_1 = y_0 + hF(x_0, y_0)$ and continue that pattern.

Let's focus on what is happening in step 3. $y_1 = y_0 + hF(x_0, y_0)$ is really just in the point-slope form of an equation of the line $y = m(x - x_0) + y_0$. In this case, we are substituting h for $x - x_0$ and $F(x_0, y_0)$ as the slope m. Then we solve for y_{new} as a solution of that equation.

Let's try a simple problem.

Let $y' = x + 2$ on $[0, 3]$; initial point $(x_0, y_0) = (0, 0)$ and $h = 0.5$.

$x_n = x_{n-1} + h$	$y_n = y_{n-1} + hF(x_{n-1}, y_{n-1}) = y_{old} + \Delta xm$
$x_1 = 0 + 0.5 = 0.5$	$y_1 = 0 + 0.5(2) = 1$ (2 is the slope at (0, 0))
$x_2 = 0.5 + 0.5 = 1$	$y_2 = 1 + 0.5(2.5) = 2.25$ (2.5 is the slope at 0.5, (1))
$x_3 = 1 + 0.5 = 1.5$	$y_3 = 2.25 + 0.5(3) = 3.75$
$x_4 = 1.5 + 0.5 = 2$	$y_4 = 3.75 + 0.5(3.5) = 5.50$
$x_5 = 2 + 0.5 = 2.5$	$y_5 = 5.50 + 0.5(4) = 7.50$
$x_6 = 2.5 + 0.5 = 3$	$y_6 = 7.5 + 0.5(4.5) = 9.75$

So now let's plot the points (0, 0), (0.5, 1), (1, 2.25), (1.5, 3.75), (2, 5.5), (2.5, 7.5), (3, 9.75) on the blank graph to the right.

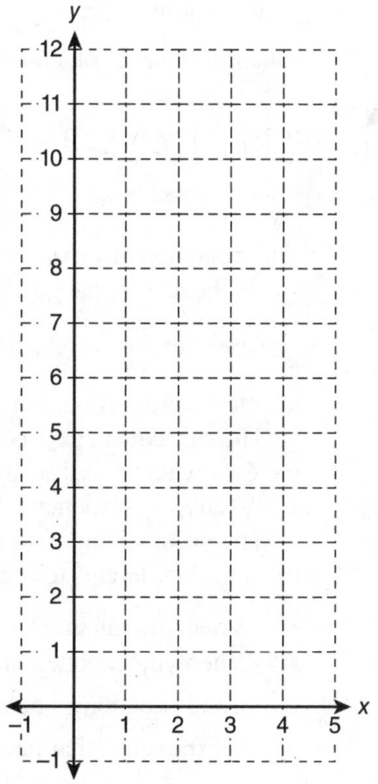

Now that you have drawn your piecewise linear graph, let's integrate the original problem. $F(x)$ becomes $\frac{x^2}{2} + 2x + C$ but $C = 0$ because of the initial condition of (0, 0); $F(x)$ is $\frac{x^2}{2} + 2x$.

If you substitute the above x-values in this particular solution, you will end up with the following set of points: (0, 0), (0.5, 1.125), (1, 2.5), (1.5, 4.125), (2, 6), (2.5, 8.125), and (3, 10.5).

Overlay your new parabola with your Euler's approximation to see how well Euler's Method approximates the solution to the differential equation.

SEPARATION OF VARIABLES

(*Calculus for AP®*, pages 618–624)

Separation of variables is a strategy of rewriting a differential equation so that each variable occurs on only one side of the equation. After separating the variables, you then integrate both sides of the equation with respect to the appropriate variable. A "constant" can be added to both sides of the equation, but then the constants are combined on one side to make a single constant value; thus you will often see it added to only one side of the equation when the integration step is completed.

For example, $\frac{dy}{dx} = \frac{2x}{y}$. Multiplying both sides by y and dx gives $ydy = 2xdx$.

Integrating both sides, $\int y\,dy = \int 2x\,dx$ leads to $\frac{y^2}{2} = x^2 + C_1$, and thus $y^2 - 2x^2 = C$.

(*Note:* You cannot really multiply by dx as it has a symbolic meaning. However, this allows us to show the integration with respect to the correct variable. If we look at it from the perspective of the Chain Rule, where y is a function of x, $dy = y'dx$, we begin the problem as $y' = \frac{2x}{y}$, multiply both sides by y, integrate with respect to x, and we get $\int yy'dx = \int 2xdx$. Then make the dy substitution and you end up with $\int ydy = \int 2xdx$.

DIFFERENTIAL EQUATIONS: GROWTH AND DECAY

(*Calculus for AP®*, pages 628–630)

The separation of variables technique is often used for growth and decay problems, where the rate of change (derivative) of a variable y is proportional to the value of y.

Consider $\frac{dy}{dt} = ky$, where the derivative (rate of change) of y with respect to t (time) is proportional to y (where k is the constant of proportionality).

The subsequent exponential model that is derived from the above equation is $y = Ce^{kt}$, where C is the initial value of y and k is the constant of proportionality.

When $k > 0$, exponential growth occurs; when $k < 0$, exponential decay occurs.

The proof of this is an important model to understand in terms of separation of variables. Things to remember:

- When you integrate $1/y$, it is $\ln|y|$.
- When you exponentiate both sides (i.e., raise e to the power of both sides of the equation), you get e^{kt+c_1} on the right side of the equation. Using rules of exponents, that becomes $e^{kt}e^{c_1}$ and e^{c_1} is just a different way of writing a constant. Thus, the right-hand side becomes Ce^{kt}.

Thus, all solutions of the equation $y' = ky$ have the form $y = Ce^{kt}$.

AP® Tips

- The applications of this form of equation can include population growth, declining sales, or other business applications, and science applications like Newton's Law of Cooling.
- Be sure to set up the equation correctly. For example, with Newton's Law of Cooling, the statement could be that the rate of change of y is proportional to the difference between y and the ambient temperature (e.g., 60) and subsequently you would use separation of variables after writing the equation as $y' = k(y - 60)$.
- Required skills for differential equations:
  - Verify that a function is or is not a solution to a given differential equation.
  - Recognize exponential growth and decay and the appropriate equations.
  - Find the general solution to a separable differential equation.
  - Find the particular solution by using the initial condition.

LOGISTIC DIFFERENTIAL EQUATIONS (BC TOPIC ONLY)

(*Calculus for AP®*, pages 630–634)

Exponential growth is unlimited. There are instances, however, when exponential growth can be used to model the first portion of a population cycle which levels off to a finite upper limit L. This maximum population L or $y(t)$ that can be sustained or supported as time t increases is called the carrying capacity.

A logistic differential equation $\frac{dy}{dt} = ky\left(1 - \frac{y}{L}\right)$ is a model that is often used for this type of growth, where k and L are positive constants. If a population satisfies this equation, it approaches the carrying capacity, L, as t increases; it does not grow without bound.

If y is between 0 and L, then $\frac{dy}{dt} > 0$, and the population increases.

If $k > L$, then $\frac{dy}{dt} < 0$, and the population decreases.

After applying the separation of variables' techniques to the logistic differential equation and using partial fractions to integrate, the general solution is of the form

$$y = \frac{L}{1 + be^{-kt}}, \quad b = \frac{L - y(0)}{y(0)}$$ by letting $t = 0$ and solving for b.

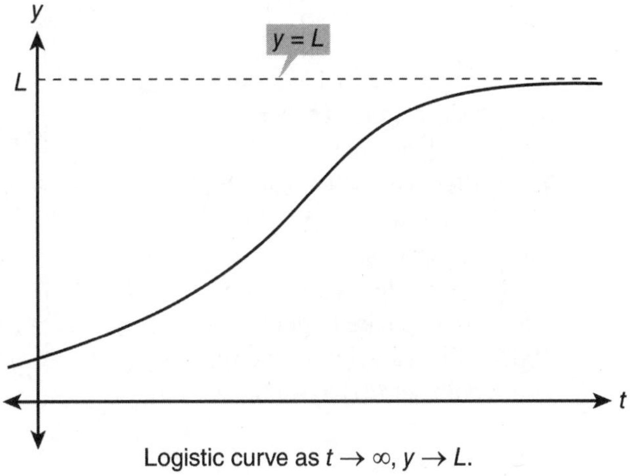

Logistic curve as $t \to \infty$, $y \to L$.

Also, note that the maximum rate of growth occurs at $\frac{L}{2}$.

The main process in the solution of a problem is as follows:

1. Take the model as written as a rate in the form of the general solution, and substitute an appropriate variable for *y*.
2. Input any known constant(s).
3. Solve for the remaining constant(s) by substituting known information (a value at a given time, for example).
4. Rewrite the solution with the correct variables and constants.
5. Answer a specific question such as the population's value at a specific time.
6. Take the limit as *t* approaches infinity to determine the carrying capacity.

Let's look at some examples.

EXAMPLE 1: Try to interpret $P(t)=\dfrac{1500}{1+24e^{-0.75t}}$.

- L (carrying capacity) = 1500 units (this comes directly from the form $y=\dfrac{L}{1+be^{-kt}}$).
- $k = 0.75$ (constant part of the exponent of e).
- Initial population is when $t = 0$ (t in years); therefore $=\dfrac{1500}{1+24e^{0}}=1500/25=60$ units.
- To determine when the population will reach 50% of its carrying capacity, let $P(t)=\dfrac{1500}{1+24e^{-0.75t}}=750$ and solve for t. Therefore $2=1+24e^{-0.75t}$, or $1/24 = e^{-0.75t}$.

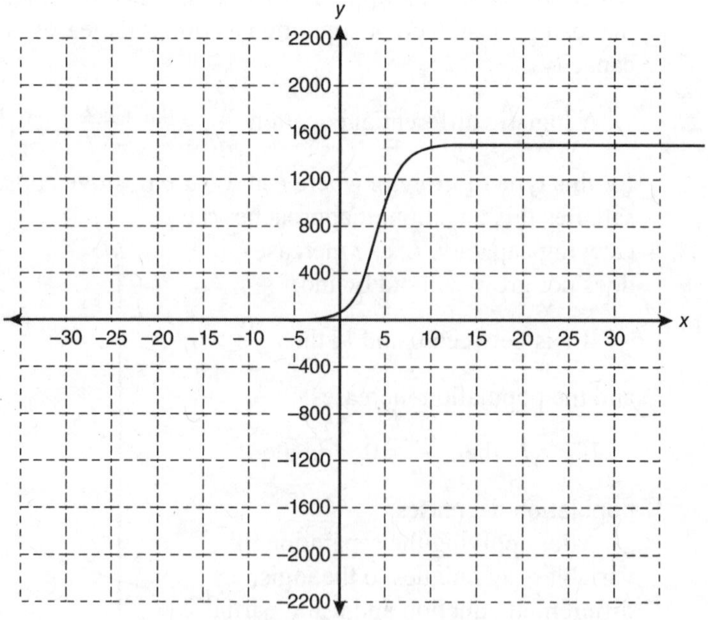

Taking the natural logarithm of both sides produces $\ln(1/24) = -0.75t$, and therefore $t \approx 4.24$. Thus, after about 4.24 years, the population is at one-half of its carrying capacity.

If you wanted to know how long it would take to get to 100% of its carrying capacity, you would set $P(t) = 1500$.

However, this won't work because you would get $0 = e^{-0.75t}$. Therefore, let's take the limit as t approaches infinity to see what happens.

As $t \to \infty$ in $P(t) = \frac{1500}{1+24e^{-0.75t}}$, then $\lim_{t\to\infty} = \frac{1500}{1+24e^{-0.75t}} = 1500$ (the carrying capacity) because $e^{-0.75t}$ approaches 0.

And finally, solve for the logistic differential equation that has a solution of $P(t) = \frac{1500}{1+24e^{-0.75t}}$.

Start with the growth rate equation $\frac{dP}{dt} = kP\left(1-\frac{P}{L}\right)$, where P is the population at a given time, k is the constant, and L is the carrying capacity.

Then substitute in the known values, and the solution is $\frac{dP}{dt} = 0.75P\left(1=\frac{P}{1500}\right)$.

EXAMPLE 2: Now let's start with the logistic differential equation and, given an initial condition, solve for the logistic equation.

$\frac{dy}{dt} = y\left(1-\frac{y}{40}\right)$, initial condition is (0, 8).

Therefore, at time $t = 0$, the population is $8 = y(0)$.

We know that $L = 40$ and $k = 1$ from the form of the equation $\frac{dP}{dt} = kP\left(1-\frac{P}{L}\right)$. (*Note: y* is equivalent to *P*.) Solving for *b* in $y = \frac{L}{1+be^{-kt}}$, we know that $b = \frac{L-y(0)}{y(0)} = \frac{40-8}{8} = 4$.

Therefore, $y = \frac{40}{1+4e^{-t}}$ is the final solution, by substitution.

AP® Tips

- Homogeneous differential equations are *not* an AP® topic.
- First-order linear differential equations are *not* an AP® topic.

PAST AP® FREE-RESPONSE PROBLEMS COVERED BY THIS CHAPTER

Note: These and other questions can be found at apcentral.com.

1998 BC 4
1999 BC 6b
2000 BC 6
2001 BC 5b,c
2002 BC 5
2004 BC 5
2005 AB 6; BC 4

2006 AB 5; BC 5
2007 AB 4b
2008 AB 5; BC 6
2009 BC 4a,c
2010 AB 6c; BC 5
2011 AB 5c
2012 AB 5a,c; BC 4c; 5
2013 AB 6; BC 5b,c
2014 AB 6

MULTIPLE-CHOICE QUESTIONS

A calculator may not be used for the following questions.

An asterisk (*) indicates the question is for BC students.

1. The general solution to the differential equation $\frac{dy}{dx} = y^2 \sin x$ is

   (A) $y = \sqrt[3]{3\cos x + C}$
   (B) $y = -\cos x + C$
   (C) $y = \sqrt[3]{\sin x + C}$
   (D) $y = \frac{1}{\cos x + C}$

2. If $e^y \frac{dy}{dx} = 2x$ and $y(1) = 2$, then the particular solution $y(x)$ is

   (A) $y = \ln(x^2) + 2$
   (B) $y = \ln(x^2 + e^2 - 1)$
   (C) $y = 2e^{x^2-1}$
   (D) $y = \ln(x^2 + e - 4)$

Questions 3–5 refer to the following information:

Consider the differential equation $\frac{dy}{dx} = \frac{4x}{y}$, for $y \geq 1$ only, with initial value $y(0) = 1$.

3. Which of the following is the slope field for the general solution to the given differential equation?

(A)

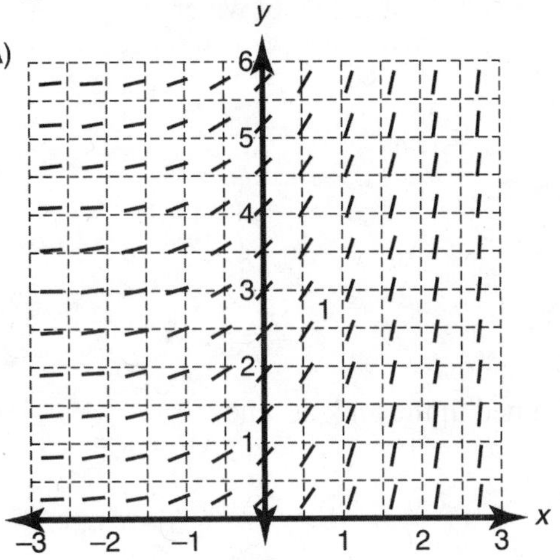

(C)

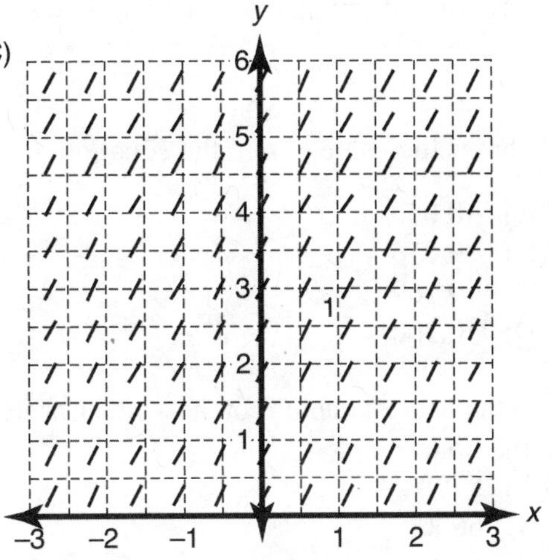

(B)

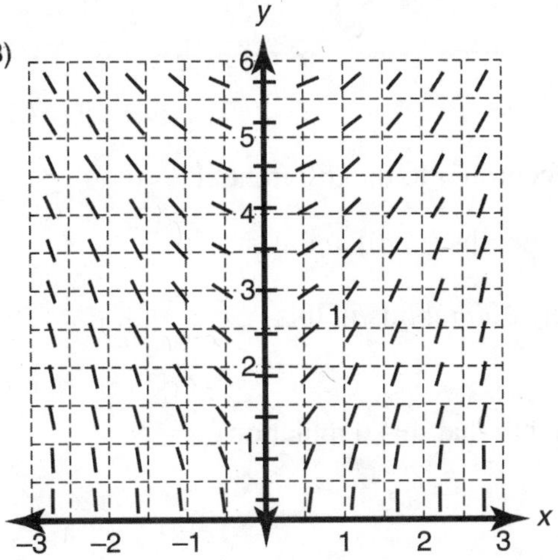

(D)

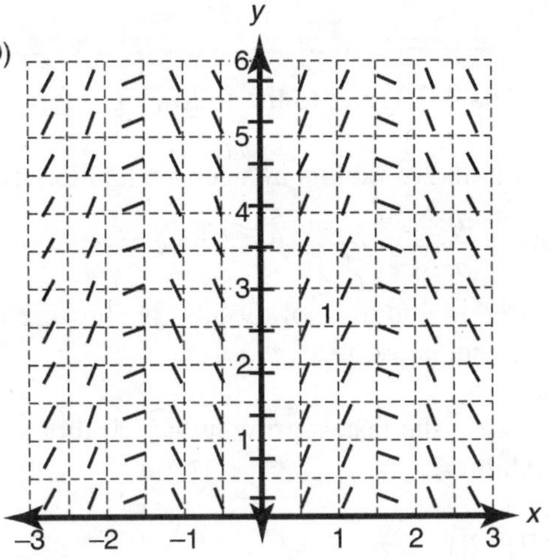

4. Using Euler's Method with step size $\Delta x = 1/2$, what is the estimate for $y(1)$?
   (A) 1
   (B) 2
   (C) $\sqrt{5}$
   (D) 5/2

5. The particular solution $y(x)$ is
   (A) $y = 2x$
   (B) $y = \sqrt{4x^2 - 4}$
   (C) $y = 2x^2 + 1$
   (D) $y = \sqrt{4x^2 + 1}$

A calculator may be used for the following questions.

Questions 6–7 refer to the following information:

Water flows continuously from a large tank at a rate proportional to the amount of water remaining in the tank; that is, $\frac{dy}{dt} = ky$. There was initially 10,000 cubic feet of water in the tank, and at time $t = 4$ hours, 8000 cubic feet of water remained.

6. What is the value of k in the equation $\frac{dy}{dt} = ky$?
   (A) −0.050
   (B) −0.056
   (C) −0.169
   (D) −0.200

7. To the nearest cubic foot, how much water remained in the tank at time $t = 8$ hours?
   (A) 5778
   (B) 6000
   (C) 6400
   (D) 6458

Questions 8–10 refer to the following information:

A population of rabbits in a certain habitat grows according to the differential equation $\frac{dy}{dt} = y\left(t - \frac{1}{10}y\right)$, where t is measured in months ($t \geq 0$) and y is measured in hundreds of rabbits. There were initially 100 rabbits in this habitat; that is, $y(0) = 1$.

8. What is the fastest growth rate in rabbits per month that this population exhibits?
   (A) 100
   (B) 200
   (C) 250
   (D) 500

9. Which of the following slope fields represents an approximate general solution to the given differential equation?

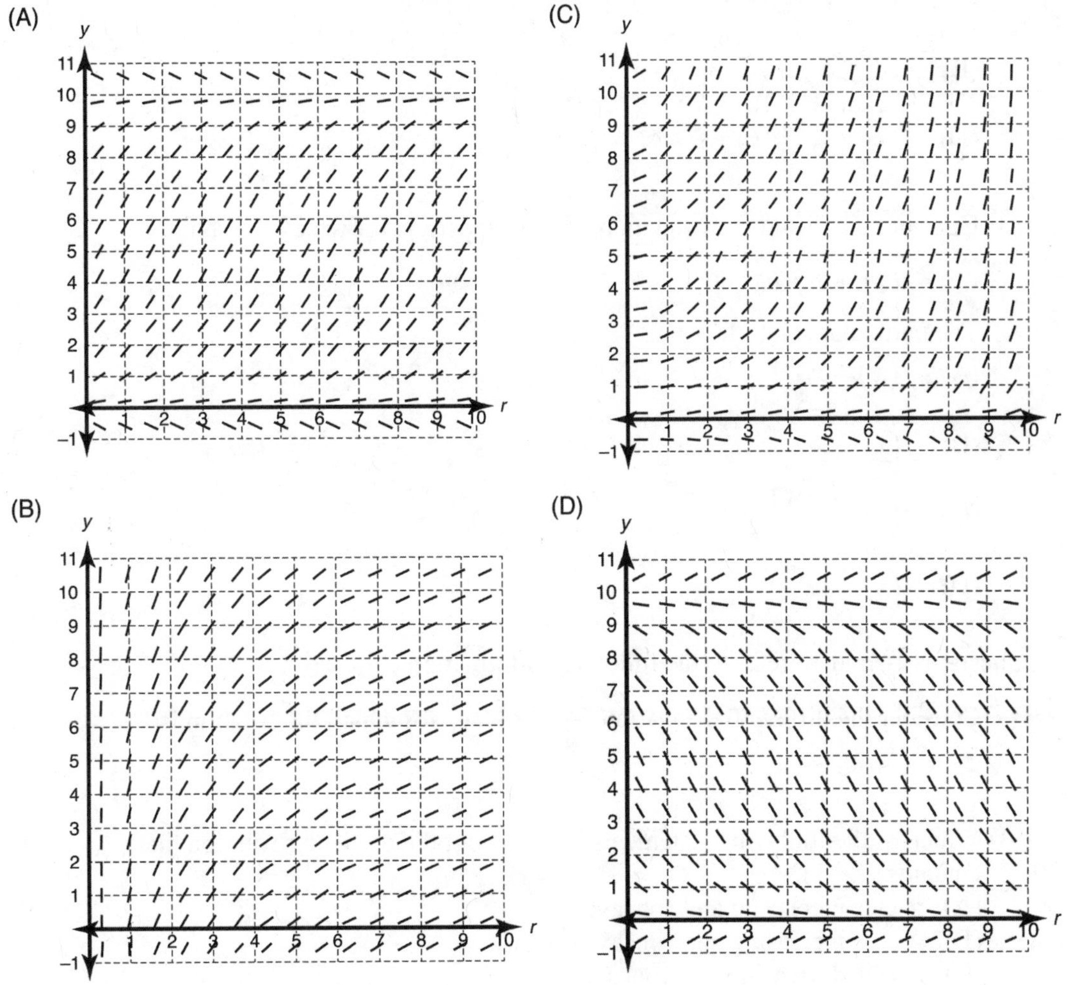

10. Estimates of $y(t)$ can be produced using Euler's Method with step size $\Delta t = 1$. To the nearest rabbit, the estimate for $y(2)$ is
(A) 281
(B) 300
(C) 344
(D) 379

11. Water is being pumped continuously into a tank at a rate that is inversely proportional to the amount of water in the tank; that is, $\frac{dy}{dt} = \frac{k}{y}$, where y is the number of gallons of water in the tank after t minutes ($t \geq 0$). Initially there were 5 gallons of water in the tank, and after 3 minutes there were 7 gallons. How many gallons of water were in the tank at time 18 minutes?
(A) $\sqrt{61}$
(B) $\sqrt{97}$
(C) 13
(D) 17

A calculator may not be used for the following questions.

12. $f'(x) = 12x^2 \sin(2x^3 - 16)$ and $f(2) = 5$ then $f(x) =$
 (A) $-4x^3 \cos(2x^3 - 16) + 5$
 (B) $2\cos(2x^3 - 16) + 3$
 (C) $-2\cos(2x^3 - 16) + 7$
 (D) $-2\cos(2x^2 - 16) + 5$

13. Consider the differential equation $\frac{dy}{dx} = \frac{1}{2}y\cos(x)$, for which the solution is $y = f(x)$. Let $f(0) = 2$.
 The particular solution is
 (A) $f(x) = x + 2$
 (B) $f(x) = 2e^{-\frac{1}{2}\sin(x)}$
 (C) $f(x) = e^{\frac{1}{2}\sin(x)}$
 (D) $f(x) = 2e^{\frac{1}{2}\sin(x)}$

Questions 14 and 15 refer to the following information:

Consider the differential equation $\frac{dy}{dx} = x + 2y$, for which the solution is $g(x)$.

14. Which of the following statements is true about the particular solution that contains $(0, -1)$?
 (A) $g(x)$ is increasing and concave up.
 (B) $g(x)$ is increasing and concave down.
 (C) $g(x)$ is decreasing and concave up.
 (D) $g(x)$ is decreasing and concave down.

15. Let $y(x)$ be the particular solution that contains $(0, 1)$. Using Euler's Method with step size $\Delta x = \frac{1}{2}$, what is the estimate for $y\left(\frac{1}{2}\right)$?
 (A) $-\frac{1}{4}$
 (B) $\frac{3}{4}$
 (C) $\frac{3}{2}$
 (D) 2

FREE-RESPONSE QUESTION

A calculator may not be used on this question.

1. A differentiable function $f(x)$ is defined such that, for all values of x in its domain, $f(x)=3+\int_{8}^{x^3} f\left(\sqrt[3]{t}\right)dt$.
   (a) What is the domain of $f(x)$?
   (b) For what value(s) of x is $f(x) = 3$?
   (c) Show that $f'(x) = 3x^2 f(x)$.
   (d) Solve the differential equation in (c) to find $f(x)$ in terms of x only.

Answers

MULTIPLE-CHOICE QUESTIONS

1. ANSWER: (D) Separating variables,
   $\int\frac{dy}{y^2} = \int\sin x dx \Rightarrow -\frac{1}{y} = -\cos x + C \Rightarrow y = \frac{1}{\cos x + C}$. (*Calculus for AP*®, pages 618–624; EU 3.5; LO 3.5A; EK 3.5A2; MPAC 2,3)

2. ANSWER: (B) Separating variables, $\int e^y dy = \int 2x dx \Rightarrow e^y = x^2 + C$. Using the initial value (1, 2), $e^2 = 1 + C \Rightarrow C = e^2 - 1$. Therefore, $e^y = x^2 + e^2 - 1 \Rightarrow y = \ln(x^2 + e^2 - 1)$. (*Calculus for AP*®, pages 618–624; EU 3.5; LO 3.5A; EK 3.5A2; MPAC 2,3)

3. ANSWER: (B) The first clear feature of the correct slope field is that all the slopes must be 0 on the y-axis (where $x = 0$). This eliminates choices (A) and (C). The appearance of a line (approximately $y = 2x$) in the slope field in (B) happens because, wherever y is twice x, the slope is 2. The sinusoidal nature of (D) should suggest a sine or cosine function in the differential equation, which eliminates (D). So, (B) is correct. (*Calculus for AP*®, pages 606–611; EU 2.3; LO 2.3F; EK 2.3F1; MPAC 4)

4. ANSWER: (B) The formula for Euler's Method with a given expression for $\frac{dy}{dx}$, a step size Δx, and an initial condition (x_0, y_0) is $y_{n+1} = y_n + \left.\frac{dy}{dx}\right|_{(x_n, y_n)} \cdot \Delta x$.

   Using this,

$x_0 = 0$	$y_0 = 1$	$\left.\frac{dx}{dy}\right|_{(0,\,1)}$
$x_1 = \frac{1}{2}$	$y_1 = 1 + 0 \times \frac{1}{2} = 1$	$\left.\frac{dx}{dy}\right|_{(\frac{1}{2},\,1)} = 2$
$x_2 = 1$	$y_2 = 1 + 2 \times \frac{1}{2} = 2$	

   Therefore, $y(1) \approx 2$. (*Calculus for AP*®, pages 611–615; EU 2.3; LO 2.3F; EK 2.3F2; MPAC 2,3)

5. ANSWER: (D) Separating variables, $\int y\,dy = \int 4x\,dx \Rightarrow \frac{1}{2}y^2 = 2x^2 + C \Rightarrow y^2 = 4x^2 + C$. Using the initial value (0, 1), $1 = 0 + C \Rightarrow C = 1$. Therefore $\sqrt{4x^2 + 1}$. (*Calculus for AP*®, pages 618–624; EU 3.5; LO 3.5A; EK 3.5A2; MPAC 2,3,4)

6. ANSWER: (B) Separating variables,
   $\int \frac{dy}{y} = \int k\,dt \Rightarrow \ln|y| = kt + C \Rightarrow y = Ce^{kt}$.
   $y(0) = 10{,}000 \Rightarrow C = 10{,}000$, so $y = 10{,}000e^{kt}$,
   $y(4) = 8000 \Rightarrow 8000 = 10{,}000e^{k \cdot 4} \Rightarrow$
   $0.8 = e^{4k} \Rightarrow k = \frac{\ln(0.8)}{4} \approx -0.056$. (*Calculus for AP*®, pages 618–624; EU 3.5; LO 3.5B; EK 3.5B1; MPAC 2,3)

7. ANSWER: (C) Using the correct equation from Question 6, $y = e^{\frac{1}{4}\ln(0.8)t} \Rightarrow y(8) = 6400$. (*Calculus for AP*®, pages 618–624; EU 3.5; LO 3.5B; EK 3.5B1; MPAC 2,3)

8. ANSWER: (C) The question asks for the maximum value of $\frac{dy}{dt}$. So the derivative of $\frac{dy}{dt}$ must be set equal to zero:

$\frac{d}{dy}\left[y-\frac{1}{10}y^2\right] \Rightarrow 1-\frac{1}{5}y=0 \Rightarrow y=5.$ Since $1-\frac{1}{5}y$ changes from positive to negative at $y = 5$, a maximum occurs at $y = 5$.

$\left.\frac{d}{dy}\right|_{y=5} = 5-\frac{1}{10}(25)=2.5,$ so the maximum growth rate is 250 rabbits per month when the number of rabbits is 500. (*Note:* You may now realize that the logistic equation increases most rapidly when it is halfway to its carrying capacity and that the carrying capacity for this particular equation is 10. Therefore, you can quickly conclude that $y = 5$.) (*Calculus for AP*®, pages 365–372; EU 3.5; LO 3.5A; EK 3.5A1; MPAC 2,3,5)

9. ANSWER: (A) The given differential equation should be recognized as having the form of logistic growth. Solutions to this should increase slowly from the initial point, then increase faster, and then finally more slowly as the population size nears its carrying capacity. Option (A) is the only choice that exhibits these characteristics. (*Calculus for AP*®, pages 630–634; EU 2.3; LO 2.3F; EK 2.3F1; MPAC 4)

10. ANSWER: (C) The formula for Euler's Method with a given expression for $\frac{dy}{dt}$, a step size Δt, and an initial condition.

(t_0, y_0) is $y_{n+1} = y_n + \left.\frac{dy}{dt}\right|_{(t_n, y_n)} \cdot \Delta t.$

Using this,

$t_0 = 0 \quad y_0 = 1 \quad \left.\frac{dy}{dt}\right|_{(0,1)} = 0.9$

$t_1 = 1 \quad y_1 = 1 + 0.9 \times 1 = 1.9 \qquad \left.\frac{dy}{dt}\right|_{(0,1)} = 1.9\left[1-\frac{1}{10}(1.9)\right] = 1.539$

$t_2 = 2y_2 = 1.9 + 1.539 \times 1 = 3.439.$

Therefore, $y(2) \approx 3.439$, so the answer is 344 rabbits. (*Calculus for AP*®, pages 611–615; EU 2.3; LO 2.3F; EK 2.3F2; MPAC 2,3)

11. ANSWER: (C) $\frac{dy}{dt} = \frac{k}{y}$. Separating variables,

$\int y\,dy = \int k\,dt \Rightarrow \frac{1}{2}y^2 = kt + C \Rightarrow y^2 = 2kt + C \Rightarrow y = \sqrt{2kt + C}.$

Using the initial condition (0, 5), $5 = \sqrt{C} \Rightarrow C \Rightarrow 25$. Using

$(3,7), 7 = \sqrt{6k+25} \Rightarrow k = 4 \Rightarrow y = \sqrt{8t+25}.$

Thus $y(18)=\sqrt{144+25}=13$. (*Calculus for AP*®, pages 618–624; EU 3.5; LO 3.5A; EK 3.5A2; MPAC 2,3)

12. ANSWER: (C)
$f(x)=\int 12x^2\sin(2x^3-16)\,dx$. Let $u=2x^3-16 \Rightarrow du=6x^2dx$
$f(x)=\int 2\sin u\,du=2\cos u+C=-2\cos(2x^3-16)+C$ using the initial condition given, $5=-2\cos 0+C=-2+C \Rightarrow C=7$ so, $f(x)=-2\cos(2x^3-16)+7$.
(*Calculus for AP*®, pages 457–461; EU 3.5; LO 3.5A; EK 3.5A2; MPAC 2,3)

13. ANSWER: (D) Separating variables,
$$\int\frac{dy}{y}=\int\frac{1}{2}\cos(x)\,dx \Rightarrow \ln|y|=\frac{1}{2}\sin(x)+C \Rightarrow y=Ce^{\frac{1}{2}\sin(x)}$$
Using the initial value (0, 2), $2=Ce^0 \Rightarrow C=2$. Therefore, $f(x)=2e^{\frac{1}{2}\sin(x)}$.
(*Calculus for AP*®, pages 618–624; EU 3.5; LO 3.5A; EK 3.5A2; MPAC 2,3)

14. ANSWER: (D) $\left.\frac{dy}{dt}\right|_{(0,\,-1)}=0-2=-2<0 \Rightarrow g(x)$ is decreasing.

To determine concavity, the sign of $\frac{d^2y}{dx^2}$ must be established.
$$\left.\frac{d^2y}{dx^2}\right|_{(0,\,-1)}=1+2\left.\frac{d^2y}{dx^2}\right|_{(0,\,-1)}=1+2(-2)=-3<0 \Rightarrow g(x) \text{ is concave down.}$$
(*Calculus for AP*®, pages 293, 322; EU 2.2; LO 2.2A; EK 2.2A1; MPAC 2,5)

15. ANSWER: (D) The formula for Euler's Method with a given expression for $\frac{dy}{dx}$, a step size Δx, and an initial condition (x_0, y_0) is $y_{n+1}=y_n+\left.\frac{dy}{dx}\right|_{(x_n,y_n)}\cdot\Delta x$.

Using this,

$x_0=0 \qquad y_0=1 \qquad \left.\frac{dy}{dx}\right|_{(0,\,1)}=2$

$x_1=\frac{1}{2} \qquad y_1=1+2\times\frac{1}{2}=2$

Therefore, $y\left(\frac{1}{2}\right)\approx 2$. (*Calculus for AP*®, pages 611–615; EU 2.3; LO 2.3F; EK 2.3F2; MPAC 2,3)

FREE-RESPONSE QUESTION

	Solution	Possible points
(a)	$\sqrt[3]{t}$ is defined for all real numbers, so x^3 can be any real number; therefore, x can be any real number.	1: answer
(b)	$f(x) = 3$ when $x^3 = 8$; therefore, $x = 2$ because the integral from 8 to 8 = 0.	1: answer
(c)	$f'(x) = f\left(\sqrt[3]{x^3}\right) \cdot 3x^2$, so $f'(x) = 3x^2 f(x)$.	$2: \begin{cases} 1: \text{argument of } f(x) \\ 1: \text{Chain Rule} \end{cases}$
(d)	Rewrite $f'(x) = 3x^2 f(x)$ as $\frac{dy}{dx} = 3x^2 y$. Separating variables, $\int \frac{dy}{y} = \int 3x^2 dx$ $\ln \lvert y \rvert = x^3 + C$ $y = e^{x^3+C} = Ce^{x^3}$. Using $f(2) = 3$ (from answer b), we get $3 = Ce^8 \Rightarrow C = 3e^{-8}$ Therefore, $y =$ $y = 3e^{-8}e^{x^3}$, hence $f(x) = 3e^{x^3-8}$.	$5: \begin{cases} 1: \text{separation of variables} \\ 2: \text{correct antiderivatives} \\ 1: \text{includes constant of integration} \\ 1: \text{solves correctly for constant} \end{cases}$

(a), (b), and (c) (*Calculus for AP*®, pages 618–624; EU 3.5,3.2,2.1,3.3; LO 3.5A,3.2C,2.1C,3.3A; EK 3.5A3,3.2C2,2.1C4,3.3A2; MPAC 2,3)(d) (*Calculus, for AP*®, pages 618–624; EU 3.5; LO 3.5A; EK 3.5A2; MPAC 2,3)

6

APPLICATIONS OF INTEGRATION

Just as the process of differentiation has many applications, so does the process of integration—from finding the area between two curves to finding the volume of a solid, and to finding an accumulation of a rate of change. For example, if you know the rate of consumption of a beverage over a time period, by integrating that function, you can find the total amount of beverage consumed over that time period (net change concept, see *Calculus for AP®* on page 496).

Objectives

- Be able to find the area of a region between two curves.
- Understand integration as an accumulation process. Integrate a rate of change to determine the total amount of change that has taken place over a time interval.
- Be able to find the volume of a solid of revolution with the disk or the washer method.
- Be able to find the volume of a solid with known cross sections.
- Be able to find the length of a curve (BC topic only).

AREA OF A REGION BETWEEN TWO CURVES

(*Calculus for AP®*, pages 477–486)

In Chapter 4, we discussed the fact that the area of a continuous, nonnegative function in a closed integral was given by the definite integral $\int_a^b f(x)\,dx$ and a value was found by applying the Fundamental Theorem of Calculus. Remember that the idea was taking the heights of the rectangles (the value of $f(x)$ at a given x) and multiplying by a determined width. Following are three figures that represent two functions, f and g, and we want to find the area *between* the curves, given a closed interval $[a, b]$, or determine points of intersection that would then give us an interval.

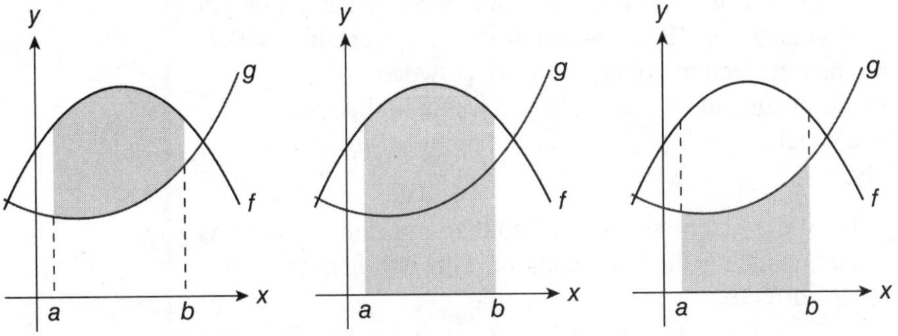

Intuitively, it would be reasonable to assume that if you took the area under the top curve (which is more than the total area) and subtracted the area under the bottom curve (which is the excess of the area), you would be able to solve for the area between the curves.

The representative rectangle would be one of length $f(x) - g(x)$.

This idea works no matter what the relative position of the functions is to the x-axis (above or below), as long as $g(x) < f(x)$ for all x in $[a, b]$ and that area will be $\int_a^b \left[f(x) - g(x)\right]dx$.

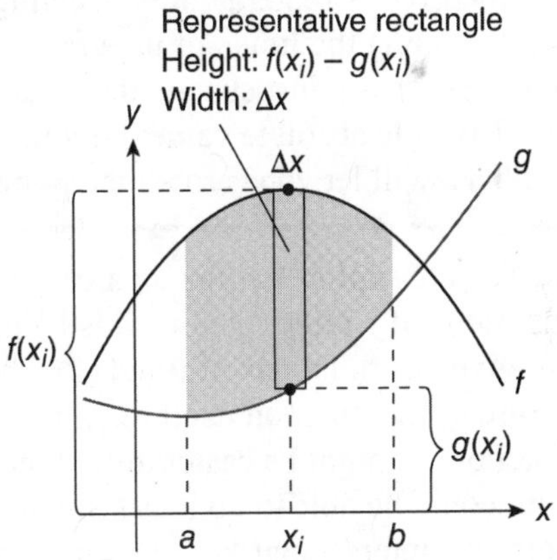

Following are samples of various positions of the functions relative to the x-axis and the representative rectangles.

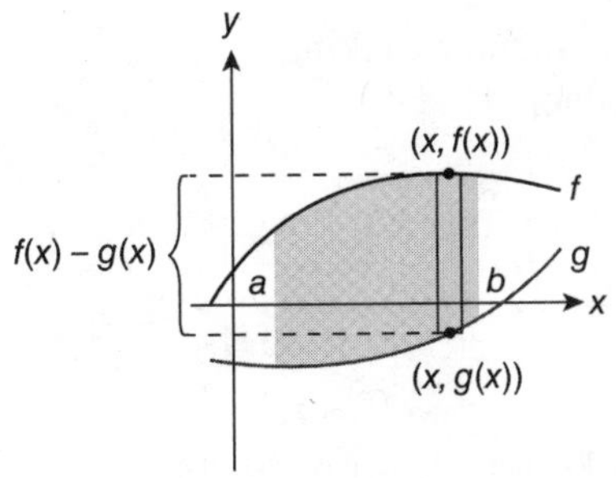

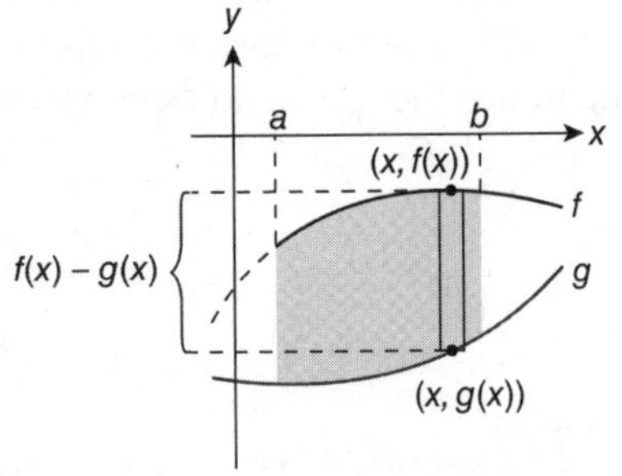

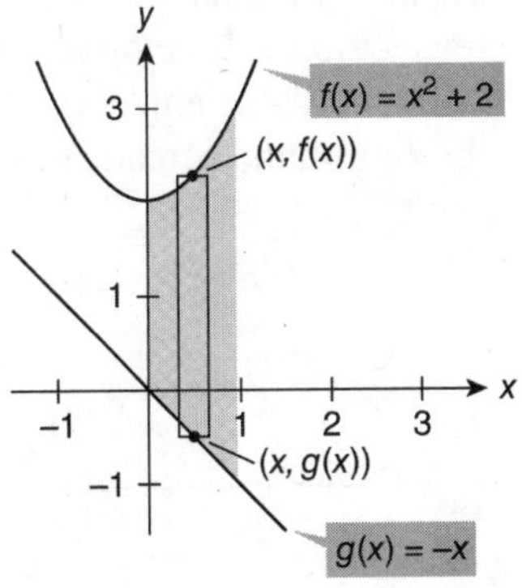

It is possible for the curves to intersect more than once and this could reverse their relative positions to each other. In this case, you must use two integrals corresponding to each of the intervals and the appropriate top curve minus bottom curve. See Example 6 in *Calculus for AP®* on page 483.

AP® Tips

- Know how to find the points of intersection of two graphs: graphically and analytically. You can use your calculator's intersect or zero function, once graphed, for this purpose as well as its solving capability. This kind of question may be on the free-response calculator section, and you should know how to solve for it on your calculator. If a calculator is used, make sure to write the equation you are solving on your paper. "Bald" answers are not acceptable. Make sure to store the intersection points you find. However, if it is a quadratic or linear function or an easily factorable higher degree function, you should be able to solve for the points of intersection algebraically.
- Sketch a graph of the functions involved so that you can see which is the top curve and which is the bottom curve. This will help you set the problem up correctly.
- Remember that area is always positive. If you solve the problem incorrectly (e.g., by interchanging the top and bottom curves or reversing the limits of integration) and you get a negative number for area, *do not* just change the negative number to a positive number. Take the absolute value of all the steps that you already worked out. This will let you earn all the points for the problem.

The concept of finding an area between two curves can be extended to functions of y rather than x. This helps in two cases: (1) where the equations are given as functions of y and (2) where the math might be easier either by the nature of the function itself (e.g., if you need to integrate a square root function, it might be easier to find the inverse and then integrate) or because you would be able to do it as a single integral because of the location of the points of intersection.

If the rectangles are vertically oriented, take the top (greater) value minus the bottom (smaller) value to get the height of the rectangle, and integrate with respect to x (dx being the width of the rectangle). If the rectangles are horizontally oriented, the "height," or in this case the length, is found by taking the right-hand (greater) value minus the left-hand (smaller) value.

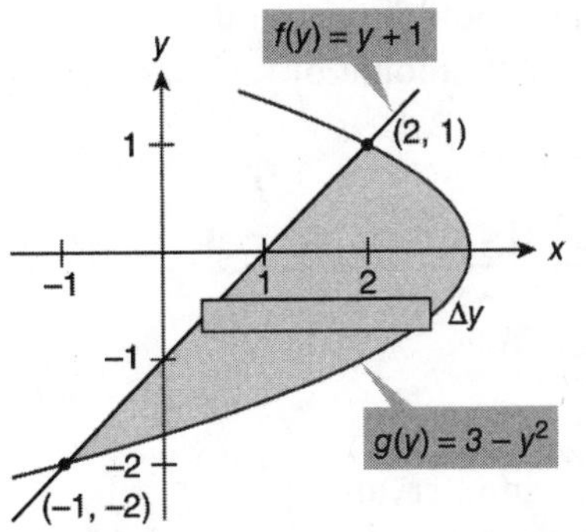

Figure 1

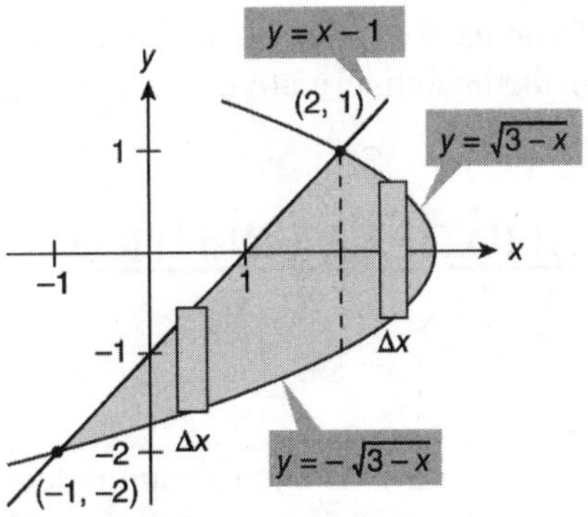

Figure 2

In Figure 1, you can see that only one integral is needed (a horizontal orientation) because there is no change in which curve has the greater values, whereas in Figure 2 (a vertical orientation), the top curve changes (from −1 to 2, it is the line; after that, it is the same curve), and this means you need two distinct integrals.

Remember, when you have horizontally oriented rectangles, your integral is in terms of *y*, and *dy* is your variable of integration (it also represents the width of your rectangles). This also means that the upper and lower bounds of integration are now the *y*-values of the ordered pairs.

INTEGRATION AS AN ACCUMULATION PROCESS

(*Calculus for AP*®, pages 450–454)

As introduced in the textbook, the concept of integration as an accumulation process can be thought of as finding the area under a curve by accumulating the areas of the rectangles formed in the interval.

Here are other ways to think of this process:

1. When integrating the absolute value of a velocity function, the area under the curve, or definite integral, would be the total distance traveled during a given time period (see the following free-response questions, available at https://ap student.collegeboard.org/ap course/ap-calculus-ab/exam-practice: 2009 BC 1, AB 1; 2011 AB 1, 2001 BC 1; 2003 AB 2, 3).
2. When integrating a function that represents the rate of water flow out of a pipe, then the definite integral would be the total flow during a given time period (see the following free-response questions: 1999 AB and BC 3).
3. When integrating a function that models the rate at which people enter a park, then the definite integral represents the total number of people who enter the park during a given interval (see the following free-response questions: 2002 AB and BC 2).
4. When integrating a function that represents the rate of traffic flow through an intersection, then the definite integral would accumulate the number of cars that pass through that intersection during the given time interval (see the following free-response questions: 2004 AB and BC 1).
5. When integrating a function that represents the rate at which gravel arrives at a gravel processing plant, then the definite integral represents the total amount of processed gravel.

In other words, if you have a function, which is a rate, then the definite integral accumulates or totals the antiderivative concept (like distance or amount of water flow, etc.).

VOLUME OF A SOLID OF REVOLUTION—THE DISK METHOD

(*Calculus for AP®*, pages 522–525)

Imagine a curve above the x-axis and its region defined over an interval between the curve and the axis. If you rotate that region around the x-axis, it would form a "solid of revolution." Our goal is to find the volume of that solid. This concept will be extended to other horizontal axes of revolution as well as to vertical axes of revolution.

To begin the analysis, consider a rectangle and revolve it around the x-axis; this will form a disk of a given width (i.e., a circular cylinder). To find the volume of that solid, you would multiply the area of the base times the height (the volume of a cylinder). The area of a circle is πr^2, and if you envision this rectangle, the width of the rectangle (dx) is the same as the height of the cylinder.

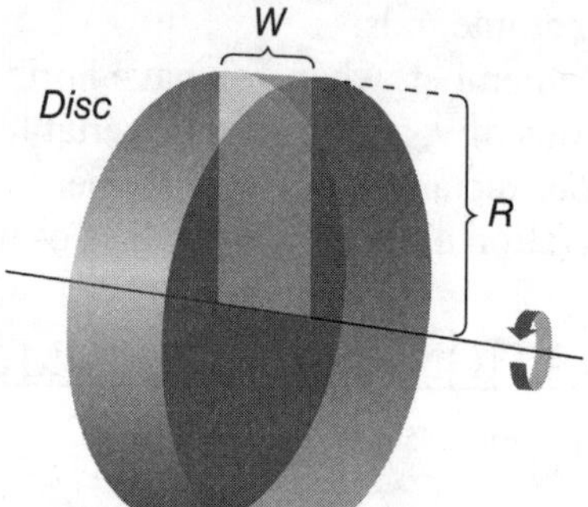

Remember how we found the area under the curve by adding up representative rectangles to approximate the area? Now, we want to add up the volumes of representative disks (cylinders) to get the volume of the entire solid. Just as we wanted the rectangles to get smaller and smaller and the width to "disappear" by taking the limit of the sums as the number of rectangles went to infinity, we now want the heights of the disks to go to zero as well. In essence, think of an infinite number of circles on top of each other filling in the cylinder. Thus, as you sum the areas of the infinite number of circles, you will get the volume of the revolved region.

$$\text{Volume of a solid} \approx \sum_{i=1}^{n} \pi\left[R(x_i)\right]^2 \Delta x = \pi \sum_{i=1}^{n}\left[R(x_i)\right]^2 \Delta x$$

(You can factor the π out because it is a constant.) Thus, the volume of a solid $= \lim_{\|\Delta\| \to 0} \sum_{i=1}^{n} \pi\left[R(x_i)\right]^2 \Delta x = \pi \int_a^b \left[R(x)\right]^2 dx$. Therefore, to find the volume of the solid, integrate the radius squared with respect to x in the interval $[a, b]$ times π, thus accumulating the areas of circles over the entire interval.

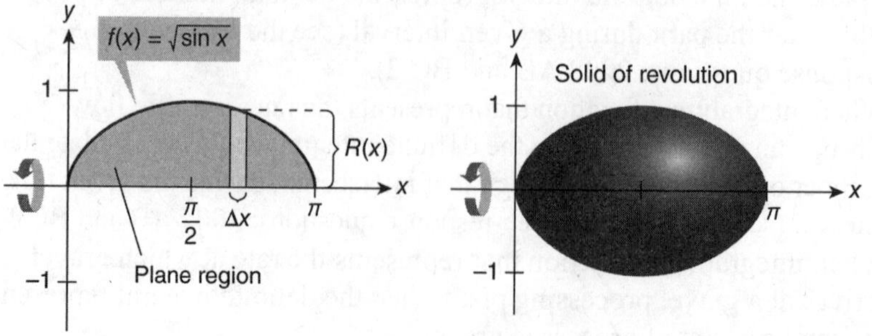

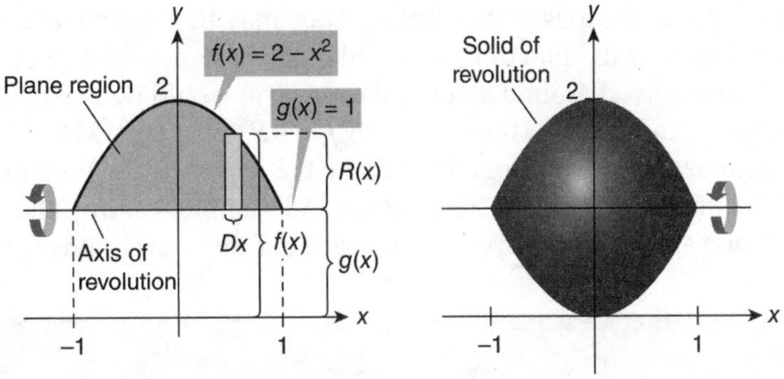

Note that the difficult part with this formula is in determining $R(x)$. Remember, it is always the distance from the curve to the axis of revolution. Thus, if you are just going from the curve to the x-axis, it is the $f(x)$ value. However, if you revolve around the line $y = -2$ for example, then $R(x) = f(x) - (-2)$, or in other words $f(x) + 2$ would be what you would square. Again, a picture is a great way to see what is occurring. If you *always* draw in your representative rectangle, you will have a clear idea of what $R(x)$ should be.

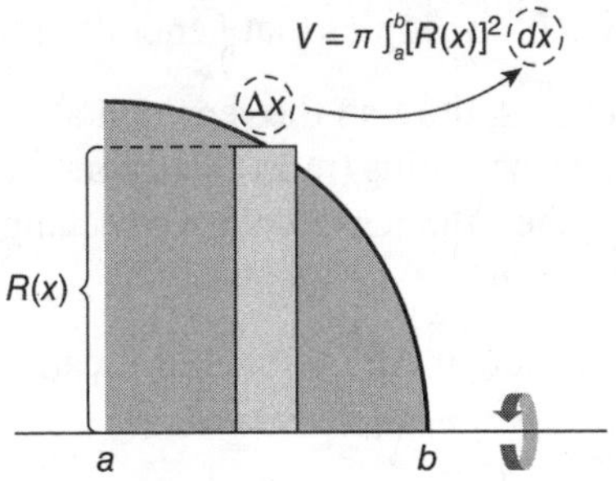

Another important point to remember is that the representative rectangle must always be *perpendicular* to the axis of revolution. Thus, if the axis of revolution is horizontal, you will use a vertical representative rectangle, and subsequently will use $R(x)$, dx, and the appropriate x-values for the definite integral.

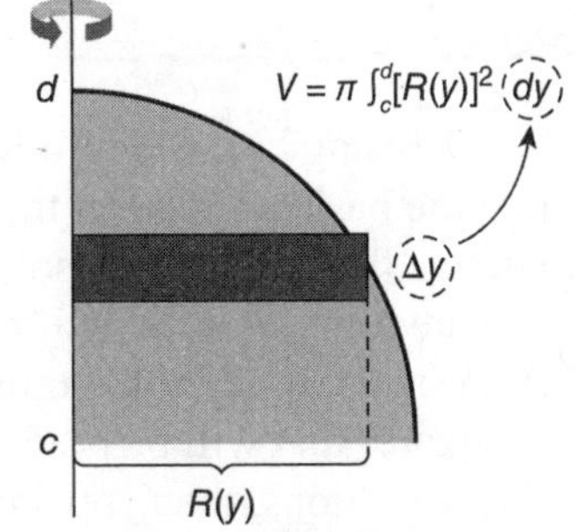

If the axis of revolution is vertical, then the representative rectangle is horizontal (thus the width is dy) and you will use $R(y)$, dy, and the appropriate y-values for the definite integral.

Volume of a vertical axis of revolution $= \pi \int_c^d \left[R(y)\right]^2 dy$, where the ordered pairs of the end points are (a, c) and (b, d).

THE WASHER METHOD

(*Calculus for AP*®, pages 525–528)

The washer method is similar to the disk method, but is used to find the area of a solid with a hole in it. Just as we found the area between two curves by taking the area under the top curve and subtracting the area under the bottom curve, we now need to subtract the volume of the piece cut out of the solid from the volume of the whole solid.

Thus, the formula would become $\pi \int_a^b \left[R(x)\right]^2 - \left[r(x)\right]^2 dx$, where $R(x)$ is the outer radius and $r(x)$ is the inner radius. Remember, $R(x)$ is equal to the distance from the outer curve to the axis of revolution, and $r(x)$ is the distance from the inside curve to the axis of revolution. They may be the actual functions, or they may be the functions adjusted by a constant (either + or −).

If the region is revolved around a vertical axis, $R(y)$ would be used to solve the problem. Examples 8–10 in *Calculus for AP®* on pages 526–528 are good examples of needing two integrals because the length of the rectangle changes over the interval. The particular region in Example 4 shows the difference in shape and volume if you revolve around the x-axis rather than the y-axis.

AP® Tips

- Know how to calculate the definite integral on a graphing calculator. Area and volume are two of the topics that generally require the ability to do this.
- When sketching curves, draw in the representative rectangle to get a clear idea of the length of the radius (radii) that you need to apply to the formula for volume. Remember, the representative rectangle is always perpendicular to the axis of revolution.
- The Shell method is not an AP® topic, but it can be used on the exam.

SOLIDS WITH KNOWN CROSS SECTIONS

(*Calculus for AP®*, pages 518–522)

This section can be confusing because it follows the solid of revolution section. However, go back to the basic premise in the disk method, which is to add the areas of circles to derive the volume of a solid. With this concept, you are not revolving or rotating anything. A solid will be described to you, and you want to take a cross section (in a cylinder, that cross section would be a circle; in a cube, it would be a square) that will be predetermined. If you take the sum of the areas of those cross sections, then you should get the volume of the solid.

Within this concept, you will be asked to find the volume of a solid formed with a given base but with different cross sections. The solutions will vary by the type of cross section because a different solid is formed.

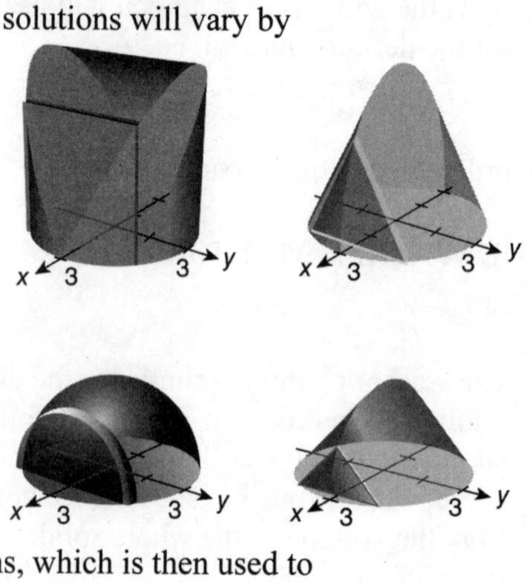

Find the volume of the solid whose base is bounded by the circle $x^2 + y^2 = 9$ with the indicated cross sections taken perpendicular to the x-axis.

Here, the base is circular in each case, but the area you sum will vary. However, this volume formula is just $\int_a^b A(x)\,dx$ for a cross section perpendicular to the x-axis, and $\int_c^d A(y)\,dy$ for cross sections perpendicular to the y-axis, where $A(x)$ and $A(y)$ are the areas of the cross sections. The base that is given is used to find the length of one side of the cross sections, which is then used to find the equation for the area of the cross sections.

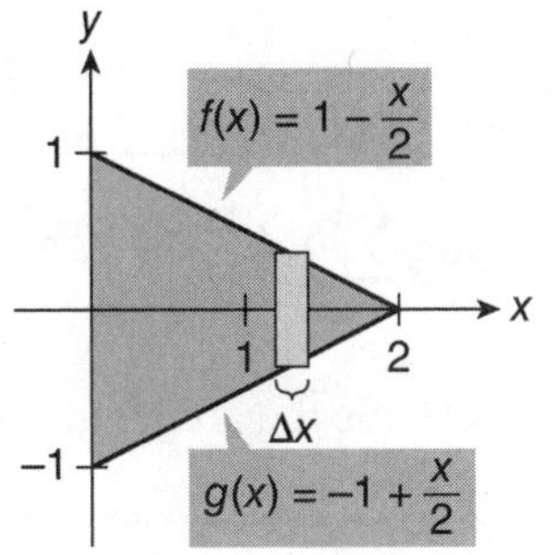

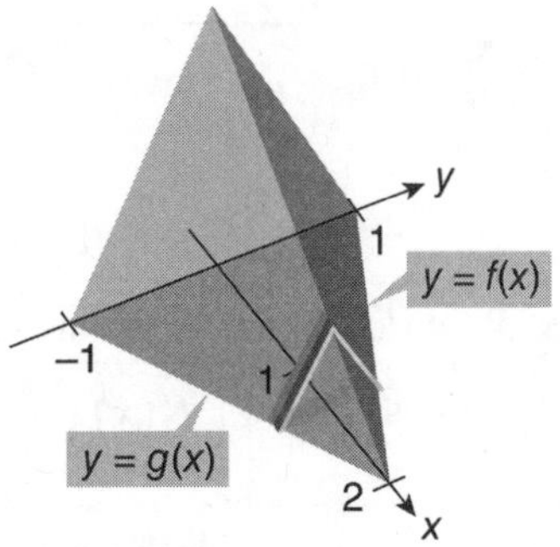

In the above figure, the base of the solid is determined by the functions $f(x)=1-\frac{x}{2}$, $g(x)=-1+\frac{x}{2}$, and $x = 0$. If you look at the 3-D picture, you see equilateral triangular cross sections. The area of an equilateral triangle is $\frac{\sqrt{3}}{4}(\text{side})^2$, so the major skills needed here are the following:

1. To determine the length of the side and then plug the area formula into the integral. If you refer to the 2-D picture and draw in the representative rectangle, it becomes more obvious that the length of the side is $f(x) - g(x)$ or in this case $2 - x$.
2. To find the interval that is determined by the $x = 0$ boundary and the intersection of $f(x)$ and $g(x)$.

Thus, the volume becomes $\int_a^b A(x)\,dx$ or $\int_0^2 \frac{\sqrt{3}}{4}(2-x)^2\,dx$, and this is an integral you could solve either by hand or with a calculator.

AP® Tip

When working in the calculator section of the exam, the expectation is that you will write the integral in the proper form (above) and then use your calculator to find the value of the definite integral. Although you may want to show that you can do it by hand, that will not only take valuable time, but you could also make an error along the way.

ARC LENGTH (BC TOPIC ONLY)

(*Calculus for AP®*, pages 532–537)

Recall how we discussed the concept of local linearity, that in any small interval, the curve can be approximated by a line? If we continue that idea and want to approximate the length of a curve, we could find the length of line segments between two given points, consecutively over the entire interval. Once we sum each of those lengths, we would have an approximation for the length of the curve.

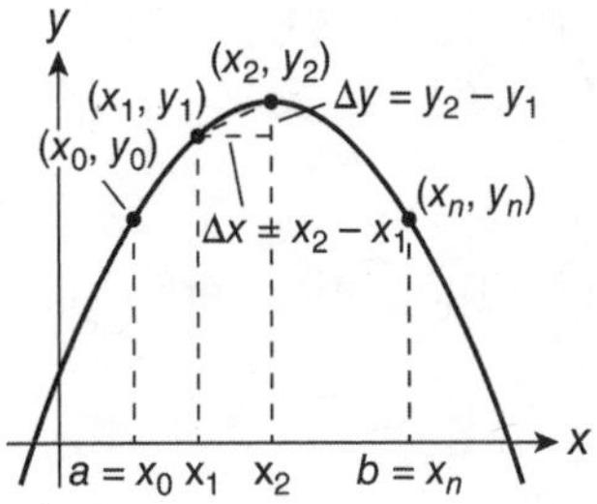

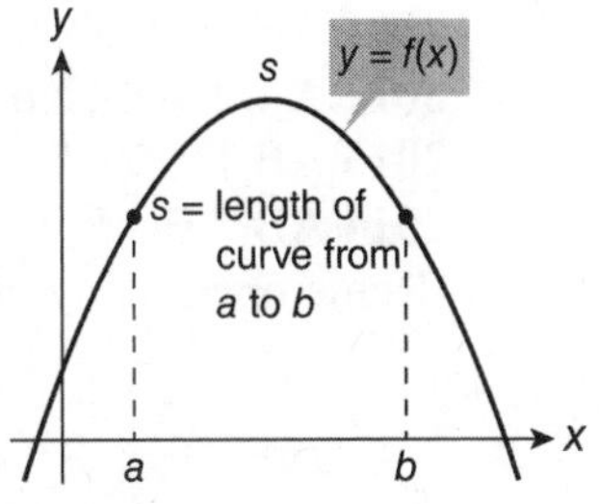

Arc length $\approx \sum_{i=1}^{n} \sqrt{(x_i - x_{i-1})^2 + (y_i - y_{i-1})^2}$

With lots of algebra, this becomes arc length $= \lim_{\|\Delta\| \to 0} \sum_{i=1}^{n} \sqrt{1 + \left(\frac{\Delta y_i}{\Delta x_i}\right)^2} \Delta x_i$,
which in turn becomes $\int_a^b \sqrt{1 + [f'(x)]^2}\, dx = s$, where s is the arc length of f between a and b.

This can be used in a form for the curve given by $x = f(y)$ as well:

$$s = \int_c^d \sqrt{1 + [g'(y)]^2}\, dy$$

(Again, note the use of the y-values in the definite integral.)

AP® Tip

It is assumed that students can adapt the knowledge and techniques they have learned to solve similar application problems. This could be an application to work, or fluid pressure, or force; although they generally are not topics on the exam, they could be in some form.

PAST AP® FREE-RESPONSE PROBLEMS COVERED BY THIS CHAPTER

Note: These and other questions can be found at apcentral.com.

1998 AB 1; 5d; BC 1
1999 AB 2
2000 AB 1; 4a
2001 AB 1
2002 AB 1; 2a
2003 AB 1; 3d
2004 AB 1a; 2
2005 AB 1
2006 AB 1; 3a,c
2007 AB 1; 2a
2008 AB 1; 2d; 3c; 4a
2009 AB 1b,d; 3a,b,c; 4
2010 AB 4; 5a,c
2011 AB 1c,d; 3b,c; 4a BC 1c,d; 3a,b
2012 AB 2; 3a; 6b,d BC 2b,d
2013 AB 1b; 4b; 5
2014 AB 2 BC 5
(Remember, many of the AB questions are also BC questions.)

MULTIPLE-CHOICE QUESTIONS

A calculator may not be used for the following questions.

For Questions 1 and 2, region R is bounded by $f(y) = y^2 - 3$ and $g(y) = 3y + 1$.

1. Which of the following expressions gives the area of region R?

   (A) $\int_{-2}^{13} (3y+1)-(y^2-3)\,dy$

   (B) $\int_{-2}^{13} (y^2-3)-(3y+1)\,dy$

   (C) $\int_{-1}^{4} (3y+1)-(y^2-3)\,dy$

   (D) $\int_{-1}^{4} (y^2-3)-(3y+1)\,dy$

2. Which of the following expressions gives the volume when region R is rotated about the line $x = 13$?

   (A) $\pi\int_{-2}^{13} (7-y^2)^2-(3-3y)^2\,dy$

   (B) $\pi\int_{-1}^{4} (1-y^2)^2-(5-3y)^2\,dy$

   (C) $\pi\int_{-1}^{4} (16-y^2)^2-(12-3y)^2\,dy$

   (D) $\pi\int_{-2}^{13} (3y+1)^2-(y^2-3)^2\,dy$

For Problems 3 and 4, region Q is bounded by $y = \sin 2x$, $y = 0$, $x = \frac{\pi}{2}$, and $x = \pi$.

3. What is the area of region?

   (A) 0

   (B) $\frac{1}{2}$

   (C) $\frac{\pi}{2}$

   (D) 1

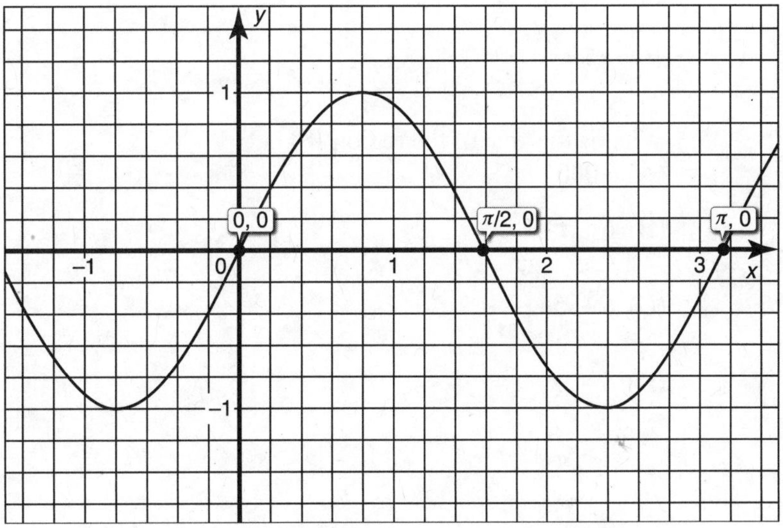

4. Which of the following expressions gives the volume of a solid whose base in the xy-plane is region Q and whose cross sections, perpendicular to the x-axis, are squares with a side in the xy-plane?
   (A) $\pi \int_{\frac{\pi}{2}}^{\pi} \left(1-\cos^2 2x\right) dx$
   (B) $\int_{\frac{\pi}{2}}^{\pi} (-\sin 2x)^2 \, dx$
   (C) $\pi \int_{\frac{\pi}{2}}^{\pi} (1-\cos 2x) \, dx$
   (D) $\pi \int_{\frac{\pi}{2}}^{\pi} (-\sin 2x)^2 \, dx$

For Question 5, region W is bounded by $f(x)=3+\sqrt{4-x^2}$, $g(x)=\cos\left(\frac{\pi}{4}x\right)$, $x=0$, and $x=2$.

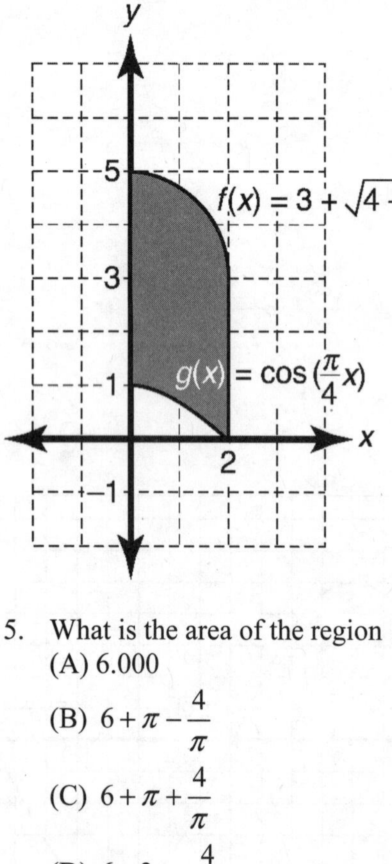

5. What is the area of the region W?
   (A) 6.000
   (B) $6+\pi-\frac{4}{\pi}$
   (C) $6+\pi+\frac{4}{\pi}$
   (D) $6+2\pi-\frac{4}{\pi}$

6. In the closed interval $0 \le x \le 2$, if $h(x) = k\cos\left(\frac{\pi}{4}x\right)$, for what value of k does the region bounded by $f(x)$ and the line $y = 3$ have the same area as that bounded by $h(x)$ and the x-axis?

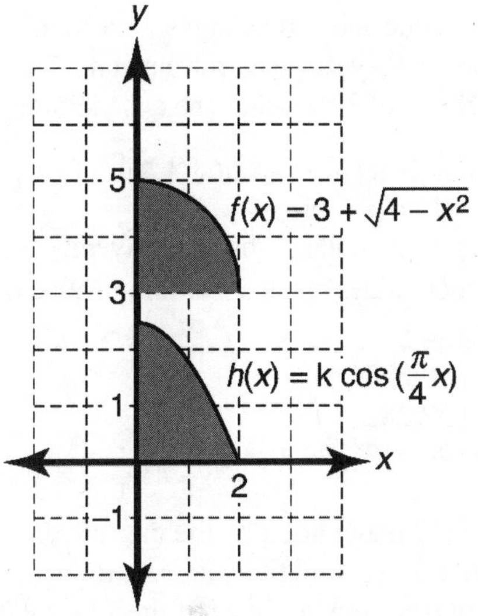

(A) $\frac{1}{2}$

(B) $\frac{\pi}{4}$

(C) $\frac{\pi^2}{4}$

(D) $\frac{\pi^2}{2}$

A calculator may be used on the following questions.

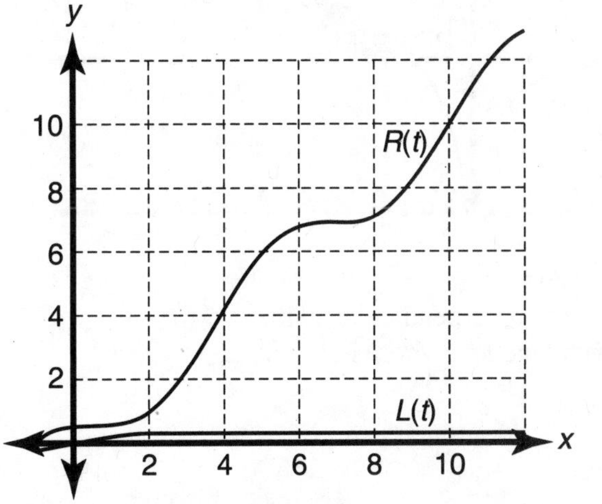

7. Air is being pumped into a spherical balloon at the rate of $R(t) = t + \cos(t + 1)$ cm^3/min, but there is a small hole in the balloon and at the same time air is leaking out at the rate of $L(t) = 0.25\tan^{-1}(t)$ cm^3/min. Which of the following is true for $0 \le t \le 10$, where t is measured in minutes?

(A) $\int_0^{10} R(t) - L(t)\,dt$ represents the volume of the balloon after the first 10 minutes.

(B) $\frac{1}{10}\int_0^{10} R(t) - L(t)\,dt$ represents the increase in volume each minute during the first 10 minutes.

(C) $\int_0^{10} R(t) - L(t)\,dt$ represents the increase in volume during the first 10 minutes.

(D) $R(0) - L(0) = 1$

8. The revenue and expenditures for a small company are analyzed and predicted for the next 5 years. The current annual revenue is \$125,000 and growing at an annual rate of 30%, while the expenditures are modeled with a sinusoidal function. If $R(t) = 125{,}000(1.3)^t$ and $E(t) = 25{,}000e^{\frac{t}{2}}\left(\sin\left(\frac{t}{2}\right) + \cos\left(\frac{t}{3}\right)\right)$, to the nearest dollar, what is the average annual profit for the company when the expenditures reach a maximum value on the interval $0 \le t \le 5$?
(A) \$434,691
(B) \$340,827
(C) \$127,282
(D) \$106,613

9. Region G is bounded by the curve $y = \ln x$, $x = e$, and the x-axis. I, II, III represent the volumes of the solids generated when Region G is rotated about the lines $y = 0$, $y = 1$ and $y = e$ respectively. Order the volumes from smallest to largest.
(A) III < I < II
(B) II < I < III
(C) I < II < III
(D) I < III < II

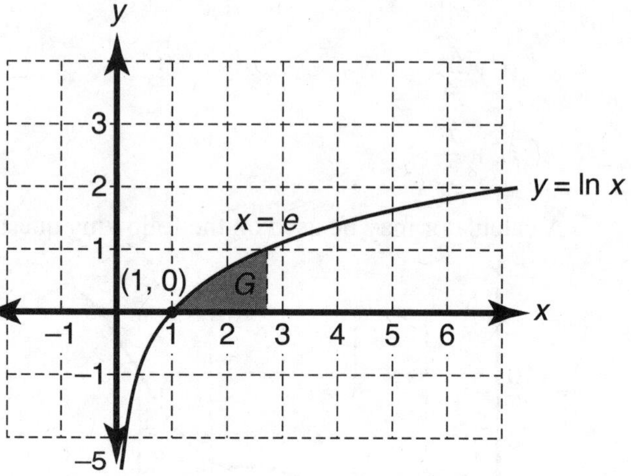

10. The base of a solid is bounded by $y = \tan^2 x$ and $y = 4 - x^2$ in the xy-plane, as shown in the figure below. Each cross section perpendicular to the x-axis is a rectangle with one side in the xy-plane and whose height is 2. What is the volume of the solid?
(A) 3.121
(B) 4.454
(C) 6.243
(D) 12.486

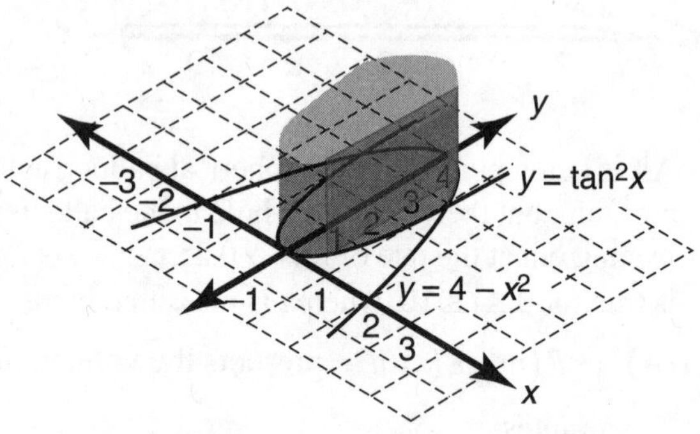

A calculator is required for the following questions.

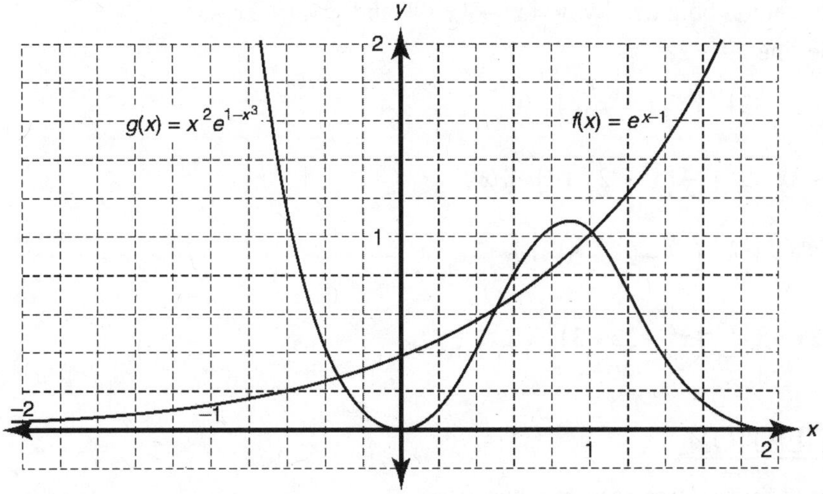

11. Find the combined area of the two regions bounded by the curves $f(x) = e^{x-1}$ and $g(x) = x^2e^{1-x^3}$ as shown in the figure above.
(A) 0.073
(B) 0.203
(C) 0.276
(D) 0.931

Questions 12–14 refer to the following information:
The velocity of a particle moving along a line is given by $v(t) = e^t \sin(e^t)$ for the interval $0 \le t \le \frac{\pi}{2}$.

12. How far to the right of the starting point will the particle be at $t = \frac{\pi}{2}$?
(A) 0.442
(B) 0.540
(C) 1.145
(D) 1.540

13. What is the total distance that the particle has traveled in this time interval?
(A) 0.442
(B) 1.145
(C) 1.540
(D) 2.638

14. If the position of the particle at time $t = 0$ is -1, then what is the position of the particle when it is farthest to the right on this time interval?
(A) 0.442
(B) 0.540
(C) 1.145
(D) 1.540

15. Which of the following expressions represents the volume of the solid generated when the region bounded by $y = x^2 - 2x + 3$ and $y = 1 + 3x - x^2$ is rotated about the line $y = -2$?

(A) $V = \pi \int_{\frac{1}{2}}^{2} \left[\left(1 + 3x - x^2\right) - \left(x^2 - 2x + 3\right) \right] dx$

(B) $V = \pi \int_{\frac{1}{2}}^{2} \left[\left(-1 + 3x - x^2\right)^2 - \left(x^2 - 2x + 1\right)^2 \right] dx$

(C) $V = \pi \int_{\frac{1}{2}}^{2} \left[\left(3 + 3x - x^2\right) - \left(x^2 - 2x + 5\right)^2 \right] dx$

(D) $V = \pi \int_{\frac{1}{2}}^{2} \left[\left(1 + 3x - x^2\right) - \left(x^2 - 2x + 3\right) \right]^2 dx$

FREE-RESPONSE QUESTION

A calculator may be used for this free-response question.

Let f be the function given by $f(x) = e^x + 1$ as shown in the sketch below, where the region R is bounded by the graph of $f(x)$, the y-axis, and the horizontal line $y = 4$.

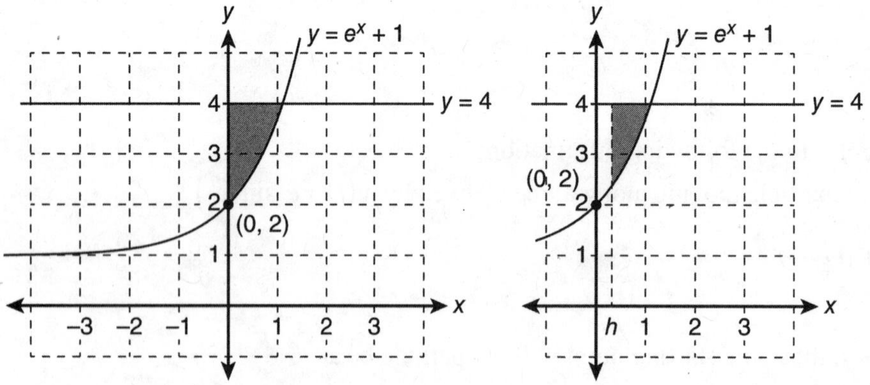

(a) Find the area of the region R.

(b) A vertical line $x = h$, where $h > 0$ is chosen so that the area of the region bounded by $f(x)$, the y-axis, the horizontal line $y = 4$, and the line $x = h$ is half the area of region R. What is the value of h?

(c) Find the volume of the solid formed when region R is rotated about the line $y = 4$.

(d) A horizontal line $y = k$, where k is greater than 4, is chosen so that the volume of the solid formed when region R is rotated about the line $y = k$ is twice the volume of the solid found in part (c). Set up, but do *not* evaluate, an integral expression in terms of a single independent variable that represents the volume of this solid.

Answers

MULTIPLE-CHOICE QUESTIONS

1. ANSWER: (C) Find points of intersection by equating the two functions: $y^2 - 3 = 3y + 1$. Solve the quadratic equation $y^2 - 3y - 4 = 0 = (y - 4)(y + 1)$.

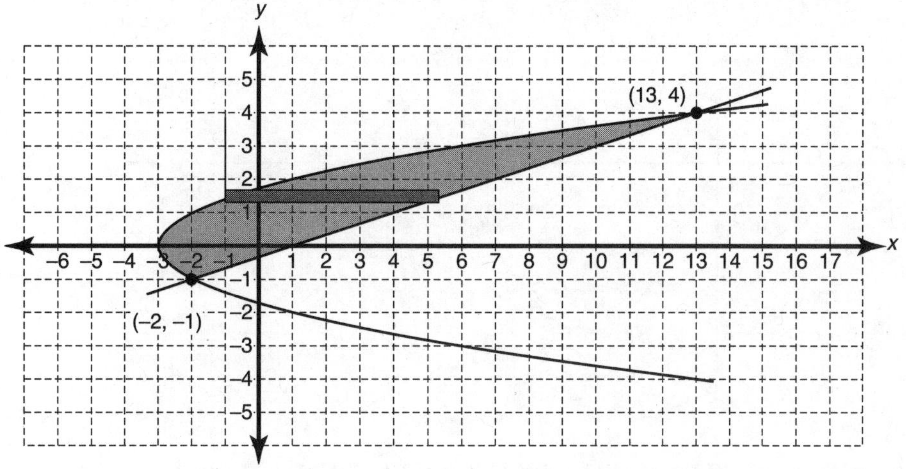

The points of intersection are $(-2, -1)$ and $(13, 4)$. With $g(y) \geq f(y)$, integrate with respect to y: $\int_{-1}^{4} (3y+1)-(y^2-3)\,dy$.
(*Calculus for AP*®, pages 477–486; EU 3.4; LO 3.4D; EK 3.4D1; MPAC 2,3,4)

2. ANSWER: (C)

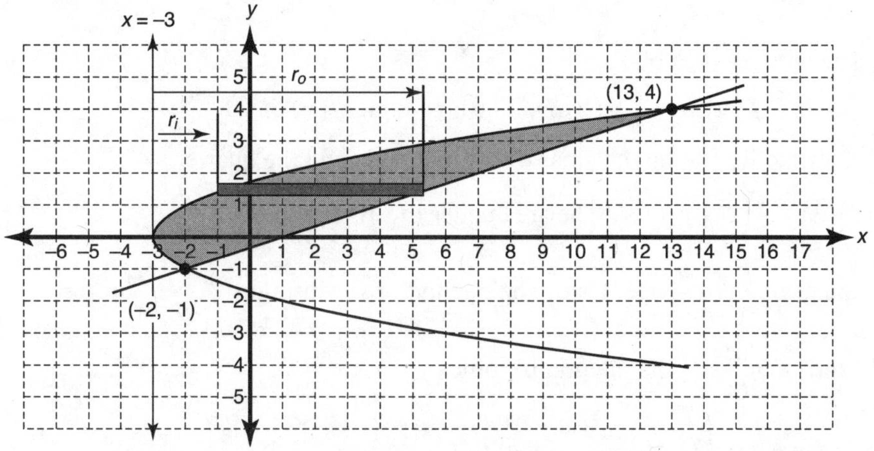

Using the same discussion from the explanation to Question 1 and the method of volume by washers, the volume is $\pi \int_{-1}^{4} \left(16-y^2\right)^2 - (12-y)^2\,dy$

where each radius is of the form $r = 13 - x$. The outside radius is $r_0 = 13 - f(y) = 13 - (y^2 - 3) = 16 - y^2$, and the inside radius is $r_i = 13 - g(y) = 13 - (3y + 1) = 12 - 3y$. (*Calculus for AP*®, pages 525–528; EU 3.4; LO 3.4D; EK 3.4D2; MPAC 2,3,4)

3. ANSWER: (D) $\int_{\frac{\pi}{2}}^{\pi} (0 - \sin 2x)\,dx$

By substitution of $u = 2x$ and $du = 2dx$, the integral becomes
$\frac{1}{2}\int_{\pi}^{2\pi} -\sin u\,du = \frac{1}{2}\cos u\Big|_{\pi}^{2\pi} = \frac{1}{2}(1-(-1)) = \frac{1}{2}(2) = 1.$

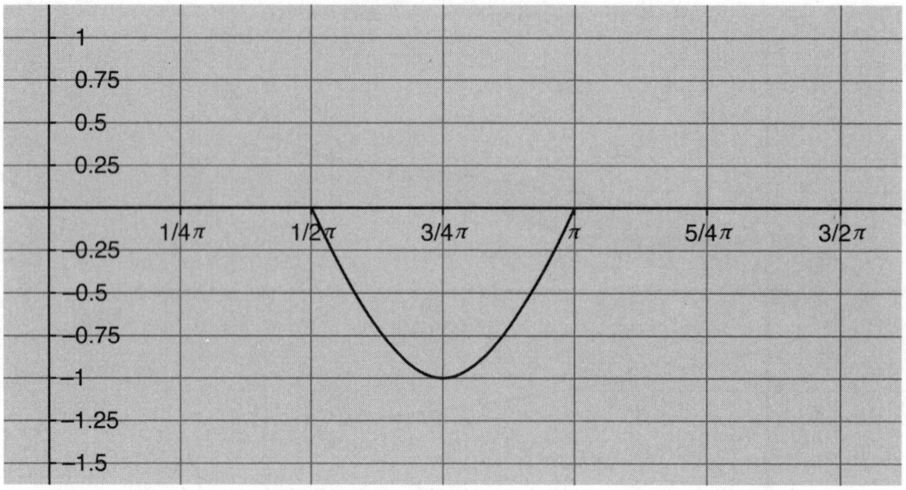

(*Calculus for AP*®, pages 477–486; EU 3.4; LO 3.4D; EK 3.4D1; MPAC 2,3,4)

4. ANSWER: (B) The side of the square is $s = \sin 2x$, and the area of each cross-sectional square is $A = s^2 = \sin^2 2x$. The volume is determined by $\int_0^{\frac{\pi}{2}} \sin^2 2x\,dx$. (*Calculus for AP*®, pages 518–522; EU 3.4; LO 3.4D; EK 3.4D2; MPAC 2,3,4)

5. ANSWER: (B) The area is given by $\int_0^2 f(x) - g(x)\,dx = \int_0^2 f(x)\,dx - \int_0^2 g(x)\,dx$. The area under $f(x)$ is determined geometrically, adding the areas of the rectangle and the quarter circle, to get $(2)(3) + \frac{\pi}{4}(2^2) = 6 + \pi$. The area under $g(x)$ is found by evaluating the integral $\int_0^2 \cos\frac{\pi x}{4}\,dx$. Using the method of substitution where $u = \frac{\pi}{4}x$ and $du = \frac{\pi}{4}dx$, the integral becomes
$\frac{4}{\pi}\int_0^{\frac{\pi}{2}} \cos u\,dx = \frac{4}{\pi}\sin u\Big|_0^{\frac{\pi}{2}} = \frac{4}{\pi}(1-0) = \frac{4}{\pi}$. Finally,
$\int_0^2 f(x) - g(x)\,dx = 6 + \pi - \frac{4}{\pi}$. (*Calculus for AP*®, pages 477–486; EU 3.4; LO 3.4D; EK 3.4D1; MPAC 2,3,4)

6. ANSWER: (C) It follows from Question 5 that the area bounded by $f(x)$ and the line $y = 3$ is equal to π. Setting the integral for the area under $h(x) = k\cos\left(\frac{\pi}{4}x\right)$ in the interval $0 \le x \le 2$ to π, solve for k.

   $\int_0^2 k\cos\left(\frac{\pi}{4}x\right)dx = \pi$ and making the substitutions, as in Problem 5,

   $\frac{4}{\pi}\int_0^{\frac{\pi}{2}} k\cos u\, du = \pi$

   $\frac{4}{\pi}\sin u\Big|_0^{\frac{\pi}{2}} = \frac{4k}{\pi}(1-0) = \pi$

   Solving for k, $k = \frac{\pi^2}{4}$. (*Calculus for AP*®, pages 477–486; EU 3.4; LO 3.4D; EK 3.4D1; MPAC 2,3,4)

7. ANSWER: (C) The area between the functions $R(t)$ and $L(t)$ defines the total change in volume over the first 10 minutes. Since the initial volume is unknown, nothing more can be stated about the total volume at $t = 10$ minutes. (*Calculus for AP*®, page 496; EU 3.4; LO 3.4A; EK 3.4A1; MPAC 2,3,4)

8. ANSWER: (D) Using the calculator, the expenditures are maximized at $t \approx 4.077$ years. Thus, $P(t)_{\text{ave}}$, the average annual profit, is $\frac{1}{4.077-0}\int_0^{4.077}\left[R(t)-E(t)\right]dt \approx \frac{\$434{,}660.60}{4.077} \approx \$106{,}613$. (*Calculus for AP*®, pages 490–494; EU 3.4; LO 3.4A; EK 3.4A2; MPAC 2,3)

9. ANSWER: (C) Case I: For rotation about the line $y = 0$ (the x-axis), the radius is $r = y = \ln x$. This is a volume by disks, as the inner radius is 0.

   $$V_{y-0} = \pi\int_1^e (\ln x)^2\,dx \approx 0.718\pi \approx 2.257$$

   Case II: For rotation about the line $y = 1$, the inner radius is $r_i = 1 - y = 1 - \ln x$. This is a volume by washers, where the outer radius is $r_0 = 1$.

   $$V_{y=0} = \pi\int_1^e \left[1^2 - (1-\ln x)^2\right]dx \approx 1.282\pi \approx 4.027$$

   Case III: For rotation about the line $y = e$, the inner radius is $r_i = e - y = e - \ln x$. This is a volume by washers, where the outer radius is $r_0 = e$.

   $$V_{y=0} = \pi\int_1^e \left[e^2 - (e-\ln x)^2\right]dx \approx 4.718\pi \approx 14.823$$

   Therefore, the order from smallest to largest is I < II < III.

   The problem can also be done by inspection.

Looking at Case I versus Case II first: $V_{\text{II}} > V_{\text{I}}$ because the shape is fuller at the outside radius.

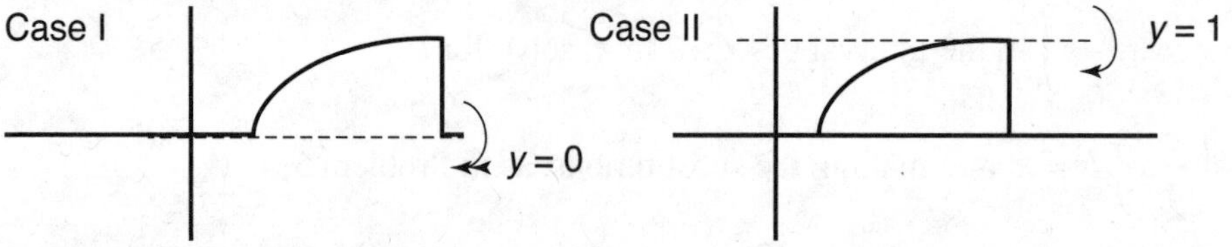

Looking at Case III versus Case II: $V_{\text{III}} > V_{\text{II}}$ with the outside radius in Case III more than twice as large as that in Case II.

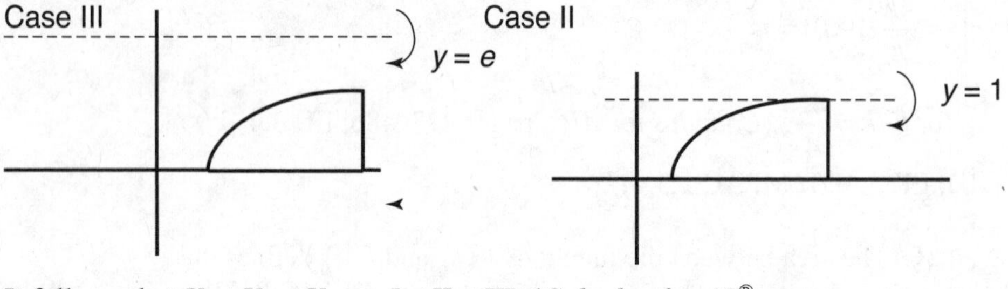

It follows that $V_{\text{I}} < V_{\text{II}} < V_{\text{III}}$, or I < II < III. (*Calculus for AP*®, pages 522–528; EU 3.4; LO 3.4D; EK 3.4D2; MPAC 2,3,4)

10. ANSWER: (D) The points of intersection are (±1.041, 2.916). The area of each cross section is $2(4 - x^2 - \tan^2 x)$. The volume is then

$$\int_{-1.041}^{1.041} 2\left(4 - x^2 - \tan^2 x\right) dx = 2\int_{0}^{1.041} 2\left(4 - x^2 - \tan^2 x\right) dx \approx 12.486.$$

(*Calculus for AP*®, pages 518–522; EU 3.4; LO 3.4D; EK 3.4D2; MPAC 2,3)

11. ANSWER: (C) The x-coordinates of the points of intersection are $x =$ −0.3103, 0.5051, and 1. The area bounded by the curves is given by

$$\int_{-.3103}^{.5051} \left[f(x) - g(x)\right] dx + \int_{.5051}^{1} \left[g(x) - f(x)\right] dx \approx 0.2029 + 0.0728 = 0.2757 \approx 0.276.$$

(*Calculus for AP*®, pages 477–486; EU 3.4; LO 3.4D; EK 3.4D1; MPAC 2,3,4)

12. ANSWER: (A) Change in position on $0 \le t \le \frac{\pi}{2}$ is given by

$\int_{0}^{\frac{\pi}{2}} e^t \sin\left(e^t\right) dt \approx 0.442$. (*Calculus for AP*®, pages 508–511; EU 3.4; LO 3.4E; EK 3.4E1; MPAC 2,3)

13. ANSWER: (D) Distance $= \int_{t_1}^{t_2} |v(t)|\, dt = \int_{0}^{\frac{\pi}{2}} \left|e^t \sin(e^t)\right| dt \approx 2.638.$

(*Calculus for AP*®, pages 508–511; EU 3.4; LO 3.4E; EK 3.4E1; MPAC 2,3)

14. ANSWER: (B) The particle moves to the right when $v(t) > 0$, which is on the interval $0 < t < 1.1447$. Thus
$s(1.1447) \approx -1 + \int_0^{1.1447} e^t \sin(e^t)\,dt = -1 + 1.540 = 0.540.$
(*Calculus for AP*®, pages 508–511; EU 3.4; LO 3.4E; EK 3.4E1; MPAC 2,3)

15. ANSWER: (C) The x-coordinates of the points of intersection are $x = \frac{1}{2}$ and 2. The radius for rotation is $r = 2 + y$. Therefore, $r_o = 1 + 3x - x^2 + 2 = 3 + 3x - x^2$ and $r_i = x^2 - 2x + 3 + 2 = x^2 - 2x + 5$.
The volume is found by the washer method where $V = \pi \int_a^b \left(r_0^2 - r_i^2\right)dx$.
Thus, the volume is given by $V = \pi \int_{\frac{1}{2}}^{2} \left[\left(3 + 3x - x^2\right)^2 - \left(x^2 - 2x + 5\right)^2\right]dx$.
(*Calculus for AP*®, pages 525–528; EU 3.4; LO 3.4D; EK 3.4D2; MPAC 2,3)

FREE-RESPONSE QUESTION

	Solution	Possible points
(a)	**Point of intersection:** $e^x + 1 = 4 \Rightarrow x = \ln 3 \approx 1.099$ $A = \int_0^{1.099}\left[4 - \left(e^x + 1\right)\right]dx \approx 1.296$	1: {Limits and constant in all parts 2: {1: integrand; 1: answer
(b)	$\int_0^h 4 - \left(e^x + 1\right)dx \approx 0.648$ $\left(3x - e^x\right)\Big\vert_0^h = 3h - e^h - (0 - 1)$ $= 3h - e^h + 1 \approx 0.648$ $h \approx 0.361$	2: {1: antiderivative; 1: answer
(c)	$V = \pi \int_0^{1.099}\left[4 - \left(e^x + 1\right)\right]^2 dx \approx 1.888\pi$, or 5.930	2: {1: integrand; 1: answer
(d)	$V = \pi \int_0^{1.099}\left\{\left[k - \left(e^x + 1\right)\right]^2 - (k - 4)^2\right\}dx = 11.86$	2: {0/2 if not difference of two squares; 1/2 $f^2 - g^2$; 1/2 if reversal

(a) (*Calculus for AP*®, pages 477–486; EU 3.4; LO 3.4D; EK 3.4D1; MPAC 2,3,4)
(b) (*Calculus for AP*®, pages 477–486; EU 3.4; LO 3.4D; EK 3.4D1; MPAC 2,3,4)
(c) (*Calculus for AP*®, pages 522–525; EU 3.4; LO 3.4D; EK 3.4D2; MPAC 2,3,4)
(d) (*Calculus for AP*®, pages 525–528; EU 3.4; LO 3.4D; EK 3.4D2; MPAC 2,4)

7

ADVANCED INTEGRATION TECHNIQUES

(The material in this chapter is tested only on the BC exam.)

There are many ways to integrate beyond the typical "recognize the integral." You can simplify, use the Log or Power Rule, or do a change of variables. This chapter will increase the number of tools you have to solve integration problems.

Objectives

- Be able to integrate by parts.
- Be able to integrate by using simple partial fractions (only nonrepeating linear factors).
- Be able to work with improper integrals.

BASIC INTEGRATION RULES, TECHNIQUES

(*Calculus for AP*®, pages 580–583)

Success at integration comes from practicing enough problems so that you can recognize which technique to use. For example, $\frac{3}{x^2+9}$, $\frac{3x}{x^2+9}$, and $\frac{3x^2}{x^2+9}$, are similar looking but require different techniques to solve. Generally, try the following:

- First try to integrate using one of the following rules: Power Rule, a trig or inverse trig rule, General Power Rule, or Log Rule.

- If that doesn't work, try to simplify (by factoring, using a trig identity, or performing an algebraic technique that will change the form to one you can integrate).
- Then, try a change of variable (u-substitution).

Thus, you have to memorize the basic integration rules (these should be in your own notes but are also listed in *Calculus for AP®* on page 543), as well as know the strategies of integration (see *Calculus for AP®* on pages 580–583) that will allow you to fit an integrand to one of the basic rules. The basic rules of simplifying include

- multiplying the parts of the problem [such as $x(x^2 - 3)$] together;
- using simple trigonometric identities (e.g., know the $\int \tan x\,dx$ rule rather than having to use the quotient rule for $\int \frac{\sin x}{\cos x}dx$);
- changing a root to a fractional exponent;
- multiplying and dividing by a convenient form of the number 1 such as a constant or a conjugate;
- factoring and dividing out common factors;
- separating an absolute value problem using the correct intervals;
- expanding [e.g., $(e^x+1)^2 = e^{2x} + 2e^x + 1$];
- separating the numerator $\left(\text{e.g., } \frac{1+x}{x^2+1} = \frac{1}{x^2+1} + \frac{x}{x^2+1}\right)$ and applying the appropriate integral rules to each (but remember, you *cannot* separate the denominator);
- completing the square (generally to get the integrand to match an inverse trig form);
- dividing the rational function if the numerator's degree is ≥ the denominator's degree (this is called an improper rational function); and
- adding and subtracting terms in the numerator (to get the form of a u'/u^n), then separating the fraction $\left(\text{e.g., } \frac{2x}{x^2+2x+1} = \frac{2x+2-2}{x^2+2x+1} = \frac{2x+2}{x^2+2x+1} - \frac{2}{(x+1)^2}\right)$ and applying the appropriate integral rules to each part.

Study the following problems:

a. $\int \frac{3}{x^2+9}dx$

b. $\int \frac{3x}{x^2+9}dx$

c. $\int \frac{3x^2}{x^2+9}dx$

a. This is in the form of an inverse trig problem where the denominator is $a^2 + x^2$ and the numerator is just a constant.
b. This is of the form u'/u where the Log Rule needs to be applied.
c. This is one where you will want to divide first because the degree of the numerator is greater than or equal to the degree of the denominator.

INTEGRATION BY PARTS

(*Calculus for AP*®, pages 544–548)

Integration by parts is a technique that can be applied to a wide variety of functions. It is particularly useful when an integrand involves products of algebraic and transcendental functions, such as $x \ln x$ or $e^x \cos x$.

The rule is $udv = uv - \int v\,du$.

It is based on the formula for the derivative of a product:

$$\frac{d}{dx}(uv) = uv' + vu'$$

and therefore

$$\int \frac{d}{dx}(uv) = uv = \int uv'dx + \int vu'dx = \int udv + \int vdu$$

(because $v'dx = dv$ and $u'dx = du$).

Thus, $uv = \int udv + \int vdu$, and solving for $\int udv$ means that $\int udv = uv - \int vdu$. In other words, the integral $\left(\int udv\right)$ of a function (u) times the derivative of a function (dv) is equal to the product of u and v (the integral of dv) minus the integral of v with respect to u. The key to success here is to let the dv part be the most complicated factor of the problem that fits a basic integration rule and then let u be the factor whose derivative is simpler than u itself.

This is actually a relatively easy technique once you memorize the rule itself and practice the procedure of choosing the u and the dv. There are times you will make a selection for u and dv and it won't work, so you will have to restart the problem with an alternate choice of u and dv.

For example, $\int xe^x dx$. Let e^x be the dv part because it is the "most complicated factor of the problem that fits a basic integration rule" and let x be the u because the derivative is "simpler than itself."

Thus, $u = x$ and $dv = e^x dx$; therefore, $du = 1\ dx$ and $v = \int dv = \int e^x dx = e^x$.

Following the form of the solution $\int udv = uv - \int vdu$,

$\int xe^x dx = xe^x - \int e^x \cdot 1dx = xe^x - e^x + C$ (which is uv) (which is $\int vdu$).

Let's look at one more: $\int x^2 \ln x dx$. First ask yourself which part is the most complicated factor of the problem that fits a basic integration rule. In this case, we don't yet know how to integrate $\ln x$, even though it is the more complicated factor; therefore, we must choose x^2 as dv and $u = \ln x$ which does have a simpler derivative than itself.

Thus,

$$u = \ln x \text{ and } dv = \int x^2 dx = \frac{x^3}{3}.$$

And therefore $du = \frac{1}{x}dx$ and $v = \int x^2 dx = \frac{x^3}{3}$.

Following the form of the solution $\int u dv = uv - \int v du$,

$$\int x^2 \ln x dx = \ln x\left(\frac{x^3}{3}\right) - \int \frac{x^3}{3}\left(\frac{1}{x}dx\right).$$

Sometimes, the integrand is a hidden product, where one part can be seen as being multiplied by 1 or having a power that can be separated (like $\sec^3 x$ that can be written as $\sec^2 x$ times $\sec x$). (See Example 5 in *Calculus for AP®* on page 548.)

There are also problems where you must have a repeated use of the technique. After the first attempt, if the integral part of your original answer is "simpler" than the original problem but a product still exists, try to repeat the procedure of integration by parts. When you use it a second time, the substitutions must follow the same pattern as the first use. (See Examples 3 and 4 in *Calculus for AP®* on page 546 for a sequencing of this process.)

AP® Tips

- The tabular method is not a required technique but may facilitate your use of the integration by parts method.
- Trigonometric integrals and trigonometric substitution are not part of the AP® curriculum.
- Integration by tables is not on the AP® exam.

PARTIAL FRACTIONS

(*Calculus for AP®*, pages 569–572)

The method of partial fractions allows you to "separate" the denominator by using a valid algebraic method to let you decompose, or break down, a rational function into two or more simpler rational functions.

For example, $\frac{1}{x^2 - 5x + 6} = \frac{1}{x-3} - \frac{1}{x-2}$. You can test this by subtracting the two rational functions on the right side of the equation. If you use the technique of $\frac{a}{b} \pm \frac{c}{d} = \frac{ad \pm bc}{bd}$, you will get

$$\frac{(x-2)-(x-3)}{(x-3)(x-2)} = \frac{x-2-x+3}{x^2-5x+6} = \frac{1}{x^2-5x+6}.$$

AP® is a trademark registered by the College Board, which is not affiliated with, and does not endorse, this product.

As you approach an integration problem that involves a rational function, again go through the process of looking for a simple rule or a basic algebraic technique that will allow you to solve the problem (like the Log Rule, u'/u). If none of the other techniques fit the problem, then try decomposing the rational function.

The following are the steps to the method of partial fractions:

1. Divide the rational function if it is improper and separate the integral; generally one part will be done by a previous method and a second part may need to be done by the partial fractions technique.
2. Factor the denominator into its linear factors (you will see only this basic technique on the AP® exam).
3. Set up an equation where the rational function is equal to the sum of two rational functions whose numerators are unknown constants. (*Note:* Only the use of nonrepeating linear factors will be on the AP® exam): $\frac{1}{x^2-5x+6}=\frac{A}{x-3}-\frac{B}{x-2}$.
4. Multiply both sides of the equation by the factors $(x-3)(x-2)$ and get $1=A(x-2)+B(x-3)=Ax-2A+Bx-3B$, therefore $1=x(A+B)+(-2A-3B)$.
5. Solve for A and B.

There are two ways to solve for A and B.

- The first entails organizing like terms: $x(A+B)+(-2A-3B)$, which is equal to $0x+1$. Therefore, $A+B=0$ and $-2A-3B=1$ (equating like terms of the two equations). Setting up a system of two equations and two unknowns,

$$\begin{array}{rcrcr} 2A & + & 2B & = & 0 \\ -2A & - & 3B & = & 1 \\ \hline & & -B & = & 1 \\ & & \text{or } B & = & -1 \end{array}$$

  Solving for A, $A=1$; therefore,

  $\int\frac{1}{x^2-5x+6}dx=\int\frac{1}{x-3}dx-\int\frac{1}{x-2}dx$ and the two integrals on the right side of the equation can be integrated using the Log Rule.
- The second method of solving $1=A(x-2)+B(x-3)$ is based on the premise that this is a true equation for all x; thus you can substitute any convenient value for x to obtain equations in A and B. The most convenient values would be those x's which make one of the factors 0. So let $x=2$ and the equation becomes $1=-B$ or $B=-1$. Let $x=3$ and the equation becomes $1=1A$ or $A=1$. Then proceed as above.

Remember to use the technique of partial fractions if

- no other previous technique works and
- the denominator factors nicely.

IMPROPER INTEGRALS

(*Calculus for AP®*, pages 586–594)

Improper integrals are integrals that possess either the property that one or both of the limits of integration are infinite or the property that the interval is not continuous (it has a finite or infinite number of discontinuities in the interval).

Let's look at the improper integrals with infinite limits of integration. They will appear as $\int_a^{\infty} f(x)\,dx = \lim\limits_{b\to\infty} \int_a^{\infty} f(x)\,dx$ or $\int_{-\infty}^{b} f(x)\,dx = \lim\limits_{a\to-\infty} \int_a^{b} f(x)\,dx$ or $\int_{-\infty}^{\infty} f(x)\,dx = \int_{-\infty}^{c} f(x)\,dx + \int_{c}^{\infty} f(x)\,dx$, and then apply the first two rules.

They will converge if, when you take the limit, it exists. If the limit does not exist due to unbounded behavior or oscillation, then the integral diverges. In other words, this enables us potentially to find the area of an unbounded region (in a way, it is similar to finding the sum of an infinite sequence). Because of the use of limits, be sure to review all of your rules on limits, including how to find them (direct substitution, etc.) as well as your understanding of the principle that as $x \to \infty$ in a problem such as $y = 1/x$, then y approaches 0 because as the denominator gets larger, $1/x$ gets smaller and approaches 0. Also review the concept of right- and left-handed limits.

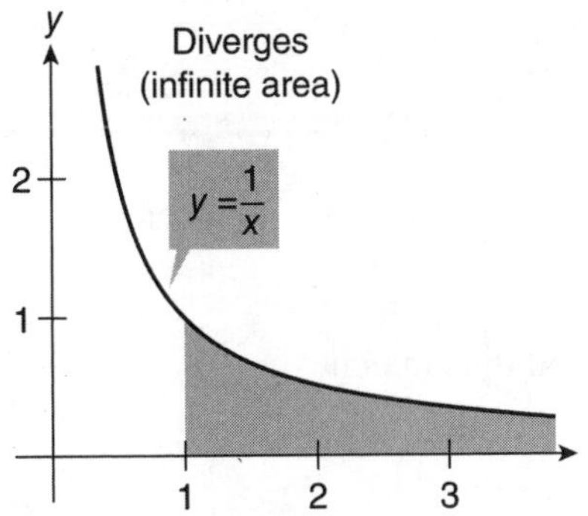

Figure 1

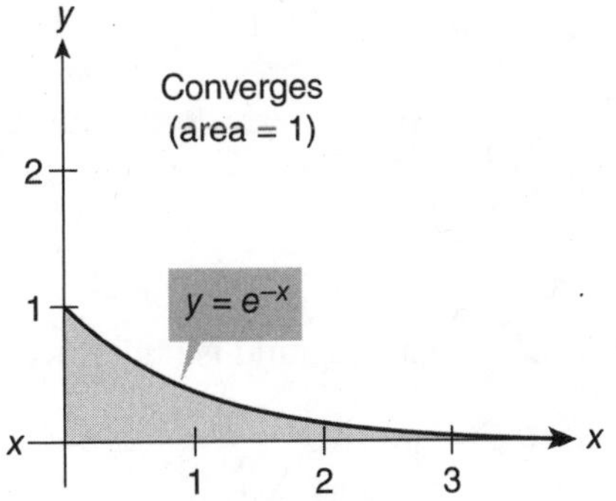

Figure 2

Let's determine the area under the curve $y = 1/x$ from 1 to infinity (see Figure 1).

$$\int_1^{\infty} \frac{1}{x}dx = \lim_{b\to\infty} \int_1^{b} \frac{1}{x}dx = \lim_{b\to\infty}[\ln x]_1^b = \lim_{b\to\infty}(\ln\, b - \ln\, 1) = \infty - 0 = \infty$$

Therefore, the unbounded region has an infinite area.

Let's look at the graph of $y = e^{-x}$ (Figure 2) and determine the area under this curve from 0 to ∞.

$$\int_0^{\infty} e^{-x}dx = \lim_{b\to\infty} \int_0^{b} e^{-x}dx = \lim_{b\to\infty}\left[-e^{-x}\right]_0^b = \lim_{b\to\infty}\left(-e^{-b} + e^{0}\right) = \lim_{b\to\infty}\left(\frac{-1}{e^b} + 1\right) = 0 + 1 = 1$$

Therefore, the area of this unbounded region is 1. Comparing the graphs, the areas look similar but have very different values.

This same process can work if both the upper and lower limits of integration are ∞. Integration by parts, L'Hôpital's Rule, or other integration techniques may be necessary to work through the problem.

Now we'll tackle improper integrals with infinite discontinuities, improper integrals that have one or more discontinuities at or between the limits of integration. They will appear as

$$\int_a^b f(x)\,dx = \lim_{c\to b^-} \int_a^c f(x)\,dx$$

if the function has an infinite discontinuity at b, we need to approach b from the left (b^-) or

$$\int_a^b f(x)\,dx = \lim_{c\to a^+} \int_c^b f(x)\,dx$$

if the function has an infinite discontinuity at a, we need to approach a from the right (a^+) or

$$\int_a^b f(x)\,dx = \int_a^c f(x)\,dx + \int_c^b f(x)\,dx$$

if there is an infinite discontinuity at some c in (a, b), we need to split the integral at c and apply one of the first two rules to each subsequent interval. Again, the improper integral converges if the limits exist.

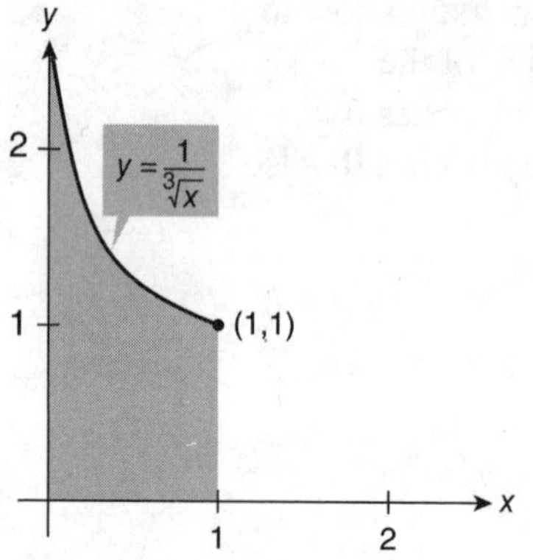

Let's evaluate $\int_0^1 \frac{1}{\sqrt[3]{x}}dx$. This integrand is undefined at 0 and thus matches our second case above. Therefore,

$$\int_0^1 \frac{1}{\sqrt[3]{x}}dx = \lim_{c\to 0^+} \int_c^1 \frac{1}{\sqrt[3]{x}}dx = \lim_{c\to 0^+}\left[\frac{x^{2/3}}{2/3}\right]_c^1 = \lim_{c\to 0^+}\frac{3}{2}\left(1^{2/3} - c^{2/3}\right) = \frac{3}{x}(1-0) = \frac{3}{2}.$$

The key components to solving improper integrals are the following:

1) *Recognition* that there is a part that has a limit of integration that is infinite or that there is an infinite discontinuity within the interval.
2) *Ability* to rewrite the integral in a form involving limits.
3) *Previous knowledge* and understanding about limits at infinity or infinite limits.

PAST AP® FREE-RESPONSE PROBLEMS COVERED BY THIS CHAPTER

2007 BC 4c
2008 BC 5c
2013 BC 5a

MULTIPLE-CHOICE QUESTIONS

A calculator may not be used for the following questions.

1. $9x\cos(3x+1)\,dx =$

   (A) $9x\cos(3x+1)+\sin(3x+1)+C$

   (B) $3x\sin(3x+1)-\cos(3x+1)+C$

   (C) $3\sin(3x+1)-\frac{1}{3}\cos(3x+1)+C$

   (D) $3x\sin(3x+1)+\cos(3x+1)+C$

2. Which of the following integral expressions represents the area of the region bounded by the graphs of $y=\frac{9}{x^2+x-20}$, $x=-3$, $x=2$, and the x-axis?

   (A) $\left|\int_{-3}^{2}\left(\frac{1}{x-4}+\frac{1}{x+5}\right)dx\right|$

   (B) $\left|\int_{-3}^{2}\left(\frac{1}{x-4}-\frac{1}{x+5}\right)dx\right|$

   (C) $\left|\int_{-3}^{2}\left(\frac{5}{x-4}+\frac{4}{x+5}\right)dx\right|$

   (D) $\left|\int_{-3}^{2}\left(\frac{1}{x+4}-\frac{1}{x-5}\right)dx\right|$

x	$g(x)$	$g'(x)$	$g''(x)$
0	1	−3	5
1	3	8	−2

3. Let g be a twice-differentiable function with the selected values of g and its derivatives shown in the table above. What is the value of $\int_0^1 2xg''(x)\,dx$?

   (A) 10
   (B) 12
   (C) 8
   (D) −4

4. Let $f(x)=\frac{k}{\sqrt{x}}$, where $x>0$ and k is some finite positive constant, as pictured at the right. Let $L=\int_0^1 f(x)\,dx$ and $M=\int_1^\infty f(x)\,dx$. Which one of the following statements is true?
(A) $L<M$
(B) $L=M$
(C) $L>M$
(D) No conclusion can be made about the relative values of L and M.

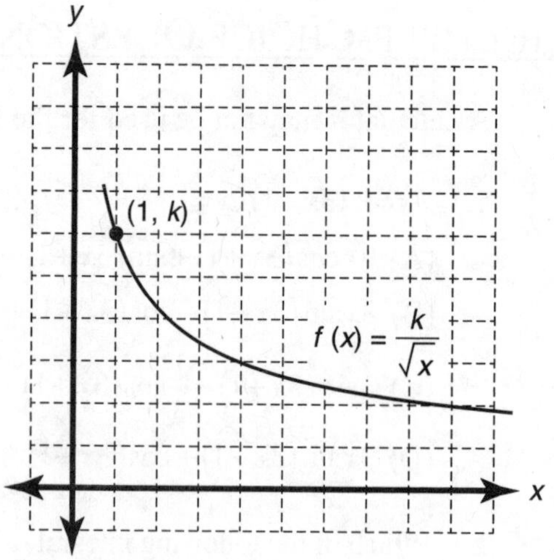

5. What is the area of the region in the first quadrant between the x-axis, y-axis, $y=\frac{1}{x^2}$, and $x=1$.
(A) 1
(B) 2
(C) 0
(D) ∞

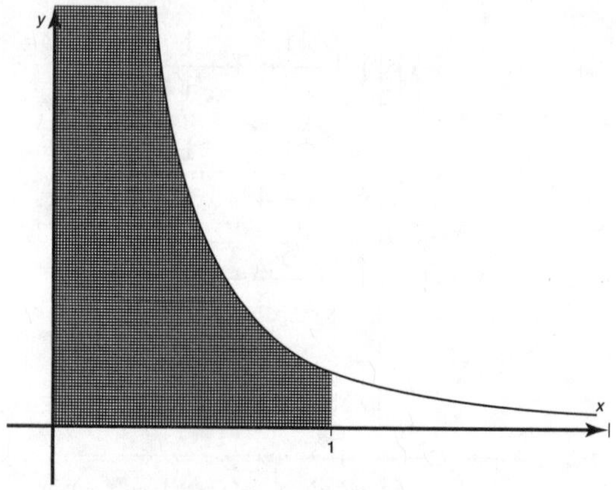

6. $\int \frac{4dx}{(x-3)(x+1)}=$
(A) $\ln|x-3|+\ln|x+1|+C$
(B) $\ln\left|\frac{x-3}{x+1}\right|+C$
(C) $4\ln|x-3|+\ln|x+1|+C$
(D) $4\ln\left|\frac{x-3}{x+1}\right|+C$

7. What is the area of the region in the first quadrant between the x-axis, the graph $y=\frac{1}{x^2}$, and $x=1$?
(A) 1
(B) 2
(C) 0
(D) ∞

8. Let $f(x)$ be a differentiable function with the properties that $f(1)=5$ and $\lim_{x\to\infty} f(x)=-8$.

$\int_1^\infty f'(x)\,dx=$
(A) -13
(B) -8
(C) 5
(D) ∞

9. The area of the region bounded by the graphs of $y = xe^x$, $x = 0$, $x = \ln 2$, and the x-axis is
(A) 2 ln (2) − 1.
(B) 2 ln (2).
(C) 2 ln (2) + 1.
(D) $[\ln (2)]^2 - 1$.

10. $\int \frac{2}{x^2+4x+3}dx =$
(A) $\ln|x+1| + \ln|x+3| + C$
(B) $(\ln|x+1|)(\ln|x+3|) + C$
(C) $\ln\left|\frac{x+1}{x+3}\right| + C$
(D) $\frac{\ln|x+1|}{\ln|x+3|} + C$

11. The area of the Quadrant I region under the function $f(x) = \frac{e^x}{1+e^{2x}}$ is
(A) $\frac{\pi}{4}$
(B) 1
(C) $\frac{\pi}{2}$
(D) divergent

12. $\int 2x^2e^{3x}dx =$
(A) $\frac{2}{3}x^2e^{3x} - \frac{4}{9}xe^{3x} + \frac{4}{27}e^{3x} + C$
(B) $2x^2e^{3x} + 4xe^{3x} + C$
(C) $6x^2e^{3x} - 36xe^{3x} + 108e^{3x} + C$
(D) $\frac{2}{3}x^2e^{3x} - \frac{4}{3}xe^{3x} + \frac{4}{3}e^{3x} + C$

13. $f(x)$ is a twice-differentiable function on $x \in [2, 6]$ with selected values given in the table below.

x	$f(x)$	$f'(x)$	$f''(x)$
2	8	1	−1
6	3	2	3

$\int_2^6 x \cdot f''(x)\,dx =$

(A) 15
(B) 20
(C) 26
(D) 34

14. Let R be the region bounded by the graphs of the function $f(x)=\dfrac{1}{\sqrt{x^2-1}}$, the x-axis, and the lines $x=p$ and $x=q$, where $1<p<q$. An expression for the volume of the solid generated by revolving R about the x-axis is

(A) $\int_p^q \frac{1}{x^2-1}dx$

(B) $\frac{\pi}{2}\int_p^q \left[\frac{1}{x-1}+\frac{1}{x+1}\right]dx$

(C) $\pi\int_p^q \left[\frac{1}{x-1}-\frac{1}{x+1}\right]dx$

(D) $\frac{\pi}{2}\int_p^q \left[\frac{1}{x-1}-\frac{1}{x+1}\right]dx$

15. The base of a certain solid is the region bounded by the coordinate axes, the line $x=16$, and the graph of $y=x^{-\frac{1}{4}}$. For this solid, each cross section perpendicular to the x-axis is a square whose side is across the base. The volume of this solid is

(A) 8

(B) $\frac{32}{3}$

(C) 8π

(D) divergent

FREE-RESPONSE QUESTION

A calculator may not be used for this question.

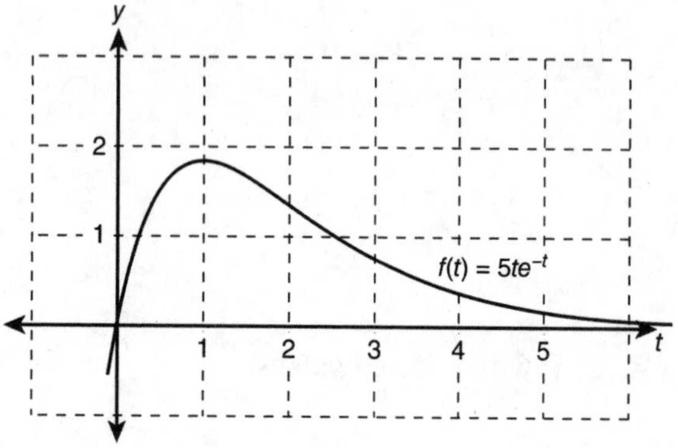

Let $F(x)=\int_0^x 5te^{-t}\,dt$ for $t\ge 0$ and $x\ge 0$.

(a) Find an expression for $F'(x)$ in terms of x only.

(b) Is the graph of $F(x)$ concave up or concave down at $x=2$? Explain your answer.

(c) Find an expression for $F(x)$, in terms of x only, that does not involve an integral.

(d) Using your answer to (c), find $\lim_{x\to\infty}F(x)$. Justify your answer.

(e) Using your answer to (d), explain what is meant by the expression $\lim_{x\to\infty}F(x)$.

Answers

MULTIPLE-CHOICE QUESTIONS

1. ANSWER: (D) Integrate by parts: Let $u = 9x$ and $dv = \cos(3x + 1)dx$.

   Then $du = 9dx$ and $v = \frac{1}{3}\sin(3x+1)$. Therefore,

   $$\int 9x\cos(3x+1)\,dx = 3x\sin(3x+1) - \int 3\sin(3x+1)dx$$
   $$= 3x\sin(3x+1) + \cos(3x+1) + C.$$

   (*Calculus for AP*®, pages 544–548; EU 3.3; LO 3.3B; EK 3.3B5; MPAC 2,3)

2. ANSWER: (B) Area $= \left|\int_{-3}^{2} \frac{9}{x^2+x-20}dx\right|$. Express the integrand using partial fractions.

   $$\frac{9}{x^2+x-20} = \frac{A}{x-4} + \frac{B}{x+5} \Rightarrow 9 = A(x+5) + B(x-4).$$

   Let $x = 4$:$9 = A(9) \Rightarrow A = 1$; Let $x = -5$:$9 = B(-9) \Rightarrow B = -1$.

   Thus, the area is $\left|\int_{-3}^{2}\left(\frac{1}{x-4} - \frac{1}{x+5}\right)dx\right|$.

   (*Calculus for AP*®, pages 569–572; EU 3.3,3.4; LO 3.3B,3.4D; EK 3.3B5,3.4D1; MPAC 2)

3. ANSWER: (B) This requires integrating by parts.

   $$\int_0^2 2xg''(x)\,dx = \left[2xg'(x)\right]_0^1 - \int_0^1 2g'(x)\,dx$$
   $$= \left[2xg'(x) - 2g(x)\right]_0^1$$
   $$= \left[(2(1)g'(1) - 2g(1)) - (2(0)g'(0) - 2g(0))\right]$$
   $$= \left[(2(1)(8) - 2(3)) - (2(0)(-3) - 2(1))\right] = 12.$$

   (*Calculus for AP*®, pages 544–548; EU 3.3; LO 3.3B(b); EK 3.3B5; MPAC 3,4)

4. ANSWER: (A) Both integrals are improper.

   $$L = \lim_{b\to 0^+}\int_b^1 kx^{\frac{1}{2}}dx = \lim_{b\to 0^+} 2kx^{\frac{1}{2}}dx\Big|_b^1$$
   $$= \lim_{b\to 0^+} 2k(1) - 2k\sqrt{b}$$
   $$= 2k - 0 = 2k.$$

$$M = \lim_{b\to\infty} \int_1^b kx^{\frac{1}{2}}dx = \lim_{b\to\infty} 2kx^{\frac{1}{2}}\Big|_1^b$$
$$= \lim_{b\to\infty} 2k\sqrt{b} - 2k(1)$$
$$= 2k(\infty) - 2k(1) = \infty.$$

Thus L is finite and M is infinite, so $L < M$.
(*Calculus for AP®*, pages 586–594; EU 3.2; LO 3.2D; EK 3.2D1, 3.2D2; MPAC 2,3,4)

5. ANSWER: (D) To determine the area of the region requires an improper integral due to one of the limits occurring at a discontinuity at $x = 0$

$$\int_0^1 \frac{1}{x^2}dx = \lim_{a\to 0^+} \int_a^1 \frac{1}{x^2}dx$$
$$= \lim_{a\to 0^+}\left[-\frac{1}{x}\right]_a^1$$
$$= \lim_{a\to 0^+} -\frac{1}{1} + \frac{1}{a}$$
$$= -1 + \infty \Rightarrow \infty$$

(*Calculus for AP®*, pages 586–594; EU 3.2; LO 3.2D; EK 3.2D2; MPAC 3,4)

6. ANSWER: (B) Use integration by partial fractions. Reexpress the integrand,

$$\frac{4}{(x-3)(x+1)} = \frac{A}{x-3} + \frac{B}{x+1}.$$

Clearing denominators, $A(x + 1) + B(x - 3) = 4$.
$x = 3$: $A(4) = 4 \Rightarrow A = 1$ $x = -1$: $B(-4) = 4 \Rightarrow B = -1$

$$\int \frac{4dx}{(x-3)(x+1)} = \int \left(\frac{1}{x-3} - \frac{1}{x+1}\right)dx$$
$$= \ln|x-3| - \ln|x+1| + C$$
$$= \ln\left|\frac{x-3}{x+1}\right| + C$$

(*Calculus for AP®*, pages 569–572; EU 3.3; LO 3.3B; EK 3.3B5; MPAC 2,3)

7. ANSWER: (A) To determine the area, if possible, of the region requires an improper integral due to one of the limits occurring at a discontinuity at $x = 0$.

$$\int_1^\infty \frac{1}{x^2}dx = \lim_{a\to\infty} \int_1^a \frac{1}{x^2}dx$$
$$= \lim_{a\to\infty}\left[-\frac{1}{x}\right]_1^a$$
$$= \lim_{a\to\infty} -\frac{1}{a} + \frac{1}{1}$$
$$= 0 + 1 = 1$$

(*Calculus for AP®*, pages 586–594; EU 3.2; LO 3.2D; EK 3.2D2; MPAC 3,4)

8. ANSWER: (A) This is an improper integral.
$\lim\limits_{b\to\infty}\int_1^b f'(x)\,dx = \lim\limits_{b\to\infty} f(x)\Big|_1^b = \lim\limits_{b\to\infty} f(b) - f(1) = -8-5=-13.$
(*Calculus for AP®*, pages 586–594; EU 3.2; LO 3.2D; EK 3.2D1,3.2D2; MPAC 2,3)

9. ANSWER: (A) Area = $\int_0^{\ln 2} xe^x\,dx$, so integrate by parts: Let $u = x$ and $dv =$ $e^x dx$.
Then $du = dx$ and $v = e^x$.
Therefore, $\int xe^x\,dx = xe^x - \int e^x\,dx = xe^x - e^x$.
Thus $\int_0^{\ln 2} xe^x\,dx = xe^x - e^x\Big|_0^{\ln 2} = (\ln 2\times 2 - 2) - (0-1) = 2\ln 2 - 1.$
(*Calculus for AP®*, pages 544–548; EU 3.3,3.4; LO 3.3B,3.4D; EK 3.3B5,3.4D1; MPAC 2,3)

10. ANSWER: (C) Use integration by partial fractions. Reexpress the integrand
$\frac{2}{x^2+4x+3} = \frac{A}{x+1} + \frac{B}{x+3}$
Clearing denominators: $2 = A(x+3) + B(x+1)$
$x=-3{:}\,2=-2\mathrm{B} \Rightarrow B - 1$
$x=-1{:}\,2=2A \Rightarrow A = 1$

$$\int\frac{2}{x^2+4x+3}dx = \int\left(\frac{1}{x+1} - \frac{1}{x+3}\right)dx$$
$$= \ln|x+1| - \ln|x+3| + C$$
$$= \ln\left|\frac{x+1}{x+3}\right| + C$$

(*Calculus for AP®*, pages 569–572; EU 3.3; LO 3.3B(a); EK 3.3B5; MPAC 3)

11. ANSWER: (A) Area $= \int_0^\infty \frac{e^x}{1+e^{2x}}dx = \int_1^\infty \frac{du}{1+u^2} = \tan^{-1}(u)\Big|_1^\infty$. Integrating by substitution, let $u = e^x \Rightarrow du = e^x dx$. Then
$\int_0^\infty \frac{e^x}{1+e^{2x}}dx = \int_1^\infty \frac{du}{1+u^2} = \tan^{-1}(u)\Big|_1^\infty.$
Recognizing the improper integral, this is
$\lim\limits_{k\to\infty}\tan^{-1}(k) - \tan^{-1}(1) = \frac{\pi}{2} - \frac{\pi}{4} = \frac{\pi}{4}.$

(*Calculus for AP®*, pages 543, 586–594; EU 3.2,3.4; LO 3.2D,3.4D; EK 3.2D1,3.2D2,3.4D1; MPAC 2,3)

12. ANSWER: (A) $\int 2x^2 e^{3x}dx$ = Integrate by parts: Let $u = 2x^2$ and $dv = e^{2x}dx$. The tabular method can be used.

+/−	u	dv
+	$2x^2$	e^{3x}
−	$4x$	$\frac{e^{3x}}{3}$
+	4	$\frac{e^{3x}}{9}$
−	0	$\frac{e^{3x}}{27}$

$$\int 2x^2 e^{3x}dx = \frac{2x^2e^{3x}}{3} - \frac{4e^{3x}}{9} + \frac{4e^{3x}}{27} + C$$

(*Calculus for AP*®, pages 544–548; EU 3.3; LO 3.3B(b); EK 3.3B5; MPAC 3)

13. ANSWER: (A) Integrate by parts using the formula $\int udv = uv - \int vdu$. Let $u = x$ and $dv = f''(x)dx$.

Thus $du = dx$ and $v = f'(x)$.

$$\int_2^6 x \cdot f''(x)dx$$

Then $= x \cdot f'(x)\big|_2^6 - \int_2^6 f'(x)dx$

$$= x \cdot f'(x)\big|_2^6 - f(x)\big|_2^6$$
$$= 6f'(6) - 2f'(2) - f(6) + f(2)$$
$$= 6\times 2 - 2\times 1 - 3 + 8 = 15.$$

(*Calculus for AP*®, pages 544–548; EU 3.3; LO 3.3B; EK 3.3B5; MPAC 2,3)

14. ANSWER: (D) Using disks, the volume is

$$\pi\int_p^q \frac{1}{x^2-1}dx = \pi\int_p^q \frac{1}{(x-1)(x+1)}dx.$$

The partial fraction decomposition for the integrand is

$\frac{1}{(x-1)(x+1)} = \frac{\frac{1}{2}}{x-1} - \frac{\frac{1}{2}}{x+1} = \frac{1}{2}\left[\frac{1}{x-1} + \frac{1}{x+1}\right]$. Thus the expression for the volume is $\frac{\pi}{2}\int_p^q\left[\frac{1}{x-1} - \frac{1}{x+1}\right]dx$.

(*Calculus for AP*®, pages 522–525, 569–572; EU 3.3,3.4; LO 3.3B,3.4D; EK 3.3B5,3.4D2; MPAC 2,3)

15. ANSWER: (A) Using cross sections and recognizing the improper integral,

$$v = \lim_{k\to 0^+} \int_k^{16} \left(x^{\frac{1}{4}}\right)^2 dx = \lim_{k\to 0} \int_k^{16} x^{\frac{1}{2}} dx = \lim_{k\to 0^+} 2x^{\frac{1}{2}}\Big|_k^{16} = \lim_{k\to 0^+} (8-k) = 8.$$

(*Calculus for AP*®, pages 518–522, 586–594; EU 3.2,3.4; LO 3.2D,3.4D; EK 3.2D1,3.2D2,3.4D2; MPAC 2,3)

FREE-RESPONSE QUESTION

	Solution	Possible points
(a)	By the Second Fundamental Theorem, $F'(x) = 5xe^{-x}$.	1: answer
(b)	Using the Product Rule, $F''(x) = \frac{d}{dx}\left[F'(x)\right] = 5x\cdot\left(-e^{-x}\right) + 5e^{-x} = 5e^{-x}(1-x)$ $F''(2) = 5e^{-2}(1-2) < 0$; therefore, the graph of $F(x)$ is concave down at $x = 2$.	2: { 1: $F''(x)$ 1: answer with reason
(c)	Integration by parts $u = 5t$ $\quad v = -e^{-t}$ $du = 5dt$ $\quad dv = e^{-t}\,dt$ $F(x) = \int_0^x 5te^{-t}dt = -5te^{-t}\Big\vert_0^x + \int_0^x 5e^{-t}dt$ $= -5te^{-t} - 5e^{-t}\Big\vert_0^x = \left(-5xe^{-x} - 5e^{-x}\right) - (0-5)$ $= -5e^{-x}(x+1) + 5$	3: { 1: parts setup 1: antiderivative 1: answer
(d)	$\lim_{x\to\infty}\left[-5e^{-x}(x+1)+5\right] = 5 + \lim_{x\to\infty}\frac{-5(x+1)}{e^x}$ Using L'Hôpital's Rule, this is equal to $5 + \lim_{x\to\infty}\frac{-5}{e^x} = 5 + 0 = 5.$	2: { 1: recognition of indeterminate form 1: answer
(e)	Since $F(x) = \int_0^x 5te^{-t}dt$ for $t \ge 0$ and $x \ge 0$. If $x \Rightarrow \infty$, then this becomes the improper integral $\lim_{x\to\infty}\int_0^x 5te^{-t}dt$, which will yield the area from $x = 0$ to $x = \infty$ between the graph of $f(t)$ and the horizontal axis. Based on the limit value in part (c), this area is 5.	1: answer

(a) (*Calculus for AP*®, pages 436–438; EU 3.3; LO 3.3A; EK 3.3A2; MPAC 1,2)
(b) (*Calculus for AP*®, pages 322–324; EU 2.2; LO 2.2A; EK 2.2A1; MPAC 2,3)
(c) (*Calculus for AP*®, pages 544–548; EU 3.3; LO 3.3B; EK 3.3B5; MPAC 2,3)
(d) (*Calculus for AP*®, pages 337–343; EU 1.1; LO 1.1C; EK 1.1C3; MPAC 2,3)
(e) (*Calculus for AP*®, pages 586–594; EU 3.2; LO 3.2D; EK 3.2D1,3.2D2; MPAC 2,3)

8

INFINITE SERIES

(The material in this chapter is tested only on the BC Exam.)

A series is defined as a sequence of partial sums. The convergence of a series is defined in terms of the limit of the sequence of partial sums.

Objectives

- Know how to identify types of series: geometric, harmonic, alternating, and *p*-series.
- Be able to determine convergence and divergence of series using various tests.
- Be able to use and analyze Taylor and Maclaurin series, including differentiation, antidifferentiation, and the formation of a new series from a known series.
- Understand and use intervals of convergence and error analysis.

SEQUENCES

(*Calculus for AP®*, pages 646–657)

A sequence is a function whose domain is the set of positive integers. It is common to represent sequences with subscript notation: $a_1, a_2, a_3, \ldots, a_n, \ldots$, which are called the terms of the sequence. A sequence is denoted by $\{a_n\}$. The subscript represents the position of the term (like 3, the third term) and the symbol { } represents a list.

A sequence can also be defined recursively where you must define a first term and then each subsequent term is dependent on the prior term. For example, $d_1 = 10$ and $d_{n+1} = d_n - 2$. The sequence would be $\{10, 8, 6, \ldots\}$.

Our main concern with sequences in this chapter is whether or not they converge, whether terms approach a limiting value such as the terms of the sequence, $\left\{\frac{1}{2^n}\right\}$, and where the terms $\frac{1}{2}, \frac{1}{4}, \frac{1}{8}, \frac{1}{16}, \ldots$ converge to 0.

To determine convergence, you can

- see if the sequence is bounded: $|a_n| \le M$; a sequence converges if it is bounded and monotonic,
- determine if it alternates; it could be unbounded,
- divide the numerator and denominator by the highest power and take its limit,
- use L'Hôpital's Rule when taking the limit, and
- apply the squeeze theorem.

When working with sequences, it is important to discover the pattern of the terms so that you can determine the formula for the nth term of the sequence. Without this general term, it is not possible to determine the convergence or divergence of a sequence from its first few terms. For example, $\frac{1}{2}, \frac{1}{4}, \frac{1}{8}, \ldots$ could actually lead to various general sequences dependent on the fourth term:

$$\frac{1}{2}, \frac{1}{4}, \frac{1}{8}, \frac{1}{16}, \ldots \frac{1}{2^n}$$

but

$$\frac{1}{2}, \frac{1}{4}, \frac{1}{8}, \frac{1}{15}, \ldots \frac{6}{(n+1)(n^2-n+6)}$$

or

$$\frac{1}{2}, \frac{1}{4}, \frac{1}{8}, 0, \ldots \frac{-n(n+1)(n-4)}{6(n^2+3n-2)}$$

Here are some ideas to help determine the nth term:

- For odd integers: use $2n-1$ or $2n+1$, depending on the initial value of n
- For even integers: $2n$
- For alternating series: $(-1)n$
- For other patterns:

$$-1,-1,+1,+1,-1,-1: \quad (-1)^{\frac{n(n+1)}{2}}$$

$$1,2,6,24,120: n!$$

$$2(1\cdot 2\cdot 3\cdot 4\cdot\cdots\cdot(n-2)(n-1)(n): 2n!$$

$$1\cdot 2\cdot 3\cdot 4\cdot\cdots\cdot(2n-2)(2n-1)(2n):(2n)!$$

SERIES AND CONVERGENCE

(*Calculus for AP®*, pages 660–710)

If $\{a_n\}$ is an infinite sequence, then $\sum_{n=1}^{\infty} a_n = a_1 + a_2 + \cdots + a_n + \cdots$ is an infinite series (or series).

In some cases, the initial index n will be equal to zero (or any other integer) rather than 1, depending on the situation/context.

We want to determine if a series converges, and, if it does, we want to find the sum or value of the series. If the limit of the sequence of partial sums $\{S_n\}$ converges, then the series converges; if the limit of the sequence of partial sums $\{S_n\}$ diverges, then the series diverges. The limit S is called the sum of the series.

Sequence of partial sums:

$$S_1 = a_1$$
$$S_2 = a_1 + a_2$$
$$S_3 = a_1 + a_2 + a_3$$
$$\vdots$$
$$S_n = a_1 + a_2 + a_3 + \cdots + a_n$$

(i.e., the nth term of the sequence of partial sums is the sum of the first n terms. S_3 is the sum of the first three terms of the sequence.)

SERIES

There are many different kinds of series.

TELESCOPING SERIES

(*Calculus for AP®*, page 666)

The form of a telescoping series is $(b_1 - b_2) + (b_2 - b_3) + \cdots + (b_n - b_{n+1}) + \cdots$ where intermediate terms cancel out and the nth partial sum S_n is $b_1 - b_{n+1}$. If the series is to converge to S, then $S = b_1 - \lim_{n\to\infty} b_{n+1}$ as long as b_n approaches a finite number as $n \to \infty$.

GEOMETRIC SERIES

(*Calculus for AP®*, pages 662–666)

In a geometric series of the form ar^n, its sum equals $a + ar + ar^2 + \cdots + ar^n + \cdots,\ a \neq 0$ where the ratio is r. If $|r| \geq 1$, then the series diverges (it would not be bounded); but if $0 < |r| < 1$, then the series converges to the sum: $\frac{a}{1-r} = \sum_{n=0}^{\infty} ar^n$. An interesting application of a geometric series is to use it to represent a repeating decimal, such as $0.\overline{08} = \frac{8}{10^2} + \frac{8}{10^4} + \frac{8}{10^6} + \cdots$ where

$r = \frac{1}{100}$ and thus the sum is $\frac{a}{1-r} = \frac{8/10^2}{1-(1/100)} = \frac{8}{99}$, which turns out if you divide 8 by 99 to be the rational number that is equivalent to $0.\overline{08}$.

p-SERIES

(*Calculus for AP*®, pages 677–678)

The form of a *p*-series is $\sum_{n=1}^{\infty} \frac{1}{n^p} = \frac{1}{1^p} + \frac{1}{2^p} + \frac{1}{3^p} + \cdots$ where p is a positive constant.

If $p = 1$, it is a harmonic series: $\sum_{n=1}^{\infty} \frac{1}{n} = \frac{1}{1} + \frac{1}{2} + \frac{1}{3} + \cdots$

A *p*-series converges if $p > 1$ and diverges if $0 < p \leq 1$.

ALTERNATING SERIES

(*Calculus for AP*®, pages 692–695)

An alternating series is one whose terms alternate in signs, like the geometric series $\sum_{n=0}^{\infty} \left(-\frac{1}{2}\right)^n$ where $r = -1/2$. An alternating series either has its odd terms negative or its even terms negative. The alternating series converges if two conditions are met: (1) $\lim_{n\to\infty} a_n = 0$ and (2) $a_{n+1} \leq a_n$ for all n (in other words, the subsequent term is less than or equal to the previous term). An example where the test does not work is $\sum_{n=1}^{\infty} \frac{(-1)^{n+1}(n+1)}{n} = \frac{2}{1} - \frac{3}{2} + \frac{4}{3} - \frac{5}{4} + \frac{6}{5} - \cdots$, which satisfies the second condition because $a_{n+1} \leq a_n$, but because it fails the first condition, you cannot apply the Alternating Series Test and therefore you have to use a different test.

Alternating series remainder: For a convergent alternating series, the sum S of the series can be approximated by the partial sum S_N but there is an error involved in using just n terms as opposed to using the entire series. That error is given by the remainder $|R_n| = |S - S_N|$. If a convergent alternating series satisfies the condition $a_{n+1} \leq a_n$ (remember that it can be determined to be convergent by something other than the Alternating Series Test, where this must be a condition), then the absolute value of the remainder R_N is less than or equal to the first term neglected. In other words, $|S - S_N| = |R_N| \leq a_{N+1}$. Another way to say this is that if you want to approximate the sum S of the series by the sum S_6 of the first six terms, then the remainder would be $|R_6|$, which has to be less than a_7 and thus the sum S would lie between $S_6 - a_7$ and $S_6 + a_7$.

TESTS FOR CONVERGENCE

(*Calculus for AP*®, pages 660–710)

The most difficult task in tests for convergence is choosing the correct test to use. If you can identify the type of series (such as telescoping, geometric, *p*-series, or alternating series), then you have very specific rules for determining convergence or divergence. However, other series will require you to match their form to an appropriate test.

THE *n*TH-TERM TEST FOR DIVERGENCE

(*Calculus for AP*®, page 667)

If $\sum_{n=0}^{\infty} a_n$ converges, then $\lim_{n\to\infty} a_n = 0$.

The contrapositive of the above statement is the *n*th-Term Test for Divergence, which says that if c then $\sum_{n=0}^{\infty} a_n$ diverges.

The first part just lets you know that if the series converges, the limit of the *n*th term must be 0. What is most important here is the *n*th-Term Test for Divergence, which allows you to quickly determine if a series diverges by looking at the limit of the *n*th term; if that limit does not go to zero, then the series diverges and you are done.

THE INTEGRAL TEST

(*Calculus for AP*®, pages 675–678)

If f is positive, continuous, and decreasing for $x \geq 1$ and $a_n = f(n)$, then $\sum_{n=0}^{\infty} a_n$ and $\int_1^{\infty} f(x)\,dx$; either both converge or both diverge. To use this test, be sure to apply the integration techniques for improper integrals.

An example of a problem where this might be used is $\sum_{n=2}^{\infty} \frac{1}{n(\ln n)}$. If the terms were larger than a divergent harmonic series, then you might expect this to diverge, but the terms are smaller, so you must reconsider. To see if it matches the conditions for the Integral Test, see if the function is positive and continuous; use its derivative to determine whether it is decreasing. It is, so integrate it; since the limit goes to infinity, the series diverges by the Integral Test. You may find that you will try one test and the conditions don't match, so you will have to try another test. Note that $\int_1^{\infty} f(x)\,dx$ and $\sum_{n=0}^{\infty} a_n$ don't necessarily converge to the same sum if they both converge.

DIRECT COMPARISON TEST

(*Calculus for AP*®, pages 685–688)

Given two sequences, if $0 < a_n \le b_n$ for all n, then

- if $\sum_{n=1}^{\infty} b_n$ converges, $\sum_{n=1}^{\infty} a_n$ converges. Since the larger-termed ($b_n > a_n$) series converged, the smaller-termed series must converge.
- if $\sum_{n=0}^{\infty} a_n$ diverges, then $\sum_{n=1}^{\infty} b_n$ diverges. Since the smaller-termed series diverged, the larger-termed series must diverge.

This test allows you to compare a series with complicated terms to a series which is simpler and whose convergence or divergence is known. For example, $\sum_{n=1}^{\infty} \frac{1}{2+3^n}$ can be compared with the convergent geometric series $\sum_{n=1}^{\infty} \frac{1}{3^n}$ (which might look like a p-series but it is not because the base in a p-series changes, not the exponent). Because each term in $\frac{1}{3^n}$ is larger than its comparable term in $\frac{1}{2+3^n}$ and the geometric series is convergent, $\sum_{n=1}^{\infty} \frac{1}{2+3^n}$ must also be convergent by the Direct Comparison Test.

Now let's take a look at another example: Determine whether $\sum_{n=1}^{\infty} \frac{1}{2+\sqrt{n}}$ converges or diverges. If you try to compare it with the divergent p-series $\sum_{n=1}^{\infty} \frac{1}{n^{1/2}}$, (this is divergent because $p < 1$), each of the terms must be smaller than the original problem, but when $n = 2$, for example, $\frac{1}{2+\sqrt{2}} < \frac{1}{2^{1/2}}$, and therefore it does not meet the requirements for divergence. Thus, you would have to look for another series to compare it to. Try the divergent harmonic series $\sum_{n=1}^{\infty} \frac{1}{n}$ (it is divergent because $p = 1$). In this case, each of the terms of the divergent series is smaller than the original problem's comparable terms and thus the Direct Comparison Test works. There are times when you can eliminate a finite number of terms of a series first to set yourself up to do the Direct Comparison Test.

LIMIT COMPARISON TEST

(*Calculus for AP*®, pages 688–689)

In this test, both a_n and b_n must be > 0 (positive) and the $\lim_{n\to\infty} \frac{a_n}{b_n} = L$, where L is finite and positive. Then the two series $\sum a_n$ and $\sum b_n$ either both converge or both diverge. You take the ratio of the terms of the series whose convergence is in question and a series with a known convergence/divergence.

If the limit of that ratio is a positive, finite number, then the series you are testing has the same convergence or divergence as the known series.

ABSOLUTE CONVERGENCE: If a series has positive and negative terms but is not an alternating series, you may need to test its convergence by evaluating the convergence of the absolute value of the series. If $\sum |a_n|$ converges, then the series $\sum a_n$ also converges.

RATIO TEST

(*Calculus for AP®*, pages 701–704)

Let $\sum a_n$ be a series with nonzero terms.

- If $\lim_{n\to\infty}\left|\frac{a_{n+1}}{a_n}\right| < 1$, then Σa_n converges absolutely.
- If $\lim_{n\to\infty}\left|\frac{a_{n+1}}{a_n}\right| > 1$ or $\lim_{n\to\infty}\left|\frac{a_{n+1}}{a_n}\right| = \infty$, then Σa_n diverges.
- The Ratio Test is inconclusive if the $\lim_{n\to\infty}\left|\frac{a_{n+1}}{a_n}\right| = 1$.

Because this test applies to any series with nonzero terms, it is a widely used and convenient test for series that are not of the "special" kind (telescoping, geometric, etc.). In this test, you will often simplify factorials or powers to get a reduced expression to evaluate. If the test is inconclusive, you would then try to use a different test for convergence.

ROOT TEST

(*Calculus for AP®*, page 704)

The Root Test is used to test for convergence and divergence of series with *n*th powers. Let $\sum a_n$ be a series.

- If $\lim_{n\to\infty}\sqrt[n]{|a_n|} < 1$, then $\sum a_n$ converges absolutely.
- If $\lim_{n\to\infty}\sqrt[n]{|a_n|} > 1$ or $\lim_{n\to\infty}\sqrt[n]{|a_n|} = \infty$, then $\sum a_n$ diverges.
- If $\lim_{n\to\infty}\sqrt[n]{|a_n|} = 1$, then the Root Test is inconclusive.

GUIDELINES FOR TESTING FOR CONVERGENCE

Although more than one test may work, you should always try to choose the most efficient one. Below are a few guidelines to help you decide which test to use.

- Determine if the *n*th term approaches 0; if it does not, then the series diverges.
- Determine if the series is one of the special ones listed above: telescoping, geometric, *p*-, or alternating; if it is, apply its specific test.

- Determine if the conditions exist for the Integral, Root, or Ratio Test and then apply the appropriate test.
- Determine if the series can be compared to one of the special series.

Test	Series	Condition(s) of convergence	Conditions of divergence	Comment
*n*th-Term	$\sum_{n=1}^{\infty} a_n$		$\lim_{n\to\infty} a_n \neq 0$	Although this test cannot show convergence, it does show divergence.
Telescoping series	$\sum_{n=1}^{\infty} (b_n - b_{n+1})$	$\lim_{n\to\infty} b_n = L$		Sum: $S = b_1 - L$
Geometric series	$\sum_{n=1}^{\infty} ar^n$	$\|r\| < 1$	$\|r\| \geq 1$	Sum: $S = \frac{a}{1-r}$
p-series	$\sum_{n=1}^{\infty} \frac{1}{n^p}$	$p > 1$	$p \leq 1$	
Alternating series	$\sum_{n=1}^{\infty} (-1)^{n-1} a_n$	$0 < a_{n+1} \leq a_n$ and $\lim_{x\to\infty} a_n = 0$		Remainder: $\|R_N\| \leq a_{N+1}$
Integral (*f* is continuous, positive, and decreasing)	$\sum_{n=1}^{\infty} a_n$, $a_n = f(n) \geq 0$	$\int_1^{\infty} f(x)\,dx$ converges	$\int_1^{\infty} f(x)\,dx$ diverges	Remainder: $0 < R_N < \int_N^{\infty} f(x)\,dx$
Ratio	$\sum_{n=1}^{\infty} a_n$	$\lim_{n\to\infty} \left\|\frac{a_{n+1}}{a_n}\right\| < 1$	$\lim_{n\to\infty} \left\|\frac{a_{n+1}}{a_n}\right\| > 1$	Test is inconclusive if $\lim_{n\to\infty} \left\|\frac{a_{n+1}}{a_n}\right\| = 1$
Root	$\sum_{n=1}^{\infty} a_n$	$\lim_{n\to\infty} \sqrt[n]{\|a_n\|} < 1$	$\lim_{n\to\infty} \sqrt[n]{\|a_n\|} > 1$	Test is inconclusive if $\lim_{n\to\infty} \sqrt[n]{\|a_n\|} = 1$
Direct comparison ($a_n, b_n > 0$)	$\sum_{n=1}^{\infty} a_n$	$0 < a_n \leq b_n$ and $\sum_{n=1}^{\infty} b_n$ converges	$0 < b_n \leq a_n$ and $\sum_{n=1}^{\infty} b_n$ diverges	
Limit comparison ($a_n, b_n > 0$)	$\sum_{n=1}^{\infty} a_n$	$\lim_{n\to\infty} \frac{a_n}{b_n} = L > 0$ and $\sum_{n=1}^{\infty} b_n$ converges	$\lim_{n\to\infty} \frac{a_n}{b_n} = L > 0$ and $\sum_{n=1}^{\infty} b_n$ diverges	

The following example will help you "sort out" which method to use.

EXAMPLE

Determine the convergence or divergence of each series.

a. $\sum_{n=1}^{\infty} \frac{n+1}{3n+1}$ b. $\sum_{n=1}^{\infty} \left(\frac{\pi}{6}\right)^n$ c. $\sum_{n=1}^{\infty} ne^{-n^2}$

d. $\sum_{n=1}^{\infty} \frac{1}{3n+1}$ e. $\sum_{n=1}^{\infty} (-1)^n \frac{3}{4n+1}$ f. $\sum_{n=1}^{\infty} \frac{n!}{10^n}$

g. $\sum_{n=1}^{\infty} \left(\frac{n+1}{2n+1}\right)^n$

SOLUTION

a. For this series, the limit of the nth term is not 0 $\left(a_n \to \frac{1}{3} \text{ as } n \to \infty\right)$. So, by the nth-Term Test, the series diverges.

b. This series is geometric. Moreover, because the ratio $r = \pi/6$ of the terms is less than 1 in absolute value, you can conclude that the series converges.

c. Because the function $f(x) = xe^{-x^2}$ is easily integrated, you can use the Integral Test to conclude that the series converges.

d. The nth term of this series can be compared to the nth term of the harmonic series. After using the Limit Comparison Test, you can conclude the series diverges.

e. This is an alternating series whose nth term approaches 0. Because $a_{n+1} \leq a_n$, you can use the Alternating Series Test to conclude that the series converges.

f. The nth term of this series involves a factorial, which indicates that the Ratio Test may work well. After applying the Ratio Test, you can conclude that the series diverges.

g. The nth test of this series involves a variable that is raised to the nth power, which indicates that the Root Test may work well. After applying the Root Test, you can conclude the series converges.

AP® Tips

- Most of the preceding series and tests are evaluated in the multiple-choice sections of the AP® exam.
- Taylor and Maclaurin series and tests for convergence are tested in both the multiple-choice and the free-response sections of the test.
- Look for and recognize the harmonic series (which diverges) and the alternating harmonic series (which converges) as these are often used for comparisons.

AP® is a trademark registered by the College Board, which is not affiliated with, and does not endorse, this product.

TAYLOR POLYNOMIALS AND APPROXIMATIONS

(*Calculus for AP*®, pages 728–737)

The goal is to find a polynomial function that can approximate elementary functions such as e^x or trigonometric functions near or expanded about some center c. The function should look like the graph at and near this point. Generally, you begin by requiring that your new function $P(x)$ equals $f(x)$ at c. The higher the degree of the polynomial, the better the approximation at or near the "center." Thus to get to a first-degree approximation, you want $P(c) = f(c)$, as well as $P'(c) = f'(c)$ (slopes to be equal at c) and substituting the values in the point-slope form of a line to find the linear approximation of f near c. This again flows from the concept of local linearity. The values close to a given point on a curve can be approximated by a line through that given point. A graphing calculator can be used to see this phenomenon but can also be used to check higher order approximations as well.

The trick is to have a way to determine a polynomial approximation, and that is what the Taylor and Maclaurin polynomials do. The Taylor polynomial is an approximation centered around a value c; the Maclaurin polynomial is just a Taylor polynomial centered around "zero."

Definition of an nth Taylor polynomial: If f has n derivatives at c, then the polynomial

$$P_n(x) = f(c) + f'(c)(x-c) + \frac{f''(c)}{2!}(x-c)^2 + \cdots + \frac{f^{(n)}(c)}{n!}(x-c)^n$$

is the nth Taylor polynomial for f at c.

If you let $c = 0$, it would be called the nth Maclaurin polynomial for f.

Let's look at a Taylor approximation for $f(x) = \ln x$ centered at $x = 1$. In other words, let's try to find polynomial approximations that are of degree 0, 1, 2, 3, and 4 and then graph them simultaneously with $\ln x$. As you graph the various approximations against $\ln x$, you will see that the higher the degree, the larger the neighborhood of "good" approximate values.

First, find the derivatives of $\ln x$.

$$f(x) = \ln x \quad f'(x) = \frac{1}{x} \quad f''(x) = \frac{-1}{x^2} \quad f'''(x) = \frac{2!}{x^3} \quad f^{iv}(x) = \frac{-3!}{x^4}$$

Then substitute in the Taylor polynomial formula with $c = 1$.

$$P_0(1) = f(1) = 0$$

$$P_1(1) = f(1) + f'(1)\cdot(x-1) = 0 + 1(x-1) = x-1$$

$$P_2(1) = f(1) + f'(1)\cdot(x-1) + \frac{f''(1)}{2!}(x-1)^2 = 0 + 1(x-1) + \frac{-1}{2!}(x-1)^2$$

$$P_3(1) = f(1) + f'(1)\cdot(x-1) + \frac{f''(1)}{2!}(x-1)^2 + \frac{f'''(1)}{3!}(x-1)^3$$

$$= 0 + 1(x-1) + \frac{-1}{2!}(x-1)^2 + \frac{2!}{3!}(x-1)^3$$

$$P_4(1) = f(1) + f'(1)\cdot(x-1) + \frac{f''(1)}{2!}(x-1)^2 + \frac{f'''(1)}{3!}(x-1)^3$$
$$+\frac{f^{(iv)}(1)}{4!}(x-1)^4$$
$$= 0 + 1(x-1) + \frac{-1}{2!}(x-1)^2 + \frac{2!}{3!}(x-1)^3 + \frac{-3!}{4!}(x-1)^4$$

Thus, in the pre-calculator days, one could make a very good numerical approximation of ln (0.9) by finding $P_4(0.9)$. (*Note:* Calculators themselves use Taylor polynomial approximations to determine the value of ln (0.9).)

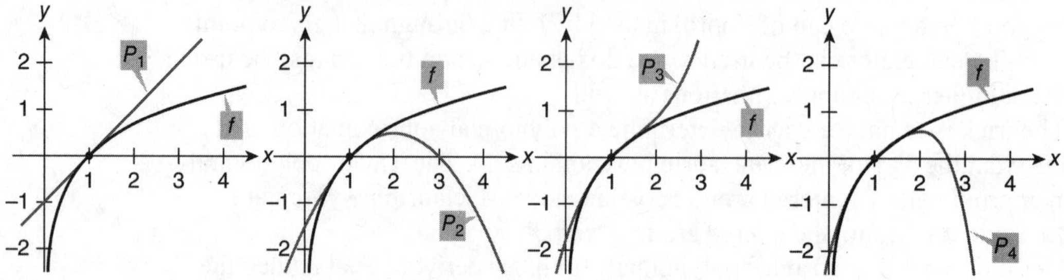

AP® Tips

- Know the Maclaurin series for e^x, sin x, cos x, and $1/(1-x)$.

LAGRANGE ERROR BOUND FOR TAYLOR POLYNOMIALS

Approximations have little value if you do not have an idea of the accuracy of the approximation. The error associated with Taylor's approximation is the absolute value of the remainder, $|R_n(x)| = |f(x) - P_{n(x)}|$ = error; in other words, the actual value of f minus the approximated value is equal to the remainder. However, if we knew that exact amount, we wouldn't need the approximating Taylor polynomial. Thus, we find an interval of approximation for the error:

$$R_n(x) = \frac{f^{n+1}(z)}{(n+1)!}(x-c)^{n+1}$$, where z is between x and c.

POWER SERIES

(*Calculus for AP*®, pages 711–717)

Although Taylor polynomials can give us very good approximations of a function near the center c, we can exactly represent some important functions, such as e^x, with an infinite series called a power series.

$1 + x + \frac{x^2}{2!} + \frac{x^3}{3!} + \cdots + \frac{x^n}{n!} + \cdots$ is the power series representation for e^x.

$\sum_{n=0}^{\infty} a_n(x-c)^n = a_0 + a_1(x-c) + a_2(x-c)^2 + \cdots + a_n(x-c)^n + \cdots$ is called a power series centered at c, where c is a constant.

A power series in x can be viewed as a function of x, $\sum_{n=0}^{\infty} a_n(x-c)^n = f(x)$, where the domain of f is the set of all x that make the power series converge. We must determine the domain of a power series so that we can know where it converges. For a power series centered at c, only one of the following can be true:

- It converges only at c.
- For some real number R, where $R > 0$, the series converges absolutely if $|x - c| < R$ and diverges if $|x - c| > R$.
- The series converges for all x.

R is called the radius of convergence. $R = 0$ if the series converges only at c; if it converges for all x, then $R = \infty$. The interval of convergence is the set of all values x for which the power series converges. The radius of convergence is determined by the Ratio Test. The interval of convergence is determined by checking the behavior of the end points.

You solve for the interval of convergence by determining where a given series converges by using one of the tests for convergence mentioned earlier. There should be examples in your textbook that show how the Ratio Test leads to the determination of the intervals of convergence.

One of the easiest ways to create a power series occurs when the function has the form of the sum of an infinite geometric series. You often have to adjust the original form to create the correct series form. For example, let $f(x) = \frac{1}{1-x}$ which looks similar to $\sum_{n=0}^{\infty} ar^n = \frac{a}{1-r}, |r| < 1$ where $a = 1$, and $r = x$, centered at zero.

Therefore, $\frac{1}{1-x} = \sum_{n=0}^{\infty} x^n = 1 + x + x^2 + x^3 + \cdots, |x| < 1$, which means that this series represents the original function in the interval $(-1, 1)$. To represent f in a different interval, you would center it at a different c.

Another example is $f(x) = \frac{4}{3x+2} = \frac{2}{1 - \left(-\frac{3}{2}x\right)}$ by dividing each term by 2, and using the commutative property in the denominator. Now $a = 2$ and $f = -\frac{3}{2}x$ and this can now also be applied to the geometric series form.

$f(x) = \sum_{n=0}^{\infty} 2\left(-\frac{2}{3}\right)^n = 2 - 3x + \frac{9}{2}x^2 - \frac{27}{4}x^3 + \cdots$ and it converges when $|r| < 1$ or in this case when $\left|\frac{-3}{2}x\right| < 1$ or $|x| < \frac{2}{3}$ and thus the interval of convergence is $\left(-\frac{2}{3}, \frac{2}{3}\right)$.

Differentiation and integration of power series is a matter of differentiating or integrating term by term. The radius of convergence remains the same as the original power series, but the interval of convergence could vary depending on the behavior at the end points.

POWER SERIES OF ELEMENTARY FUNCTIONS

(*Calculus for AP®*, page 738)

Function	Interval of convergence
$\frac{1}{x}=1-(x-1)+(x-1)^2-(x-1)^3+(x-1)^4-\cdots+(-1)^n(x-1)^n+\cdots$	$0<x<2$
$\frac{1}{x+1}=1-x+x^2-x^3+x^4-x^5+\cdots+(-1)^n x^n+\cdots$	$-1<x<1$
$\ln x=(x-1)-\frac{(x-1)^2}{2}+\frac{(x-1)^3}{3}-\frac{(x-1)^4}{4}+\cdots+\frac{(-1)^{(n-1)}(x-1)^n}{n}+\cdots$	$0<x\le 2$
$e^x=1+\frac{x^2}{2!}+\frac{x^3}{3!}+\frac{x^4}{4!}+\cdots+\frac{x^n}{n!}+\cdots$	$-\infty<x<\infty$
$\sin x=x-\frac{x^3}{3!}+\frac{x^5}{5!}-\frac{x^7}{7!}+\frac{x^9}{9!}-\cdots+\frac{(-1)^n x^{2n+1}}{(2n+1)!}+\cdots$	$-\infty<x<\infty$
$\cos x=1-\frac{x^2}{2!}+\frac{x^4}{4!}-\frac{x^6}{6!}+\frac{x^8}{8!}-\cdots+\frac{(-1)^n x^{2n}}{(2n)!}+\cdots$	$-\infty<x<\infty$

In general, if f is represented by a power series for all x in an open interval I containing c, $f(x)=\sum a_n(x-c)^n$. Then, $a_n=\frac{f^n(c)}{n!}$ and therefore,

$f(x)=f(c)+f'(c)(x-c)+\frac{f''(c)}{2!}(x-c)^2+\cdots+\frac{f^n(c)}{n!}(x-c)^n$, which should look like the Taylor polynomial, and is called the Taylor series for f at c. If $c=0$, then it is called the Maclaurin series.

Many AP® free-response questions ask about developing or finding specific coefficients for Taylor (or Maclaurin) polynomials, or ask you to work with the Lagrange or alternating series error, or to determine convergence, the radius, and interval of convergence, or apply other calculus concepts like derivative, extrema, etc. At this point, you should review and understand the sample problems in this chapter as well as released AP® problems to get a sense of the importance of these major topics.

PAST AP® FREE-RESPONSE PROBLEMS COVERED BY THIS CHAPTER

Note: These and other questions can be found at apcentral.com.

1998 BC 3
1999 BC 4

2000 BC 3
2001–2005 BC 6
2006 BC 5c; 6
2007 BC 6
2008 BC 6c
2009 BC 4b; 6
2010–2011 BC 6
2012 BC 4d; 6
2013–2014 BC 6

MULTIPLE-CHOICE QUESTIONS

A calculator may not be used for the following questions.

1. Which of the following series is absolutely convergent?

(A) $\sum_{k=0}^{\infty}(-1)^k \dfrac{k+3}{k+\sqrt{k}}$

(B) $\sum_{k=0}^{\infty}(-1)^k \dfrac{3}{\sqrt{k}}$

(C) $\sum_{k=0}^{\infty}(-1)^{k+1} \dfrac{\sqrt{k}}{k+3}$

(D) $\sum_{k=0}^{\infty}(-1)^{k+1} \dfrac{3}{k\sqrt{k}}$

2. The power series $\sum_{k=1}^{\infty}\dfrac{x^k}{k}$ converges for which values of x?

(A) $-1 < x < 1$

(B) $-1 \le x < 1$

(C) $-1 \le x \le 1$

(D) x is any real number

3. Which of the following series is the power series expansion for $f(x) = x(\cos x - 1)$?

(A) $x - \dfrac{x^3}{2} + \dfrac{x^5}{24} - \cdots$

(B) $-x^3 + x^5 - x^7 - \cdots$

(C) $\dfrac{x^3}{2} - \dfrac{x^5}{24} + \dfrac{x^7}{720} - \cdots$

(D) $-\dfrac{x^3}{2} + \dfrac{x^5}{24} - \dfrac{x^7}{720} + \cdots$

4. What are all values of a for which the series $\sum_{k=0}^{\infty}\left(\frac{5}{9-a}\right)^k$ converges?

(A) $a < 4$
(B) $4 < a < 14$
(C) $a < 9$
(D) $a < 4$ or $a > 14$

5. The Maclaurin series for $f(x) = \frac{1}{1+x^2}$ is $\sum_{k=0}^{\infty}(-1)^k x^{2k}$. What is the Maclaurin series for $g(x) = \tan^{-1} x$?

(A) $C + \sum_{k=0}^{\infty}(-1)^k (2k) x^{2k-1}$

(B) $C + \sum_{k=0}^{\infty}(-1)^k \frac{x^{2k+1}}{2k+1}$

(C) $C + \sum_{k=0}^{\infty}(-1)^{k+1} \frac{x^{2k+1}}{2k}$

(D) $C + \sum_{k=0}^{\infty}(-1)^{k-1} \frac{x^{2k-1}}{2k}$

6. The Maclaurin series $\sum_{k=0}^{\infty}(-9)^k \frac{x^{4k}}{(2k)!}$ represents which function below?

(A) $\cos(3x^2)$
(B) $\sin(3x^2)$
(C) $\cos(9x^4)$
(D) e^{-3x^2}

7. If the first five terms of the Taylor expansion for $f(x)$ about $x = 0$ are $3 - 7x + \frac{5}{2}x^2 + \frac{3}{4}x^3 - 6x^4$, then $f'''(0) =$

(A) $\frac{1}{8}$.

(B) $\frac{3}{4}$.

(C) $\frac{9}{2}$.

(D) 6.

8. Which of the following series diverge?

I. $\sum_{k=0}^{\infty} \frac{k^{\frac{3}{2}}+1}{5k^2+7}$

II. $\sum_{k=2}^{\infty} (-1)^k \frac{1}{\ln(k)}$

III. $\sum_{k=0}^{\infty} (-1)^k \left(\frac{4}{3}\right)^k$

(A) I only
(B) II only
(C) I and II only
(D) I and III only

A calculator may be used for the following questions.

9. The sixth-degree term of the Taylor series expansion $f(x) = e^{-\frac{1}{2}x^2}$ about $x = 0$ has coefficient

(A) $-\frac{1}{48}$.

(B) $-\frac{1}{6}$.

(C) $\frac{1}{720}$.

(D) $-\frac{1}{4608}$.

10. Let $T_n(x)$ represent the Taylor Polynomial of degree n about $x = 0$ for $f(x) = e^{-x}$. If $T_n(2)$ is used to approximate the value of $f(2) = e^{-2}$, then all of the following expressions are less than $\frac{2^7}{7!}$ EXCEPT

(A) $f(2) - T_6(2)$.
(B) $T_6(2) - f(2)$.
(C) $f(2) - T_5(2)$.
(D) $T_5(2) - f(2)$.

*11. For function $f(x)$, $f(0) = 3, f'(0) = 2, f''(0) = 5$, and $f'''(0) = 4$. Using the Taylor series expansion for $f(x)$ about $x = 0$, the second degree estimate for $f'(0.1)$ is
(A) 2.500.
(B) 2.520.
(C) 3.120.
(D) 3.225.

A calculator may not be used for the following questions.

12. The Maclaurin series $\sum_{k=0}^{\infty}(-5)^k \frac{x^{3k+2}}{k!}$ represents which expression below?

(A) $x^2 e^{-5x^3}$
(B) $-5e^{3x+2}$
(C) $x^2 \sin(-5x^3)$
(D) $-5\cos(x^3)+2$

13. If $f(x)=\sin(x^2)$, the first three terms of the Taylor series expansion about $x = 0$ for $f'(x)$ are

(A) $2x - x^3 + \frac{1}{2}x^5$.

(B) $1 - \frac{1}{2}x^4 + \frac{1}{16}x^8$.

(C) $2x - x^5 + \frac{1}{12}x^9$.

(D) $x^2 - \frac{1}{6}x^6 + \frac{1}{120}x^{10}$.

14. Which of the following series is conditionally convergent?

(A) $\sum_{k=1}^{\infty}(-1)^k \frac{k^2+1}{k+4}$

(B) $\sum_{k=1}^{\infty}(-1)^{k-1} \frac{2}{k+1}$

(C) $\sum_{k=1}^{\infty}(-1)^{k+1}\ln(k+1)$

(D) $\sum_{k=1}^{\infty}(-1)^k \frac{k+3}{k^3+7}$

15. The radius of convergence of the power series $\sum_{k=0}^{\infty}\frac{x^{2k}}{k\cdot 4^k}$ is

(A) 0.
(B) 1.
(C) 2.
(D) 4.

FREE-RESPONSE QUESTION

A calculator may be used for this question.
Let $f(x)$ be a function that is differentiable for all x. The Taylor expansion for $f(x)$ about $x = 0$ is given by $T(x) = \sum_{k=0}^{\infty} (-1)^k \frac{(k+1)x^{3k}}{k!}$. The first four nonzero terms of $T(x)$ are given by $T_4(x) = 1 - 2x^3 + \frac{3x^6}{2!} - \frac{4x^9}{3!}$.

(a) Show that $T(x)$ converges for all x.
(b) Let $W(x)$ be the Taylor expansion for $x^2 f'(x)$ about $x = 0$. Find the general term for $W(x)$ and find $W_3(x)$.
(c) $f(0.5) \approx T_4(0.5)$ and $f(1) \approx T_4(1)$. Find the values of $T_4(0.5)$ and $T_4(1)$.
(d) Which value is smaller, $|f(0.5) - T_4(0.5)|$ or $|f(1) - T_4(1)|$? Give a reason for your answer.

Answers

MULTIPLE-CHOICE QUESTIONS

1. ANSWER: (D) All of the choices are variations on the p-series. Because the question asks for absolute convergence, the $(-1)^k$ or $(-1)^{k+1}$ factors can be ignored. The p-series of the form $\sum_{k=0}^{\infty} \frac{1}{k^p}$ converges if $p > 1$ and diverges if $0 < p \le 1$. Using the Limit Comparison Test, each of the choices can be compared to a series where p is the degree of the denominator minus the degree of the numerator. In (A), $p = 0$. In (B) and (C), $p = 1/2$. In (D), $p = 3/2$. Thus (D) is correct. [*Note:* The series in (B) and (C), are conditionally convergent, because they converge as alternating series but not as absolutes. The series in (A) is divergent, because $\lim_{k\to\infty} \frac{k+3}{k+\sqrt{k}} = 1 \neq 0$.]
(*Calculus for AP*®, pages 677–678; EU 4.1; LO 4.1A; EK 4.1A4,4.1A5; MPAC 2)

2. ANSWER: (B) The interval of convergence of a power series is obtained by solving the inequality below using the Ratio Test for absolute convergence.

$$\lim_{k\to\infty}\left|\frac{a_{k+1}}{a_k}\right| < 1 \Rightarrow \lim_{k\to\infty}\left|\frac{\frac{x^{k+1}}{k+1}}{\frac{x^k}{k}}\right| < 1 \Rightarrow \lim_{d\to\infty}\left|\frac{x^{k+1}}{k+1}\cdot\frac{k}{x^k}\right| < 1 \Rightarrow |x| < 1 \Rightarrow x \in (-1,1).$$

End points must be evaluated separately. If $x = -1$, the series is $\sum_{k=1}^{\infty} \frac{(-1)^k}{k}$, which converges (alternating harmonic series). If $x = 1$, the series is $\sum_{k=1}^{\infty} \frac{1}{k}$, which diverges (harmonic series). Thus, the series converges for $x \in [-1, 1)$.
(*Calculus for AP*®, pages 715–717; EU 4.2; LO 4,2C; EK 4.2C2; MPAC 2,3)

3. ANSWER: (D) Using the known Maclaurin series,

$$\cos x = \sum_{k=0}^{\infty}(-1)^k \frac{x^{2k}}{(2k)!} = 1 - \frac{x^2}{2} + \frac{x^4}{4!} - \cdots$$ Therefore,

$$x(\cos x - 1) = x\left(1 - \frac{x^2}{2} + \frac{x^4}{4!} - \cdots - 1\right) = -\frac{x^3}{2} + \frac{x^5}{24} - \frac{x^7}{720} + \cdots$$

(*Calculus for AP*®, pages 728–737; EU 4.2; LO 4.2B; EK 4.2B2,4.2B5; MPAC 2,3)

4. ANSWER: (D) The geometric series $\sum_{k=0}^{\infty} r^k$ converges if $|r| < 1$.

$$\left|\frac{5}{9-a}\right| < 1 \Rightarrow |9-a| > 5 \Rightarrow 9-a > 5 \text{ or } 9-a < -5 \Rightarrow a < 4 \text{ or } a > 14$$

(*Calculus for AP*®, pages 662–666; EU 4.1; LO 4.1A,4.1B; EK 4.1A3,4.1B1; MPAC 2,3,5)

5. ANSWER: (B)

$\tan^{-1} x$ is the antiderivative of $\frac{1}{1+x^2}$. Therefore,

$$\tan^{-1} x = \int \sum_{k=0}^{\infty}(-1)^k x^{2k}\,dx = C + \sum_{k=0}^{\infty}(-1)^k \frac{x^{2k+1}}{2k+1}$$

(*Calculus for AP*®, pages 721–724; EU 4.2; LO 4.2B,4.2C; EK 4.2B5,4.2C4; MPAC 2,3)

6. ANSWER: (A) The Maclaurin series for $\cos x$ is $\sum_{k=0}^{\infty}(-1)^k \frac{x^{2k}}{(2k)!}$. By substitution,

$$\cos\left(3x^2\right) = \sum_{k=0}^{\infty}(-1)^k \frac{\left(3x^2\right)^{2k}}{(2k)!}$$

$$= \sum_{k=0}^{\infty}(-1)^k \frac{9^k x^{4k}}{(2k)!}$$

$$= \sum_{k=0}^{\infty} \frac{(-9)^k x^{4k}}{(2k)!}$$

(*Calculus for AP*®, pages 728–737; EU 4.2; LO 4.2B; EK 4.2B2; MPAC 2,3)

7. ANSWER: (C) The Taylor expansion for $f(x)$ about $x = 0$ is given by

$f(0)+f'(0)x+\dfrac{f''(0)x^2}{2!}+\dfrac{f'''(0)x^3}{3!}+\cdots$. Therefore,

$$\frac{f'''(0)x^3}{3!}=\frac{3}{4}x^3 \Rightarrow$$

$$f'''(0)=3!\frac{3}{4}=\frac{9}{2}$$

(*Calculus for AP*®, pages 728–737; EU 4.2; LO 4.2A; EK 4.2A1; MPAC 2,3)

8. ANSWER: (D)

I: Because the degree of the numerator is less by 1/2 than the degree of the denominator, the series diverges using the Limit Comparison Test with comparison to the known divergent series $\sum_{k=0}^{\infty}\frac{1}{k^{\frac{1}{2}}}$.

II: Since the sequence $\left\{\frac{1}{\ln(k)}\right\}$ is monotone, decreasing and

$\lim_{k\to\infty}\frac{1}{\ln(k)}=0$, the series converges by the Alternating Series Test.

III: The series is geometric with $|r|=\frac{4}{3}>1$, so it diverges. Therefore, series I and III diverge.

(*Calculus for AP*®, pages 688–689, 692–695, 662–666; EU 4.1; LO 4.1A; EK 4.1A6; MPAC 2)

9. ANSWER: (A) $e^x=\sum_{k=0}^{\infty}\frac{x^k}{k!}$. By substitution

$$e^{\frac{1}{2}x^2}=\sum_{k=0}^{\infty}\frac{\left(-\frac{1}{2}x^2\right)^k}{k!}=1-\frac{1}{2}x^2+\frac{1}{4}\cdot\frac{x^4}{2!}-\frac{1}{8}\cdot\frac{x^6}{3!}+\cdots, c$$

so the coefficient of the sixth-degree term is $-\frac{1}{48}$. (*Calculus for AP*®, pages 728–737; EU 4.2; LO 4.2A; EK 4.2A1; MPAC 2,3)

10. ANSWER: (C) The Maclaurin series for e^{-x} is $\sum_{k=0}^{\infty}(-1)^k\frac{x^k}{k!}$, so

$T_n(x)=\sum_{k=0}^{n}(-1)^k\frac{x^k}{k!}$. The seventh-degree term of this series is $-\frac{2^7}{7}$.
Because this is an alternating series, $|f(2)-T_n(2)<|a_{n+1}(2)|$, hence for $n\ge 6$, all such magnitudes are less than $-\frac{2^7}{7}$. This leaves only choices (C) and (D). But (D) is negative, since the last term of $T_5(2)$ is negative, making the estimate less than $f(2)$. See below for expanded series:

$$e^{-x}=1-x+\frac{x^2}{2!}-\frac{x^3}{3!}+\frac{x^4}{4!}-\frac{x^5}{5!}+\frac{x^6}{6!}-\frac{x^7}{7!}+\frac{x^8}{8!}-\cdots$$

$$e^{-2}=1-2+\frac{2^2}{2!}-\frac{2^3}{3!}+\frac{2^4}{4!}-\frac{2^5}{5!}+\frac{2^6}{6!}-\frac{2^7}{7!}+\frac{2^8}{8!}-\cdots$$

$$T_6(2)=1-2+\frac{2^2}{2!}-\frac{2^3}{3!}+\frac{2^4}{4!}-\frac{2^5}{5!}+\frac{2^6}{6!}\text{ and }R_6(2)=-\frac{2^7}{7!}+\frac{2^8}{8!}-\cdots$$

Since $f(2)=T_6(2)+R_6(2)$, then $|f(2)-T_6(2)|=|R_6(2)|<|a_7(2)|=\frac{2^7}{7!}$

and all subsequent remainders would be smaller than $\frac{2^7}{7}$.

Note: $R_5(2)=f(2)-T_5(2)=\frac{2^6}{6!}-\frac{2^7}{7!}+\cdots>\frac{2^7}{7!}$ [(C) is the answer.]
$T_5(2)-f(2)=-R_5(2)<0$ [(D) is not the answer.] As an alternative solution, evaluate e^{-2}, $T_5(2)$ and $T_6(2)$ on the calculator using the $T_n(x)$ expansion. The value of (C) is 0.069 and all others are less than $\frac{2^7}{7}\approx 0.025$. (*Calculus for AP*®, pages 695–697; EU 4.2; LO 4.2A,4.2B; EK 4.2A2,4.2B2; MPAC 2,3)

11. ANSWER: (B) $f(x)\approx 3+2x+\frac{5x^2}{2!}+\frac{4x^3}{3!}\Rightarrow f'(x)\approx 2+5x+2x^2$
(*Calculus for AP*®, pages 728–737; EU 4.2; LO 4.2A; EK 4.2A1; MPAC 2,3)

12. ANSWER: (A) $\sum_{k=0}^{\infty}(-5)^k\frac{x^{3k+2}}{k!}=x^2\sum_{k=0}^{\infty}(-1)^k\frac{5^k x^{3k}}{k!}=x^2\sum_{k=0}^{\infty}\frac{(-5x^3)^k}{k!}=x^2e^{-5x^3}$
(*Calculus for AP*®, pages 728–737; EU 4.2; LO 4.2B; EK 4.2B2; MPAC 2,3)

13. ANSWER: (C) $f'(x) = 2x\cos(x^2)$. Using the Taylor series expansion for $\cos x$ about $x = 0$, $f'(x) = 2x\sum_{k=0}^{\infty}(-1)^k \frac{(x^2)^{2k}}{(2k)!} = 2x\left(1 - \frac{x^4}{2!} + \frac{x^8}{4!} - \cdots\right)$. The first three terms are $= 2x - x^5 + \frac{1}{12}x^9$. Alternatively, using the Taylor series expansion for $\sin x$ about $x = 0$, $f(x) = \sin(x^2) = \sum_{k=0}^{\infty}(-1)^k \frac{(x^2)^{2k+1}}{(2k+1)!} = x^2 - \frac{x^6}{3!} + \frac{x^{10}}{5!} - \cdots$.

Therefore, $f'(x) = 2x - \frac{6x^5}{3!} + \frac{10x^9}{5!} - \cdots$. The first three terms are $= 2x - x^5 + \frac{1}{12}x^9$. (*Calculus for AP®*, pages 728–737; EU 4.2; LO 4.2B; EK 4.2B2,4.2B5; MPAC 2,3)

14. ANSWER: (B) Choices (A) and (C) are divergent by the nth-Term Test for Divergence, as the terms of each one approach a limit other than 0. Choice (D) is absolutely convergent. In (D), the conclusion follows from the Limit Comparison Test using the convergent series $\sum_{k=1}^{\infty}\frac{1}{k^2}$. To justify the remaining choice (B), compare $\sum_{k=1}^{\infty}\frac{2}{k+1}$ to $\sum_{k=1}^{\infty}\frac{1}{k}$, a known divergent series.

Using the Limit Comparison Test, $\lim_{k\to\infty}\frac{\frac{2}{k+1}}{\frac{1}{k}} = \lim_{k\to\infty}\frac{2k}{k+1} = 2$, which is finite and positive. Therefore, $\sum_{k=1}^{\infty}\frac{2}{k+1}$ also diverges. However, the terms of $\sum_{k=1}^{\infty}\frac{2}{k+1}$ are positive and decreasing with $\lim_{k\to\infty}\frac{2}{k+1} = 0$. Hence, $\sum_{k=1}^{\infty}(-1)^{k-1}\frac{2}{k+1}$ converges by the Alternating Series Test and is conditionally convergent. (*Calculus for AP®*, pages 699–701; EU 4.1; LO 4.1A; EK 4.1A4,4.1A6; MPAC 2)

15. ANSWER: (C) Using the Ratio Test for Absolute Convergence,

$$\lim_{k\to\infty}\left|\frac{a_{k+1}}{a_k}\right| < 1 \Rightarrow \lim_{k\to\infty}\left|\frac{\frac{x^{2k+2}}{(k+1)\cdot 4^{k+1}}}{\frac{x^{2k}}{k\cdot 4^k}}\right| < 1 \Rightarrow \lim_{k\to\infty}\left|\frac{x^{2k+2}\cdot k\cdot 4^k}{x^{2k}(k+1)\cdot 4^{k+1}}\right| < 1$$

Hence $\lim_{k\to\infty}\left|\frac{x^2}{4}\right|\cdot\lim_{k\to\infty}\left|\frac{k}{k+1}\right| < 1 \Rightarrow \left|\frac{x^2}{4}\right|\cdot 1 < 1 \Rightarrow |x^2| < 4 \Rightarrow |x| < 2.$

Therefore, the radius of convergence is 2. (*Calculus for AP®*, pages 701–704; EU 4.2; LO 4.2C; EK 4.2C2; MPAC 2,3)

FREE-RESPONSE QUESTION

	Solution	Possible points
(a)	Using the Ratio Test for absolute convergence, $\lim_{k\to\infty}\left\|\dfrac{\frac{(k+2)x^{3(k+1)}}{(k+1)!}}{\frac{(k+1)x^{3k}}{k!}}\right\|<1\Rightarrow$ $\lim_{k\to\infty}\left\|\dfrac{(k+2)x^{3k+3}}{(k+1)!}\cdot\dfrac{k!}{(k+1)x^{3k}}\right\|<1\Rightarrow$ $\lim_{k\to\infty}\left\|\dfrac{k+2}{k+1}\cdot\dfrac{x^3}{k+1}\right\|<1\Rightarrow 1\cdot 0<1$, which is true for all x. Therefore, $T(x)$ converges for all real numbers.	$2:\begin{cases}1:\text{correct use of Ratio Test for Absolute Convergence}\\1:\text{answer}\end{cases}$
(b)	$f'(x)=-3\cdot 2x^2+\dfrac{6\cdot 3x^5}{2!}-\dfrac{9\cdot 4x^8}{3!}+\cdots=$ $\sum_{k=1}^{\infty}(-1)^k\dfrac{3k(k+1)x^{3k-1}}{k!}$. Therefore, $W(x)=x^2f'(x)=\sum_{k=1}^{\infty}(-1)^k\dfrac{3k(k+1)x^{3k+1}}{k!}$ and $W_3(x)=-6x^4+9x^7-6x^{10}$.	$4:\begin{cases}1:\text{expanded } f'(x)\\1:\text{general term of } f'(x)\\1:\text{general term of } W(x)\\1: W_3(x)\end{cases}$
(c)	Using direct substitution or a graphing calculator evaluation, $T_4(0.5)=0.772$ and $T_4(1)=-0.167$.	1: both answers correct
(d)	Because $T(x)$ is an alternating series, each difference above is smaller than the fifth term of the expansion, $\dfrac{5x^{12}}{4!}$, and $\dfrac{5(0.5)^{12}}{4!}<\dfrac{5(1)^{12}}{4!}$ $(0.00005<0.20833)$. Therefore, $\|f(0.5)-T_4(0.5)\|$ is smaller. Alternatively, $\|f(0.5)-T_4(0.5)\|$ is smaller because 0.5 is closer than 1 to the center $x=0$ of the interval of convergence. Therefore, the series converges to $f(x)$ more quickly.	$2:\begin{cases}1:\text{answer}\\1:\text{reason}\end{cases}$

(a), (b) (*Calculus for AP*®, pages 701–704, 728–737; EU 4.2; LO 4.2; EK 4.2C2,4.2B5; MPAC 2,3)

(c), (d) (*Calculus for AP*®, pages 728–737, 695–697; EU 4.2; LO 4.2A,4.2B; EK 4.2A2,4.2B4; MPAC 2,3)

9

PARAMETRIC EQUATIONS, VECTORS, AND POLAR COORDINATES

(The material in this chapter is tested only on the BC exam.)

Objectives

- Understand parametric equations: their form, differentiation, and integration.
- Understand polar equations: their form, differentiation, and integration.
- Understand and use vector-valued functions, as well as velocity and acceleration vectors.

PARAMETRIC EQUATIONS

(*Calculus for AP®*, pages 754–764, 769–782)

Up to this point, a graph has been represented by a single equation with two variables. Now we want to represent a curve in a plane with three variables. Parametric equations allow us to look at a situation with a broader perspective. Previously, if we wanted to track a softball hit in the *xy*-plane, we plotted the ball's height as a function of its horizontal displacement OR plotted the ball's height as a function of time OR plotted the ball's horizontal displacement as a function of time. With parametric equations, we will be able to know both the vertical height and the horizontal displacement of the ball at a given time. The third variable, time in this case, is called the parameter, and we can write both x and y equations in terms of t.

For example, to graph a basic set of parametric equations, let $x(t) = 2t + 3$ and $y(t) = -4t$. Substituting t into the equations beginning at $t = -3$, you can plot this set of points on the axes,

t	$x(t) = 2t + 3$	$y(t) = -4t$
−3	−3	12
−2	−1	8
−1	1	4
0	3	0.
1	5	−4
2	7	−8
3	9	−12
4	11	−16

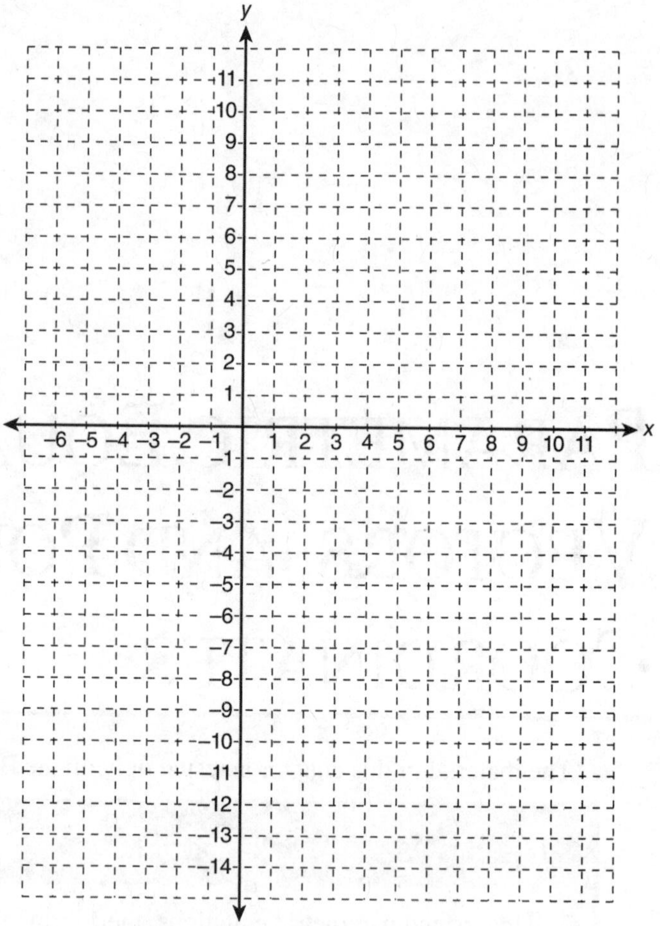

If f and g are continuous functions of t in the interval I, then the equations $x = f(t)$ and $y = g(t)$ are parametric equations and t is the parameter. The set of points (x, y) derived from the equations is the graph of the parametric equations. (*Note:* t is hidden from the graphical view; however, on your calculator, using the trace button, you can identify t at any given (x, y)). What is important to note with parametric equations is that, depending on the context of the problem, t could be limited in its domain. For example, if it represents time, it generally would not include negative values and subsequently the graph (of the x and y values) would not be infinite.

If $x = 24t$ and $y = -16t^2 + 24t + 48$ and those equations define the horizontal and vertical distances, respectively, of the movement of a ball, then t begins at 0 and ends when the ball hits the ground between 2.6 and 2.7 seconds. You can draw the graph representing other t values, including negative values, but they would not be pertinent to the problem.

t	$x = 24t$	$y = -16t^2 + 24t + 48$
0	0	48
0.2	4.8	52.16
0.4	9.6	55.04
0.6	14.4	56.64
0.8	19.2	56.96
1	24	56
1.2	28.8	53.76
1.4	33.6	50.24
1.6	38.4	45.44
1.8	43.2	39.36
2	48	32
2.2	52.8	23.36
2.4	57.6	13.44
2.6	62.4	2.24
2.8	67.2	−10.24
3	72	−24
3.2	76.8	−39.04
3.4	81.6	−55.36
3.6	86.4	−72.96
3.8	91.2	−91.84
4	96	−112

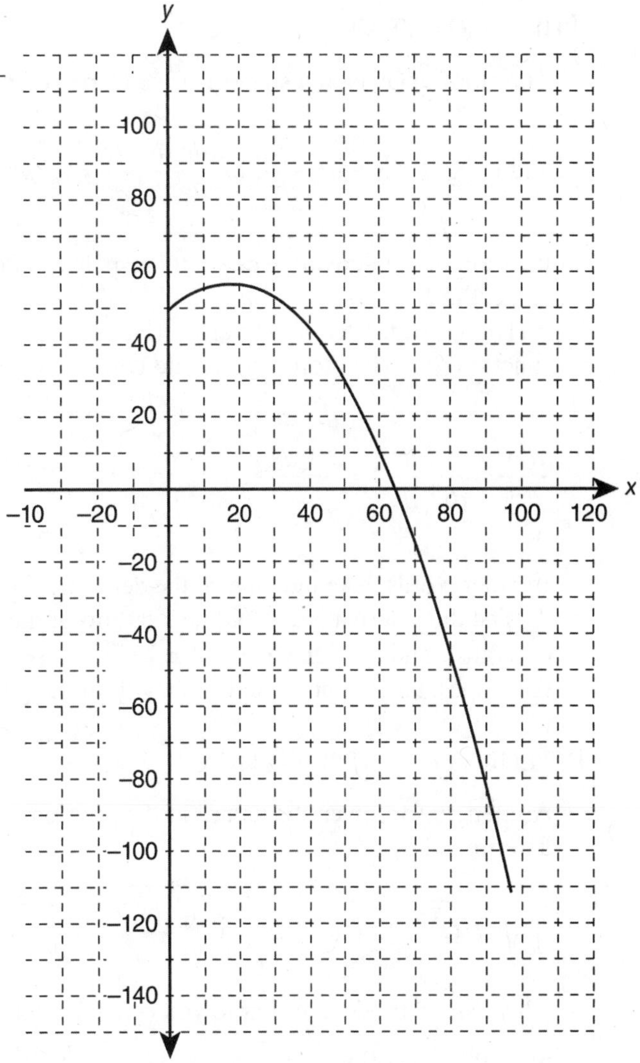

Important things to note about parametric equations:

- Two different sets of equations could have the same graph.
- The domain of t is critical.
- They show direction of movement.
- The parameter is not always t for time; parametric equations used in trigonometry use θ (representing the angle) as the parameter.

There are situations in which you will want to convert a set of parametric equations to a rectangular equation, and you do that by eliminating the parameter. Solve one of the parametric equations for t and substitute that into the other equation.

Once you understand the nature of parametric equations, their calculus applications are similar to what you already know.

THE DERIVATIVE

The slope at (x, y) of a smooth curve C, represented by the equations $x = f(t)$ and $y = g(t)$, is $\dfrac{dy}{dx} = \dfrac{\frac{dy}{dt}}{\frac{dx}{dt}}$, or $\dfrac{dy/dt}{dx/dt}, \dfrac{dx}{dt} \neq 0$, which means that you should take the ratio of the derivative of y with respect to t and the derivative of x with respect to t.

Higher-order derivatives are derived based on the fact that dy/dx is a function of t. Therefore, the second derivative would be

$$\frac{d^2y}{dx^2} = \frac{d}{dx}\left(\frac{dy}{dx}\right) = \frac{\frac{d}{dt}\left(\frac{dy}{dx}\right)}{\frac{dx}{dt}}.$$

In other words, take the ratio of the derivative of y and the derivative of x.

The third derivative would be the ratio of the derivative of the second derivative and the derivative of x. Using these derivatives you can now find the slopes, tangent lines, and concavity of the plane curves at given points.

INTEGRATION APPLICATION

Arc length (or, given the nature of the problem, distance traveled) can be determined by

$$\int_a^b \sqrt{\left[f'(t)\right]^2 + \left[g'(t)\right]^2}\, dt = \int_a^b \sqrt{\left(\frac{dx}{dt}\right)^2 + \left(\frac{dy}{dt}\right)^2}\, dt,$$

which should seem familiar to you (see Chapter 7). To interpret this further, the magnitude of velocity is speed $= \|v(t)\| = \sqrt{\left[x'(t)\right]^2 + \left[y'(t)\right]^2}$, and thus if you integrate velocity as above, you are accumulating the distance traveled.

POLAR EQUATIONS

(*Calculus for AP*®, pages 785–800, 803–810)

We now want to look at the polar coordinate system. Instead of plotting a collection of points (x, y) on a rectangular coordinate system, we will assign points (r, θ) where $r =$ the directed distance from O, the origin, to P and $\theta =$ the directed angle, counterclockwise from the polar axis to segment $\overline{OP}$.

Generally, the origin (0, 0), is called the pole, and the x-axis is called the polar axis.

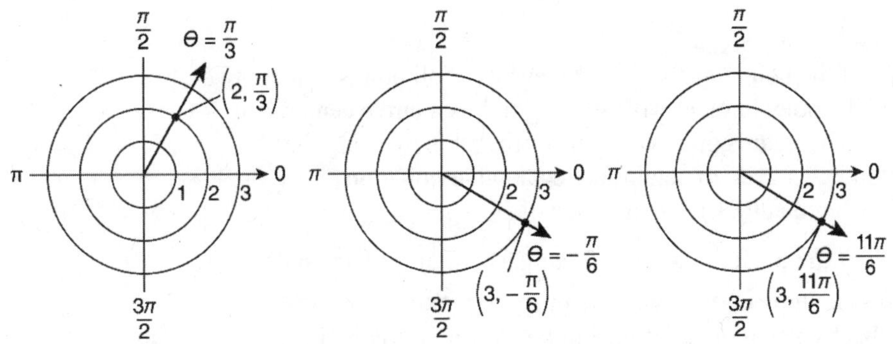

- In the left-hand figure above, r is equal to 2 (the point is on the circle having a radius of 2 from the pole (0, 0) and θ is $\pi/3$).
- In the center figure, r is equal to 3 and θ is the angle $-\pi/6$.
- In the right-hand figure, the point is at the same location as in the center figure, but is represented by a different ordered pair, where r remains 3 but the angle is now represented by $\frac{11\pi}{6}$.

In the polar coordinate system, unlike the rectangular system, each point does not have a unique representation.

AP® Tip

Although the ordered pair is (r, θ), it is often easier to graph by locating the angle θ first, then counting out the distance r from the origin.

By considering the right triangle (see figure), you can determine the relationship between the rectangular coordinate system and the polar coordinate system.

Since $\cos\theta = \text{adj/hyp} = x/r$, you can solve for x as $x = r\cos\theta$. And since $\sin\theta = \text{opp/hyp} = y/r$, you can solve for y as $y = r\sin\theta$. Looking at the tangent relationship, $\tan\theta = \text{opp/hyp} = y/x$. Finally using the Pythagorean theorem, $r^2 = x^2 + y^2$.

All of these relationships will allow you to convert from polar to rectangular coordinates or vice versa.

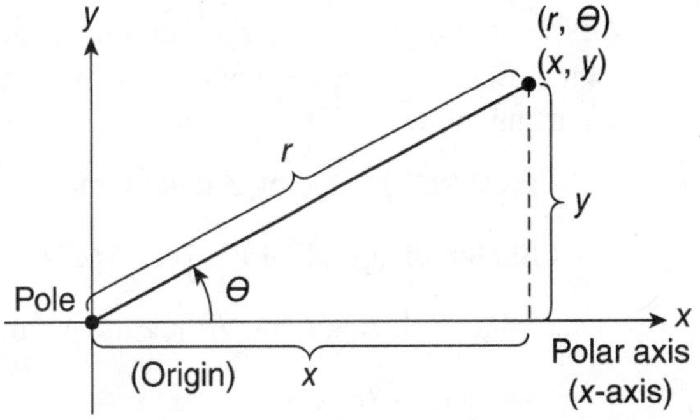

EXAMPLE: Graphing Polar Equations

Describe the graph of each polar equation. Confirm each description by converting to a rectangular equation.

a. $r = 2$ b. $\theta = \frac{\pi}{3}$ c. $r = \sec\theta$

AP® is a trademark registered by the College Board, which is not affiliated with, and does not endorse, this product.

SOLUTION:

a. The graph of the polar equation $r = 2$ consists of all points that are two units from the pole. In other words, this graph is a circle centered at the origin with a radius of 2. You can confirm this by using the relationship $r^2 = x^2 + y^2$ to obtain the rectangular equation $x^2 + y^2 = 2^2$ [a circle centered at (0, 0) with a radius of 2].

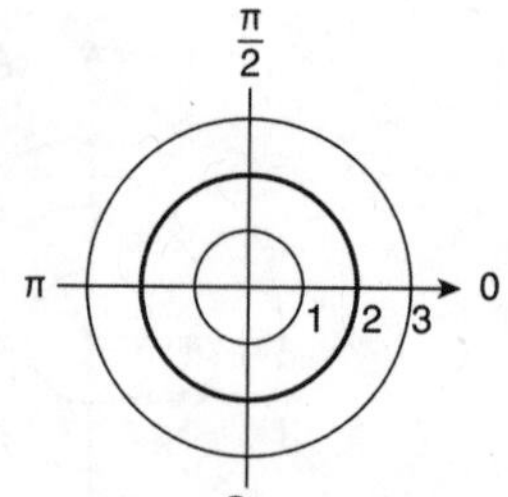

b. The graph of the polar equation $\sqrt{3}$ consists of all points on the line that makes an angle of $\pi/3$ with the positive x-axis. You can confirm this by using the relationship $\tan\theta = y/x$ to obtain the rectangular equation: $\tan\frac{\pi}{3} = \sqrt{3} = y/x$; therefore $y = \sqrt{3}x$.

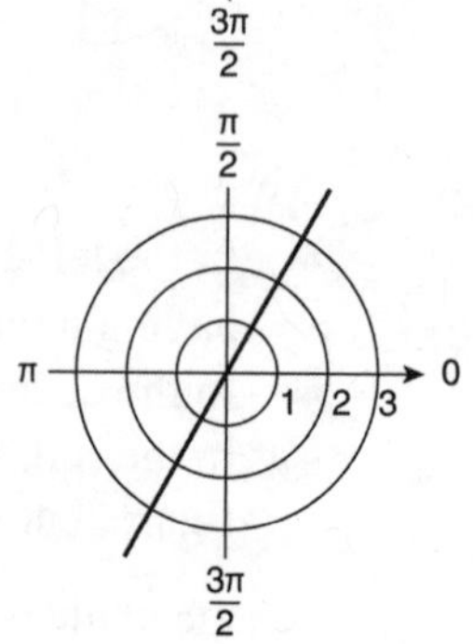

c. The graph of the polar equation $r = \sec\theta$ is not evident by simple inspection, so you can begin by converting to rectangular form using the relationship $r\cos\theta = x$.

$r = \sec\theta$ Polar equation

$r\cos\theta = 1$

$x = 1$ Rectangular equation

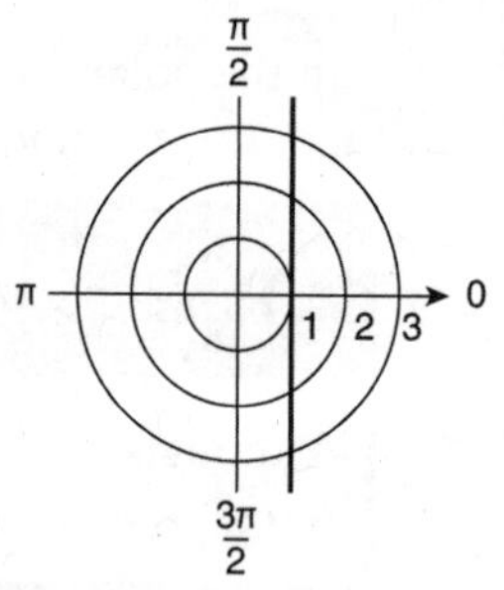

From the rectangular equation, you can see that the graph is a vertical line.

Most polar graphs can be plotted via a table of values. Generally, if you are graphing by hand, you need to determine the "end" of the graph because you will see that it begins to repeat its curve. However, on the calculator, you must understand θ and its domain. For example, in the following example, you can see that the domain of θ affects the totality of the graph. On your calculator, experiment with your polar graphing function by changing the domain of θ, including going beyond one cycle of π and using a number less than 0 as a starting value.

EXAMPLE: Sketching a Polar Graph

Sketch the graph of $r = 2\cos 3\theta$.

SOLUTION: Begin by writing the polar equation in parametric form.

$x = 2\cos 3\theta\cos\theta$ and $y = 2\cos 3\theta\sin\theta$

After some experimentation, you will find that the entire curve, which is called a **rose curve**, can be sketched by letting θ vary from 0 to π, as shown on the next page. If you try duplicating this graph, with a graphing utility, you will find that by letting θ vary from 0 to 2π, you will actually trace the entire curve *twice*.

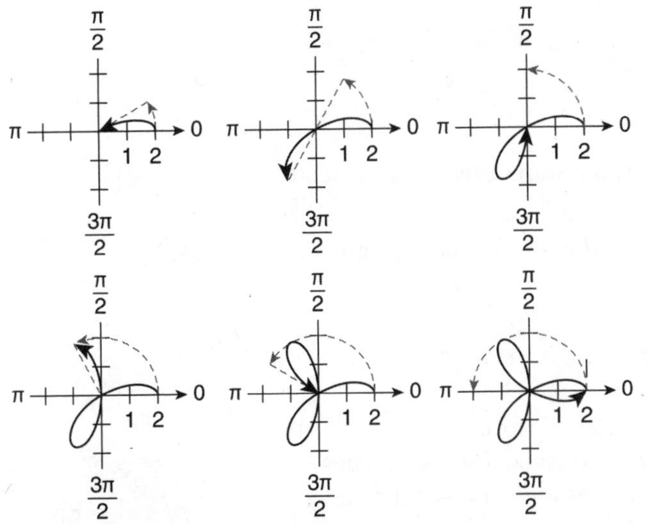

SLOPES AND TANGENT LINES

To solve for a slope, we need a differentiable function, which we will call $x = f(\theta)\cos\theta$ and $y = f(\theta)\sin\theta$ where $f(\theta) = r$.

Applying the parametric form of the derivative given above and noting that you need to use the product rule in both the numerator and denominator as $f(\theta)$, $\cos\theta$, and $\sin\theta$ are functions. $\dfrac{dy}{dx} = \dfrac{dy/d\theta}{dx/d\theta} = \dfrac{f(\theta)\cos\theta + f'(\theta)\sin\theta}{-f(\theta)\sin\theta + f'(\theta)\cos\theta}$

(again note that you are taking the derivative of x and the derivative of y separately and placing them in the numerator and the denominator, respectively).

Due to the nature of the derivative above, when the numerator $dy/d\theta = 0$, there will be a horizontal tangent line (as long as the denominator is not equal to 0) and when the denominator $dy/d\theta = 0$, a vertical tangent will occur (as long as the numerator is not 0).

> **AP® Tip**
>
> This is where a review of how to solve trigonometric equations would be appropriate. Remember your basic trig identities and how to factor.

A slope and subsequently, the equation of the tangent line at a given, θ can be found by using the above equation for a derivative.

AREA OF A POLAR REGION

Solving for the area of a polar region is similar to what we reviewed for the area of a region in the rectangular coordinate system. The difference is that we use sectors of a circle instead of rectangles as the basic element of area. The area of a sector of a circle is equal to $\dfrac{1}{2}\theta r^2$.

(*Note*: The area of a circle is πr^2, and so the area of a sector should be a portion of that based proportionately on the sector's size, according to the angle involved.) (Essentially, it is $\frac{\theta}{2\pi}\pi r^2$, the π's cancel, and you are left with $\frac{1}{2}\theta r^2$.)

Thus the integration concept uses the sum of the areas of sectors.

The area of a polar region bounded by the graph of $r = f(\theta)$ between the radial lines $\theta = \alpha$ and $\theta = \beta$, if f is continuous and nonnegative in the interval $[\alpha, \beta]$ and $0 < \beta - \alpha \leq 2\pi$, is

$$\frac{1}{2}\int_{\alpha}^{\beta}\left[f(\theta)\right]^2 d\theta = \frac{1}{2}\int_{\alpha}^{\beta} r^2 d\theta, \text{where } 0\beta - \alpha \leq 2\pi.$$

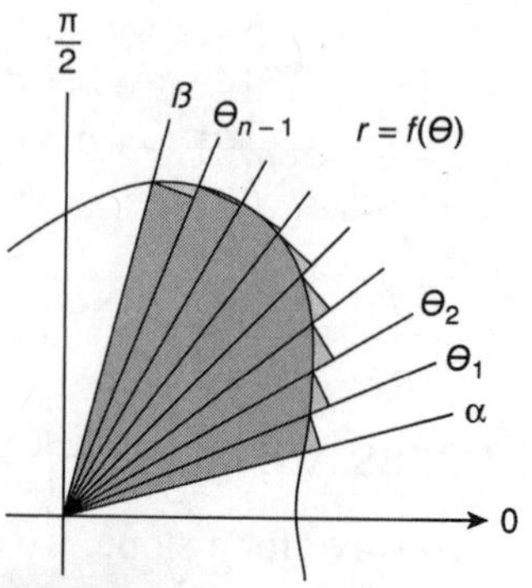

This is generally a straightforward application with the information given. However, just as in rectangular coordinates, you need to watch for overlapping regions, position of the curves, and so on, as well as add or subtract appropriate regions, to find the actual area of the region specified. You may also have to find the points of intersection between two graphs to determine the appropriate α and β.

AP® Tips

- Arc length in polar form and area of a surface of revolution in parametric or polar form are not AP® topics.
- Polar equations of conics are not AP® topics.

VECTOR-VALUED FUNCTIONS

(*Calculus for AP®*, pages 772–782)

GENERAL REVIEW OF VECTORS

A vector is a directed line segment used to represent quantities such as force, velocity, and acceleration that involve both magnitude and direction.

$\overline{PQ}$ has $P(x_1, y_1)$ as its initial point and $Q(x_2, y_2)$ as its terminal point. Its length (or magnitude) is denoted by $\left\|\overline{PQ}\right\|$. A vector in the plane can be represented by a variety of directed line segments, all of the same length and pointing in the same direction.

$$\left\|\overline{PQ}\right\| = \sqrt{(x_2 - x_1)^2 + (y_2 - y_1)^2}$$

A vector, v, whose initial point is the origin and whose terminal point is (v_x, v_y), can be written in the component form $v = \langle v_x, v_y \rangle$.

You can add and subtract vectors as well as multiply them by a constant. A unit vector has a length of 1. Standard unit vectors are denoted $\mathbf{i} = \langle 1, 0 \rangle$ and $\mathbf{j} = \langle 0, 1 \rangle$, and thus any vector can be represented uniquely by $v = v_1\mathbf{i} + v_2\mathbf{j}$, which is called a linear combination of **i** and **j**. The scalars v_1 and v_2 are the horizontal and vertical components of v.

VECTOR-VALUED FUNCTIONS: PROPERTIES, DIFFERENTIATION, AND INTEGRATION

A function of the form $\mathbf{r}(t) = f(t)\mathbf{i} + g(t)\mathbf{j}$ is a planar vector-valued function where the component functions f and g are real-valued functions of the parameter t. It can also be denoted as $\mathbf{r}(t) = \langle f(t), g(t)\rangle$. Thus vector-valued functions are parametric. $x(t) = \cos t$ and $y(t) = \sin t$, $0 < t \leq 2\pi$, can be represented as a vector: $\mathbf{r}(t) = \langle x(t), y(t)\rangle = (\cos t, \sin t)$. Using this set of parametric equations, you would get the unit circle in a smooth set of points traced out in a counterclockwise direction starting and finishing at (1, 0). In the vector representation, it is essentially graphing a series of vectors, each of whose initial point is at the origin and whose terminal point is on the unit circle, thus forming a circle from each of the terminal points.

Vector-valued functions not only graph a function but also indicate the curve's orientation by pointing in the direction of increasing values of t. Arrows should be used to show the direction in which the function is plotted.

Sketch the following example by hand first and see how the values are derived.

EXAMPLE: Sketching a Plane Curve

Sketch the plane curve represented by the vector-valued function
$\mathbf{r}(t) = 2\cos t\mathbf{i} - 3\sin t\mathbf{j}\quad 0 \leq t \leq 2\pi$

SOLUTION: From the position vector $\mathbf{r}(t)$, you can write the parametric equations $x = 2\cos t$ and $y = -3\sin t$. Solving for $\cos t$ and $\sin t$ and using the identity $\cos^2 t + \sin^2 t = 1$ you will get the rectangular equation

$$\frac{x^2}{2^2} + \frac{y^2}{3^2} = 1.$$

The graph of this rectangular equation is the ellipse shown in the figure to the right. The curve has a clockwise orientation. That is, as t increases from 0 to 2π, the position vector $\mathbf{r}(t)$ moves clockwise and its terminal point traces the ellipse.

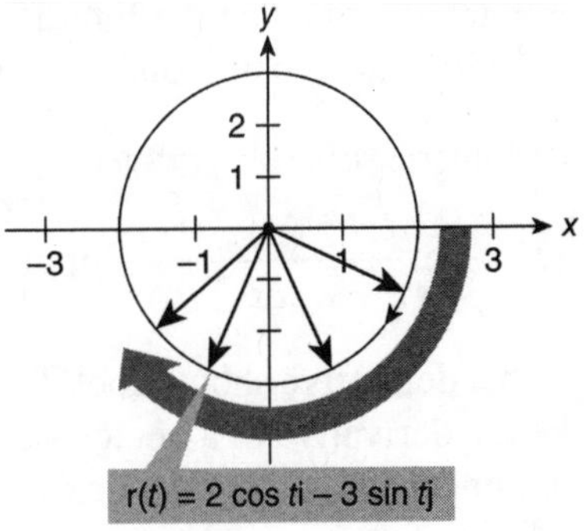

Taking a graph and representing it as a vector is demonstrated in the example below. Note that the orientation would vary depending on the choice of x.

EXAMPLE: Representing a Graph by a Vector-Valued Function

Represent the parabola given by $y = x^2 + 1$ by a vector-valued function.

SOLUTION: Although there are many ways to choose the parameter t, a natural choice is to let $x = t$. Then $y = t^2 + 1$ and you have the vector-valued function

$$\mathbf{r}(t) = t\mathbf{i} + (t^2+1)\mathbf{j}$$

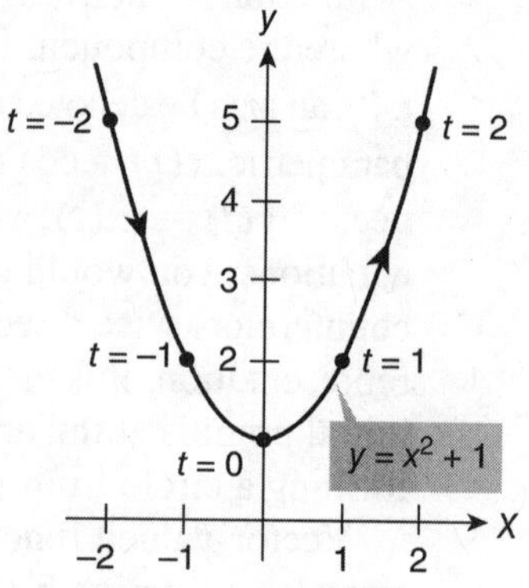

Note in the figure the orientation produced by this particular choice of parameter. Had you chosen $x = -t$ as the parameter, the curve would have oriented in the opposite direction.

Most of the techniques used in calculus for real-valued functions can be applied to vector-valued functions, such as adding, subtracting, multiplying by a scalar, taking the limit, and differentiating.

DEFINITION OF THE LIMIT OF A VECTOR-VALUED FUNCTION If $\mathbf{r}$ is a vector-valued function, $\mathbf{r}(t) = f(t)\mathbf{i} + g(t)\mathbf{j}$, then $\lim_{t\to a} \mathbf{r}(t) = \left[\lim_{t\to a} f(t)\right]\mathbf{i} + \left[\lim_{t\to a} g(t)\right]\mathbf{j}$,

provided f and g have limits as t approaches a.

DEFINITION OF CONTINUITY OF A VECTOR-VALUED FUNCTION A vector-valued function $\mathbf{r}$ is continuous at the point $t = a$ if the limit of $\mathbf{r}(t)$ exists as t approaches a and that the limit is $\mathbf{r}(a)$. The function $\mathbf{r}$ is continuous in an interval I if it is continuous at every point in that interval.

DIFFERENTIATION OF VECTOR-VALUED FUNCTIONS The derivative of $\mathbf{r}$ is

$\mathbf{r}'(t) = \lim_{\Delta t\to 0} \dfrac{\mathbf{r}(t+\Delta t) - \mathbf{r}(t)}{\Delta t}$ for all t for which the limit exists.

This derivative should look familiar to you, and subsequently when you take the derivative of a vector-valued function, you will be differentiating on a component-by-component basis.

Thus, if $\mathbf{r}(t) = f(t)\mathbf{i} + g(t)\mathbf{j}$ where f and g are differentiable functions of t, then $\mathbf{r}'(t) = f'(t)\mathbf{i} + g'(t)\mathbf{j}$. For example, if $\mathbf{r}(t) = t^2\mathbf{i} - 4\mathbf{j}$, then $\mathbf{r}'(t) = 2t\mathbf{i} - 0\mathbf{j} = 2t\mathbf{i}$.

Higher-order differentiation would continue in the same manner; take the derivative of the component parts.

INTEGRATION OF A VECTOR-VALUED FUNCTION This, too, follows the same procedure as real-valued functions. If $\mathbf{r}(t) = f(t)\mathbf{i} + g(t)\mathbf{j}$ where f and g are continuous in $[a, b]$, then the indefinite integral of $\mathbf{r}$ is

$$\int \mathbf{r}(t)\,dt = \left[\int f(t)\,dt\right]\mathbf{i} + \left[\int g(t)\,dt\right]\mathbf{j}.$$

The definite integral over the interval $a \le t \le b$ would be

$$\int_a^b \mathbf{r}(t)\,dt = \left[\int_a^b f(t)\,dt\right]\mathbf{i} + \left[\int_a^b g(t)\,dt\right]\mathbf{j}.$$

VELOCITY AND ACCELERATION VECTORS

Again, these work just like real-valued functions.

If

- x and y are twice-differentiable functions of t
- $\mathbf{r}$ is a vector-valued function, $\mathbf{r}(t) = x(t)\mathbf{i} + y(t)\mathbf{j}$

Then

- Velocity $= v(t) = \mathbf{r}'(t) = x'(t)\mathbf{i} + y'(t)\mathbf{j} = \langle x(t), y(t)\rangle$.
- Acceleration $= a(t) = \mathbf{r}''(t) = x''(t)\mathbf{i} + y''(t)\mathbf{j} = \langle x(t), y(t)\rangle$.
- Speed $= \|v(t)\| = \|r'(t)\| = \sqrt{[x'(t)]^2 + [y'(t)]^2}$.
- Distance traveled $= \int_{t_2}^{t_1} \|v(t)\| dt = \int_{t_2}^{t_1} \sqrt{\left(\frac{dx}{dt}\right)^2 + \left(\frac{dy}{dt}\right)^2}\, dt$ (which is the same formula for parametric equations).

AP® Tips

- The topics covered on the multiple-choice sections from the 1997, 1998, 2003, and 2008 exams include
  - finding the area between two polar curves,
  - finding the derivative of a vector-valued function,
  - finding the speed of a particle or information about the motion of a particle from parametric equations for its position or velocity,
  - finding the derivative and tangent line at a given point on a parametric equation, and
  - converting between polar and rectangular coordinates or vice versa.
- There have been three or four of these types of questions on the multiple-choice section each year. On the BC exam, there is usually at least one free-response question (out of six) that deals with polar, parametric, or vector forms.

PAST AP® FREE-RESPONSE PROBLEMS COVERED BY THIS CHAPTER

***Note*:** These and other questions can be found at apcentral.com.

2000 BC 4
2001 BC 1
2002 BC 3
2003 BC 2; 3
2004 BC 3
2005 BC 2
2007 BC 3
2008 BC 3
2009 BC 3c,d
2010 BC 3
2011 BC 6
2012 BC 4d; 6
2013 BC 2
2014 BC 2
2015 BC 2

MULTIPLE-CHOICE QUESTIONS

A calculator may not be used on the following questions.

1. A particle moves in the *xy*-plane such that its position for time $t \geq 0$ is given by $x(t) = 3t^2 - 19t$ and $y(t) = e^{2t-7}$. What is the slope of the tangent to the path of the particle when $t = 4$?

   (A) $-\frac{e}{28}$

   (B) $-\frac{28}{e}$

   (C) $\frac{e}{5}$

   (D) $\frac{2e}{5}$

2. The path of a particle in the *xy*-plane is given by the parametric equations $x(t) = \ln t$ and $y(t) = 5t^2 + 11$ for $t > 0$. An integral expression that represents the length of the path from $t = 2$ to $t = 6$ is

   (A) $\int_2^6 \sqrt{\frac{1}{t^2} + 100t^2}\, dt.$

   (B) $\int_2^6 \sqrt{(\ln t)^2 + (5t^2 + 11)^2}\, dt.$

   (C) $\int_2^6 \sqrt{1 + \frac{1}{t^2}}\, dt.$

   (D) $\int_2^6 \sqrt{1 + 100t^2}\, dt.$

3. The position vector of a particle moving in the *xy*-plane is $(t - \cos t, t^3 - 12t)$ for $t \in [0, 2\pi]$. For what value of *y* does the path of the particle have a horizontal tangent?

   (A) -16

   (B) $\frac{3\pi}{2}$

   (C) 2

   (D) 16

4. A plane curve has parametric equations $x(t) = t^2$ and $y(t) = t^4 + 3t^2$. An expression for the rate of change of the slope of the tangent to the path of the curve is

   (A) $2t^2 + 3$.

   (B) $4t$.

   (C) 2.

   (D) $t^2 + 3$.

5. A particle moves in the xy-plane for $t > 0$ so that $x(t) = t^2 - 4t$ and $y(t) = \ln t$. At time $t = 1$, the particle is moving
(A) to the right and up.
(B) to the left and up.
(C) to the left and down.
(D) to the right and down.

6. The velocity vector of a particle moving in the xy-plane is $(\sqrt[3]{t},\ 6e^{2t-2})$ for all real t. If the position of the particle at $t = 1$ is $(0, 5)$, then the position vector of the particle is
(A) $\left(t^{\frac{4}{3}} - 1,\ \ 3e^{2t-1} + 2\right)$.
(B) $\left(\frac{3}{4}t^{\frac{4}{3}},\ \ 3e^{2t-2}\right)$.
(C) $\left(\frac{3}{4}t^{\frac{4}{3}},\ \ 6e^{2t-2} - 1\right)$.
(D) $\left(\frac{3}{4}t^{\frac{4}{3}} - \frac{3}{4},\ \ 3e^{2t-2} + 2\right)$.

7. A particle moving in the xy-plane has position vector $(e^{2t},\ \sqrt{t}\,)$ for $t \geq 0$. The acceleration vector of the particle is
(A) $\left(4e^{2t},\ \ \frac{1}{4t^{\frac{3}{2}}}\right)$.
(B) $\left(e^{2t},\ \ -\frac{1}{4t^{\frac{3}{2}}}\right)$.
(C) $\left(4e^{2t},\ \ -\frac{1}{4t^{\frac{3}{2}}}\right)$.
(D) $\left(2e^{2t},\ \ \frac{1}{2\sqrt{t}}\right)$.

A calculator may be used for the following questions.

8. A polar curve is given by $r = \frac{3}{2 - \cos\theta}$. The slope of the curve at $\theta = \frac{\pi}{2}$ is
(A) 0.
(B) 0.5.
(C) 0.75.
(D) −0.75.

9. The position vector of a particle moving in the xy-plane is $(t^2, \sin t)$. What is the distance traveled by the particle from $t = 0$ to $t = \pi$?
(A) 9.870
(B) 10.354
(C) 12.335
(D) 42.912

10. The area inside the polar curve $r = 3 + 2\cos\theta$ is
(A) 9.425.
(B) 18.850.
(C) 28.274.
(D) 34.558.

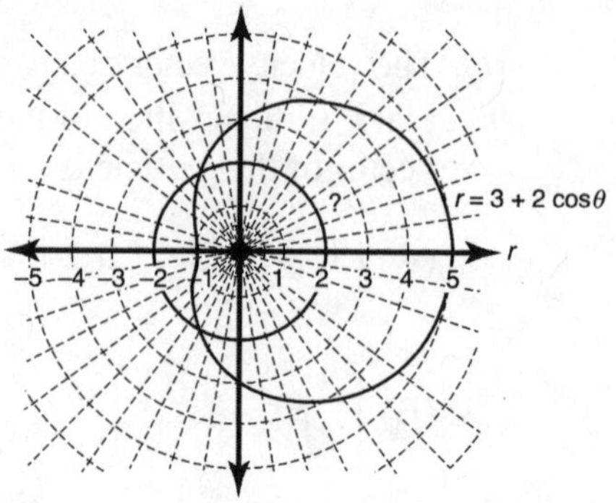

11. A particle moves in the xy-plane so that its acceleration vector for time $t > 0$ is $\left(6t^2, \frac{20}{t}\right)$. If the velocity vector at $t = 1$ is (5,0), then how fast is the particle moving when $t = 3$?
(A) 36.069
(B) 54.410
(C) 58.299
(D) 61.088

A calculator may not be used on the following questions.

12. A particle moves in the xy-plane so that its velocity for time $t \geq 0$ is given by the parametric equations $x'(t) = e^{2t}$ and $y'(t) = \sqrt{3t+1}$. An expression for the distance traveled by the particle on the interval $t \in [1,5]$ is
(A) $\int_1^5 \left(e^{4t} + 3t + 1\right) dt.$
(B) $\int_1^5 \left(e^{2t} + \sqrt{3t+1}\right)^2 dt.$
(C) $\int_1^5 \sqrt{e^{4t} + 3t + 1}\, dt.$
(D) $\int_1^5 \left(\frac{1}{2}e^{2t} + \frac{2}{9}(3t+1)^{\frac{3}{2}}\right) dt.$

13. The area enclosed inside the polar curve $r^2 = 10 \cos(2\theta)$ is
(A) 10.
(B) 5π.
(C) 20.
(D) 10π.

14. A particle moves in the xy-plane so that its velocity vector for time $0 \le t \le 10$ is $(\sqrt{100-10t},\ 2t)$. Which one of the following statements is true about the particle when $t = 1$?
(A) The particle is slowing down.
(B) The particle is speeding up.
(C) The particle is at rest.
(D) The speed of the particle is $\sqrt{90}+2$.

15. A particle moves in the xy-plane for values of time t in the interval $1.25 \le t \le 3.75$ according to the parametric equations $x(t) = \cos(\pi t)$ and $y(t) = t^3 - 24t^2 + 45t$. For what value(s) of t in this interval is the line tangent to the path of the particle vertical?
(A) 3 only
(B) 2 and 3 only
(C) 1.5, 2.5, and 3.5 only
(D) 1.5, 2.5, 3, and 3.5 only

FREE-RESPONSE QUESTION

A calculator may be used on this question.

1. A particle moving in the xy-plane has acceleration vector $\left(\sqrt{t}, \dfrac{1}{1+t^2}\right)$ for all $t \ge 0$. The particle is at rest at time $t = 0$.
   (a) Give the velocity vector of the particle at time $t = 0$.
   (b) Give the velocity vector of the particle at time $t = 3$.
   (c) How fast is the particle moving at time $t = 3$?
   (d) What is the total distance traveled by the particle in the time interval $0 \le t \le 3$?

Answers

MULTIPLE-CHOICE QUESTIONS

1. ANSWER: (D) The slope of the tangent for parametric equations is $dy/dx = \dfrac{dy/dt}{dx/dt} = \dfrac{2e^{2t-7}}{6t-19}$. When $t = 4$, the slope of the tangent is $\dfrac{2e}{5}$.
(*Calculus for AP*®, pages 769–782; 5 EU 2.3; LO 2.3C; EK 2.3C4; MPAC 2,3)

2. ANSWER: (A) $L = \int_{t=a}^{t=b} \sqrt{\left(\dfrac{dx}{dt}\right)^2 + \left(\dfrac{dy}{dt}\right)^2}\,dt; \dfrac{dx}{dt} = \dfrac{1}{t}, \dfrac{dy}{dt} = 10t,$ $a = 2$ and $b = 6$.
$L = \int_2^6 \sqrt{\left(\dfrac{1}{t}\right)^2 + (10t)^2}\,dt = \int_2^6 \sqrt{\dfrac{1}{t^2} + 100t^2}\,dt.$
(*Calculus for AP*®, page 775; EU 3.4; LO 3.4D; EK 3.4D3; MPAC 2,3)

3. ANSWER: (A) A horizontal tangent occurs when $\dfrac{dy}{dt} = 0$.
$\dfrac{dy}{dt} = 3t^2 - 12t = 0 \Rightarrow t = \pm 2$. Since $t = 2$ is the only solution in the domain, the horizontal tangent is $y(2) = 2^3 - 12 \cdot 2 = -16$.
(*Calculus for AP*®, pages 772–782; EU 2.1; LO 2.1C; EK 2.1C7; MPAC 2,3)

4. ANSWER: (C) The slope of the path is $\dfrac{dy}{dx} = \dfrac{dy/dt}{dx/dt} = \dfrac{4t^3 + 6t}{2t} = 2t^2 + 3$. The rate of change of the slope is $\dfrac{d^2y}{dx^2} = \dfrac{\dfrac{d}{dt}\left[\dfrac{dy}{dx}\right]}{dx/dt} = \dfrac{4t}{2t} = 2$. (*Note*: Because this is positive for all t, the path is concave upward for all t. The sign of $\dfrac{d^2y}{dx^2}$ at any point determines the concavity of the path at that point.)
(*Calculus for AP*®, pages 769–782; EU 2.3; LO 2.3C; EK 2.3C4; MPAC 2,3)

5. ANSWER: (B) $x'(t) = 2t - 4 \Rightarrow x'(1) = -2 < 0 \Rightarrow$ the particle is moving *left*. $y'(t) = \dfrac{1}{t} \Rightarrow y'(1) = 1 > 0 \Rightarrow$ the particle is moving up.
(*Calculus for AP*®, pages 769–782; EU 2.3; LO 2.3C; EK 2.3C4; MPAC 2,3)

6. ANSWER: (D) To find the position vector $[x(t),\ y(t)]$, integrate the components of the velocity vector $\left(\frac{dx}{dt}, \frac{dy}{dt}\right)$. $\int t^{\frac{1}{3}}dt = \frac{3}{4}t^{\frac{4}{3}} + C_1$, and since $x(1) = 0, \frac{3}{4}(1)^{\frac{4}{3}} + C_1 = 0 \Rightarrow C_1 = 1\frac{3}{4}$.
Similarly, $\int 6e^{2t-2}\,dt = 3e^{2t-2} + C_2$, and since $y(1) = 5$, $3e^{2(1)-2} + C_2 = 5 \Rightarrow C_2 = 2$. Thus, the vector is $\left(\frac{3}{4}t^{\frac{4}{3}} - \frac{3}{4}, 3e^{2t-2} + 2\right)$.

(*Calculus for AP*®, pages 777–782; EU 3.4; LO 3.4C; EK 3.4C2; MPAC 2,3)

7. ANSWER: (C) An acceleration vector requires that the position vector be differentiated twice. $\frac{d}{dt}\left(e^{2t}\right) = 2e^{2t}$ and $\frac{d}{dt}\left(3e^{2t}\right) = 4e^{2t}$; $\frac{d}{dt}\left(\sqrt{t}\right) = \frac{1}{2}t^{\frac{1}{2}}$ and $\frac{d}{dt}\left(\frac{1}{2}t^{\frac{1}{2}}\right) = -\frac{1}{4}t^{\frac{3}{2}} = -\frac{1}{4t^{\frac{3}{2}}}$. The acceleration vector is $\left(4e^{2t}, -\frac{1}{4t^{\frac{3}{2}}}\right)$.

(*Calculus for AP*®, pages 777–782; EU 2.3; LO 2.3C; EK 2.3C4; MPAC 2,3)

8. ANSWER: (B) The preferred solution is to sketch the curve in polar mode on the calculator. The calculator can be asked for the value of $\left.\frac{dy}{dx}\right|_{\theta=\frac{\pi}{2}}$, which is 0.5. (*Note:* The analytic solution requires that $\frac{dy}{dx}$ be expressed as $\left.\frac{dy/d\theta}{dx/d\theta}\right)$ To find these expressions, the polar conversions of x and y are $x = r\cos\theta = \frac{3\cos\theta}{2-\cos\theta}$ and $y = r\sin\theta = \frac{3\sin\theta}{2-\cos\theta}$. From these, $\frac{dy}{dt}$ and $\frac{dx}{dt}$ can be determined, divided, and evaluated at $\theta = \pi/2\ \frac{dy}{dx} = 0.5$.

(*Calculus for AP*®, pages 803–810; EU 2.2; LO 2.2A; EK 2.2A4; MPAC 2,3)

9. ANSWER: (B) Total distance in plane motion is the integral of the speed function, thus $\int_{t1}^{t2}\sqrt{\left[x'(t)\right]^2 + \left[y'(t)\right]^2}\,dt = \int_0^{\pi}\sqrt{4t^2 + \cos^2 t}\,dt = 10.354$.
(*Calculus for AP*®, pages 777–782; EU 3.4; LO 3.4D; EK 3.4D3; MPAC 2,3)

$$A = \frac{1}{2}\int_{\theta_1}^{\theta_2} r^2\, d\theta = \frac{1}{2}\int_0^{2\pi} (3+2\cos\theta)^2\, d\theta = 34.5575.$$

10. ANSWER: (D) (*Calculus for AP*®, pages 804–809; EU 3.4; LO 3.4D; EK 3.4D1; MPAC 2,3,4)

11. ANSWER: (D) The velocity vector is $(2t^3 + C_1,\ 20\ \ln t + C_2)$. Using the vector (5,0) for $t = 1$, $2(1)^3 + C_1 = 5 \Rightarrow C_1 = 3$ and $20\ \ln(1) + C_2 = 0 \Rightarrow C_2 = 0$. The velocity vector is $(2t^3 + 3,\ 20\ \ln t)$. At $t = 3$, this vector is $(57,\ 20\ \ln 3)$ and the speed is $\sqrt{57^2 + (20\ \ln 3)^2} = 61.088$.

(*Calculus for AP*®, pages 777–782; EU 3.4; LO 3.4C; EK 3.4C2; MPAC 2,3)

12. ANSWER: (C) Distance traveled $= \int_1^5 \sqrt{[x'(t)]^2 + [y'(t)]^2}\ dt$

$$= \int_1^5 \sqrt{e^{4t} + 3t + 1}\ dt.$$

(*Calculus for AP*®, pages 777–782; EU 3.4; LO 3.4D; EK 3.4D3; MPAC 2,5)

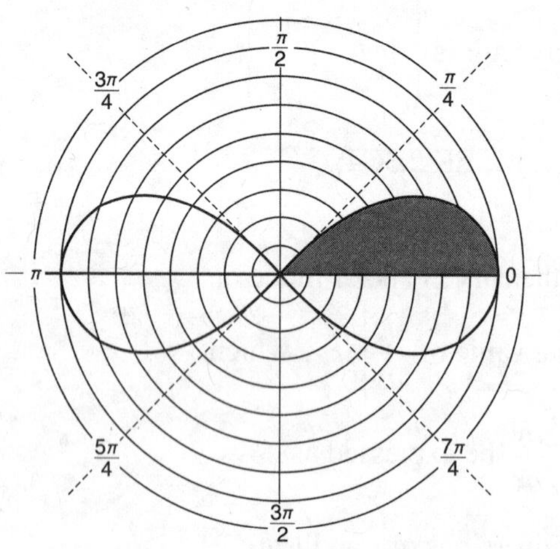

13. ANSWER: (A) The graph of the curve is a lemniscate with axis of symmetry $\theta = 0$ and loop radius $\sqrt{10}$ as shown on the graph. It is sufficient to calculate the area of the shaded region, bounded by the lines $\theta = 0$ and $\theta = \frac{\pi}{4}$, and multiply by 4. Using the polar area formula,

$$A = \int_{\theta_1}^{\theta_2} \frac{1}{2} r^2 d\theta = 4\int_0^{\frac{\pi}{4}} \frac{1}{2}\cdot 10\cos(2\theta)\, d\theta$$

$$= \int_0^{\frac{\pi}{4}} 20\cos(2\theta)\ d\theta = 10\sin(2\theta)\Big|_0^{\frac{\pi}{4}}$$

$$= 10(1-0) = 10.$$

(*Calculus for AP*®, pages 804–809; EU 3.4; LO 3.4D; EK 3.4D1; MPAC 2,3,4)

14. ANSWER: (A) The speed of the particle is $\sqrt{100-10t+4t^2}$

$$\frac{d}{dt}[\text{speed}]\bigg|_{t=1} = \frac{-10+8t}{2\sqrt{100-10t+4t^2}}\bigg|_{t=1} = \frac{-2}{2\sqrt{94}} < 0.$$

Since the derivative of speed is negative, the speed is decreasing. In other words, the particle is slowing down.

(*Calculus for AP*®, pages 777–782; EU 2.3; LO 2.3C; EK 2.3C4; MPAC 2)

15. ANSWER: (B) $\dfrac{dy}{dx} = \dfrac{\frac{dy}{dt}}{\frac{dx}{dt}} = \dfrac{3t^2-24t+45}{-\pi\sin(\pi t)}$. The path has a vertical tangent

when $\dfrac{dx}{dt} = -\pi\sin(\pi t) = 0 \Rightarrow t = 0, 1, 2, 3, \ldots$

For $1.25 \le t \le 3.75$, the solutions are $t = 2$ and 3.

(*Calculus for AP*®, pages 769–782; EU 2.1,2.3; LO 2.1C,2.3B; EK 2.1C7,2.3B1; MPAC 2,3)

FREE-RESPONSE QUESTION

	Solution	Possible points
(a)	The velocity vector at time $t = 0$ is (0, 0), because when the particle is at rest, both components of the velocity vector must be zero.	1: answer with reason
(b)	$\int\sqrt{t}\,dt = \frac{2}{3}t^{\frac{3}{2}} + C_1 \Rightarrow \frac{2}{3}(0)^{\frac{3}{2}} + C_1 = 0 \Rightarrow C_1 = 0$ $\int\frac{1}{1+t^2}\,dt = \tan^{-1}t + C_2 \Rightarrow \tan^{-1}(0) + C_2 = 0, C_2 = 0$ The velocity vector at $t = 3$ is $\left(\frac{2}{3}(3)^{\frac{3}{2}}, \tan^{-1}3\right) \approx (3.464,\ 1.249)$	$4:\begin{cases}1:\text{antiderivative of }\sqrt{t}\\1:\text{antiderivative of }\frac{1}{1+t^2}\\1:\text{both constants of integration}\\\quad <-1> \text{ first error}\\1:\text{answer}\end{cases}$
(c)	$\sqrt{\left(\frac{2}{3}3^{\frac{3}{2}}\right)^2 + \left(\tan^{-1}3\right)^2} = 3.682$	$2:\begin{cases}1:\text{expression for speed}\\1:\text{answer}\end{cases}$
(d)	$\int_0^3\sqrt{\left(\frac{2}{3}t^{\frac{3}{2}}\right)^2 + \left(\tan^{-1}t\right)^2}\,dt = 5.006$	$2:\begin{cases}1:\text{integrand with limits}\\1:\text{answer}\end{cases}$

(a), (b), (c), (d) (*Calculus for AP*®, pages 777–782; EU 2.3,3.4; LO 3.4C,3.4D,2.3; EK 3.4C2,2.3C4,3.4D3; MPAC 2,3)

Part III

Practice Tests

AP® CALCULUS AB PRACTICE TEST 1
Section I, Part A: Multiple-Choice Questions
Time: 60 minutes
Number of Questions: 30

A calculator may not be used on this part of the examination.

1. What is $\int \frac{x-3}{x}\,dx$?

   (A) $1 - 3\ln|x| + C$
   (B) $x - 3\ln|x| + C$
   (C) $1+\frac{3}{x^2}+C$
   (D) $\frac{x^2}{2}-3\ln|x|+C$

2. What is the value of $\lim_{x\to 1}\frac{x^2-3x-4}{x^2-1}$?

   (A) $\frac{5}{2}$
   (B) 0
   (C) $-\frac{5}{2}$
   (D) The limit does not exist.

3. What is the equation of the normal to $f(x) = 3x - 5\cos 2x$ at $x = 0$?

   (A) $x = -5x - 3$
   (B) $y = (-1/5)x + 3$
   (C) $y = 3x + 5$
   (D) $y = (-1/3)x - 5$

4. A particle moves along the y-axis so that its position at any time t, for $0 \le t \le 5$, is given by $y(t) = t^4 - 18t^2$. In which interval(s) is the particle speeding up?

   (A) $0 < t < \sqrt{3}$
   (B) $0 < t < \sqrt{3}$ and $3 < t < 5$
   (C) $3 < t < 5$
   (D) $\sqrt{3} < t < 3$ and $3 < t < 5$

5. Which of the following statements is (are) false for $f(x) = e^x \sin x$?

   I. $\lim_{x\to 0} f(x) = 0$
   II. $\lim_{x\to 0} f(x) = 1$
   III. $\lim_{x\to 0} f(x) = 2$

   (A) I only
   (B) II only
   (C) III only
   (D) None of the statements is false.

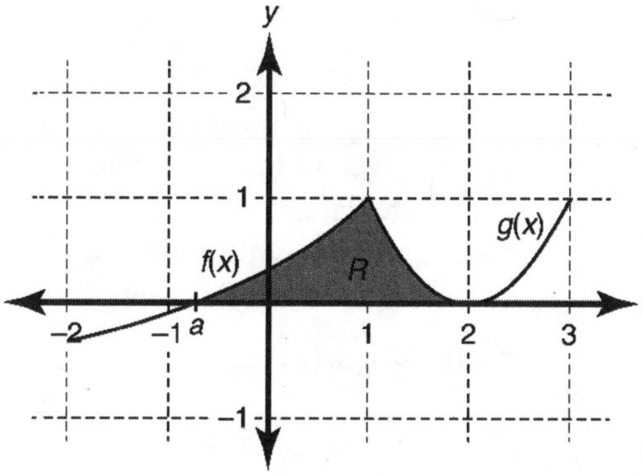

6. The region R, bounded by $f(x)$, $g(x)$, and the x-axis, is shown in the diagram above. Which one of the following integrals represents the volume of the solid generated when R is rotated about the line $y = 1$?

   (A) $\pi\int_a^1[1-f(x)]^2\,dx + \pi\int_1^2[1-g(x)]^2\,dx$
   (B) $\pi\int_a^1\left\{1^2-\left[1-f(x)\right]^2\right\}dx + \pi\int_1^2\left\{1^2-\left[1-g(x)\right]^2\right\}dx$
   (C) $\pi\int_a^1\left\{1-\left[f(x)\right]^2\right\}dx + \pi\int_1^2\left\{1-\left[g(x)\right]^2\right\}dx$
   (D) $\pi\int_a^1\left[1-f(x^2)\right]dx + \pi\int_1^2\left[1-g(x^2)\right]dx$

AP® is a trademark registered by the College Board, which is not affiliated with, and does not endorse, this product.

7. Let $f(x) = (3 + 2x - x^2)^3$ be defined for the closed interval $-2 \le x \le 3$. If M is the y-coordinate of the absolute maximum and m is the y-coordinate of the absolute minimum, what is $|M + m|$?
(A) 189
(B) 125
(C) 64
(D) 61

8. Find the equation of the curve that passes through the point (1, 2) and has a slope of $\left(3+\frac{1}{x}\right)y$ at any point(x, y) on the curve.
(A) $2xe^{3x-3}$
(B) $2xe^{3x+3}$
(C) $2xe^{3}$
(D) $2e^{3x-3}$

9. A continuous function $h(t)$ is defined in the closed interval $10 \le t \le 16$ with values given in the table below. Using the data, find the trapezoidal approximation with three subintervals of unequal length to estimate $\int_{10}^{16} h(t)\,dt$.

t	h(t)
10	10
12	20
15	50
16	80

(A) $\frac{359}{3}$
(B) 130
(C) 200
(D) 270

10. Find the coordinates of the point on $f(x)=\frac{4}{\sqrt{x}}$ that is closest to the origin.
(A) (1,4)
(B) $\left(2,2\sqrt{2}\right)$
(C) $\left(\sqrt{2},2\right)$
(D) $\left(2\sqrt{2},2\sqrt[4]{8}\right)$

11. Evaluate $\lim_{x\to\infty}\frac{3-\sqrt{x^2-1}}{2x+5}$.
(A) $-\frac{1}{2}$
(B) 0
(C) $\frac{3}{5}$
(D) The limit does not exist.

12. If $\tan y + x^3 = y^2 + 1$ and $\frac{dx}{dt} = -2$, what is the value of $\frac{dy}{dt}$ at the point (1, 0)?
(A) −6
(B) −2.5
(C) 6
(D) $\frac{1}{2(\cos 1)^2}$

13. A particle moves in a line with velocity $v(t) = 3t^2 - e^t$. What is the average velocity of the particle in the closed interval $0 \le t \le 2$?
(A) $\frac{8-e^2}{2}$
(B) $\frac{9-e^2}{2}$
(C) $\frac{11-e^2}{2}$
(D) $\frac{13-e^2}{2}$

14. What is the value of $k + c$ if
$$f(x)=\begin{cases}2kx^2 - x, & x>3\\ x^3 + cx, & x\le 3\end{cases}$$ is
everywhere differentiable?
(A) $\frac{5}{4}$
(B) 3
(C) 8
(D) 11

15. A particle moves along the x-axis with a velocity given by $v(t) = t - \sqrt[3]{t}$ for $0 \le t \le 8$. If the particle is 4 units to the left of the origin at $t = 0$, where is the particle at $t = 8$?
(A) 24 units to the right of the origin
(B) 20 units to the right of the origin
(C) 16 units to the right of the origin
(D) $1\frac{3}{4}$ units to the left of the origin

16. $\int_{-2}^{5} |x + 1|\, dx =$
(A) 17
(B) 17.5
(C) 18.5
(D) 19

17. $\int \frac{x+2}{x^2+1} dx =$
(A) $\ln(x^2 + 1) + C$
(B) $\frac{1}{2}\ln(x^2+1) + 2\tan^{-1}(x^2) + C$
(C) $\frac{1}{2}\ln(x^2+1) + 2\tan^{-1}(x) + C$
(D) $\frac{1}{2}\ln(x^2+1) + C$

18. The tangent line to the graph of $g(x)$ at the point (3, 5) has a slope of −2. Use the equation of the tangent to estimate $g(2.98)$.
(A) 2.50
(B) 4.98
(C) 5.02
(D) 5.04

19. Which of the following is the slope field for $\frac{dy}{dx} = \frac{e^x}{y}$?

(A)
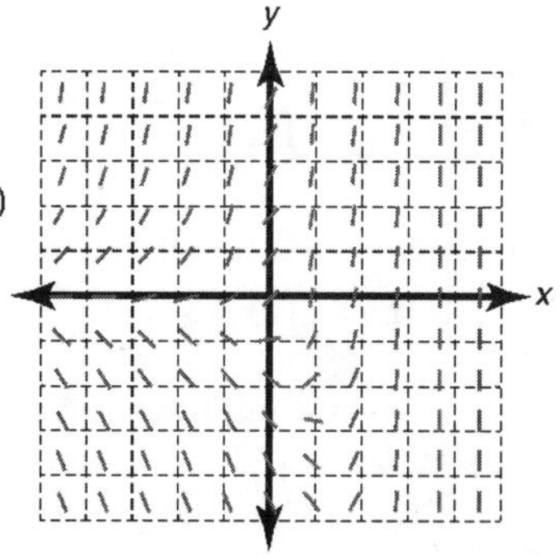

(B)
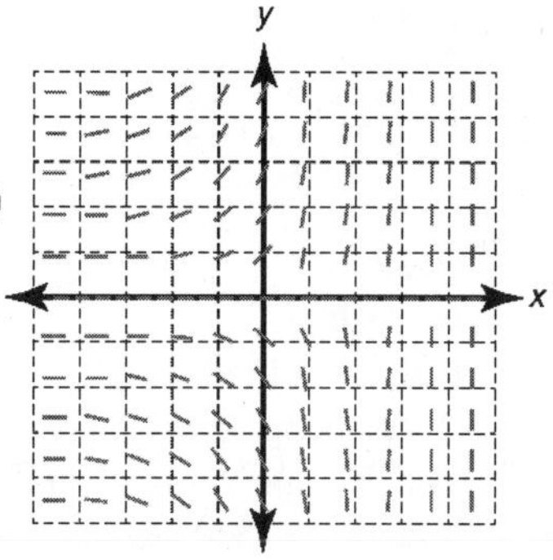

(C)
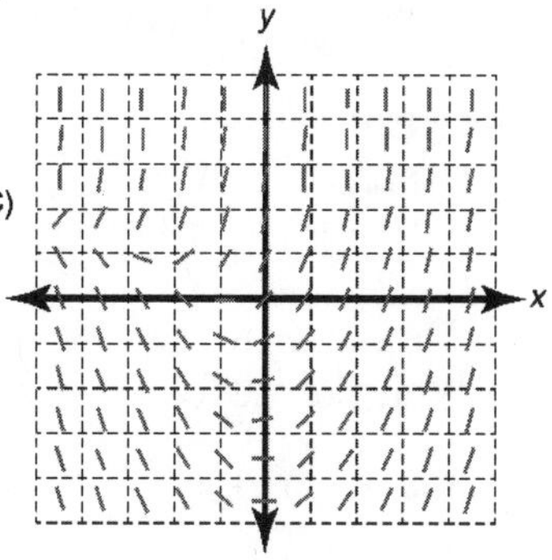

(D)
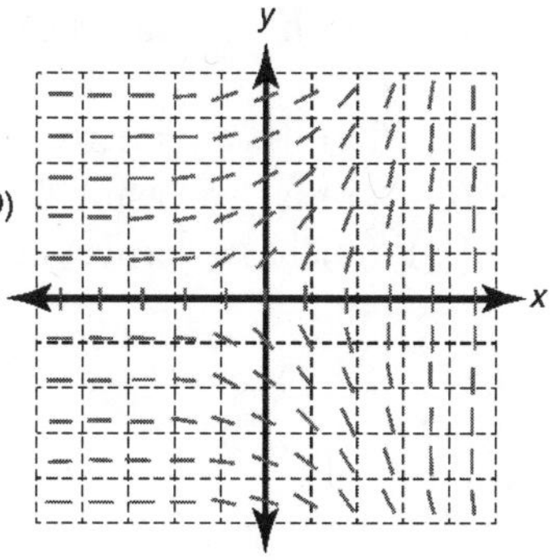

GO ON TO NEXT PAGE

20. Consider the piecewise function,

$$g(x)=\begin{cases} e^{\left(\frac{x}{10}+C\right)}, & x<10 \\ 3, & x=10 \\ \log(x)+1, & x>10. \end{cases}$$

Find the value of C so that $\lim_{x\to 10} g(x)$ exists.

(A) The limit does not exist.
(B) 2
(C) 1
(D) ln 2 − 1

21. If $y=4^{x^2}$, what is $y'(1)$?

(A) 0
(B) ln 4
(C) 8 ln 4
(D) 1 + 2 ln 4

22. What is the value of $g(2)$ if $g(x)=3+\frac{d}{dx}\left[\int_1^{x^2}(1+t^2)\,dt\right]$?

(A) 20
(B) 23
(C) 24
(D) 71

23. Which of the following statements is true for $f(x)=\frac{1+e^x}{e^x-1}$?

(A) $f(x)$ has a relative maximum at $x=1$.
(B) $f(x)$ has a y-intercept at $x=0$.
(C) $f(x)$ is decreasing for all x, $x\neq 0$.
(D) $f(x)$ has a vertical asymptote at $x=1$.

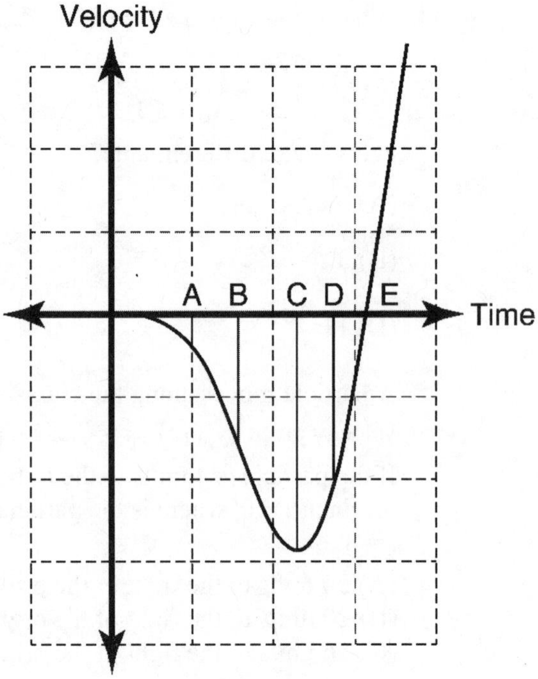

24. A particle moves along the x-axis. At which time on the velocity versus time graph given above is the particle farthest left of its starting point?

(A) C
(B) E
(C) A
(D) D

25. If $\sin xy = x + y$, what is $\frac{dy}{dx}$?

(A) $\frac{y\cos xy+1}{1-x\cos xy}$

(B) $\frac{y\cos xy-1}{1-x\cos xy}$

(C) $\frac{\cos xy-1}{1-x\cos xy}$

(D) $\frac{\cos x-1}{1-\cos y}$

The graph of $f(x)$ consists of four line segments as shown below. Let g be the function given by $g(x)=\int_{-4}^{x} f(t)\,dt$. Use this information for problems 26–28.

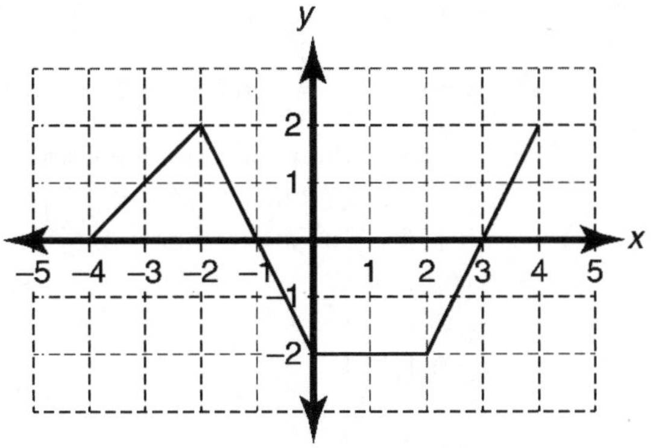

26. What is $g(0)$?
    (A) 4
    (B) 2
    (C) 6
    (D) −2

27. What is the equation of the tangent to $g(x)$ at the point $(3, g(3))$?
    (A) $y=0$
    (B) $y=-3$
    (C) $y=x-3$
    (D) $y=x+3$

28. Which of the following is false for $g(x)$?
    (A) $g(x)$ has a relative maximum at $x=-1$.
    (B) $g(x)$ has a relative minimum at $x=3$.
    (C) $g(x)$ has a relative maximum at $x=-2$.
    (D) $g(x)$ is decreasing in the interval $2<x<3$.

29. $\lim_{x\to 0}\frac{\sin 6x}{x^2-3x}$
    (A) −2
    (B) −1/2
    (C) −1/3
    (D) Does not exist

30. $\lim_{x\to 1}\frac{\int_{2}^{4-2x}\sqrt{t+7}\,dt}{x-1}$
    (A) 3
    (B) −3
    (C) −6
    (D) Does not exist

END OF SECTION I PART A

GO ON TO NEXT PAGE

Section I, Part B: Multiple-Choice Questions
Time: 45 minutes
Number of Questions: 15

A calculator may be used on this part of the examination.

31. What is the area of the first closed region to the left of the y-axis, bounded by the curves $f(x) = -\tan x$ and $g(x) = 2x^4$?
(A) 1.206
(B) 0.240
(C) 0.691
(D) 0.452

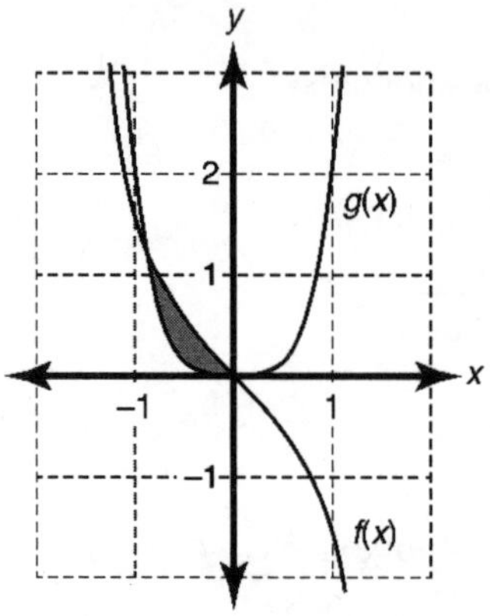

32. What is the average rate of change of $f(x) = \dfrac{e^{\frac{1}{x}}}{x^2}$ in the interval $-4 \le x \le -1$?
(A) 0.106
(B) 0.137
(C) 0.319
(D) 0.411

33. Consider the integral expression $\int_0^{\frac{\pi}{2}} \sin(2x)\, e^{\cos(2x)} dx$. If $u = \cos(2x)$, then which integral below is equivalent to the given integral?
(A) $-\dfrac{1}{2}\int_0^{\pi} e^u du$
(B) $-2\int_0^{\pi} e^u du$
(C) $-\dfrac{1}{2}\int_{-1}^{1} e^u du$
(D) $\dfrac{1}{2}\int_{-1}^{1} e^u du$

34. Let $f(x) = \dfrac{1}{x}$ and $k > 1$. If the area between the x-axis and the graph of $f(x)$ in the closed interval $k \le x \le k+1$ is 0.125 where $k > 1$, then what is the value of k?
(A) 1.133
(B) 1.134
(C) 2.998
(D) 7.510

35. A solid has its base in the xy-plane, bounded by the x-axis, the y-axis, and the function $y = 3 - x^5$. If cross sections taken perpendicular to the x-axis are semicircles whose diameters are in the xy-plane, what is the volume of this solid?
(A) 3.335
(B) 4.247
(C) 5.239
(D) 6.671

36. Shampoo drips from a crack in the side of a plastic bottle at a rate modeled by $Y(t) = \dfrac{t}{\sqrt{1+t^{\frac{3}{2}}}}$, where $Y(t)$ is in ounces per minute. If there are 32 ounces in the bottle at $t = 0$, how many ounces are left in the bottle after 5 minutes?
(A) 26.937 ounces
(B) 24.355 ounces
(C) 7.645 ounces
(D) The bottle will be empty before 5 minutes has elapsed.

37. Consider the function $f(x) = x^3 + 2$ in the closed interval $0 < a \le c \le 2$. If the value guaranteed by the Mean Value Theorem in the closed interval is $c = 1.720$, then what is the value of a?
    (A) 1.260
    (B) 1.424
    (C) 1.602
    (D) 1.680

38. The sketch of $f(x)$ is shown below, with regions bounded by $f(x)$ and the x-axis indicated by P, Q, and R. If $\int_a^d f(x)\,dx = -7$, $\int_b^d f(x)\,dx = -2$, and $\int_c^a f(x)\,dx = 17$, what is $\int_b^c f(x)\,dx$?

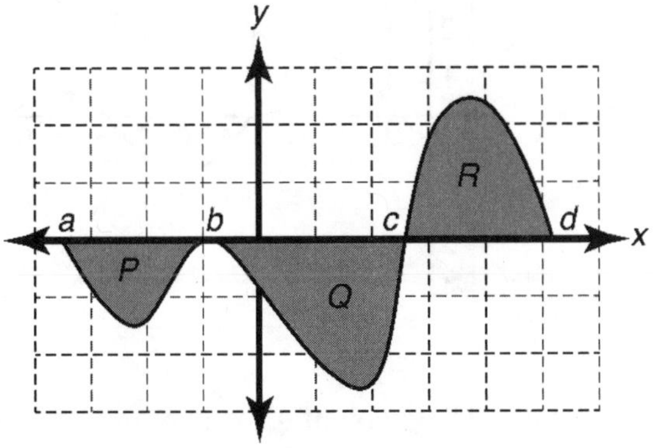

    (A) −12
    (B) −6
    (C) −3
    (D) 4

39. Let $h(x) = xg(x)$, where $g(x) = f^{-1}(x)$. Use the table of values below to find $h'(5)$.

x	$f(x)$	$f'(x)$
2	4	−1
3	5	2
5	1	3

    (A) $\frac{1}{2}$
    (B) 2.5
    (C) 3
    (D) 5.5

40. The height of a conical sand pile is always twice the radius. If sand is being added to the pile at a rate of 30π cm^3/min, how fast is the height of the pile increasing when the circumference of the base of the sand pile is 120π cm? $\left(V_{\text{cone}} = \frac{\pi}{3}r^2h\right)$
    (A) $\frac{1}{120\pi}$ cm/min
    (B) $\frac{1}{120}$ cm/min
    (C) $\frac{2}{15}$ cm/min
    (D) $\frac{1}{4\pi}$ cm/min

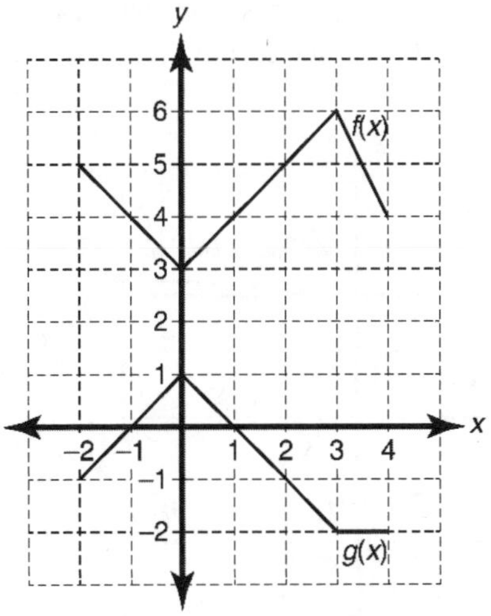

41. The graphs of $f(x)$ and $g(x)$ are shown above. If $h(x) = \frac{g(2x)}{f(x)}$, use the graphs to find $h'(1)$.
    (A) $-\frac{7}{4}$
    (B) $-\frac{9}{16}$
    (C) $-\frac{7}{16}$
    (D) $-\frac{5}{16}$

GO ON TO NEXT PAGE

42. The number of home fires each day in a certain city increases as the temperature drops. The rate of home fires is modeled by $F(t) = 4\cos\left(\frac{t}{58} - 2\right) + 6$, for $0 \le t \le 365$ days, where midnight on January 1st corresponds to $t = 0$. Which of the following is *closest* to the approximate number of fires in the first quarter of the year?

(A) 910
(B) 660
(C) 540
(D) 330

43. The graphs of the derivatives of three functions, *f*, *g*, and *h*, are given below. Which of the functions has at least one point of inflection in the open interval $-3 < x < 2$?

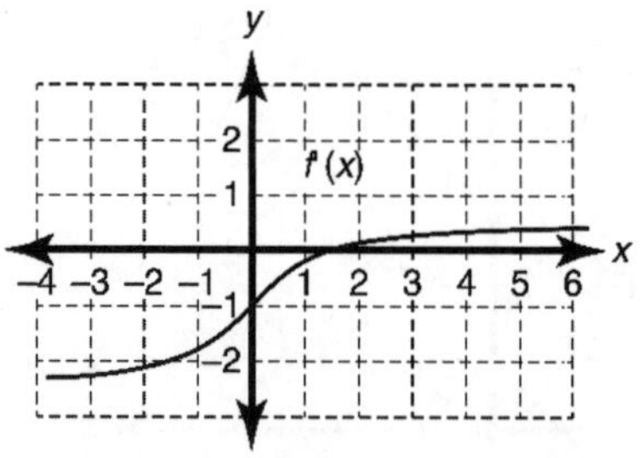

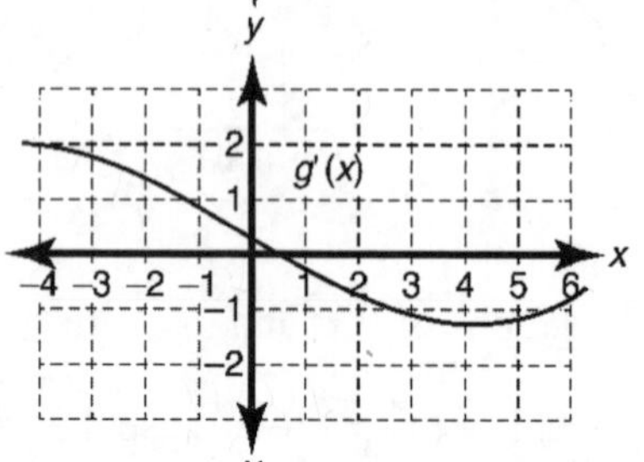

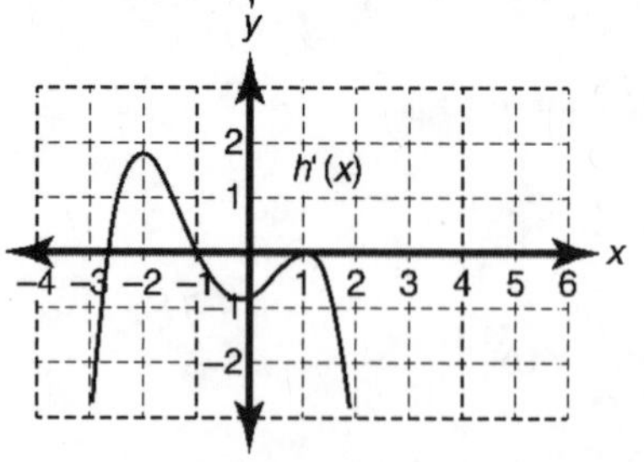

(A) Only $f(x)$
(B) Only $g(x)$
(C) Only $h(x)$
(D) Only $f(x)$ and $g(x)$

44. The price of a newly issued stock varies during the first 10 days after its initial offering and is modeled by $P(t) = \log(2t + 1)\sin t + 20$, where t is in days. To the nearest cent, what is the price of the stock when the price of the stock is decreasing most rapidly in the interval $0 < t < 10$?

(A) \$7.98
(B) \$9.49
(C) \$19.91
(D) \$20.12

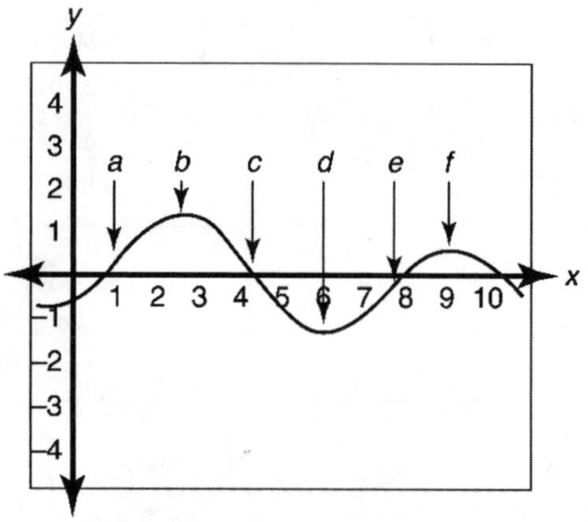

45. The graph of $g'(x)$ is shown on the graph above. For which of the stated interval(s) is the function $g(x)$ both increasing and concave up?

(A) $a < x < b$
(B) $e < x < f$
(C) $a < x < b$ and $e < x < f$
(D) $a < x < b$ and $d < x < f$

END OF SECTION I PART B

GO ON TO NEXT PAGE

Section II
Free-Response Questions
Time: 1 hour and 30 minutes
Number of Problems: 6

Part A
Time: 30 minutes
Number of Problems: 2

You may use a calculator for any problem in this section.

1. The velocity of a particle moving on the y-axis is given by $v(t)=\dfrac{e^{t-2}}{2t^2+3}-4$ on the interval $1\le t\le 11$. At time $t = 1$, the particle is 3 units above the origin.
   (a) During what time interval is the particle moving down?
   (b) What is the position of the particle when it is farthest south of the origin?
   (c) At what time is the particle's average velocity twice the instantaneous velocity on $2\le t\le 8$?
   (d) Find the total distance traveled by the particle during the time where $1\le t\le 11$.

2. A solution is draining through a conical filter into an identical conical container as shown in the diagram to the right. The solution drips from the upper filter into the lower container at a rate of $\pi\ \text{cm}^3/\text{sec}\left(V_{\text{cone}}=\dfrac{\pi}{3}r^2h\right)$.
   (a) How fast is the level in the upper filter dropping when the solution level in the upper filter is at 6 cm?
   (b) If the conical filter is initially full, what is the level of the solution in the lower level when the solution level in the upper filter is at 6 cm and how fast is the level in the lower filter rising?
   (c) How fast is the surface area of the solution in the lower filter increasing when the volume in the upper filter equals the volume in the lower container?

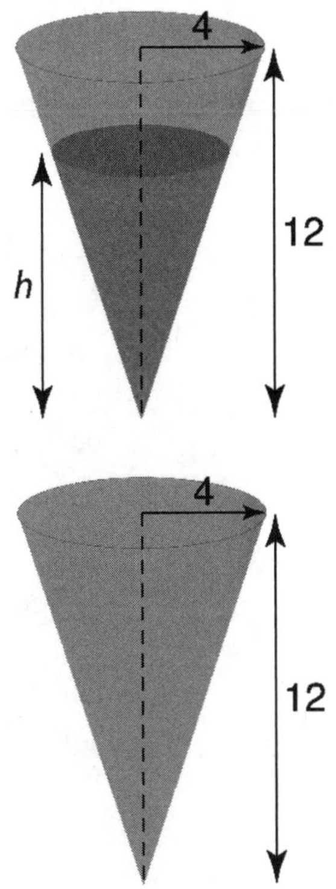

END OF SECTION II PART A

Section II
Part B
Time: 60 minutes
Number of Problems: 4

You may not use a calculator for any problem in this section. During the timed portion for Section II, Part B, you may continue to work on the problems in Section II, Part A without the use of a calculator.

3. A 1,000 gallon tank is initially empty. A valve is opened and water begins to flow into the tank at a variable rate, $R(t)$, in gallons per minute, where t is the number of minutes since the valve was opened. The rate is recorded in the chart and graph below.

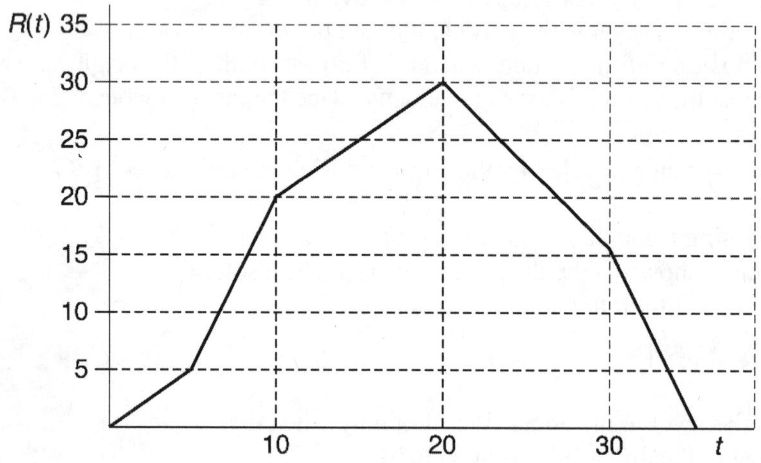

t min	$R(t)$ gal/min
0	0
5	5
10	20
20	30
30	16
35	0

(a) Approximate the volume of water that flows into the tank for the time interval $0 \le t \le 35$ using a right Riemann sum for the five unequal subintervals indicated by the data in the chart. Indicate units of measure.

(b) Approximate the value of $\frac{1}{20}\int_{10}^{30} R(t)\,dt$ using the Trapezoidal Rule. Indicate units of measure with your answer. Interpret the meaning of your answer in the context of the problem.

(c) At time $t = 20$ minutes, a drain is opened at the bottom of the tank and water leaves the tank at a rate of $(t + 10)$ gallons per minute. Set up, but do not evaluate, an integral expression in terms of a single independent variable that represents the volume of the water in the tank at time $t = 35$ minutes.

4. Consider the curve defined by $x^2 + 4xy + y^2 = -12$.
   (a) Find $\frac{dy}{dx}$ in terms of x and y.
   (b) Find the equations of all horizontal tangent lines.
   (c) Find the equation of the tangent line at the point (−4, 14).
   (d) If $\frac{dy}{dt} = -\frac{1}{2}$ at the point (−4, 14), find $\frac{dx}{dt}$.
   (e) Use the tangent in part c to estimate the value of k for the point (−4.01, k) on the curve.

5. Let L be the tangent to $f(x) = \sqrt{x}$ at any point on the curve as shown in the diagram to the right.
   (a) Show that the x-intercept of the tangent to the curve at the point $(h, \sqrt{h})$ is $-h$.
   (b) Find the area of the region bounded by the tangent to the curve at $x = 4$, the curve, and the x-axis.
   (c) What is the volume when the region found in part b is rotated about the line $x = 4$?

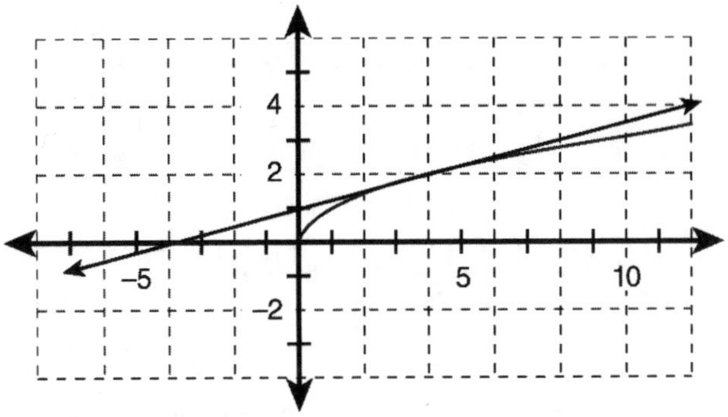

6. Let f be a function defined in the closed interval $0 \le x \le 6$. The graph of f consists of three line segments and a semicircle. Let $g(x) = 3 + \int_2^x f(t)\,dt$.
   (a) Find $g(1)$, $g'(1)$, and $g''(1)$.
   (b) What is the average rate of change of $g(x)$ in the interval $2 \le x \le 6$?
   (c) Identify the x-coordinate of any extrema of $g(x)$ in $0 < x < 6$. Explain your reasoning.
   (d) Identify the x-coordinate of any points of inflection of $g(x)$ in $0 < x < 6$.

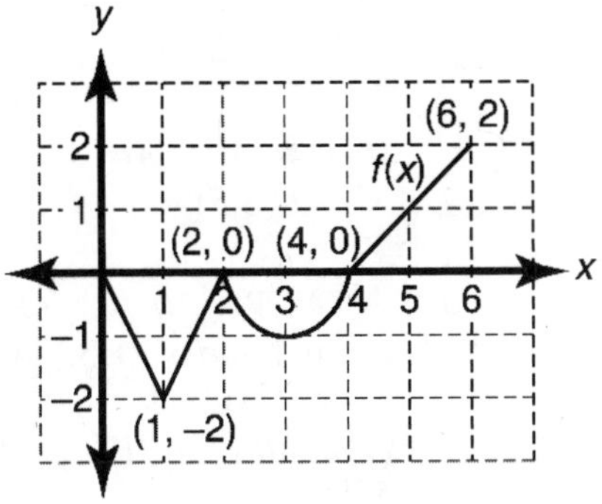

END OF EXAMINATION

Answers and Answer Explanations

Using the table below, score your test. Determine how many questions you answered correctly and how many you answered incorrectly. Additional information about scoring is at the end of the Practice Test.

1. B	2. A	3. D	4. B	5. D
6. B	7. D	8. A	9. C	10. B
11. A	12. C	13. B	14. D	15. C
16. C	17. C	18. D	19. D	20. D
21. C	22. D	23. C	24. B	25. B
26. B	27. B	28. C	29. A	30. C
31. B	32. A	33. D	34. D	35. A
36. A	37. B	38. A	39. D	40. B
41. C	42. B	43. C	44. C	45. C

MULTIPLE-CHOICE QUESTIONS

1. ANSWER: (B) $\int \frac{x-3}{x}\,dx = \int (1-\frac{3}{x})\,dx = x - 3\ln|x| + C$
(*Calculus for AP*®, pages 386–389; EU 3.3; LO 3.3B; EK 3.3B5; MPAC 3,5)

2. ANSWER: (A) Rewrite the limit into factored form, simplify, and substitute $x = -1$.

$$\lim_{x\to -1}\frac{x^2-3x-4}{x^2-1} = \lim_{x\to -1}\frac{(x-4)(x+1)}{(x-1)(x+1)} = \lim_{x\to -1}\frac{(x-4)}{(x-1)} = \frac{-5}{-2} = \frac{5}{2}$$

(*Calculus for AP*®, pages 105–113; EU 1.1; LO 1.1C; EK 1.1C2; MPAC 3,5)

3. ANSWER: (D) $f'(x) = 3 + 10\sin 2x$, and $f'(0) = 3$. The slope of the normal line is $-1/3$. For $f(0) = -5$, the normal is $y + 5 = (-1/3)(x - 0)$, or $y = (-1/3)x - 5$.
(*Calculus for AP*®, pages 165–167; EU 2.3; LO 2.3B; EK 2.3B1; MPAC 2,3)

4. ANSWER: (B) A particle speeds up in any interval when the velocity and acceleration have the same sign. Take the first and second derivative to find velocity and acceleration. Set $v(t) = 4t^3 - 36t = 4t(t^2 - 9) = 0$ and $a(t) = 12t^2 - 36 = 12(t^2 - 3) = 0$ and use the interval chart to analyze the motion of the particle.

	$0 < t < \sqrt{3}$	$\sqrt{3} < t < 3$	$3 < t < 5$
$v(t)$	negative	negative	positive
$a(t)$	negative	positive	positive
Particle	*speeding up*	slowing down	*speeding up*

(*Calculus for AP*®, page 105; EU 2.3; LO 2.3C; EK 2.3C1; MPAC 2,3)

5. ANSWER: (D) Find $f'(x)$ and $f''(x)$ and evaluate each limit.

Case I: $f(x) = e^x \sin x$ and $\lim_{x\to 0} e^x \sin x = e^0(0) = 1(0) = 0$

Case II: $f'(x) = e^x \sin x + e^x \cos x = e^x(\sin x + \cos x)$ and $\lim_{x\to 0} f'(x) = e^0(0+1) = 1$

Case III: $f''(x) = e^x(\sin x + \cos x) + e^x(\cos x - \sin x) = 2e^x \cos x$ and $\lim_{x\to 0} f'(x) = 2e^0(1) = 2$

Therefore, none of the statements is false.
(*Calculus for AP*®, pages 105–113; EU 1.1,2.1; LO 1.1C,2.1C; EK 1.1C1,2.1C3; MPAC 2,3,5)

6. ANSWER: (B) Using the Washer Method,

$$V = \pi \int_a^1 \left[1^2 - (1 - f(x))^2\right] dx + \pi \int_1^2 \left[1^2 - (1 - g(x))^2\right] dx,$$

where $r_0 = 1$ and $r_1 = 1 - y$.

(*Calculus for AP*®, pages 525–528; EU 3.4; LO 3.4D; EK 3.4D2; MPAC 2,4)

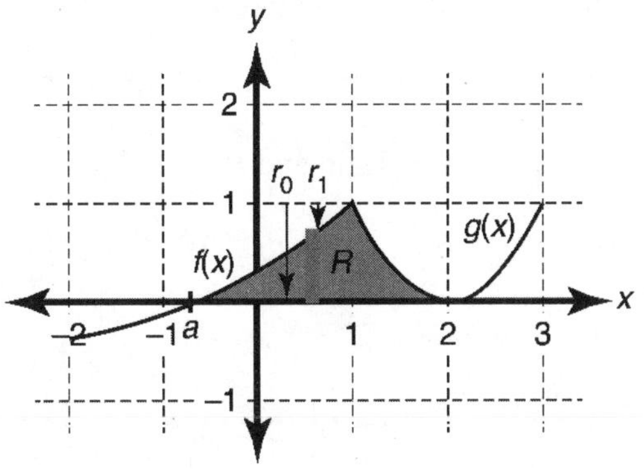

7. ANSWER: (D)

$$f'(x) = 3(3 + 2x - x^2)^2 (2 - 2x)$$
$$= 3(3 - x)^2 (1 + x)^2 \cdot 2(1 - x)$$
$$= 0$$

Evaluate $f(x)$ at the critical points and the end points of the closed interval.

x	-2	-1	1	3
$f(x)$	-125	0	64	0
extrema	absolute minimum		absolute maximum	

Therefore, $M = -125$, $m = 64$, and $|M + m| = 61$.
(*Calculus for AP*®, pages 292–293; EU 2.3; LO 2.3C; EK 2.3C3; MPAC 1,2,3)

8. ANSWER: (A) If the slope of the curve is $\left(3 + \frac{1}{x}\right)y$, then $\frac{dy}{dx} = \left(3 + \frac{1}{x}\right)y$.

Separating the variables yields $\int \frac{dy}{y} = \int 3 + \frac{1}{x}\, dx$, for $x > 0$. Therefore,

$\ln|y| = 3x + \ln x + C_1$ and $y = e^{3x + \ln x + C_1} = Ce^{3x}e^{\ln x} = Cxe^{3x}$. Using the

initial condition (1, 2), it follows that $2 = Ce^3 \Rightarrow C = \frac{2}{e^3}$. By substitution and the rules for exponents, we simplify and get $y = \frac{2}{e^3}xe^{3x} = 2xe^{3x-3}$.
(*Calculus for AP*®, pages 618–624; EU 3.5; LO 3.5A; EK 3.5A1,3.5A2; MPAC 2,3)

9. ANSWER: (C) Evaluate the sum using trapezoids.
$\frac{1}{2}[2(10+20)+3(20+50)+1(50+80)] = \frac{1}{2}(400) = 200$
(*Calculus for AP*®, pages 400–401; EU 3.2; LO 3.2B; EK 3.2B1,3.2B2; MPAC 2,4)

10. ANSWER: (B) Let the point of the curve be given by $P\left(x, \frac{4}{\sqrt{x}}\right)$. Let the square of the distance between the origin and P be defined by
$D(x) = (x-0)^2 + \left(\frac{4}{\sqrt{x}} - 0\right)^2 = x^2 + \frac{16}{x}$. Therefore,
$D'(x) = 2x - \frac{16}{x^2} = 0$ and then $x = 2$. With $D'(x) = 2 + \frac{32}{x^3}$ and $D''(2) > 0$, then $x = 2$ is the x coordinate of the point on

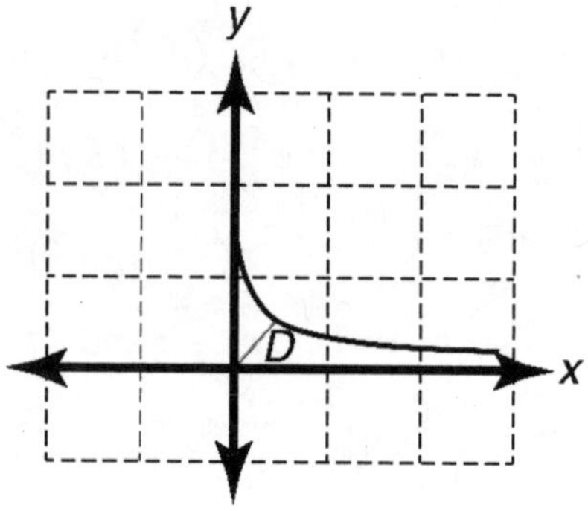

the curve that is closest to the origin. And the y coordinate is $\frac{4}{\sqrt{2}} = 2\sqrt{2}$.
(*Calculus for AP*®, pages 365–372; EU 2.3; LO 2.3C3; EK 2.3C3; MPAC 1,2,3)

11. ANSWER: (A) Since the degree of the numerator is equal to the degree of the denominator $\left(\sqrt{x^2} = x\right)$, divide each term in the numerator and denominator by x. The resulting limit can then be evaluated:

$$\lim_{x\to\infty} \frac{\frac{3}{x} - \sqrt{\frac{x^2}{x^2} - \frac{1}{x^2}}}{\frac{2x}{x} + \frac{5}{x}} = \lim_{x\to\infty} \frac{\frac{3}{x} - \sqrt{1 - \frac{1}{x^2}}}{2 + \frac{5}{x}} = \frac{0 - \sqrt{1-0}}{2+0} = -\frac{1}{2}.$$

(*Calculus for AP*®, pages 117–128; EU 1.1; LO 1.1C; EK 1.1C2,1.1C3; MPAC 2,3,5)

12. ANSWER: (C) Differentiating implicitly with respect to t,
$\sec^2 y\left(\frac{dy}{dt}\right) + 3x^2\left(\frac{dx}{dt}\right) = 2y\left(\frac{dy}{dt}\right)$. Substituting
$\sec^2 0\left(\frac{dy}{dt}\right) + 3(1)^2(-2) = 2(0)\left(\frac{dy}{dt}\right) \Rightarrow \frac{dy}{dt} - 6 = 0$; therefore, $\frac{dy}{dt} = 6$.

(*Calculus for AP*®, pages 240–245; EU 2.3; LO 2.3C; EK 2.3C2; MPAC 2,3,5)

13. ANSWER: (B) $v_{avg} = \frac{1}{2-0}\int_0^2 3t^2 - e^t\,dt$ becomes

$$\frac{1}{2}\left(t^3 - e^t\right)\Big|_0^2 = \frac{1}{2}\left[\left(2^3 - e^2\right) - \left(0 - e^0\right)\right] = \frac{1}{2}\left(8 - e^2 + 1\right) = \frac{9 - e^2}{2}.$$

(*Calculus for AP*®, pages 490–494; EU 2.1; LO 2.1A; EK 2.1A1; MPAC 2,3,5)

14. ANSWER: (D) $f'(x) = \begin{cases} 4kx - 1, & x > 3 \\ 3x^2 + c, & x \le 3 \end{cases}$. If $f(x)$ is differentiable at $x = 3$, then $\lim_{x\to 3^-} f(x) = \lim_{x\to 3^+} f(x)$ and $\lim_{x\to 3^-} f'(x) = \lim_{x\to 3^+} f'(x)$. The solution of the system $18k - 3 = 27 + 3c$ and $12k - 1 = 27 + c$, is $k = 3$ and $c = 8$. Thus, $(k + c) = 11$.
(*Calculus for AP*®, pages 182–184; EU 1.2,2.2; LO 1.2A,2.2B; EK 1.2A1,2.2B2; MPAC 1,2,3)

15. ANSWER: (C) $x(8) = x(0) + \int_0^8 v(t)\,dt$

$$x(8) = -4 + \int_0^8 \left(t - t^{\frac{1}{3}}\right) dt$$

$$= -4 + \left(\frac{t^2}{2} - \frac{3}{4}t^{\frac{4}{3}}\right)\Bigg|_0^8$$

$$= -4 + \left[\frac{64}{2} - \frac{3}{4}\left(8^{\frac{4}{3}}\right)\right]$$

$$= -4 + 32 - 12 = 16$$

Therefore, the particle is 16 cm to the right of the origin.
(*Calculus for AP*®, pages 277–287; 11th ed., pages 281–291; EU 3.3; LO 3.3B; EK 3.3B2; MPAC 2,3)

16. ANSWER: (C) Solving the problem geometrically, the integral given equals the sum of the areas of two right triangles. For $f(x) = |x + 1|$, the x-intercept is -1, and the dimensions of the triangles are labeled on the diagram.

An alternate method would be to express $f(x)$ as a piecewise function and perform the integration. Thus, $f(x) = \begin{cases} -x - 1, & x < -1 \\ x + 1, & x \ge -1 \end{cases}$ and the area $= \int_{-2}^{-1}(-x-1)\,dx + \int_{-1}^{5}(x+1)\,dx$. Then,

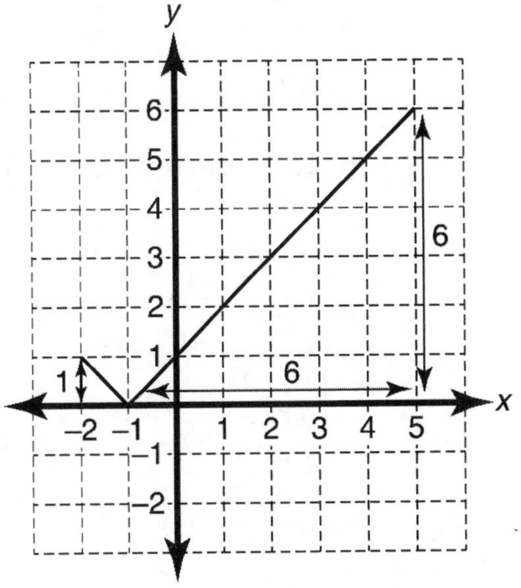

$$\text{Area} = \frac{1}{2}(1)(1) + \frac{1}{2}(6)(6) = 18.5$$

$$\left(-\frac{x^2}{2}-x\right)\Bigg|_{-2}^{-1}+\left(\frac{x^2}{2}+x\right)\Bigg|_{-1}^{5}$$

$$=\left[-\frac{1}{2}+1-(-2+2)\right]+\left[\frac{25}{2}+5-\left(\frac{1}{2}-1\right)\right]$$

$$\Rightarrow\frac{1}{2}+12+6=18.5.$$

(*Calculus for AP*®, pages 450–454; EU 3.2; LO 3.2C; EK 3.2C1; MPAC 4,5)

17. ANSWER: (C) $\int\left(\frac{x+2}{x^2+1}\right)dx=\int\left(\frac{x}{x^2+1}\right)dx+\int\left(\frac{2}{x^2+1}\right)dx$. For the first integral, let $u=x^2+1$, and $du=2x\,dx$. After substitution, or $\frac{1}{2}\int\frac{du}{u}+\int\frac{2}{x^2+1}dx=\frac{1}{2}\ln u+2\tan^{-1}x+C$ or $\frac{1}{2}\ln\left(x^2+1\right)+2\tan^{-1}x+C.$
(*Calculus for AP*®, pages 457–461, 447; EU 3.3; LO 3.3B; EK 3.3B5; MPAC 2,3)

18. ANSWER: (D) The equation of the tangent at $x=3$ is given by $y-5=-2(x-3)$. When $x=2.98$, $y=5+(-2)(0-0.02)=5.04$.
(*Calculus for AP*®, pages 165–167; EU 2.3; LO 2.3B; EK 2.3B2; MPAC 2,3)

19. ANSWER: (D) The slope field for $\frac{dy}{dx}=\frac{e^x}{y}$ will have vertical segments at all points on the x-axis because $y=0$. Those points above the x-axis will have segments with positive slopes, and those below will have negative slopes, as e^x is always positive.
(*Calculus for AP*®, pages 606–611; EU 2.3; LO 2.3F; EK 2.3F1; MPAC 4)

20. ANSWER: (D) Although the function may be discontinuous at $x=10$, the limit does exist if $\lim_{x\to10^-}g(x)=\lim_{x\to10^+}g(x)$. Therefore, $\lim_{x\to10^-}e^{\left(\frac{x}{10}+C\right)}=$ $\lim_{x\to10^+}\left(\log(x)+1\right)$. Then, $e^{\left(\frac{10}{10}+C\right)}=\log(10)+1\Rightarrow e^{1+C}=1+1\Rightarrow e^{1+C}=2.$
Finally, $1+C=\ln 2$, and $C=\ln 2-1$.
(*Calculus for AP*®, pages 111–112; EU 1.1; LO 1.1A; EK 1.1A2; MPAC 2,3)

21. ANSWER: (C) For $y=4^{x^2}$, $y'=4^{x^2}(\ln 4)(2x)$ and $y'=4(\ln 4)(2)=8\ln 4$.
(*Calculus for AP*®, pages 227–233; EU 2.1; LO 2.1C; EK 2.1C2; MPAC 2,3)

22. ANSWER: (D) By the Second Fundamental Theorem,
$g(x)=3 + [1 + (x^2)^2](2x) = 3 + (1 + x^4)(2x)$.
Then, $g(2) = 3 + (1 + 16)(4) = 71$.
(*Calculus for AP®*, pages 436–437; EU 3.3; LO 3.3A; EK 3.3A2; MPAC 3,5)

23. ANSWER: (C) There is no root for $f(x)$, because $e^x+1 \neq 0$. There is a vertical asymptote at $x = 0$ because $e^0 - 1 = 0$. And there is no y-intercept at $x = 0$ because $f(x)$ is not defined at $x = 0$. The only true statement is found by taking the derivative and analyzing it:
$f'(x) = \dfrac{e^x\left(e^x - 1\right) - e^x\left(1 + e^x\right)}{\left(e^x - 1\right)^2} = \dfrac{-2e^x}{\left(e^x - 1\right)^2}$. There are no critical points for $f(x)$ and $f'(x)$ is always less than 0, so $f(x)$ is decreasing for all x, provided $x \neq 0$.
(*Calculus for AP®*, pages 350–362; EU 1.1,2.2; LO 1.1D,2.2A; EK 1.1D1,2.2A1; MPAC 2,3)

24. ANSWER: (B) The particle moves to the left until time E because the velocity is less than 0 and is therefore farthest to the left of its starting position.
(*Calculus for AP®*, page 509; EU 3.4; LO 3.4A; EK 3.4A2; MPAC 4)

25. ANSWER: (B) Differentiating implicitly yields
$(\cos xy)\left[y + x\dfrac{dy}{dx}\right] = 1 + \dfrac{dy}{dx}$. Therefore, $\dfrac{dy}{dx} = \dfrac{y\cos xy - 1}{1 - x\cos xy}$.
(*Calculus for AP®*, pages 240–245; EU 2.1; LO 2.1C; EK 2.1C5; MPAC 2,3)

26. ANSWER: (B) $g(0) = \int_{-4}^{0} f(t)\,dt = \frac{1}{2}(3)(2) - \frac{1}{2}(1)(2) = 2$
(*Calculus for AP®*, pages 422–423; EU 3.2; LO 3.2C; EK 3.2C1; MPAC 2,4)

27. ANSWER: (B) $g(3) = \int_{-4}^{3} f(t)\,dt = \frac{1}{2}(3)(2) - \frac{1}{2}(2)(4 + 2) = 3 - 6 = -3$, and by the Second Fundamental Theorem, $g'(3) = f(3) = 0$, so the tangent is $y = -3$.
(*Calculus for AP®*, pages 436–437, 165–167; EU 2.3; LO 2.3B; EK 2.3B1; MPAC 2,3,4)

28. ANSWER: (C) A relative maximum or minimum occurs where the first derivative of a function changes sign. Since $g(x)=\int_2^x f(t)\,dt$ and $g'(x)=f(x)$, analyze the behavior of $g(x)$ using an interval chart.

	$-4<x<-1$	$x=-1$	$-1<x<3$	$x=3$	$3<x<4$
$g'(x)=f(x)$	positive	0	negative	0	positive
$g(x)$	increasing	rel.max	decreasing	rel.min	increasing

Statement C is therefore false, as there is no relative maximum at $x=-2$. (*Calculus for AP*®, pages 436–437, 293–300; EU 2.2; LO 2.2A; EK 2.2A1; MPAC 2,3,4)

29. ANSWER: (A) Using L'Hopital's Rule for the indeterminate form

$$\frac{0}{0},\ \lim_{x\to 0}\frac{\sin 6x}{x^2-3x}=\lim_{x\to 0}\frac{\frac{d}{dx}(\sin 6x)}{\frac{d}{dx}\left(x^2-3x\right)}=\lim_{x\to 0}\frac{6\cos 6x}{2x-3}=\frac{6}{-3}=-2$$

(*Calculus for AP*®, pages 337–343; EU 1.1; LO 1.1A; EK 1.1C3; MPAC 1,2,3,4)

30. ANSWER: (C) Using L'Hopital's Rule for the indeterminate form 0/0 and the Fundamental Theorem of Calculus

$$\lim_{x\to 1}\frac{\int_2^{4-2x}\sqrt{t+7}\,dt}{x-1}=\lim_{x\to 1}\frac{\frac{d}{dx}\left(\int_2^{4-2x}\sqrt{t+7}\,dt\right)}{\frac{d}{dx}(x-1)}=\lim_{x\to 1}\frac{-2\sqrt{4-2x+7}}{1}=\frac{-2\sqrt{9}}{1}=-6$$

(*Calculus for AP*®, pages 337–343, 436–437; EU 1.1; LO 1.1A; EK 1.1C3,3.3A2; MPAC 1,2,3,4)

31. ANSWER: (B) Finding the intersection point (−0.8834, 1.2181), the area is determined by evaluating the integral $\int_{-0.8834}^{0} -\tan x - 2x^4\,dx \approx 0.240$. (*Calculus for AP*®, pages 447–486; EU 3.4; LO 3.4D; EK 3.4D1; MPAC 3,4)

32. ANSWER: (A) The average rate of change is equivalent to the slope of the secant on the given interval. Thus, $\frac{f(-1)-f(-4)}{-1-(-4)}=\frac{e^{-1}-\frac{e^{-\frac{1}{4}}}{16}}{3}\approx 0.106$.
(*Calculus for AP*®, page 167; EU 3.4; LO 3.4B; EK 3.4B1; MPAC 2,3)

33. ANSWER: (D) $u = \cos 2x \Rightarrow du = -2\sin 2x\,dx$; and for $x = 0 \Rightarrow u = 1$ and for $x = \frac{\pi}{2} \Rightarrow u = -1$.

Then by substitution $\int_0^{\frac{\pi}{2}} \sin 2x e^{\cos 2x}\,dx = -\frac{1}{2}\int_1^{-1} e^u\,du \Rightarrow \frac{1}{2}\int_{-1}^{1} e^u\,du.$

(*Calculus for AP*®, pages 463–465; EU 3.3; LO 3.3B; EK 3.3B5; MPAC 3,5)

34. ANSWER: (D) Area = $\int_k^{k+1} \frac{1}{x}\,dx = \ln(k+1) - \ln k = 0.125$. Then

$\ln\left(\frac{k+1}{k}\right) = 0.125 \Rightarrow e^{0.125} = \frac{k+1}{k}$ and $k \approx 7.510$.

(*Calculus for AP*®, pages 447–486; EU 3.4; LO 3.4D; EK 3.4D1; MPAC 2,3)

35. ANSWER: (A) The function crosses the x-axis at $x = 3^{\frac{1}{5}} \approx 1.2457$. The radius of each semicircle $= \frac{3-x^5}{2}$ and the area of each cross section is $\frac{\pi}{2}\left(\frac{3-x^5}{2}\right)^2$, so the volume is given by

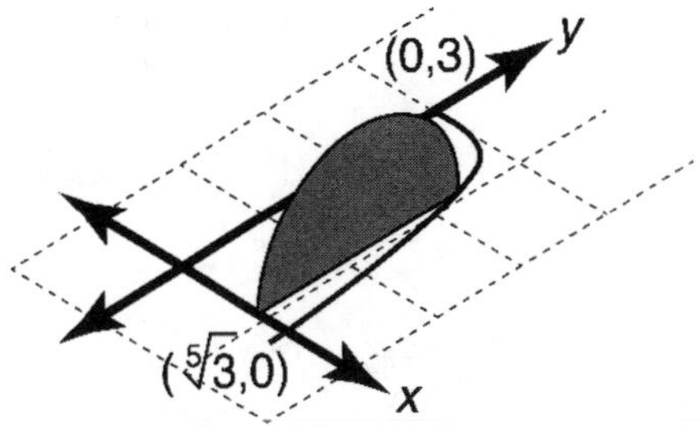

$\frac{\pi}{8}\int_0^{1.2457} \left(3 - x^5\right)^2\,dx \approx 3.335.$

(*Calculus for AP*®, pages 518–522; EU 3.4; LO 3.4D; EK 3.4D2; MPAC 2,3)

36. ANSWER: (A) The amount left in the bottle is given by

$32 - \int_0^5 Y(t)\,dt \approx 32 - 5.063 = 26.937$ ounces.

(*Calculus for AP*®, pages 437–440; EU 3.3; LO 3.3B; EK 3.3B2; MPAC 2,3)

37. ANSWER: (B) By the Mean Value Theorem $f'(c) = \frac{f(b) - f(a)}{b-a}$ for $a \le c \le 2$, we have $f'(1.720) = \frac{f(2) - f(a)}{2-a} \Rightarrow 8.875 = \frac{8-a^3}{2-a}$. The solution to this equation is $a = 1.424$.

(*Calculus for AP*®, pages 308–311; EU 1.2,2.4; LO 1.2B,2.4A; EK1.2B1,2.4A1; MPAC 2,3)

38. ANSWER: (A) If $f(x)$ is integrable on $p \le x \le q$, then $\int_q^p f(x)\,dx = -\int_q^p f(x)\,dx$. The given information yields the following system: $P + Q + R = -7$, $Q + R = -2$, and $-(P + Q) = 17$. Solving the system, $P = -5$, $Q = -12$, and $R = 10$, and then $\int_b^c f(x)\,dx = Q = -12$.
(Calculus *for AP*®, pages 450–454; 247–248; EU 3.2; LO 3.2C; EK 3.2C1; MPAC 2,4,5)

39. ANSWER: (D) For $g(5) = 3$, then $f(3) = 5$ and $g'(5) = \frac{1}{f'(3)} = \frac{1}{2}$.
Differentiating,
$h'(x) = g(x) + xg'(x) \Rightarrow h'(5) = g(5) + 5 \cdot g'(5) = 3 + 5\left(\frac{1}{2}\right) = 5.5.$
(*Calculus for AP*®, pages 207–210; EU 2.1; LO 2.1C; EK 2.1C6; MPAC 2,4,5)

40. ANSWER: (B) $V = \frac{1}{3}\pi r^2 h = \frac{\pi}{3}\left(\frac{h}{2}\right)^2 h = \frac{\pi h^3}{12} \Rightarrow \frac{dV}{dt} = \frac{\pi h^2}{4}\left(\frac{dh}{dt}\right)$. If $C = 120\pi = 2\pi r$, $\Rightarrow r = 60$ and $h = 120$. Substituting,
$30\pi = \frac{\pi}{4}120^2\left(\frac{dh}{dt}\right) \Rightarrow \frac{dh}{dt} = \frac{1}{120}$ cm/sec.
(*Calculus*, 10th ed., pages 247–279; EU 2.3; LO 2.3C; EK 2.3C2; MPAC 2,3)

41. ANSWER: (C) By the Quotient and Chain Rules,
$h'(x) = \frac{g'(2x) \cdot 2 \cdot f(x) - f'(x)g(2x)}{(f(x))^2}$ and
$h'(1) = \frac{g'(2) \cdot 2 \cdot f(1) - f'(1) \cdot g'(2)}{(f(1))^2} = \frac{-1(2)(4) - (1)(-1)}{16} = -\frac{7}{16}.$
(*Calculus for AP*®, pages 207–210; 227–233; EU 2.1; LO 2.1C; EK 2.1C3,2.1C4; MPAC 2,3,4)

42. ANSWER: (B) The total number of fires for the first quarter of the year is determined by $\int_0^{91.25}\left[4\cos\left(\frac{t}{58} - 2\right) + 6\right]dt \approx 660.$
(*Calculus for AP*®, pages 450–454; EU 3.4; LO 3.4A; EK 3.4A2; MPAC 2,3)

43. ANSWER: (C) The slope of the graph of the derivative of a function must change signs in order for the graph of the original function to have a point of inflection. Thus only $h(x)$ has at least one point of inflection as the graph of $h'(x)$ changes slope from positive to negative, back to positive and then finally negative, showing three points of inflection in the interval $-3 < x < 2$.
(*Calculus for AP*®, pages 322–324; EU 2.2; LO 2.2A; EK 2.2A1,2.2A3; MPAC 2,4)

44. ANSWER: (C) Graph $P'(t)$ on the interval $0 \le t \le 10$ and observe that the most minimum value of $P'(t)$ occurs at $t = 9.491$ with $P'(9.491) \approx -1.301$. Finally, $P(9.491) \approx \$19.91$.
(*Calculus for AP*®, pages 292–300; EU 2.2,2.3; LO 2.2A,2.3C; EK 2.2A1,2.3C3; MPAC 2,3)

45. ANSWER: (C) $g(x)$ is increasing when $g'(x) > 0$, and concave up when the slope of $g'(x)$, or $g''(x)$, is also > 0.

	$a < x < b$	$b < x < c$	$c < x < d$	$d < x < e$	$e < x < f$	$f < x < h$
$g'(x)$	positive	positive	negative	negative	positive	positive
$g''(x)$	positive	negative	negative	positive	positive	negative
Characteristics of $g(x)$	increasing	increasing	decreasing	decreasing	increasing	increasing
	concave up	concave down	concave down	concave down	concave up	concave down

Therefore, $g(x)$ is increasing and concave up for the intervals $a < x < b$ and $e < x < f$.
(*Calculus for AP*®, pages 293–300, 322–324; EU 2.2; LO 2.2A; EK 2.2A1,2.2A3; MPAC 2,4)

FREE-RESPONSE QUESTIONS

1. The velocity of a particle moving on the y-axis is given by
$v(t) = \dfrac{e^{t-2}}{2t^2 + 3} - 4$ on the interval $1 \le t \le 11$.
At time $t = 1$, the particle is 3 units above the origin.
(a) During what time interval is the particle moving down?
(b) What is the position of the particle when it is farthest south of the origin?
(c) At what time is the particle's average velocity twice the instantaneous velocity on $2 \le t \le 8$?
(d) Find the total distance traveled by the particle during the time where $1 \le t \le 11$.

	Solution	Possible points
(a)	The particle is moving down when $v(t) < 0$. Therefore, the particle is moving to the left in the interval $1 \le t \le 8.344$	$2: \begin{cases} 1: & v(t) < 0 \\ 1: & \text{answer} \end{cases}$
(b)	$\int_1^{8.344} v(t)\,dt = y(8.344) - y(1)$ $-23.772 = y(8.344) - 3 = -20.772$ The particle is 20.772 units south of the origin.	$3: \begin{cases} 1: & \text{uses the FTC} \\ 1: & \text{integral and initial value} \\ 1: & \text{answer} \end{cases}$
(c)	$v_{av} = \frac{1}{8-2}\int_2^8 v(t)\,dt = -3.281$ $2v(t) = -3.281$ $t = 7.645$	$2: \begin{cases} 1: & \text{integral and constant} \\ 1: & \text{answer} \end{cases}$
(d)	Total distance $= \int_1^{11} \lvert v(tdt) \rvert = 49.302$	$2: \begin{cases} 1: & \text{integral on } \lvert v(t) \rvert \\ 1: & \text{answer} \end{cases}$

1. (a) (*Calculus for AP®*, page 508; EU 2.3; LO 2.3C; EK2.3C1; MPAC 2,3)
1. (b), (c), (d) (*Calculus for AP®*, pages 508–509; EU 2.3,2.4,3.4; LO2.3C,2.4A,3.4C; EK 2.3C1,2.4A1,3.4C1; MPAC 2,3)

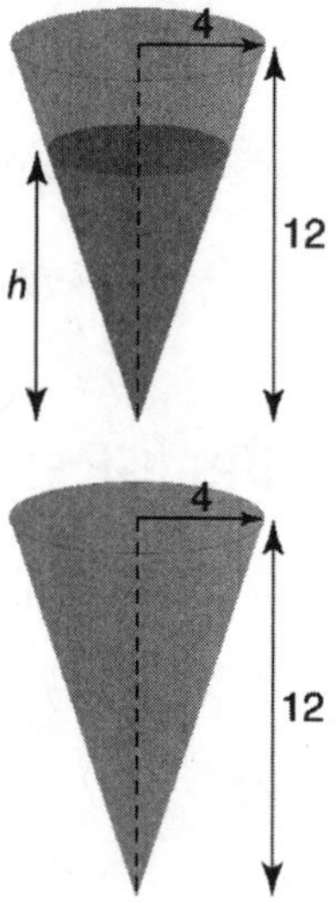

2. A solution is draining through a conical filter into an identical conical container as shown in the diagram to the right. The solution drips from the upper filter into the lower container at a rate of π cm^3/sec $\left(V_{\text{cone}} = \frac{\pi}{3} r^2 h\right)$.

   (a) How fast is the level in the upper filter dropping when the solution level in the upper filter is at 6 cm?

   (b) If the conical filter is initially full, what is the level of the solution in the lower level when the solution in the level in the upper filter is at 6 cm and how fast is the level in the lower filter rising?

   (c) How fast is the surface area of the solution in the lower filter increasing when the volume in the upper filter equals the volume in the lower container?

<table>
<tr><th></th><th>Solution</th><th>Possible points</th></tr>
<tr><td>(a)</td><td>By similar triangles for both cones:
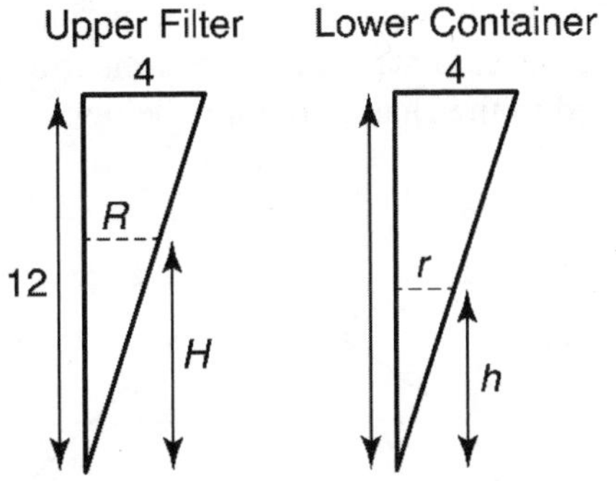

$\frac{4}{12}=\frac{1}{3}=\frac{R}{H}\Rightarrow R=\frac{1}{3}H$ and $V_{cone}=\frac{\pi}{3}R^2H\Rightarrow\frac{\pi}{27}H^3$.
Then $\frac{dV}{dt}=\frac{\pi}{9}H^2\left(\frac{dH}{dt}\right)\Rightarrow-\pi=\frac{\pi}{9}6^2\left(\frac{dH}{dt}\right)$
$\Rightarrow\frac{dH}{dt}=-\frac{1}{4}$ cm/sec.</td><td>$3:\begin{cases}1: & R=\frac{1}{3}H\\ 1: & \frac{dV}{dt}\\ 1: & \text{answer}\end{cases}$</td></tr>
<tr><td>(b)</td><td>When $H=6$, the volume left in the upper filter is
$V_{\text{upper}}=\frac{\pi}{27}6^3=8\pi\text{ cm}^3$ and the volume in the lower container is
$V_{\text{lower}}=\frac{\pi}{3}4^2(12)-8\pi=64\pi-8\pi=56\pi\text{ cm}^3$.
Solving for h in the lower container,
$56\pi=\frac{\pi}{27}h^3\Rightarrow h=6\sqrt[3]{7}\approx11.4776.$ Since
$\frac{dV}{dt}=\frac{\pi}{9}h^2\left(\frac{dh}{dt}\right)\Rightarrow\pi=\frac{\pi}{9}(11.4776)^2\left(\frac{dh}{dt}\right)$ and $\frac{dh}{dt}\approx0.068$ cm/sec.</td><td>$3:\begin{cases}1: & V_{\text{lower}}\\ 1: & h_{\text{lower}}\\ 1: & \text{answer}\end{cases}$</td></tr>
<tr><td>(c)</td><td>$V=\frac{\pi}{3}(4)^2(12)=64\pi$
Half full: $V=32\pi=\frac{\pi}{27}h^3\Rightarrow h=6\sqrt[3]{4}\approx9.5244$
$\frac{dV}{dt}=\frac{\pi}{9}h^2\left(\frac{dh}{dt}\right)\Rightarrow\pi=\frac{\pi}{9}(9.5244)^2\left(\frac{dh}{dt}\right)$ and $\frac{dh}{dt}\approx0.099$ cm/sec
and $r=\frac{1}{3}h$, then $r\approx3.175$ and $\frac{dr}{dt}=\frac{1}{3}\frac{dh}{dt}\Rightarrow0.033$ cm/sec.
$A=\pi r^2\Rightarrow\frac{dA}{dt}=2\pi r\left(\frac{dr}{dt}\right)$ and
$\frac{dA}{dt}\approx2\pi(3.175)^2(0.033)\approx0.658\text{ cm}^2/\text{sec}.$</td><td>$3:\begin{cases}1: & h\\ 1: & \frac{dh}{dt}\\ 1: & \frac{dA}{dt}\end{cases}$</td></tr>
</table>

2. (a), (b), (c) (*Calculus for AP*®, pages 274–279; EU 2.3; LO 2.3C; EK 2.3C2; MPAC 2,3)

3. A 1,000 gallon tank is initially empty. A valve is opened and water begins to flow into the tank at a variable rate, $R(t)$, in gallons per minute, where t is the number of minutes since the valve was opened. The rate is recorded in the chart and graph below.

t min	$R(t)$ gal/min
0	0
5	5
10	20
20	30
30	16
35	0

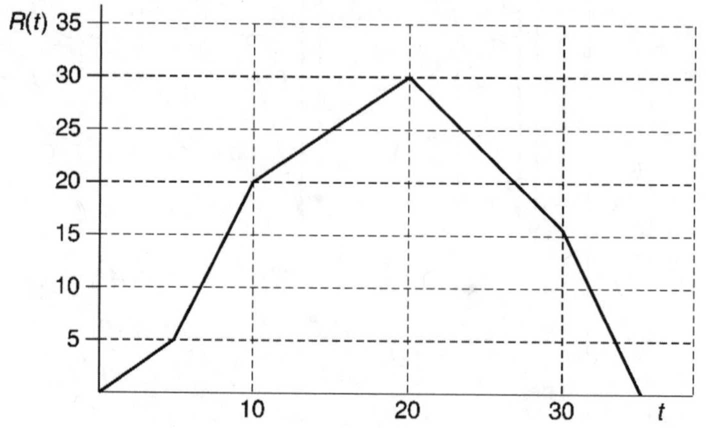

(a) Approximate the volume of water that flows into the tank for the time interval $0 \le t \le 35$ using a right Riemann sum for the five unequal subintervals indicated by the data in the chart. Indicate units of measure.

(b) Approximate the value of $\frac{1}{20}\int_{10}^{30} R(t)\,dt$ using the Trapezoidal Rule. Indicate units of measure with your answer. Interpret the meaning of your answer in the context of the problem.

(c) At time $t = 20$ minutes, a drain is opened at the bottom of the tank and water leaves the tank at a rate of $(t + 10)$ gallons per minute. Set up, but do not evaluate, an integral expression in terms of a single independent variable that represents the volume of the water in the tank at time $t = 35$ minutes.

	Solution	Possible points
(a)	Using the data from the chart, 5(5) + 5(20) + 10(30) + 10(16) + 5(0) = 585 gal.	2: {<−1> entry error
(b)	$\frac{1}{20}\int_{10}^{30} R(t)\,dt$ is the average rate that water enters the tank over the 20 minute period $10 \le t \le 30$ minutes. $\frac{1}{20}\int_{10}^{30} R(t)dt$ $\approx \frac{1}{20}\left(\frac{30-10}{2(2)}\right)\left[R(10)+2R(20)+R(30)\right]$ $= \frac{1}{20}\left(\frac{20}{4}\right)\left[20+2(30)+16\right]$ $\Rightarrow \frac{1}{4}(96) = 24$ gal/min	3: { 2: answer <−1> entry error 1: interpretation
(c)	$\left[\int_0^{35} Q(t)\,dt\right] - \left[\int_{20}^{35} (t+10)\,dt\right]$	3: { 1: integrand and interval for $Q(t)$ 1: integrand and interval for $(t+10)$ 1: correct order of functions 1: units in parts a and b

3. (a) (*Calculus for AP*®, pages 395–410; EU 3.2; LO 3.2B; EK 3.2B2; MPAC 2,3,6)
3. (b) (*Calculus for AP*®, pages 400–401; EU 3.2,3.4; LO 3.2B,3.4B; EK3.2B2,3.4B2; MPAC 2,3,6)
3. (c) (*Calculus for AP*®, pages 450–454; EU 3.4; LO 3.4E; EK 3.4E1; MPAC 2,3,6)

4. Consider the curve defined by $x^2 + 4xy + y^2 = -12$.
   (a) Find $\frac{dy}{dx}$ in terms of x and y.
   (b) Find the equations of all horizontal tangents.
   (c) Find the equation of the tangent at the point (−4, 14).
   (d) If $\frac{dy}{dt} = -\frac{1}{2}$ at the point (−4, 14), find $\frac{dx}{dt}$.
   (e) Use the tangent in part c to estimate the value of k for the point (−4.01, k) on the curve.

	Solution	Possible points
(a)	$2x+4y+4x\left(\frac{dy}{dx}\right)+2y\left(\frac{dy}{dx}\right)=0$ $\frac{dy}{dx}=\frac{-(x+2y)}{2x+y}$	$2:\begin{cases}1:\text{implicit differentiation}\\ \quad <-1> \text{ each error}\\ 1:\text{answer}\end{cases}$
(b)	$\frac{dy}{dx}=\frac{-(x+2y)}{2x+y}=0 \Rightarrow x=-2y$ $(-2y)^2+4(-2y)y+y^2=-12$ and $-3y^2=-12 \Rightarrow y \pm 2.$ Verify that both values of y yield horizontal tangent lines by showing that $\frac{dy}{dx}=0$ in both cases. When $y=2$, $x=-4$ and $\frac{dy}{dx}=\frac{-(-4+4)}{-8+2}=0.$ When $y=-2$, $x=4$ and $\frac{dy}{dx}=\frac{-(4-4)}{8-2}=0.$	$2:\begin{cases}1:\frac{dy}{dx}=0\\ 1:\text{solutions}\end{cases}$
(c)	$\left.\frac{dy}{dx}\right\|_{(-4,14}=\frac{-[-4+2(14)]}{2(-4)+14}=\frac{-24}{6}=-4$ $y-14=-4(x+4) \Rightarrow y=-4x-2$	1: answer
(d)	$\frac{dy}{dx}=\frac{dy}{dt}\cdot\frac{dt}{dx}=\frac{dy/dt}{dx/dt}$ $-4=\frac{-1/2}{dx/dt} \Rightarrow \frac{dx}{dt}=\frac{1}{8}$	$2:\begin{cases}1:\text{relationship}\\ 1:\text{answer}\end{cases}$
(e)	$y=14-4(-4.01+4) \Rightarrow y \approx 14.04$	1: answer

4. (a) (*Calculus for AP*®, pages 240–245; EU 2.1; LO 2.1C; EK 2.1C5; MPAC 2,3,5)
4. (b), (c) (*Calculus for AP*®, pages 199–200, 165–167; EU2.3; LO 2.3B; EK 2.3B1; MPAC 2,3)
4. (d) (*Calculus for AP*®, pages 274–279; EU 2.1; LO 2.1C; EK 2.1C4; MPAC 2,3,5)
4. (e) (*Calculus for AP*®, pages 165–167; EU 2.3; LO 2.3B; EK 2.3B2; MPAC 2,3)

5. Let L be the tangent to $f(x)=\sqrt{x}$ at any point on the curve as shown in the diagram to the right.
   (a) Show that the x-intercept of the tangent to the curve at the point $(h, \sqrt{h})$ is $-h$.
   (b) Find the area of the region bounded by the tangent to the curve at $x=4$, the curve, and the x-axis.
   (c) What is the volume when the region found in part b is rotated about the line $x=4$.

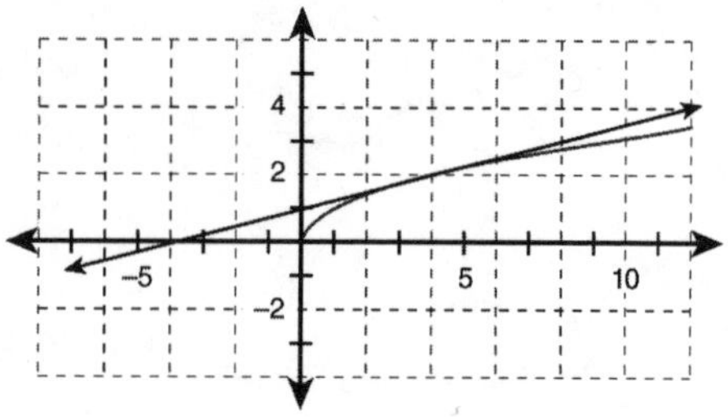

	Solution	Possible points
(a)	$y'(x)=\frac{1}{2\sqrt{x}}$ and $y'(h)=\frac{1}{2\sqrt{h}}$ $L:\ y-\sqrt{h}=\frac{1}{2\sqrt{h}}(x-h)$ The x-intercept occurs when $y = 0$. Thus, $(0-\sqrt{h})2\sqrt{h} = (x-h) \Rightarrow x = -h.$	$3:\begin{cases}1:\ y'(x)\\1:\ L\\1:\ y=0\rightarrow \text{answer}\end{cases}$
(b)	The area is found by integrating with respect to y. Rewriting the functions, $L:\ \ y-2=\frac{1}{4}(x-4)\Rightarrow x=4$ and $x=y^2$ $A=\int_0^2\left[y^2-(4y-4)\right]dy$ $=\left(\frac{y^3}{3}-2y+4y\right)\Big\vert_0^2$ $=\frac{8}{3}-8+8=\frac{8}{3}$ The area may also be determined by integrating with respect to x, but two integrals will be needed. $L: y-2=\frac{1}{4}(x-4)\Rightarrow\ y=\frac{1}{4}x+1,$ with the x-intercept of -4. $A=\int_{-4}^{0}\left(\frac{1}{4}x+1\right)dx+\int_{0}^{4}\left(\frac{1}{4}x+1-x^{\frac{1}{2}}\right)dx$ $=\left(\frac{1}{8}x^2+x\right)\Big\vert_{-4}^{0}+\left(\frac{1}{8}x^2+x-\frac{2}{3}x^{\frac{3}{2}}\right)\Big\vert_0^4$ $=0-(2-4)+\left(2+4-\frac{16}{3}\right)=\frac{8}{3}$	$3:\begin{cases}1:\ \text{integral with limits}\\1:\ \text{antiderivative}\\1:\ \text{answer}\end{cases}$
(c)	$V=\pi\int_0^2\left[4-(4y-4)\right]^2-\left(4-y^2\right)^2 dy$ $=\pi\int_0^2 16y^2-\left(16-8y^2+y^4\right)dy$ $=\pi\left(8y^3-16y-\frac{y^5}{5}\right)\Big\vert_0^2=\frac{128\pi}{5}$	$3:\begin{cases}1:\ \text{integral with limits}\\1:\ \text{antiderivative}\\1:\ \text{answer}\end{cases}$

5. (a) (*Calculus for AP*®, pages 165–167; EU 2.3; LO 2.3B; EK2.3B1; MPAC 2,3,4)
5. (b) (*Calculus for AP*®, pages 477–486; EU 3.4; LO 3.4D; EK3.4D1; MPAC 2,3,4)
5. (c) (*Calculus for AP*®, pages 525–528; EU 3.4; LO 3.4D; EK3.4D2; MPAC 2,3,4)

6. Let f be a function defined in the closed interval $0 \le x \le 6$. The graph of f consists of three line segments and a semicircle. Let

$g(x) = 3 + \int_2^x f(t)\,dt.$

(a) Find $g(1)$, $g'(1)$, and $g''(1)$.
(b) What is the average rate of change of $g(x)$ in the interval $2 \le x \le 6$?
(c) Identify the x-coordinate of any extrema of $g(x)$ on $0 < x < 6$. Explain your reasoning.
(d) Identify the x-coordinate of any points of inflection of $g(x)$ on $0 < x < 6$.

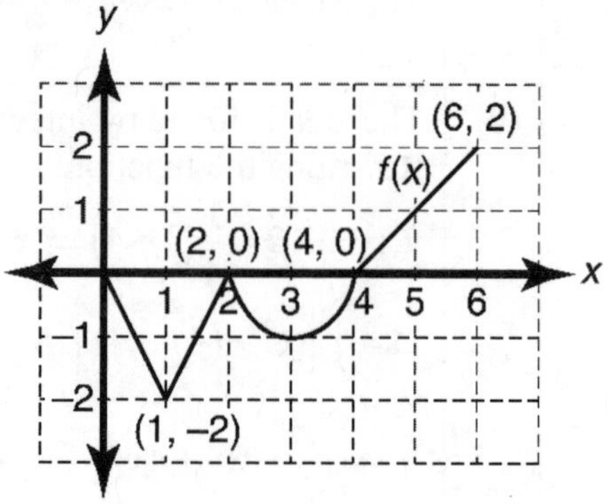

	Solution	Possible points
(a)	$g(1) = 3 + \int_2^1 f(t)dt = 3 - \int_1^2 f(t)dt = 3 + \frac{1}{2}(1)(2) = 4$ $g'(x) = f(x) \Rightarrow g'(1) = -2$ $g''(x) = f'(x) \Rightarrow g''(1)$ does not exist.	3: 1 for each answer
(b)	$\frac{g(6)-g(2)}{6-2} = \frac{\left[3 + \left(-\frac{\pi}{2}\right) + \frac{1}{2}(2)(2)\right] - (3)}{4} = \frac{4-\pi}{8}$	$2: \begin{cases} 1: \text{difference quotient} \\ 1: \text{answer} \end{cases}$
(c)	Extrema exist where $g'(x) = f(x) = 0$ or $g'(x)$ does not exist. Extrema exist at $x = 4$ because $g'(4) = f(4)$ is zero and $g'(x)$ (or $f(x)$) changes from negative values to positive values at $x = 4$. There are no sign changes at $x = 2$ so it is not an extremum even though $g'(2) = 0$.	$2: \begin{cases} 1: \text{reason} \\ 1: \text{answer} \end{cases}$
(d)	Inflection points occur where $g''(x) = f'(x)$ change sign. The points of inflection exist at $x = 1$, 2, and 3.	$2: \begin{cases} 1: \text{reason} \\ 1: \text{answer} \end{cases}$

6. (a) (*Calculus for AP*®, pages 436–437; EU 2.1,3.3; LO 2.1D,3.3A; EK 2.1D1,3.3A2; MPAC 2,3,4)
6. (b) (*Calculus for AP*®, page 171; LO 2.1A; EK2.1A1; MPAC 2,3,4)
6. (c) (*Calculus for AP*®, pages 178–179; EU 2.2; LO 2.2A; EK2.2A1; MPAC 2,3,4,6)
6. (d) (*Calculus for AP*®, pages 182–184; EU 2.2; LO 2.2A; EK2.2A1; MPAC 2,3,4)

CALCULUS AB AND BC SCORING CHART

SECTION I: MULTIPLE-CHOICE QUESTIONS

_________ $\times 1.2 =$ _________

\# correct (out of 45) — do not round (out of 54)

SECTION II: FREE-RESPONSE QUESTIONS

Question 1	Score out of 9 points =	_________
Question 2	Score out of 9 points =	_________
Question 3	Score out of 9 points =	_________
Question 4	Score out of 9 points =	_________
Question 5	Score out of 9 points =	_________
Question 6	Score out of 9 points =	_________
	Sum for Section II =	_________ (out of 54)

Composite Score

Section I total	=
Section II total	=
Composite score	= _________ (out of 108)

Grade Conversion Chart*

Composite score range	AP® exam grade
68–108	5
52–67	4
39–51	3
27–38	2
0–26	1

***Note:** The ranges listed above are only approximate. Each year the ranges for the actual AP® exam are somewhat different. The cutoffs are established after the exams are given to over 200,000 students and are based on the difficulty level of the exam each year.

AP® CALCULUS AB PRACTICE TEST 2
Section I, Part A: Multiple-Choice Questions
Time: 60 minutes
Number of Questions: 30

A calculator may not be used on this part of the examination.

1. In what interval is $f(x) = \ln(x^2 - 4)$ increasing?
   (A) $|x| > 2$
   (B) $|x| \geq 2$
   (C) $x > 2$
   (D) $x < 2$

2. Find the limit $\lim\limits_{x \to 0} \dfrac{\cos x}{|x|}$.
   (A) 0
   (B) 1
   (C) -1
   (D) The limit does not exist.

3. $\int \left[3^{-x} + \dfrac{1}{x} \right] dx = ?$
   (A) $3^{-x} + \ln|x| + C$
   (B) $-\dfrac{3^{-x}}{\ln 3} - \dfrac{1}{x^2} + C$
   (C) $-3^{-x}\ln 3 + \ln|x| + C$
   (D) $-\dfrac{3^{-x}}{\ln 3} + \ln|x| + C$

4. Find $\dfrac{dy}{dx}$ for $\cos(x + y) = x$.
   (A) $-\csc(x + y) - 1$
   (B) $\dfrac{\cos(x + y)}{\sin^2(x + y)}$
   (C) $-\sin(x + y) \cdot \cot(x + y)$
   (D) $-\sin(x + y) - 1$

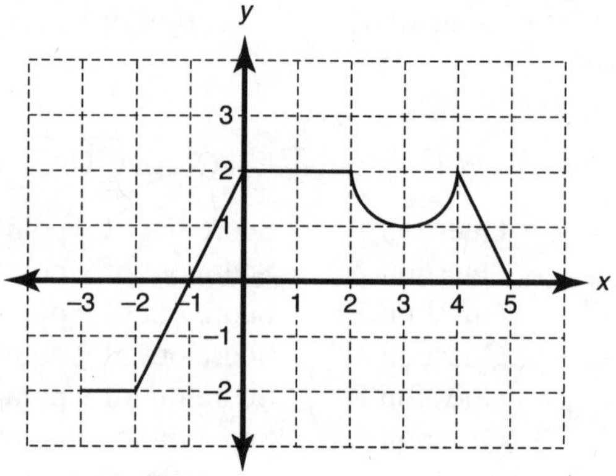

The graph of $f(x)$ consists of four line segments and a semicircle as shown above in the closed interval $-3 < x < 5$. Let g be the function given by $g(x) = \int_0^x f(t)\,dt$. Use this information for Problems 5–7.

5. What is $g(-1) + g'(-1) + g''(-1)$?
   (A) -1
   (B) 0
   (C) 1
   (D) 2

6. What is $\int_{-3}^{5} f(t)\,dt$?
   (A) $7 - \pi$
   (B) $7 - \dfrac{\pi}{2}$
   (C) $7 - \dfrac{\pi}{4}$
   (D) $12 - \dfrac{\pi}{2}$

7. Which of the following statements is false for $g(x)$?
   (A) A relative minimum for $g(x)$ occurs at $x = -1$.
   (B) A point of inflection for $g(x)$ occurs at $x = 3$.
   (C) $g(x)$ has roots at $x = 0$ and $x = -2$.
   (D) $g(x)$ is concave down in the open interval $-2 < x < -1$.

8. The position of a particle moving along the x-axis is given by $x(t) = 2 + 3t - t^3$. What is the speed of the particle at $t = 4$?
   (A) -50
   (B) -45
   (C) 32
   (D) 45

9. A region R is bounded by the curve $x = y^2 - 1$ and the y-axis. What is the volume generated when region R is rotated about the y-axis?
   (A) $\dfrac{\pi}{2}$
   (B) $\dfrac{8\pi}{15}$
   (C) π
   (D) $\dfrac{16\pi}{15}$

10. Which of the following statements is true for $f(x) = \sqrt[3]{x} + 1$?
    I. $f(x)$ is always increasing, $x \neq 0$.
    II. The tangent to the curve at $x = 0$ is horizontal.
    III. The Mean Value Theorem can be applied to $f(x)$ in the closed interval $-1 \leq x \leq 1$.
    (A) I only
    (B) II only
    (C) III only
    (D) I, II, and III

11. The acceleration of a model car along an incline is given by $a(t) = \dfrac{t^2 + t}{t^2 + t}$ cm/sec^2, for $0 \leq t < 1$. If $v(0) = 1$ cm/sec, what is $v(t)$?
    (A) $\tan^{-1} t + \frac{1}{2}\ln(t^2 + 1) + 1$ cm/sec
    (B) $t - \frac{1}{2}\ln(t^2 + 1) - \tan^{-1} t + 1$ cm/sec
    (C) $t + \frac{1}{2}\ln(t^2 + 1) + \tan^{-1} t + 1$ cm/sec
    (D) $t + \frac{1}{2}\ln(t^2 + 1) - \tan^{-1} t + 1$ cm/sec

t	$R(t)$
0	12
2	18
4	10
6	15
8	12
10	16
12	8

12. Water is dripping into a vase at a variable rate. The rate, $R(t)$ in cm^3/min, is recorded every 2 minutes for 12 minutes, as listed in the chart above. Using a right Riemann sum with 3 equal intervals, find the approximate average rate at which the water drips into the vase over the 12 minutes.
    (A) 10 cm^3/min
    (B) $10\frac{1}{3}$ cm^3/min
    (C) $16\frac{1}{3}$ cm^3/min
    (D) 40 cm^3/min

13. If $h''(x) = e^{x-1}(2x - 1)^2(x - 3)^3(4x + 5)$, then $h(x)$ has how many points of inflection?
    (A) 4
    (B) 3
    (C) 2
    (D) 1

GO ON TO NEXT PAGE

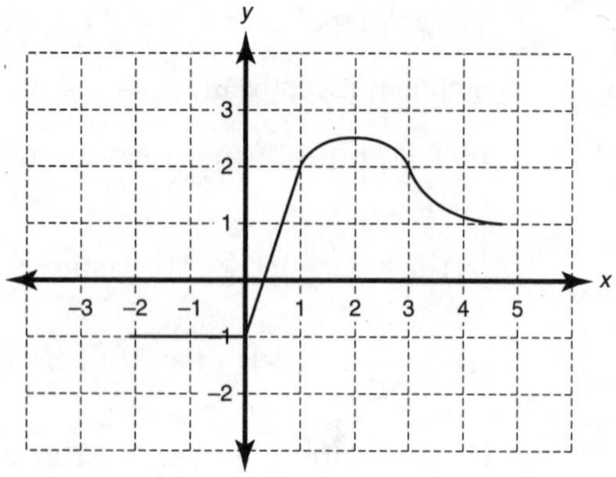

14. The graph of $f'(x)$ is shown in the figure above. If $\int_1^2 f'(x)\,dx = k$, what is $f(2) - f(-1)$?

(A) $k + \dfrac{11}{6}$

(B) $k + \dfrac{3}{2}$

(C) $k - \dfrac{1}{2}$

(D) $k - 1$

15. $\displaystyle\int \frac{1}{16 + x^2}\,dx =$

(A) $\tan^{-1} x + C$

(B) $\dfrac{1}{4}\tan^{-1}\dfrac{x}{4} + C$

(C) $\tan^{-1}\dfrac{x}{4} + C$

(D) $\dfrac{1}{4}\tan^{-1} 4x + C$

16. A particle moves along the x-axis so that its velocity for $t \geq 0$ is given by $v(t) = -t^3 + \dfrac{9}{4}t^4$. At what time is the acceleration of the particle a minimum?

(A) $\dfrac{2}{9}$

(B) $\dfrac{1}{3}$

(C) $\dfrac{4}{9}$

(D) 0

17. What is the value of $\displaystyle\lim_{h \to 0} \frac{\sin^{-1}(1+h) - \frac{\pi}{2}}{h}$?

(A) 1
(B) 0
(C) −1
(D) The limit does not exist.

18. Which of the following is the equation of the tangent to the curve of $f(x) = e^{\sin x} + x$ at $x = 0$?

(A) $y = 2x - 1$
(B) $y = 2x + 1$
(C) $y = 2x$
(D) $y = 1$

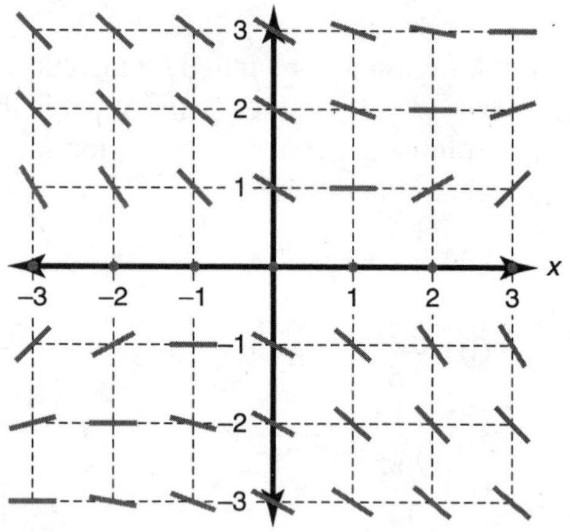

19. Which of the following statements matches the slope field shown above?

(A) $\dfrac{dy}{dx} = \dfrac{x - y}{2y}$

(B) $\dfrac{dy}{dx} = \dfrac{x + y}{2y}$

(C) $\dfrac{dy}{dx} = \dfrac{x - y}{2x}$

(D) $\dfrac{dy}{dx} = \dfrac{x + y}{2x}$

20. If $F(x) = \displaystyle\int_{3x-2}^{2} f(2t)\,dt$, what is $F'(x)$ in terms of x?

(A) $3f(6x - 4)$
(B) $f(3x - 2)$
(C) $-3f(6x - 4)$
(D) $-f(3x - 2)$

21. What is the slope of the line normal to the curve $h(x)=\sqrt{5x^3-2x+1}$ at the point where $x = 1$?

(A) $-\frac{13}{4}$
(B) $-\frac{4}{13}$
(C) $\frac{4}{13}$
(D) $\frac{13}{4}$

22. Let U in the interval $0 \le X \le \frac{\pi}{2}$. What is the average rate of change of y with respect to x in this interval?

(A) $-\pi$
(B) $-\frac{\pi}{2}$
(C) $\frac{\pi}{2}$
(D) π

23. Find k so that the relative minimum of $f(x) = x^3 - \ln(k + x)$ occurs at $x = 1$.

(A) 2
(B) $\sqrt{3}$
(C) $-\frac{2}{3}$
(D) 0

24. The concentration of an anti-inflammatory drug in the bloodstream t minutes after taking a single dose is $C(t)=\frac{2t}{8100+t^2}$, $t \ge 0$. At what time is the concentration the greatest?
(A) 90 minutes
(B) $30\sqrt{6}$ minutes
(C) $30\sqrt{3}$ minutes
(D) $15\sqrt{6}$ minutes

25. If $\lim_{x\to\infty} \frac{ae^x}{5+2e^x} = 3$, what is a?
(A) 9
(B) 6
(C) 3
(D) No such value of a exists.

x	$f(x)$	$g(x)$	$f'(x)$	$g'(x)$
1	3	4	$\frac{2}{3}$	$-\frac{5}{2}$
2	4	2	$\frac{4}{3}$	$-\frac{3}{2}$
4	8	1	$\frac{8}{3}$	$-\frac{1}{2}$

26. Use the values listed in the chart above to find the value of $\frac{d}{dx}\left[f\left(g\left(x^2\right)\right)\right]$ when $x = 2$.

(A) -8
(B) -4
(C) $-\frac{4}{3}$
(D) $\frac{2}{3}$

27. The volume of an open-topped rectangular box is 8 cm^3, and the length of the rectangular base is twice as long as its width. What is the width of the base so that the surface area of the open box is minimized?
(A) $\sqrt[3]{3}$
(B) $\sqrt[3]{6}$
(C) $\sqrt{3}$
(D) $\sqrt{6}$

GO ON TO NEXT PAGE

28. The base of a solid is bounded by the curve $y=\sqrt{x+1}$, the x-axis, and the line $x = 1$. The cross sections, taken perpendicular to the x-axis, are squares. Find the volume of the solid.
(A) $\frac{1}{2}$
(B) 1
(C) $\frac{4\sqrt{2}}{3}$
(D) 2

29. $\lim_{x\to 0}\frac{1-e^{4x}}{2x}$
(A) $\frac{1}{2}$
(B) 2
(C) −2
(D) undefined

30. $\lim_{x\to\frac{\pi}{2}}\frac{\int_0^{x-\frac{\pi}{2}}\cos 3t\,dt}{x-\frac{\pi}{2}}$
(A) 0
(B) 1
(C) 3
(D) Does not exist

END OF SECTION I PART A

Section I, Part B: Multiple-Choice Questions
Time: 45 minutes
Number of Questions: 15

A calculator may be used on this part of the examination.

31. Two cars are converging on a point P as they drive at right angles to each other. Car A is traveling at 60 miles per hour and car B is traveling at 50 miles per hour. At the instant when car A is 12 miles from the point P and car B is 10 miles from the point P, at what rate is the distance between the cars decreasing?
(A) 55 miles per hour
(B) 55.455 miles per hour
(C) 76.882 miles per hour
(D) 78.102 miles per hour

32. A line tangent to the curve $f(x) = \frac{1}{2^{2x}}$ at the point $(a, f(a))$ has a slope of -1. What is the x-intercept of this tangent?
(A) 0.236
(B) 0.500
(C) 0.721
(D) 0.957

33. Consider the function $g(x) = \tan(x + 2)$ in the open interval $-4 < x < 5$. How many times are the tangents to $g(x)$ parallel to the line $y = 2x - 1$?
(A) never
(B) 2
(C) 4
(D) 5

34. What is the sum of all k values that satisfy $\int_1^{2k} x - \frac{k}{x^2}\,dx = 15$?
(A) 3
(B) $\frac{1}{2}$
(C) 1
(D) $-\frac{1}{2}$

GO ON TO NEXT PAGE

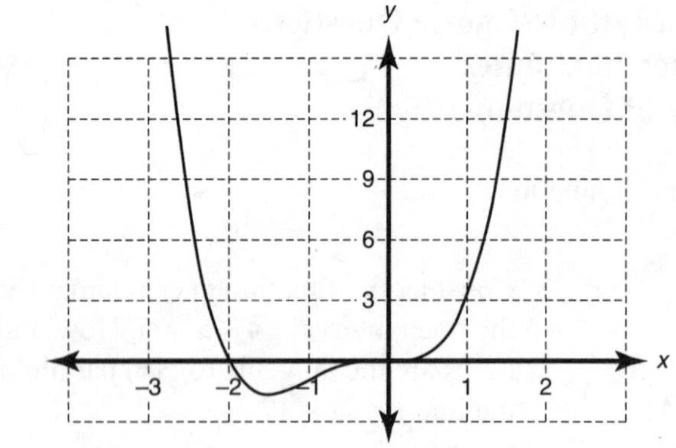

35. The graph of $f'(x)$ is shown at the bottom of the previous column. Which of the following could be a graph of $f(x)$?

(A)

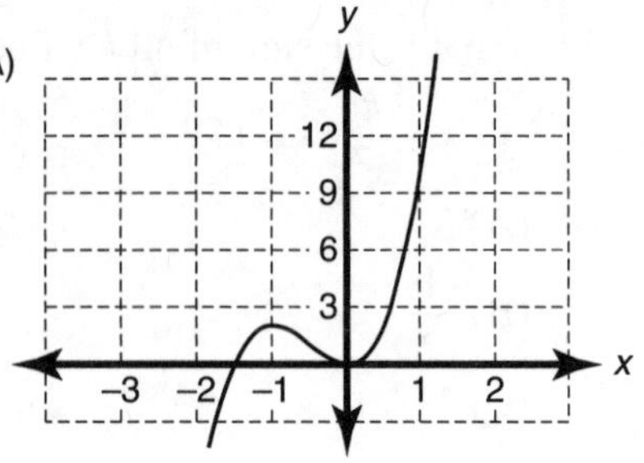

(B)

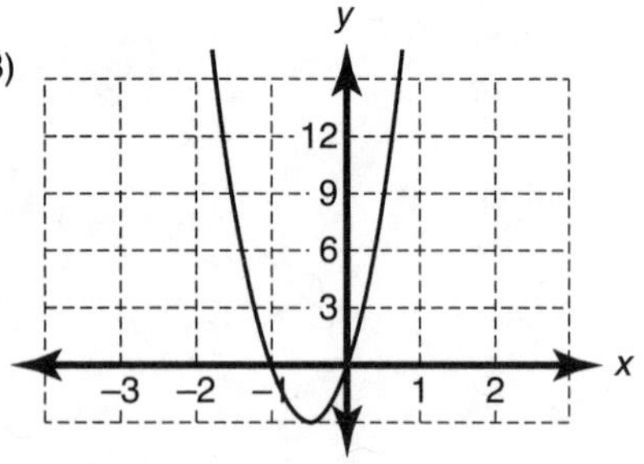

(C)

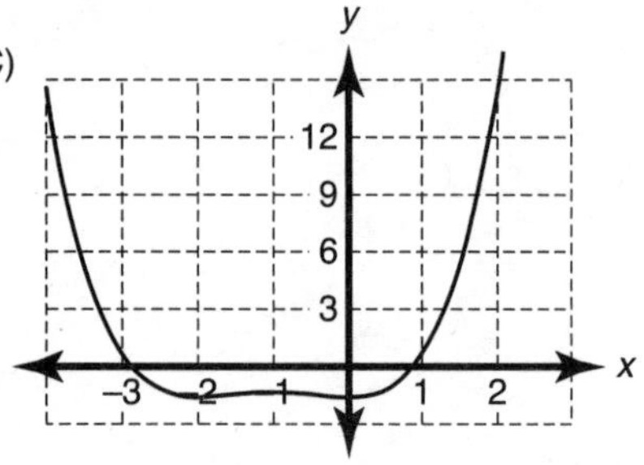

(D)

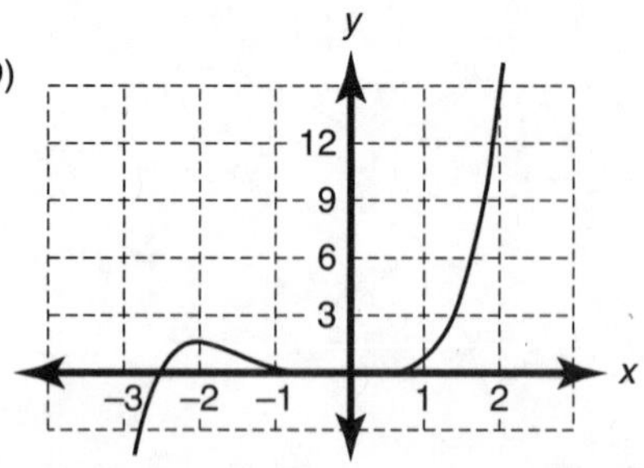

t	0	1	2	3	4
$H(t)$	0	1.3	1.5	2.1	2.6

36. A small plant is purchased from a nursery and the change in the height of the plant is measured at the end of every day for four days. The change in the height of the plant is listed in the chart at the bottom of the left column, where $H(t)$ is in inches per day and t is in days. Using the Trapezoidal Rule, which of the following represents an estimate of the average rate of growth of the plant during the four-day period?

(A) $\frac{1}{4}(0+1.3+1.5+2.1+2.6)$

(B) $\frac{1}{4}\left[\frac{1}{2}(0+1.3+1.5+2.1+2.6)\right]$

(C) $\frac{1}{4}\left\{\frac{1}{2}[0+2(1.3)+2(1.5)+2(2.1)+2.6]\right\}$

(D) $\frac{1}{4}\left\{\frac{1}{4}[0+2(1.3)+2(1.5)+2(2.1)+2.6]\right\}$

37. A bug travels along the y-axis such that its velocity, in centimeters per second, is given by $v(t) = (t-1)e^{t^2+2t}$, and t is in seconds. Find the total distance traveled by the bug in the first 1.5 sec.

(A) 3.386 cm
(B) 27.155 cm
(C) 29.412 cm
(D) 31.669 cm

38. Consider a differentiable function $f(x)$ that has an x-intercept of 2 and a y-intercept of 4. In the interval $0 < x < 2$, $f(x)$ is decreasing and concave down. Which of the following must be true?
    I. The Mean Value Theorem is satisfied when $c = 1$.
    II. $\int_0^1 f(x)\,dx > \int_1^2 f(x)\,dx$
    III. A tangent approximation of the function for any value in the interval $0 < x < 2$ will underestimate the function value.
    (A) I only
    (B) II only
    (C) III only
    (D) I and II only

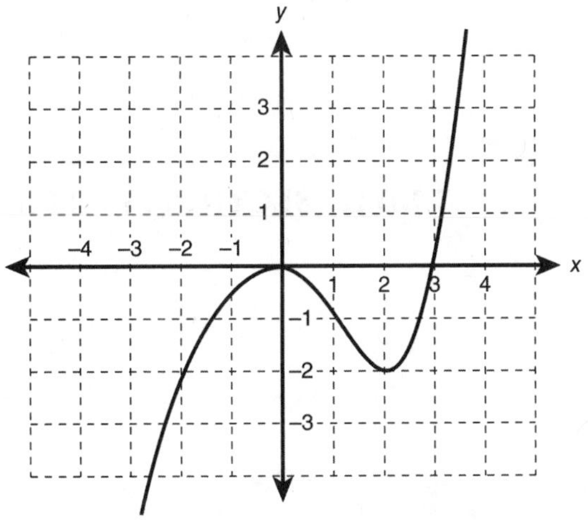

Let $f(x) = x^2 + \int_{-2}^{x} g(t)\,dt$, where $g(x)$ is shown in the graph above. Use this graph to answer Problems 39–41.

39. What is $f(-2)$?
    (A) 6
    (B) 4
    (C) 0
    (D) −4

40. What is $f'(-2)$?
    (A) −6
    (B) −4
    (C) 0
    (D) 2

41. What is $f''(2)$?
    (A) −6
    (B) −4
    (C) 0
    (D) 2

42. What is the area of the regions between $f(x) = 2x\sin(2x)$ and $g(x) = -2x\cos(2x)$ on the interval $0 \le x \le \frac{\pi}{2}$?
    (A) 0.571
    (B) 0.595
    (C) 1.761
    (D) 1.178

43. The volume of the solid generated by revolving the region enclosed between the graph of $y = x^2 + 2$, the y axis, and the lines $y = 1$ and $x = 2$ about the x axis is given by which of the following integral expression?
    (A) $\pi \int_0^2 x^4\,dx$
    (B) $\pi \int_0^2 (2 + x^2)^2\,dx$
    (C) $\pi \int_1^6 \left(1 - \sqrt{y - 2}\right)^2\,dy$
    (D) $\pi \int_0^2 \left[(2 + x^2)^2 - 1^2\right]dx$

GO ON TO NEXT PAGE

44. The rate of decay of a radioactive isotope is directly proportional to the amount remaining. If the half-life of the radioactive isotope, Einsteinium, is 276 days and a sample initially weighs 25 grams, what is its rate of decay on the 120th day?
(A) −0.046 grams per day
(B) −0.031 grams per day
(C) −0.003 grams per day
(D) −0.002 grams per day

45. A region is bounded by the function $y = \sin^{-1}(x-1) + \frac{\pi}{2}$, the line $x = 2$, and the x-axis. A solid is formed when the region is rotated about the line $x = 2$. What is the radius of the volume of rotation?
(A) $r = \sin^{-1}(x-1) + \frac{\pi}{2}$
(B) $r = 1 + \sin\left(y - \frac{\pi}{2}\right)$
(C) $r = 2 - \sin\left(y - \frac{\pi}{2}\right)$
(D) $r = 1 - \sin\left(y - \frac{\pi}{2}\right)$

END OF SECTION I PART B

Section II
Free-Response Questions
Time: 1 hour and 30 minutes
Number of Problems: 6

Part A
Time: 30 minutes
Number of Problems: 2

You may use a calculator for any problem in this section.

1. Region R is bounded by the functions $f(x) = 2(x-4) + \pi$, $g(x) = \cos^{-1}\left(\frac{x}{2} - 3\right)$, and the x-axis as shown in the figure to the right.
   (a) What is the area of region R?
   (b) Find the volume of the solid generated when region R is rotated about the x-axis.
   (c) Find all values c for $f(x)$ and $g(x)$ in the closed interval $p \le c \le q$ for which each function equals the average value in the indicated interval.

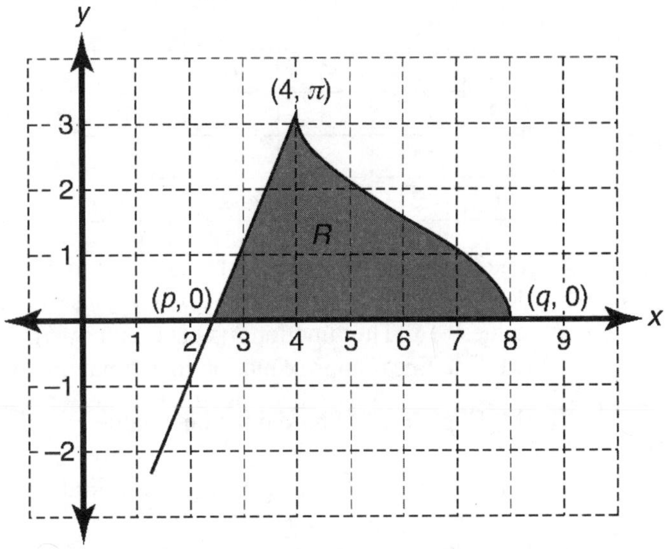

2. A particle is moving along the x-axis with velocity $v(t) = \ln(t+3) - e^{\frac{t}{2}-1}(\cos t)$, for $0 \le t \le 8$. The initial position of the particle is -1.6.
   (a) At what time(s) in the open interval $0 < t < 8$ does the particle change direction? Justify your answer.
   (b) Where is the particle when it is farthest to the left?
   (c) How far does the particle travel in the interval $3 \le t \le 6$?
   (d) At what times in the closed interval, $0 \le t \le 8$, is the speed of the particle decreasing? Justify your answer.

END OF SECTION II PART A

Section II
Part B
Time: 60 minutes
Number of Problems: 4

You may not use a calculator for any problem in this section. During the timed portion for Section II, Part B, you may continue to work on the problems in Section II, Part A without the use of a calculator.

3.

x	$f(x)$	$g(x)$	$f'(x)$	$g'(x)$
1	1	6	2	−3
2	2	4	0	−½
3	3	3	1	−1
4	4	2	0	−½
6	2	1	−2	−1

The functions $f(x)$ and $g(x)$ are differentiable for all real numbers, and $g(x)$ is strictly decreasing. The table above gives values of the functions and their first derivatives at selected values of x. The function $h(x)$ is given by $h(x) = f(g(x))$.

(a) Use linear approximation to estimate the value of $h(x)$ at $x = 5.9$.

(b) Explain why there must be a value c on the interval $1 < c < 3$ such that $h''(c) = -\frac{7}{2}$.

(c) Let $R(x) = \int_1^{f(x)} \left[g(t) + (2t) \right] dt$. Find the value of $R'(1)$.

(d) Find $\left. \frac{d}{dx}\left[g^{-1}(x) \right] \right|_{x=6}$.

4. Consider the differential equation
$\frac{dy}{dx} = (y+1)(1-x)$ for $y > -1$.
(a) On the axes provided, sketch a slope field for the given differential equation at the 11 points indicated.
(b) If $y(0) = 1$, then find the particular solution $y(x)$ to the given differential equation.
(c) Draw a function through the point (0, 1) on your slope field which represents an approximate solution of the given differential equation with initial condition $y(0) = 1$.

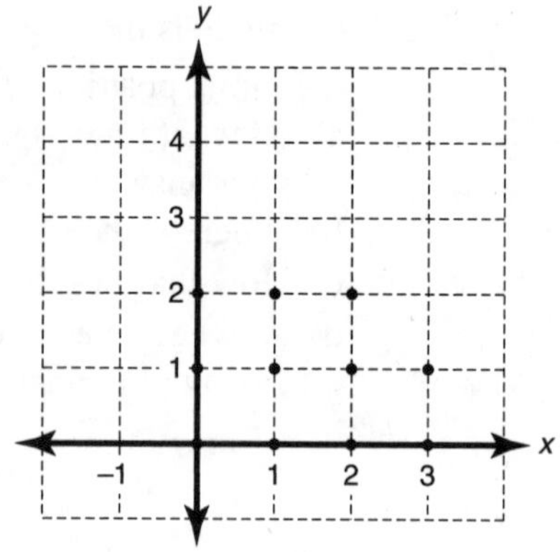

5. Consider the function $h(x) = 3x^2 - \sqrt{x+1}$.
(a) Evaluate $\frac{1}{3-(-1)} \int_{-1}^{3} (3x^2 - \sqrt{x+1})\, dx$ and interpret its meaning.
(b) What is the equation of the tangent to $h(x)$ at $x = 0$?
(c) Use the tangent found in part b to approximate $h(x)$ at $x = -0.01$.
(d) Is the approximation, found in part c, greater or less than the actual value of $h(x)$ at $x = -0.01$? Justify your answer using calculus.

6. Consider the functions $f(x) = e^x \sin x$ and $g(x) = e^x \cos x$, as shown in the sketch to the right, in the closed interval $0 \le x \le 2\pi$.

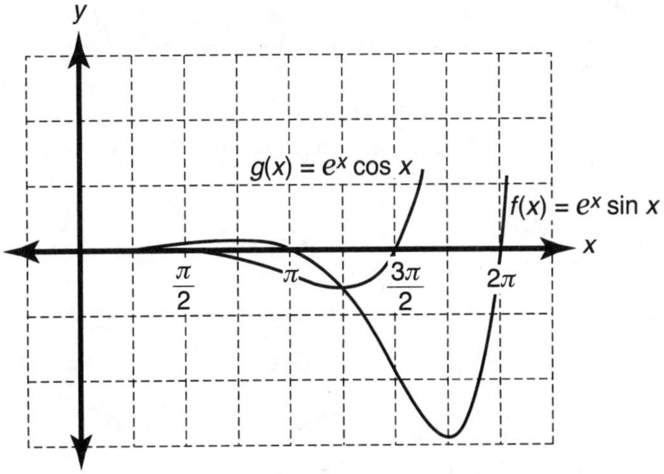

(a) Let $D(x) = f(x) - g(x)$ be the vertical distance between the functions. Find the value of x in the open interval $\frac{\pi}{4} < x < \frac{5\pi}{4}$, where $D(x)$ is a maximum value. Explain your reasoning.

(b) At what value of x in the open interval $\frac{\pi}{4} < x < \frac{5\pi}{4}$ is the rate of change of $D(x)$ increasing the most rapidly? Explain your reasoning.

(c) For $H(x) = \frac{e^x}{\sin x} + g(x)$, find the x-coordinate of all points at which $H(x)$ has horizontal tangents on the open interval $0 < x < 2\pi$.

END OF EXAMINATION

Answers and Answer Explanations

Using the table below, score your test. Determine how many questions you answered correctly and how many you answered incorrectly. Additional information about scoring is at the end of the Practice Test.

1. C	2. D	3. D	4. A	5. C
6. B	7. D	8. D	9. D	10. A
11. D	12. A	13. C	14. C	15. B
16. A	17. D	18. B	19. A	20. C
21. B	22. A	23. C	24. A	25. B
26. C	27. B	28. D	29. C	30. B
31. D	32. D	33. D	34. B	35. D
36. C	37. D	38. B	39. B	40. A
41. D	42. C	43. D	44. A	45. D

MULTIPLE-CHOICE QUESTIONS

1. ANSWER: (C) The domain for $f(x) = \ln(x^2 - 4)$ is $|x| > 2$.
With $f'(x) = \dfrac{2x}{x^2 - 4} = 0$, but $x = 0$ is not in the domain of $f(x)$. The behavior of the curve is analyzed using the sign chart below.

x	$-\infty < x < -2$	$2 < x < \infty$
$f'(x)$	negative	positive
$f(x)$	decreasing	increasing

Therefore, the curve is increasing when $x > 2$.
(*Calculus for AP®*, pages 293–300; EU 2.2; LO 2.2A; EK 2.2A1; MPAC 2,3)

2. ANSWER: (D) $\lim\limits_{x \to 0} \dfrac{\cos x}{|x|} = \dfrac{1}{0}$, which does not exist. (The value of the limit from both the left and right side of 0 is ∞.)
(*Calculus for AP®*, page 97; EU 1.1; LO 1.1C; EK 1.1C2; MPAC 2,3)

3. ANSWER: (D) By substituting $u = -x$ and $du = -dx$,
$$\int 3^{-x} + \frac{1}{x}\,dx = -\int 3^{u}\,du + \int \frac{1}{x}\,dx = -\frac{3^{-x}}{\ln 3} + \ln|x| + C$$
(*Calculus for AP®*, pages 457–465; EU 3.3; LO 3.3B; EK 3.3B3; MPAC 3)

4. ANSWER: (A)

$$\frac{d}{dx}\left[\cos(x+y)\right]=\frac{d}{dx}(x)\Rightarrow -\sin(x+y)\cdot\left(1+\frac{dy}{dx}\right)=1$$

$$1+\frac{dy}{dx}=\frac{1}{-\sin(x+y)}=-\csc(x+y)$$

$$\frac{dy}{dx}=-\csc(x+y)-1$$

(*Calculus for AP*®, pages 240–245; EU 2.1; LO 2.1C; EK 2.1C5; MPAC 2,3)

5. ANSWER: (C)

$$g(-1)=\int_0^{-1} f(t)\,dt=-\int_{-1}^{0} f(t)\,dt=-\frac{1}{2}(1)(2)=-1$$

$g'(x)=f(x)\Rightarrow g'(-1)=f(-1)=0$
$g''(x)=f'(x)\Rightarrow g''(-1)=f'(-1)=2$
$g(-1)+g'(-1)+g''(-1)=-1+0+2=1$
(*Calculus for AP*®, pages 436–440; EU 3.3; LO 3.3B; EK 3.3B1; MPAC 2,4)

6. ANSWER: (B) Solve the integral by adding up the geometric areas pictured.

$$\int_{-3}^{5} f(t)\,dt=1(-2)+\frac{1}{2}(1)(-2)+\frac{1}{2}(1)(2)+2(2)+\left(2(2)-\frac{\pi}{2}\right)+\frac{1}{2}(1)(2)$$

$$=-2-1+1+4+4-\frac{\pi}{2}+1$$

$$=7-\frac{\pi}{2}$$

(*Calculus for AP*®, pages 422–423; EU 3.3; LO 3.3B; EK 3.3B1; MPAC 2,4)

7. ANSWER: (D) The function $g(x)$ is increasing for $x > 0$, so the absolute maximum occurs at $x = 5$. The relative minimum occurs where $g'(x)$ changes from negative to positive, so the relative minimum occurs at $x = -1$. A point of inflection occurs where the slope of $f(x)$, $f'(x) = g''(x)$, changes from negative to positive, so a point of inflection occurs where $x = 3$. The roots of $g(x)$ occur where $\int_0^x f(t)\,dt = 0$, and this occurs when $x = 0$ or $x = -2$.
Therefore, the false statement is D, because $g''(x) = f'(x)$ is greater than zero in the open interval $-2 < x < -1$, which indicates that the curve is concave up.
(*Calculus for AP*®, pages 436–440; EU 2.2; LO 2.2A; EK 2.2A1,2.2A3; MPAC 2,4)

8. ANSWER: (D) Speed $= |v(t)| = |x'(t)|$. Since $x'(t) = 3 - 3t^2$, then $|v(4)| = |3 - 3(4)^2| = 45$.
(*Calculus for AP*®, page 509; EU 2.3; LO 2.3C; EK 2.3C1; MPAC 2,3)

9. ANSWER: (D) Using the disk method and integrating with respect to y:

$V=\pi\int_{-1}^{1}x^2dy=2\pi\int_0^1(y^2-1)^2\,dy$

$v=2\pi\int_0^1(y^4-2y^2+1)dy$

$=2\pi\left(\frac{1}{5}y^5-\frac{2}{3}y^3+y\right)\Big|_0^1$

$=2\pi\left(\frac{1}{5}-\frac{2}{3}+1\right)=\frac{16\pi}{15}$

(*Calculus for AP®*, pages 522–525; EU 3.4; LO 3.4D; EK 3.4D2; MPAC 2,3)

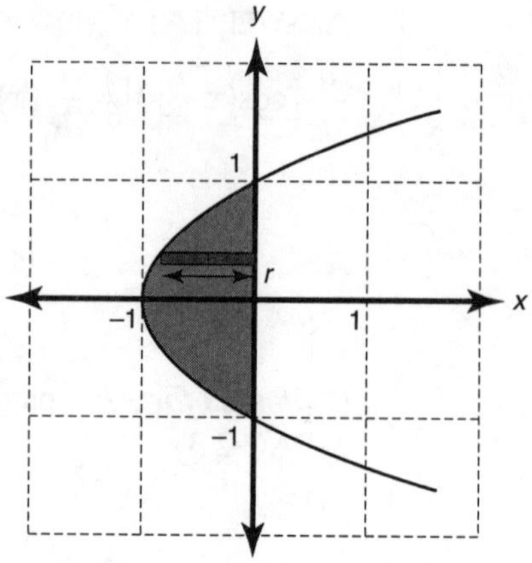

10. ANSWER: (A) **Case I:** $f'(x)|=\frac{1}{3x^{\frac{2}{3}}}$ and is not defined at $x = 0$.

Therefore, $f'(x)$ is always greater than zero, except at $x = 0$. (Therefore, the statement is true.)

Case II: The function is not differentiable at $x = 0$ and since the slope of the tangent line is undefined at $x = 0$, the tangent line is vertical. (So, the statement is false.)

Case III: The Mean Value Theorem is not applicable in the stated interval, because the function is not differentiable at $x = 0$. (Thus, the statement is false.)
(*Calculus for AP®*, pages 350–362, 308; EU 2.2,2.4; LO 2.2A,2.4A; EK 2.2A1,2.4A1; MPAC 2,3)

11. ANSWER: (D) Rewrite $a(t)$ using long division:

$\frac{t^2+t}{t^2+1}\Rightarrow 1+\frac{t-1}{t^2+1}\Rightarrow 1+\frac{t}{1+t^2}-\frac{1}{1+t^2}$

$v(t)=\int a(t)\,dt=\int\left(1+\frac{t}{1+t^2}-\frac{1}{1+t^2}\right)dt=t+\frac{1}{2}\ln(t^2+1)-\tan^{-1}t+C.$

If $v(0)=1$, then $C=1$ and finally, $v(t)=t+\frac{1}{2}\ln(t^2+1)-\tan^{-1}t+1.$

(*Calculus for AP®*, pages 388–389; EU 2.3; LO 2.3C; EK 2.3C1; MPAC 3)

12. ANSWER: (A) For $n = 3$ the width of each rectangle is 4. Since $f_{\text{avg}}=\frac{1}{b-a}\int_a^b f(x)\,dx$ and $\int_a^b f(x)\,dx$ is approximated by using a right Riemann sum, then

$R_{\text{avg}}=\frac{1}{12}\int_0^{12}R(t)\,dt\approx\frac{1}{12}(4)(10+12+8)=10\text{ cm}^3/\text{min}$

(*Calculus for AP®*, pages 395–410; EU 3.2; LO 3.2B; EK 3.2B1,3.2B3; MPAC 2,3)

13. ANSWER: (C) $h(x)$ has a point of inflection where $h''(x)$ changes sign. For $h''(x) = e^{x-1}(2x-1)^2(x-3)^3(4x+5)$, the factor e^{x-1} never equals zero.

x			$\frac{1}{2} < x < 3$	$3 < x < \infty$
$h''(x)$	positive	negative	negative	positive

Therefore, there are two points of inflection, one at $x = -\frac{5}{4}$ and the other at $x = 3$, where $h''(x)$ changes from positive to negative or negative to positive. (*Calculus for AP®*, pages 322–324; EU 2.2; LO 2.2A; EK 2.2A1; MPAC 2,3)

14. ANSWER: (C) Since $\int_a^b f'(x)\,dx = f(b) = f(a)$, then

$$f(2) - f(-1) = \int_{-1}^{2} f'(x)\,dx. \text{ Then } \int_{-1}^{2} f'(x)\,dx \Rightarrow$$

$$\int_{-1}^{1} f'(x)\,dx + \int_{1}^{2} f'(x)\,dx \Rightarrow \int_{-1}^{1} f'(x)\,dx + k. \text{ Thus,}$$

$$f(2) - f(-1) = \left[1(-1) + \frac{1}{2}\left(\frac{1}{3}\right)(-1) + \frac{1}{2}\left(\frac{2}{3}\right)(2)\right] + k$$

$$= \left[-1 - \frac{1}{6} + \frac{2}{3}\right] + k$$

$$= k - \frac{1}{2}$$

(*Calculus for AP®*, pages 266–287; pages 270–291; EU 3.3; LO 3.3B; EK 3.3B2; MPAC 2,3)

15. ANSWER: (B) Since $\int \frac{1}{a^2 + u^2}\,du = \frac{1}{a}\tan^{-1}\frac{u}{a} + C$, then

$$\int \frac{1}{16 + x^2}\,dx = \frac{1}{4}\tan^{-1}\frac{x}{4} + C$$

(*Calculus for AP®*, page 447; EU 3.3; LO 3.3B; EK 3.3B5; MPAC 2,3)

16. ANSWER: (A) Acceleration has a relative maximum or minimum when $a'(t) = 0$. So, $v(t) = -t^3 + \frac{9}{4}t^4 \Rightarrow a(t) = -3t^2 + 9t^3$ and finally, $a'(t) = -6t + 27t^2 = 0 \Rightarrow -3t(2 - 9t) \Rightarrow t = \frac{2}{9}$ or 0

t	$0 < t < \frac{2}{9}$	$\frac{2}{9} < t < \infty$
$a'(t)$	negative	positive
$a(t)$	decreasing	increasing

Therefore, $a(t)$ is at a minimum when $t=\frac{2}{9}$, where $a(t)$ changes from decreasing to increasing.
(*Calculus for AP*®, pages 293–300; EU 2.3; LO 2.3C; EK 2.3C1; MPAC 2,3)

17. ANSWER: (D) $\lim_{h\to 0}\frac{\sin^{-1}(1+h)-\frac{\pi}{2}}{h}$ is in the form of the definition of the derivative, $\lim_{h\to 0}\frac{f(x+h)-f(x)}{h}=f'(x)$, with the function, $f(x)=\sin^{-1}(x)$ and $x=1$, because $\sin^{-1}(1)=\frac{\pi}{2}$. Then, $f'(x)=\frac{1}{\sqrt{1-x^2}}$ and $f'(1)=\frac{1}{\sqrt{1-1^2}}$ does not exist.
(*Calculus for AP*®, pages 169–171; EU 2.1; LO 2.1C; EK 2.1C1; MPAC 1,2,3)

18. ANSWER: (B) For $f(x)=e^{\sin x}+x$, $f(0)=e^0+0=1$ and $f'(x)=e^{\sin x}\cos x+1$, with $f'(0)=e^0\cos 0+1=2$. Since $f(0)=1$ and $f'(0)=m=2$, then the equation of the tangent is $y-1=2(x-0)\Rightarrow y=2x+1$.
(*Calculus for AP*®, pages 165–167; EU 2.3;LO 2.3B; EK 2.3B1; MPAC 2,3)

19. ANSWER: (A) Observe that the segments with slopes of zero occur where x and y are equal and that the segments with vertical slopes occur where $y=0$. Thus, the statement that matches the slope field is $\frac{dy}{dx}=\frac{x-y}{2y}$.
(*Calculus for AP*®, pages 606–611; EU 2.3; LO 2.3F; EK 2.3F1; MPAC 1,2,4)

20. ANSWER: (C) The Second Fundamental Theorem states that if $F(x)=\int_a^{g(x)}f(u)\,du$, then $F'(x)=f[g(x)]\cdot g'(x)$. First, rewrite $F(x)=\int_{3x-2}^{2}f(2t)\,dt\Rightarrow F(x)=-\int_2^{3x-2}f(2t)\,dt$, where $g(x)=3x-2$.
By substitution of $u=2t$ and $du=2dt$, change the limits of the integral (where $t=2$, then $u=4$, and where $t=3x-2$, $u=6x-4$) and the integral becomes $F(x)=-\frac{1}{2}\int_4^{6x-4}f(u)du$. Finally,
$F'(x)=-\frac{1}{2}[f(6x-4)]\cdot 6=-3f(6x-4)$.
(*Calculus for AP*®, pages 436–440; EU 3.3; LO 3.3A; EK 3.3A2; MPAC 1,2)

21. ANSWER: (B) With $h'(x) = \dfrac{15x^2 - 2}{2\sqrt{5x^3 - 2x + 1}}$, $h'(1) = \dfrac{15 - 2}{2\sqrt{5 - 2 + 1}} = \dfrac{13}{4}$.
A normal line is perpendicular to the tangent at the point of tangency, so
$m_{\text{normal}} = -\dfrac{4}{13}$.
(*Calculus for AP*®, pages 196–197; EU 2.3; LO 2.3B; EK 2.3B1; MPAC 2,3)

22. ANSWER: (A) The average rate of change of a function in a closed interval is given by $\dfrac{f(b) - f(a)}{b - a}$. Then the average rate of change of *y* in the closed interval $0 \le x \le \dfrac{\pi}{2}$ is

$$\frac{y\left(\frac{\pi}{2}\right) - y(0)}{\left(\frac{\pi}{2}\right) - 0} = \frac{2\left(\frac{\pi}{2}\right)\left[\sin 2\left(\frac{\pi}{2}\right) + \frac{\pi}{2}\cos 2\left(\frac{\pi}{2}\right)\right] - 2(0)(\sin 0 + 0\cos 0)}{\frac{\pi}{2} - 0}$$

$$= \frac{\pi\left[0 - \frac{\pi}{2}\right] - 0}{\frac{\pi}{2}} = -\pi$$

(*Calculus for AP*®, page 171; EU 2.1; LO 2.1A; EK 2.1A1; MPAC 1,3)

23. ANSWER: (C) $f'(x) = 3x^2 - \dfrac{1}{x+k} \Rightarrow f'(1) = 3 - \dfrac{1}{K+1} = 0 \Rightarrow k = -\dfrac{2}{3}$.
Using the second derivative test, $f''(x) = 6x + (k + x)^{-2} \rightarrow f''(1) > 0$.
Therefore, $f(x)$ is concave up and a minimum occurs at $x = 1$ when
$k = -\dfrac{2}{3}$.
(*Calculus for AP*®, pages 293–300; EU 2.2; LO 2.2A; EK 2.2A1; MPAC 2,3)

24. ANSWER: (A)

$$C'(t) = \frac{2(8100 + t^2) - 2t(2t)}{(8100 + t^2)^2}$$

$$= \frac{16{,}200 - 2t^2}{(8100 + t^2)^2} = 0 \Rightarrow 16{,}200 - 2t^2$$

$$= 0 \Rightarrow t = \sqrt{8100} = 90 \text{ min}$$

To be sure that this value of *t* occurs when $C(t)$ is a relative maximum, use a sign chart.

t	$0 < t < 90$	$t > 90$
$C'(t)$	positive	negative
$C(t)$	increasing	decreasing

Since $C(t)$ increases before $t = 90$ and decreases after $t = 90$, $C(t)$ has a relative maximum at $t = 90$.
(*Calculus for AP*®, pages 293–300; EU 2.3; LO 2.3C; EK 2.3C3; MPAC 2,3)

25. ANSWER: (B) If $\lim_{x\to\infty}\frac{ae^x}{5+2e^x} = 3$ and $\lim_{x\to\infty} e^x = \infty$, then

$$\lim_{x\to\infty}\frac{\frac{ae^x}{e^x}}{\frac{5}{e^x}+\frac{2e^x}{e^x}} = \lim_{x\to\infty}\frac{a}{\frac{5}{e^x}+2} = \frac{a}{2} = 3. \text{ Thus, a} = 6.$$

The solution for this problem can be found using L'Hôpital's Rule as follows: $\lim_{x\to\infty}\frac{f(x)}{g(x)} = \lim_{x\to\infty}\frac{f'(x)}{g'(x)}$ can also be used to evaluate a limit when of the form $\frac{\infty}{\infty}$ or $\frac{0}{0}$. Thus, $\lim_{x\to\infty}\frac{ae^x}{5+2e^x} = \lim_{x\to\infty}\frac{ae^x}{2e^x} = \frac{a}{2} = 3$, and therefore, $a = 6$.
(*Calculus for AP*®, pages 117–128; EU 1.1; LO 1.1C; EK 1.1C1; MPAC 2,3)

26. ANSWER: (C)

$$\frac{d}{dx}\left[f\left(g\left(x^2\right)\right)\right] = f'(g(x^2))\cdot g'(x^2)\cdot 2x \Rightarrow f'(g(4))\cdot g'(4)\cdot 4$$

$$= f'(1)\cdot\left(-\frac{1}{2}\right)\cdot 4 = \frac{2}{3}(-2) = -\frac{4}{3}$$

(*Calculus for AP*®, pages 227–233; EU 2.1; LO 2.1C; EK 2.1C4; MPAC 2,3,4,5)

27. ANSWER: (B) $V = 2x^2h = 8 \Rightarrow h = \frac{8}{2x^2} = \frac{4}{x^2}$

$$\text{SA} = 2(2x+x)h + 2x^2$$
$$= 6x\left(\frac{4}{x^2}\right) + 2x^2$$
$$= 24x^{-1} + 2x^2$$

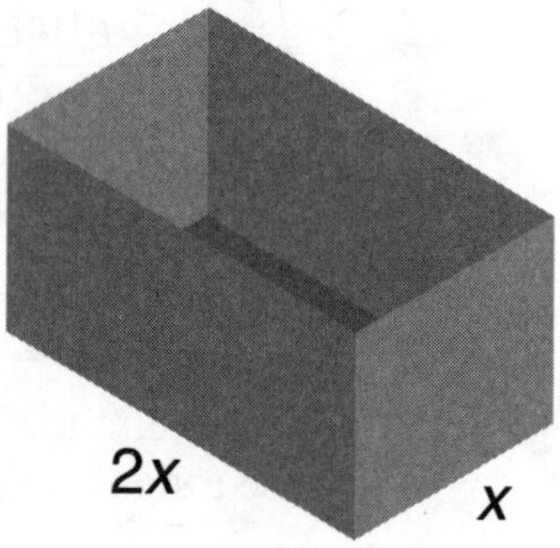

$$\text{SA}' = -24x^{-2} + 4x = 0 \Rightarrow 4\left(x - \frac{6}{x^2}\right) = 0$$

and $x = \sqrt[3]{6}$ is the width of the base. $\text{SA}'' = 48x^{-3} + 4 > 0$ for all x, and the function SA will be concave up, thus $x = \sqrt[3]{6}$ occurs at a relative minimum.
(*Calculus for AP*®, pages 365–372; EU 2.3; LO 2.3C; EK 2.3C3; MPAC 2,3)

28. ANSWER: (D) The length of the side of each square is $s = \sqrt{x+1}$ and the area of each square is $s^2 = x + 1$. Then

$$V = \int_{-1}^{1} s^2 dx \Rightarrow \int_{-1}^{1} (x+1)\,dx$$

$$= \left(\frac{x^2}{2} + x\right)\Big|_{-1}^{1}$$

$$= \left(\frac{1}{2} + 1\right) - \left(\frac{1}{2} - 1\right)$$

$$= 2$$

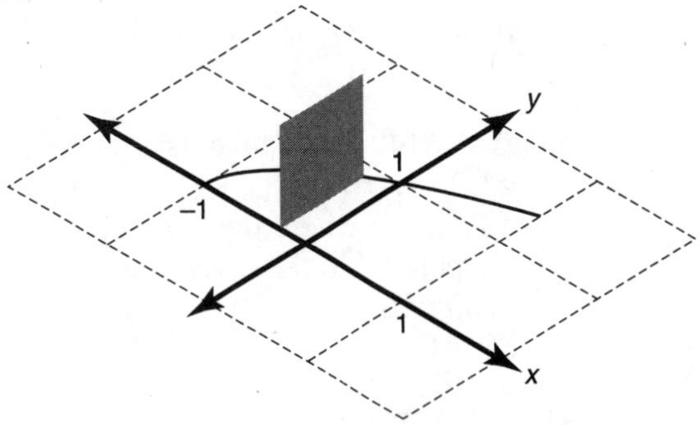

(*Calculus for AP*®, pages 518–522; EU 3.4; LO 3.4D; EK 3.4D2; MPAC 2,3)

29. ANSWER: (C) This is a quotient indeterminate form, so L'Hopital's Rule applies. So, $\lim_{x\to 0}\frac{1-e^{4x}}{2x} = \lim_{x\to 0}\frac{-4e^{4x}}{2} = \frac{-4}{2} = -2.$
(*Calculus for AP*®, pages 337–343; EU 1.1; LO 1.1A; EK 1.1C3; MPAC 1,2,3)

30. ANSWER: (B) Using L'Hopital's Rule and the Fundamental Theorem of Calculus we have

$$\lim_{x\to\frac{\pi}{2}}\frac{\int_0^{x-\frac{\pi}{2}}\cos 3t\,dt}{x-\frac{\pi}{2}} = \lim_{x\to\frac{\pi}{2}}\frac{\cos 3\left(x-\frac{\pi}{2}\right)}{1} = \cos(3.0) = \cos 0 = 1$$

(*Calculus for AP*®, pages 337–343; 436–440; EU 1.1; LO 1.1A; EK 1.1C3, 3.3A2; MPAC 1,2,3,4)

31. ANSWER: (D) Let x = the distance from car A to point P, y = the distance from car B to point P, and z = the distance between the cars at time t.

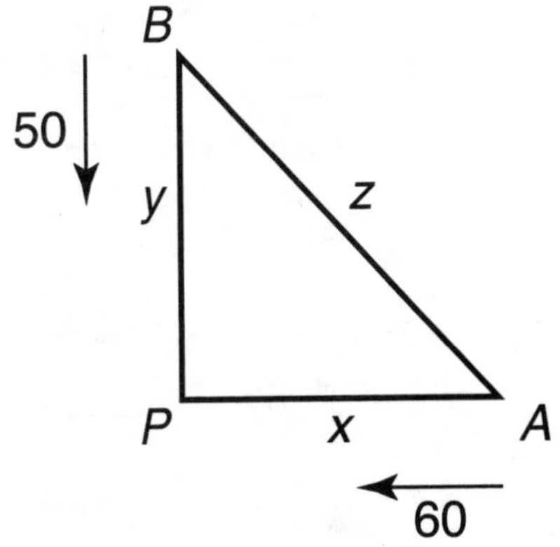

Then, $\frac{d}{dt}(x^2 + y^2 = z^2) = 2x\frac{dx}{dt} + 2y\frac{dy}{dt} = 2z\frac{dz}{dt}$,

which simplifies to $x\frac{dx}{dt} + y\frac{dy}{dt} = z\frac{dz}{dt}$. By substitution,

$12(-60) + 10(-50) = \sqrt{12^2 + 10^2}\frac{dz}{dt} \Rightarrow \frac{dz}{dt} \approx -78.102.$

Therefore, the distance between the cars is decreasing at approximately 78.102 miles per hour.
(*Calculus for AP*®, pages 274–279; EU 2.3; LO 2.3C; EK 2.3C2; MPAC 2,3)

32. ANSWER: (D) $f'(x) = 2^{-2x}(-2\ln 2) = -1 \Rightarrow x \approx 0.2356$ $f(0.2356) = 0.7124$ and the tangent is $y - 0.7214 = -1(x - 0.2356)$ with the x-intercept of $x \approx 0.957$.
(*Calculus for AP*®, pages 165–167; EU 2.3; LO 2.3B; EK 2.3B1; MPAC 2,3)

33. ANSWER: (D) Tangents are parallel when derivatives are equal; $g'(x) = y' \Rightarrow \sec^2(x+2) = 2$. There are five points in the open interval $-4 < x < 5$ where the derivatives intersect. Therefore, the tangents to $g(x)$ are parallel to the given line five times in this interval.
(*Calculus for AP*®, pages 165–167; EU 2.3; LO 2.3B; EK 2.3B1; MPAC 2,3,5)

34. ANSWER: (B)

$$\int_1^{2k}\left(x - \frac{k}{x^2}\right)dx = 15 \Rightarrow \left(\frac{x^2}{2} + \frac{k}{x}\right)\Bigg|_1^{2k}$$

$$= \left(\frac{4k^2}{2} + \frac{k}{2k}\right) - \left(\frac{1}{2} + \frac{k}{1}\right) \Rightarrow 2k^2 + \frac{1}{2} - \frac{1}{2} - k$$

$$= 15 \Rightarrow 2k^2 - k - 15 = 0$$

Factor the quadratic and solve for k. $(2k+5)(k-3) = 0$, and $k = 3$ and $-\frac{5}{2}$.

The sum of both k values is $\frac{1}{2}$.
(*Calculus for AP*®, pages 436–440; EU 3.3; LO 3.3B; EK 3.3B2; MPAC 2,3,5)

35. ANSWER: (D) Use a sign chart to analyze the curve.

	$-\infty < x < -2$	$-2 < x < -1.5$	$-1.5 < x < 0$	$X > 0$
$f'(x)$	positive	negative	negative	positive
$F''(x)$	negative	negative	positive	positive
$f(x)$	increasing concave down	decreasing concave down	decreasing concave up	increasing concave up

Therefore, a correct graph of $f(x)$ is D.
(*Calculus for AP*®, pages 316–317; EU 2.2; LO 2.2A; EK 2.2A3; MPAC 2,4)

36. ANSWER: (C) By the Trapezoidal Rule,

$$\int_0^4 H(t)\,dt \approx \frac{b-a}{2n}[H(0) + 2H(1) + 2H(2) + 2H(3) + H(4)]$$

Where $\frac{b-a}{2n} = \frac{4-0}{2(4)} = \frac{1}{2}$. If $H_{avg} = \frac{1}{b-a}\int_a^b H(t)\,dt$ then H_{avg} is approximated by

$$H_{avg} = \frac{1}{4}\int_0^4 H(t)\,dt \Rightarrow \frac{1}{4}\left\{\frac{1}{2}[0 + 2(1.3) + 2(1.5) + 2(2.1) + 2.6]\right\}.$$

(*Calculus for AP*®, pages 400–401; EU 3.2; LO 3.2B; EK 3.2B2; MPAC 2,4)

37. ANSWER: (D) Distance traveled, $x(t)=\int_0^{1.5}|v(t)|\,dt \approx 31.669$ cm.

(*Calculus for AP*®, page 452; EU 3.4; LO 3.4E; EK 3.4E1; MPAC 2,3)

38. ANSWER: (B) I. (False) The Mean Value Theorem is satisfied in the interval $0 < x < 2$, but not necessarily at $c = 1$. (The statement is true if $f(x) = 4 - x^2$ but not true for a function such as $f(x)=4-\frac{1}{4}x^4$, where

$$f'(c)=-c^3=\frac{f(2)-f(0)}{2-0}\Rightarrow -c^3=\frac{0-4}{2}\Rightarrow c=\sqrt[3]{2}.)$$

II. (True) Since $f(x)$ is decreasing and concave down, the area from $x = 0$ to $x = 1$ is always greater than from $x = 1$ to $x = 2$. Use right or left Riemann sums to visualize the statement.

III. (False) The tangent will always be above the curve in this interval and will therefore overestimate the function value.

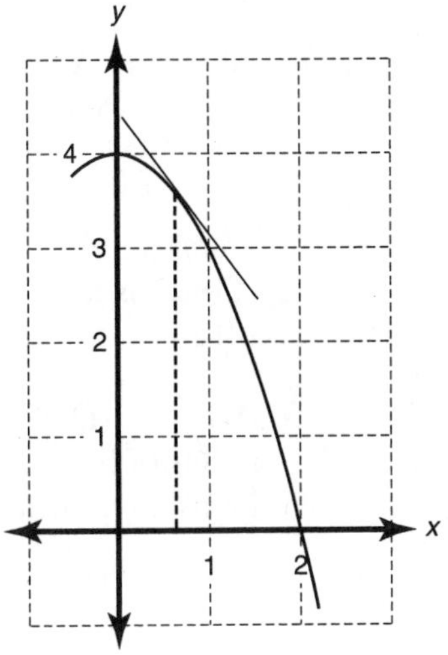

(*Calculus for AP*®, pages 308–311, 422–423, 322–324; EU 2.3,2.4,3.2; LO 2.3B,2.4A,3.2C; EK 2.3B2,2.4A1,3.2C1; MPAC 1,2,5)

39. ANSWER: (B) $f(-2)=(-2)^2+\int_{-2}^{-2} g(t)\,dt=4+0=4$

(*Calculus for AP*®, pages 436–440; EU 3.2; LO 3.2B; EK 3.2B1; MPAC 1,2,3)

40. ANSWER: (A) $f'(x) = 2x + g(x) \Rightarrow f'(-2) = 2(-2) + g(-2) = -4 - 2 = -6$
(*Calculus for AP*®, pages 436–440; EU 3.3; LO 3.3A; EK 3.3A2; MPAC 1,2,3)

41. ANSWER: (D) $f''(x) = 2 + g'(x) \Rightarrow f''(2) = 2 + g'(2) = 2 + 0 = 2$.
(*Calculus for AP*®, pages 436–440; EU 3.3; LO 3.3A; EK 3.3A2; MPAC 1,2,3)

42. ANSWER: (C) The curves intersect at $x \approx 1.1781$ and the area between the curves is found by

$$\int_0^{1.1781}(f-g)\,dx+\int_{1.1781}^{\frac{\pi}{2}}(f-g)\,dx \approx 1.1661+0.5953 \approx 1.761.$$

(The area can also be computed by evaluating the absolute value of the difference of the functions as the functions intersect in the interval $0 \le x \le \frac{\pi}{2}$:

$$\int_0^{\frac{\pi}{2}}|f(x)-g(x)|\,dx \approx 1.761.)$$

(*Calculus for AP*®, pages 477–486; EU 3.4; LO 3.4D; EK 3.4D1; MPAC 2,3)

43. ANSWER: (D) By the washer method, the outer radius is $(x^2 + 2 - 0)$ and the inner radius is $(1 - 0)$, so $V = \pi\int_0^2 \left[(2+x^2)^2 - 1^2\right]dx$.
(*Calculus for AP*®, pages 525–528; EU 3.4; LO 3.4D; EK 3.4D2; MPAC 2)

44. ANSWER: (A) Since the rate of decay is proportional to the amount present, then $y = Ce^{kt}$. When $t = 0$, $C = 25$. With a half-life of 276 days, solve for k. $12.5 = 25e^{k(276)} \Rightarrow k \approx -0.0025$ and $y = 25e^{-0.0025t}$. Then, $y'(t) = 25e^{-0.0025t}(-0.0025)$ and $y'(120) = 25e^{-0.0025(120)}(-0.0025) \approx -0.046$ grams per day.
(*Calculus for AP*®, pages 628–630; EU 3.5; LO 3.5B; EK 3.5B1; MPAC 1,2,3)

45. ANSWER: (D) When rotating about the line $x = 2$, the radius of rotation $= 2 - x$. Rewrite the function for x in terms of y. Then

$$y = \sin^{-1}(x-1) + \frac{\pi}{2} \Rightarrow y - \frac{\pi}{2}$$
$$= \sin^{-1}(x-1) \Rightarrow \sin\left(y - \frac{\pi}{2}\right) + 1$$
$$= x.$$

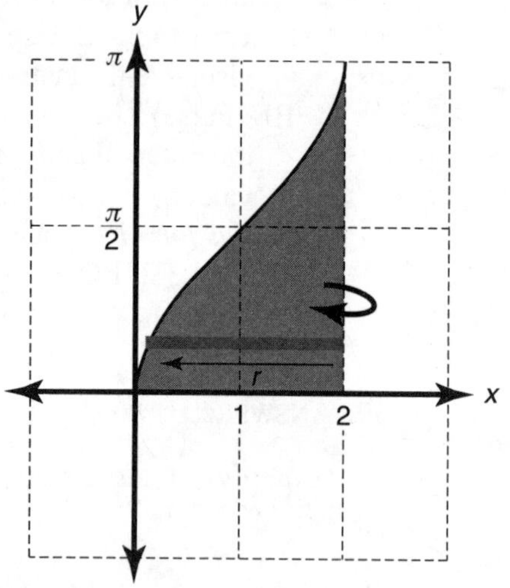

Finally, $r = 2 - x \Rightarrow 2 - \left[\sin\left(y - \frac{\pi}{2}\right) + 1\right]$

$$= 1 - \sin\left(y - \frac{\pi}{2}\right).$$

(*Calculus for AP*®, pages 446–452; pages 454–456; EU 3.4; LO 3.4D; EK 3.4D2; MPAC 2)

FREE-RESPONSE QUESTIONS

1. Region R is bounded by the functions $f(x) = 2(x-4) + \pi$, $g(x) = \cos^{-1}\left(\frac{\pi}{2} - 3\right)$, and the x-axis as shown in the figure to the right.
   (a) What is the area of region R?
   (b) Find the volume of the solid generated when region R is rotated about the x-axis.
   (c) Find all values c for $f(x)$ and $g(x)$ in the closed interval $p \le c \le q$ for which each function equals the average value in the indicated interval.

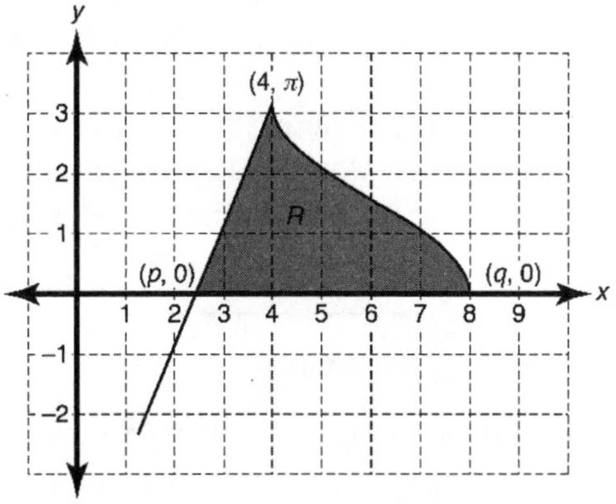

	Solution	Possible points
(a)	Root of $f(x)$ is $p = 2.4292$ and the root of $g(x)$ is $q = 8$. Area of $R = \int_{2.4292}^{4} [2(x-4)+\pi]\,dx + \int_{4}^{8}\left[\cos^{-1}\left(\frac{x}{2}-3\right)\right]dx \approx 8.751$	3: { 1: limits and integrand for left branch, $f(x)$ 1: limits and integrand for right branch, $g(x)$ 1: answer
(b)	Volume = $\pi\left\{\int_{2.4292}^{4}\left[2(x-4)+\pi\right]^2 dx + \int_{4}^{8}\left[\cos^{-1}\left(\frac{x}{2}-3\right)\right]^2 dx\right\}$ $V \approx 16.907\pi$ or 53.115	3: { 1: limits on both integrals 1: both integrands $<-1>$ for any error 1: answer
(c)	The average value of a function on an interval is given by $h(c) = \frac{1}{b-a}\int_a^b h(x)\,dx$, where $a \le c \le b$. Use the answer from part a above. For the left branch, $f(x)$: $2(c_1 - 4) + \pi = \frac{1}{8-2.4292}[8.751]$ $\Rightarrow c_1 \approx 3.215\ (p < c_1 < 4)$ For the right branch of $g(x)$: $\cos^{-1}\left(\frac{c_2}{2}-3\right) = \frac{1}{8-2.4292}(8.751)$ $\Rightarrow c_2 = 6\ (4 < c_2 < 8)$	3: { 1: use of f_{avg} 1: c_1 for left branch, $f(x)$ 1: c_2 for right branch, $g(x)$

1. (a) (*Calculus for AP®*, pages 477–486; EU 3.4; LO 3.4D; EK 3.4D1;MPAC 2,3)
1. (b) (*Calculus for AP®*, pages 522–528; EU 3.4; LO 3.4D; EK 3.4D2; MPAC 2,3)
1. (c) (*Calculus for AP®*, pages 490–494; EU 2.4; LO 2.4A; EK 2.4A1; MPAC 2,3)

2. A particle is moving along the x-axis with velocity $v(t) = \ln(t+3) - e^{\frac{t}{2}-1}(\cos t)$ for $0 \le t \le 8$. The initial position of the particle is -1.6.
   (a) At what time(s) in the open interval $0 < t < 8$ does the particle change direction? Justify your answer.
   (b) Where is the particle when it is farthest to the left?
   (c) How far does the particle travel in the interval $3 \le t \le 6$?
   (d) At what times in the closed interval $0 \le t \le 8$ is the speed of the particle decreasing? Justify your answer.

<table>
<tr><th></th><th>Solution</th><th>Possible points</th></tr>
<tr><td>(a)</td><td>The particle changes direction when $v(t)$ changes from positive to negative or negative to positive. Graph $v(t)$, then $v(t) = 0$ at $t \approx 5.160$ and $t \approx 7.718$.
<table>
<tr><td>t</td><td>$0 < t < 5.160$</td><td>$5.160 < t < 7.718$</td><td>$7.718 < t < 9$</td></tr>
<tr><td>$v(t)$</td><td>positive</td><td>negative</td><td>positive</td></tr>
</table>
The particle moves to the right from 0 to 5.160 sec, to the left from 5.160 to 7.718 sec, and to the right from 7.718 to 8 sec.</td><td>$2: \begin{cases} 1: \text{values} \\ 1: \text{reason} \end{cases}$</td></tr>
<tr><td>(b)</td><td>$$x(t) = x(0) + \int_0^{7.718} v(t)\,dt$$ $x(7.718) \approx -1.16 - .2167 \approx -1.817$
The particle is 1.817 units to the left of the origin at $t = 7.718$.</td><td>$2: \begin{cases} 1: \text{integrand, with limits} \\ 1: \text{answer, including } x(0) \end{cases}$</td></tr>
<tr><td>(c)</td><td>Distance $= \int_3^6 \lvert v(t) \rvert\, dt \approx 8.455$</td><td>$2: \begin{cases} 1: \text{integrand, with limits} \\ 1: \text{answer} \end{cases}$</td></tr>
<tr><td>(d)</td><td>The speed of the particle is decreasing when the velocity and acceleration have opposite signs.
<table>
<tr><th>t</th><th>$v(t)$</th><th>$a(t)$</th></tr>
<tr><td>$0 < t < 3.664$</td><td>positive</td><td>positive</td></tr>
<tr><td>$3.664 < t < 5.160$</td><td>positive</td><td>negative</td></tr>
<tr><td>$5.160 < t < 6.738$</td><td>negative</td><td>negative</td></tr>
<tr><td>$6.738 < t < 7.718$</td><td>negative</td><td>positive</td></tr>
<tr><td>$7.718 < t < 8$</td><td>positive</td><td>positive</td></tr>
</table>
Therefore, the speed of the particle is decreasing in the intervals $3.664 < t < 5.160$ and $6.738 < t < 7.718$.</td><td>$3: \begin{cases} 1: v(t) \text{ and } a(t) \text{ have opposite signs} \\ 1: \text{analysis} \\ 1: \text{answers} \end{cases}$</td></tr>
</table>

2. (a) (*Calculus for AP*®, pages 508–509; EU 2.3; LO 2.3C; EK 2.3C1; MPAC 2,3)
2. (b), (c) (*Calculus for AP*®, pages 508–509; EU 2.3,3.4; LO 2.3C,3.4C; EK 2.3C1,2.3C3,3.4C1; MPAC 2,3)
2. (d) (*Calculus for AP*®, pages 508–509; EU 2.3; LO 2.3C; EK 2.3C1; MPAC 2,3,6)

3.

x	$f(x)$	$g(x)$	$f'(x)$	$g'(x)$
1	1	6	2	−3
2	2	4	0	−½
3	3	3	1	−1
4	4	2	0	−½
6	2	1	−2	−1

The functions $f(x)$ and $g(x)$ are differentiable for all real numbers, and $g(x)$ is strictly decreasing. The table above gives values of the functions and their first derivatives at selected values of x. The function $h(x)$ is given by $h(x) = f(g(x))$.

(a) Use linear approximation to estimate the value of $h(x)$ at $x = 5.9$.

(b) Explain why there must be a value c on the interval $1 < c < 3$ such that $h''(c) = -\frac{7}{2}$.

(c) Let $R(x) = \int_1^{f(x)} \left[g(t) + (2t)\right] dt$. Find the value of $R'(1)$.

(d) Find $\frac{d}{dx}\left[g^{-1}(x)\right]\Big|_{x=6}$

	Solution	Possible points
(a)	$h(6) = f(g(6)) = f(1) = 1$ $h'(x) = f'(g(x))g'(x)$ $h'(6) = f'(g(6))g'(6) = f'(1)g'(6) = 2(-1) = -2$ tangent line: $y - 1 = -2(x - 6)$ $h(5.9) \approx 1 - 2(5.9 - 6) = 1.2$	$3: \begin{cases} 1: h'(x) \\ 1: \text{ tangent line} \\ 1: \text{answer} \end{cases}$
(b)	$\frac{h'(3) - h'(1)}{3-1} = \frac{-1-6}{3-1} = -\frac{7}{2}$ Since $h(x)$ is a continuous and differentiable, by the Mean Value Theorem, there exists a value c, $1 < c < 3$, such that $h''(c) = -\frac{7}{2}$.	$2: \begin{cases} 1: \frac{h'(3) - h'(1)}{3-1} \\ 1: \text{ conclusion, using MVT} \end{cases}$
(c)	$R'(x) = g(f(x)) \cdot f'(x) + 2f(x) \cdot f'(x)$ $R'(1) = g(f(1)) \cdot f'(1) + 2f(1) \cdot f'(1)$ $= g(1) \cdot 2 + 2 \cdot 2 = 6 \cdot 2 + 4 = 16$	$2: \begin{cases} 1: R'(x) \\ 1: \text{value} \end{cases}$
(d)	$g(1) = 6$ and $g'(1) = -3$ $g^{-1}(6) = 1$ $\frac{d}{dx}\left[g^{-1}(x)\right]\Big\|_{x=6} = \frac{1}{g'(1)} = -\frac{1}{3}$	$2: \begin{cases} 1: g^{-1}(6) \\ 1: \frac{d}{dx}\left[g^{-1}(x)\right]\Big\|_{x=6} \end{cases}$

3. (a) (*Calculus for AP*®, pages 282–284; EU 2.3; LO 2.3B; EK2.3B2; MPAC 2,3,4)
3. (b) (*Calculus for AP*®, pages 308–311; EU 1.2,2.4; LO 1.2B,2.4A; EK 1.2B1,2.4A1; MPAC 2,3,4,6)
3. (c) (*Calculus for AP*®, pages 436–440; EU 2.1; LO 2.1C; EK2.1C4; MPAC 1,2,3,4)
3. (d) (*Calculus for AP*®, pages 247–248; EU 2.1; LO 2.1C; EK2.1C6; MPAC 2,3,4)

4. Consider the differential equation $\frac{dy}{dx}=(y+1)(1-x)$ for $y>-1$.
   (a) On the axes provided, sketch a slope field for the given differential equation at the 11 points indicated.
   (b) If $y(0) = 1$, then find the particular solution $y(x)$ to the given differential equation.
   (c) Draw a function through the point (0, 1) on your slope field which represents an approximate solution of the given differential equation with initial condition $y(0) = 1$.

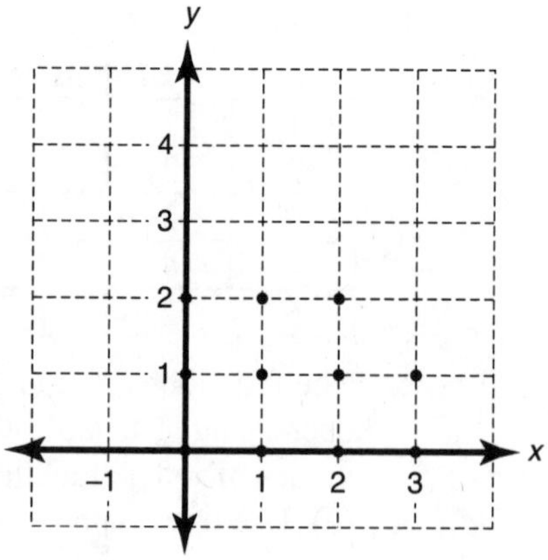

<table>
<tr><th></th><th>Solution</th><th>Possible points</th></tr>
<tr><td>(a)</td><td>

y \ x	0	1	2	3
2	3	0	−3	−6
1	2	0	−2	−4
0	1	0	−1	−2

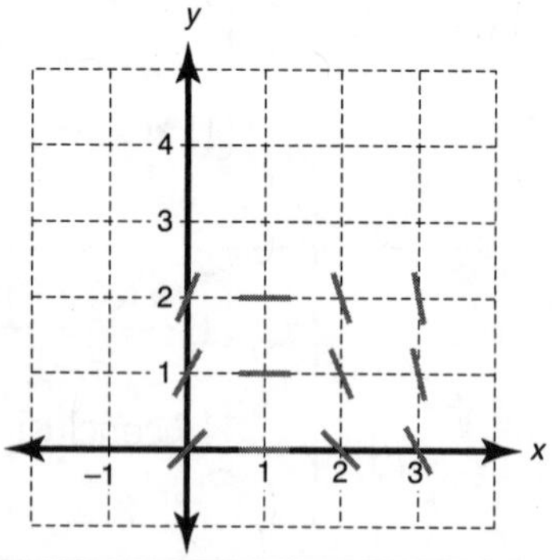

</td><td>2: { 1: zero slope at each point (x, y) where $x=1$
positive slopes at each point
1: (x, y) where $x=0$
negative slopes at each point
(x, y) where $x=2$ or 3 }</td></tr>
<tr><td>(b)</td><td>$\frac{dy}{y+1}=(1-x)\,dx \Rightarrow$

$\ln|y+1|=x-\frac{x^2}{2}+c_1$.
Recall that $y>-1$, so
$y+1=e^{x-\frac{x^2}{2}+c_1}=e^{x-\frac{x^2}{2}}e^{c_1}=Ce^{x-\frac{x^2}{2}}$.

Then, $y=-1+Ce^{x-\frac{x^2}{2}}$. Using the initial condition (0, 1), $C=2$ and
$y=-1+2e^{x-\frac{x^2}{2}}$.</td><td>5: { 1: separating variables
1: antiderivatives
1: constant of integration
1: uses initial condition
solves for y
1: 0/1 if y is not exponential }</td></tr>
</table>

	Solution	**Possible points**
(c)	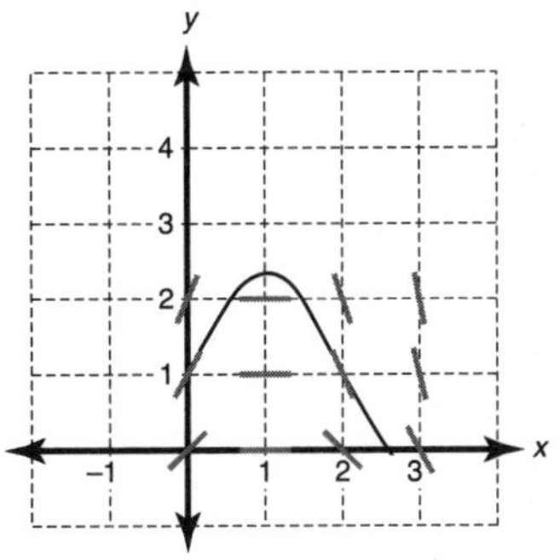 $y=-1-2e^{x-\frac{x^2}{2}}$	$2:\begin{cases}1:\text{maximum at } x=1 \text{ only} \\ \quad \text{curve above } x\text{-axis} \\ 1:\text{following slopes from} \\ \quad \text{part a}\end{cases}$

(a), (c) (Calculus *for AP*®, pages 606–611; EU 2.3,3.5; LO 2.3F,3.5A; EK 2.3F1,3.5A2,3.5A3; MPAC 2,3)
(b) (*Calculus for AP*®, pages 618–624; EU 2.3,3.5; LO 2.3F,3.5A; EK 2.3F1,3.5A2,3.5A3; MPAC 2,3)

5. Consider the function $h(x)=3x^2-\sqrt{x+1}.$
   (a) Evaluate $\frac{1}{3-(-1)}\int_{-1}^{3}\left(3x^2-\sqrt{x+1}\right)dx$ and interpret its meaning.
   (b) What is the equation of the tangent to $h(x)$ at $x = 0$?
   (c) Use the tangent found in part b to approximate $h(x)$ at $x = -0.01$.
   (d) Is the approximation, found in part c, greater or less than the actual value of $h(x)$ at $x = -0.01$? Justify your answer using calculus.

	Solution	**Possible points**
(a)	Rewrite the given integral: $\frac{1}{4}\int_{-1}^{3}\left(3x^2-(x+1)^{\frac{1}{2}}\right)dx$ $=\frac{1}{4}\left\{x^3-\left(\frac{2}{3}\right)\left[(x+1)^{\frac{3}{2}}\right]\right\}\Bigg\|_{-1}^{3}$ $=\frac{17}{3}$ The integral represents the average value of the function in the interval $-1\le x\le 3$.	$4:\begin{cases}2:\text{antiderivatives } <-1> \text{ for} \\ \quad \text{each error} \\ 1:\text{value of integral expression} \\ 1:\text{recognizing average value of} \\ \quad h(x) \text{ on interval } -1\le x\le 3\end{cases}$

	Solution	Possible points
(b)	$h(x)=3x^2-(x+1)^{\frac{1}{2}}$ and $h(0)=-1$ $h'(x)=6x-\left[\left(\frac{1}{2}\right)(x+1)^{-\frac{1}{2}}\right]$ $h'(0)=0-\frac{1}{2}(1)^{-\frac{1}{2}}=-\frac{1}{2}$ Since $h(0)=1$ and $h'(0)=-\frac{1}{2}$, then the tangent line to $h(x)$ at $x=0$ is $y+1=-\frac{1}{2}(x)\Rightarrow y=-\frac{1}{2}(x)-1.$	$2:\begin{cases}1: h'(0)\\ 1: \text{equation of}\\ \quad \text{tangent line}\end{cases}$
(c)	$h(-.01)\approx-\frac{1}{2}(-0.01)-1=0.995$	1: answer
(d)	$h''(x)=6+\frac{1}{4}(x+1)^{-\frac{3}{2}}$ and $h''(x)>0$ for all x. Therefore, $h(x)$ is concave up at $x=0$ and the tangent line will be below the curve. Thus, the value of the approximation near $x=0$ will be less than the actual value.	$2:\begin{cases}1: \text{finding } h''(x)\\ 1: \text{reason for under}\\ \quad \text{approximation}\end{cases}$

5. (a) (*Calculus for AP*®, pages 457–465; 490–494; EU 3.3,3.4; LO 3.3B,3.4B; EK 3.3B2,3.4B1; MPAC 2,3,6)
5. (b) (*Calculus for AP*®, pages 165–167; EU 2.1,2.3; LO 2.1C,2.3B; EK 2.1C2,2.1C4,2.3B1; MPAC 2,3)
5. (c), (d) (*Calculus for AP*®, pages 282–284; EU 2.2,2.3; LO2.2A,2.3B; EK 2.2A1,2.3B2; MPAC 2,6)

6. Consider the functions $f(x) = e^x \sin x$ and $g(x) = e^x \cos x$, as shown in the sketch below, in the closed interval $0 \le x \le 2\pi$.

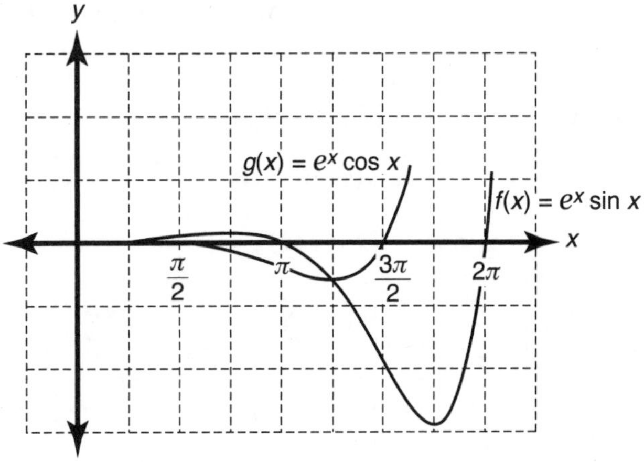

(a) Let $D(x) = f(x) - g(x)$ be the vertical distance between the functions. Find the value of x in the open interval $\frac{\pi}{4} < x < \frac{5\pi}{4}$, where $D(x)$ is a maximum value. Explain your reasoning.

(b) At what value of x in the open interval $\frac{\pi}{4} < x < \frac{5\pi}{4}$ is the rate of change of $D(x)$ increasing the most rapidly? Explain your reasoning.

(c) For $H(x) = \frac{e^x}{\sin x} + g(x)$, find the x-coordinate of all points at which $H(x)$ has horizontal tangents on the open interval $0 < x < 2\pi$.

	Solution	Possible points
(a)	$D(x) = f(x) - g(x)$ $D'(x) = f'(x) - g'(x)$ $D'(x) = e^x \sin x - e^x \cos x - (e^x \cos x - e^x \sin x)$ $= 2e^x \sin x = 0 \Rightarrow x = \pi$ (see table below) Therefore, $D(x)$ is a maximum at $x = \pi$, because $D(x)$ is increasing to the left of $x = \pi$ and decreasing to the right of $x = \pi$, which is the only critical value in the interval $\frac{\pi}{4} < x < \frac{5\pi}{4}$.	$3\begin{cases}1: \text{find } D'(x)\\1: \text{set } D'(x)=0\\1: \text{answer and reason}\end{cases}$

X	$\frac{\pi}{4} < x < \pi$	$\pi < x < \frac{5\pi}{4}$
$D'(x)$	positive	negative
$D(x)$	increasing	decreasing

	Solution	Possible points
(b)	The rate of change of $D(x)$ is given by $D'(x)$, and the absolute maximum of $D'(x)$ occurs when $D''(x) = 0$. $D''(x) = 2e^x \sin x + 2e^x \cos x = 0$ $= 2e^x(\sin x + \cos x) = 0$ $\Rightarrow \sin x = -\cos x \Rightarrow x = \dfrac{3\pi}{4}$. x: $\dfrac{\pi}{4} < x < \dfrac{3\pi}{4}$ | $\dfrac{3\pi}{4} < x < \dfrac{5\pi}{4}$ $D''(x)$: positive | negative $D'(x)$: increasing | decreasing Therefore, $D'(x)$, the rate of change in the distance, is increasing most rapidly (an absolute maximum) at $x = \dfrac{3\pi}{4}$ because $D'(x)$ is increasing to the left of $x = \dfrac{3\pi}{4}$ and decreasing to the right of $x = \dfrac{3\pi}{4}$, which is the only critical value in the interval $\dfrac{\pi}{4} < x < \dfrac{5\pi}{4}$.	$3\begin{cases} 1: \text{find } D''(x) \\ 1: \text{set } D''(x) = 0 \\ 1: \text{answer with reason} \end{cases}$
(c)	$H(x) = \dfrac{e^x}{\sin x} + g(x)$ $H'(x) = \dfrac{e^x \sin x - e^x \cos x}{\sin^2 x} + e^x \cos x - e^x \sin x$ $\Rightarrow \dfrac{e^x(\sin x - \cos x) - e^x \sin^2 x(\sin x - \cos x)}{\sin^2 x}$ $\Rightarrow \dfrac{e^x(\sin x - \cos x)(1 - \sin^2 x)}{\sin^2 x} = 0$ In the open interval $0 < x < 2\pi$, the horizontal tangents occur when $H'(x) = 0$. Then, $1 - \sin^2 x = 0 \Rightarrow x = \dfrac{\pi}{2}$ and $\dfrac{3\pi}{2}$, or $\sin x - \cos x = 0 \Rightarrow x = \dfrac{\pi}{4}$ and $\dfrac{5\pi}{4}$.	$3\begin{cases} 1: \text{find derivative of } H(x) \\ 1: \text{set } H'(x) = 0 \\ 1: \text{answers} \end{cases}$

6. (a) (*Calculus for AP®*, pages 293–300; EU 2.3; LO 2,3C; EK 2.3C3; MPAC 2,3,4,6)
6. (b) (*Calculus for AP®*, pages 293–300; EU 2.3; LO 2.3C; EK 2.3C3; MPAC 2,3,4,6)
6. (c) (*Calculus for AP®*, pages 199–200; EU 2.1,2.2; LO 2.1C,2.2A; EK 2.1C3,2.2A1; MPAC 2,3,4)

CALCULUS AB AND BC SCORING CHART

SECTION I: MULTIPLE-CHOICE QUESTIONS

_______ × 1.2 = _______

correct (out of 45)   do not round (out of 54)

SECTION II: FREE-RESPONSE QUESTIONS

Question 1	Score out of 9 points	=	_______
Question 2	Score out of 9 points	=	_______
Question 3	Score out of 9 points	=	_______
Question 4	Score out of 9 points	=	_______
Question 5	Score out of 9 points	=	_______
Question 6	Score out of 9 points	=	_______
	Sum for Section II	=	_______
			(out of 54)

Composite Score

Section I total	=
Section II total	=
Composite score	= _______ (out of 108)

Grade Conversion Chart*

Composite score range	AP® exam grade
68–108	5
52–67	4
39–51	3
27–38	2
0–26	1

***Note:** The ranges listed above are only approximate. Each year the ranges for the actual AP® exam are somewhat different. The cutoffs established after the exams are given to over 200,000 students and are based on the difficulty level of the exam each year.

AP® CALCULUS BC PRACTICE TEST 1
Section I, Part A: Multiple-Choice Questions
Time: 60 minutes
Number of Questions: 30

A calculator may not be used on this part of the examination.

1. If $f(x) = 2x \cos x$, then $f'(x) =$
   (A) $-2 \sin x$
   (B) $2x \sin x + 2 \cos x$
   (C) $2x \sin x - 2 \cos x$
   (D) $-2x \sin x + 2 \cos x$

2. If $f(x)$ is a function such that $f'(x)$ is increasing for $x < 2$ and $f'(x)$ is decreasing for $x > 2$, then which of the following could be the graph of $f(x)$?

(A)

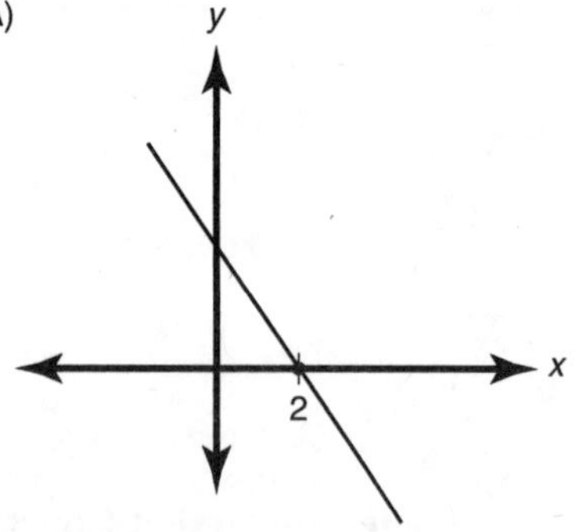

(B)

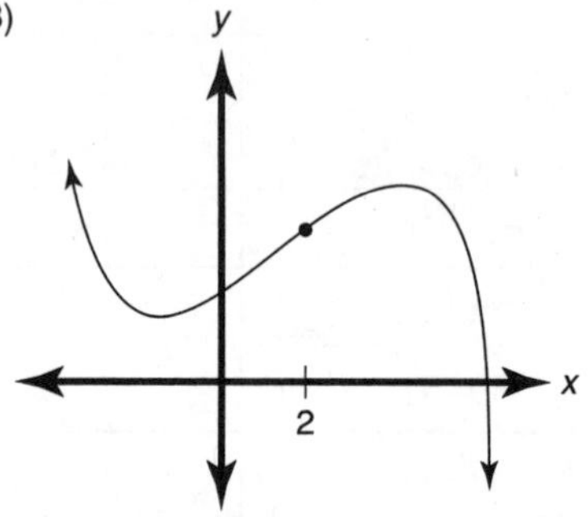

(C)

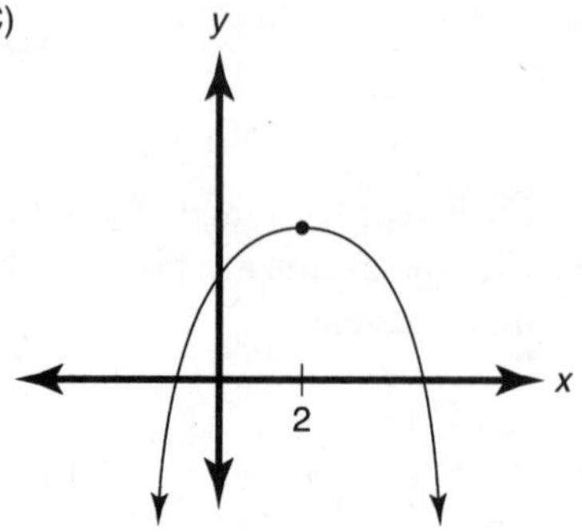

(D)

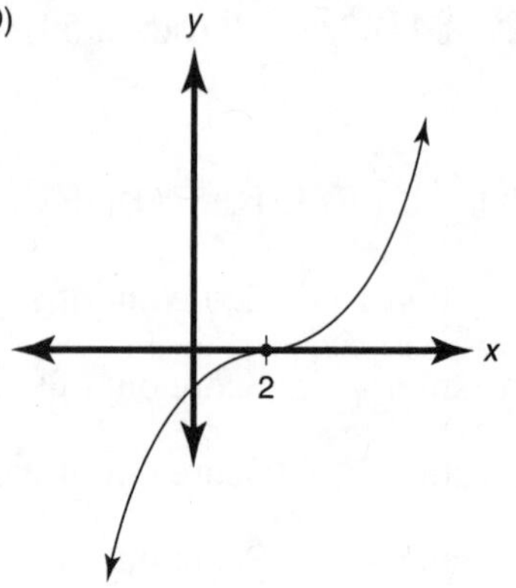

3. Find the limit $\lim_{n\to\infty} \sum_{k=1}^{n} \sqrt{\frac{k}{n}} \cdot \frac{1}{n} =$.
   (A) 0
   (B) $\frac{1}{2}$
   (C) $\frac{2}{3}$
   (D) ∞

4. Consider the differential equation $\frac{dy}{dx} = y - 2x + 3$, where $y = f(x)$ is the solution to the equation and $f(2) = 5$. Using Euler's method starting at $x_0 = 2$ with step size $\Delta x = 0.5$, what is the approximation for $f(3)$?
   (A) 7
   (B) 8.5
   (C) 9
   (D) 9.5

5. The equation of the tangent line to the function $y = 8\sqrt{3x+1}$ at $x = 5$ is
   (A) $y = 3x + 27$
   (B) $y = 3x + 17$
   (C) $y = 6x + 12$
   (D) $y = 6x + 2$

6. The position vector for a particle moving in the xy-plane for $t \geq 0$ is $\left(10\ln(1+t), 16\sqrt{t}\right)$. The slope of the tangent line to the path of the particle at $t = 4$ is
(A) $\frac{16}{5\ln 5}$
(B) $2\sqrt{5}$
(C) $\frac{8}{5}$
(D) 2

7. Evaluate $\int_0^1 \frac{3}{x}\,dx$.
(A) 0
(B) 1
(C) $3e$
(D) ∞

8. The graph of $f(x)$ is pictured below. Which of the following statements about $\int_0^4 f(x)\,dx$ are true?

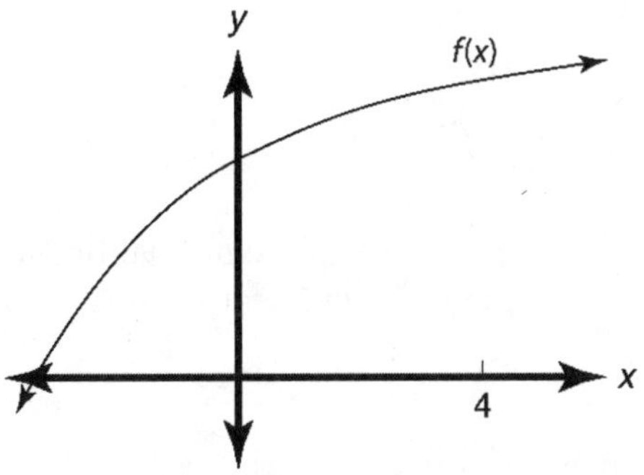

I. A left endpoint approximation is greater than $\int_0^4 f(x)\,dx$.
II. A right endpoint approximation is less than $\int_0^4 f(x)\,dx$.
III. A trapezoidal approximation is less than $\int_0^4 f(x)\,dx$.

(A) None are true
(B) III only
(C) I and III only
(D) I, II, and III

9. The general solution to the differential equation $\frac{dy}{dx} = y\left(1+\frac{1}{x^2}\right)$ is $y =$
(A) $Ce^{\tan^{-1} x}$
(B) $Ce^{x-\frac{1}{x}}$
(C) $e^{x+\frac{1}{x}} + C$
(D) $e^{x-\frac{1}{x}}$

10. What is the slope of the curve $2xy^2 = 3x^2 - y^3$ at the point (1, 1)?
(A) $\frac{1}{7}$
(B) $\frac{4}{7}$
(C) $\frac{6}{7}$
(D) $\frac{6}{5}$

11. If $f'(x) = 12x^2 \sin(2x^3-16)$ and $f(2) = 5$, then $f(x) =$
(A) $-2\cos(2x^3 - 16) + 7$
(B) $-4x^3 \cos(2x^3 - 16) + 5$
(C) $-2\cos(2x^3 - 16) + 5$
(D) $24x\cos(2x^3 - 16) + 5$

12. The first four terms of the Taylor expansion for $f(x)$ about $x = 3$ are $5 - \frac{x-3}{4} - \frac{7(x-3)^2}{3} + \frac{9(x-3)^3}{2}$.
What is the value of $f''(3)$?
(A) $-\frac{14}{3}$
(B) $-\frac{7}{3}$
(C) $-\frac{7}{6}$
(D) $-\frac{1}{2}$

GO ON TO NEXT PAGE

13. The graph of $f(x) = x^6 - 5x^4$ has inflection points at $x =$
(A) $-\sqrt{2}$ and $\sqrt{2}$ only
(B) 0 and $\sqrt{2}$ only
(C) 0 and $\sqrt{\frac{10}{3}}$ only
(D) $-\sqrt{2}$, 0, and $\sqrt{2}$

14. $\lim\limits_{x\to 0} \dfrac{\cos x - e^x}{\ln(1+x)} =$
(A) -1
(B) 0
(C) 1
(D) e

15. Which of the following series converge?
I. $\sum\limits_{k=0}^{\infty} \dfrac{3^{k+1}}{4^k}$
II. $\sum\limits_{k=0}^{\infty} (-1)^k \dfrac{k^2}{(2k+1)^2}$
III. $\sum\limits_{k=0}^{\infty} \dfrac{|\sec k|}{k}$
(A) I only
(B) I and II
(C) I and III
(D) I, II, and III

16. If $\dfrac{dy}{dt} = k(y-2)$, then $y =$
(A) Ce^{t-2}
(B) $e^{kt} + C$
(C) $\dfrac{k}{2}(t-2)^2 + C$
(D) $Ce^{kt} + 2$

Questions 17 and 18 refer to the following information:

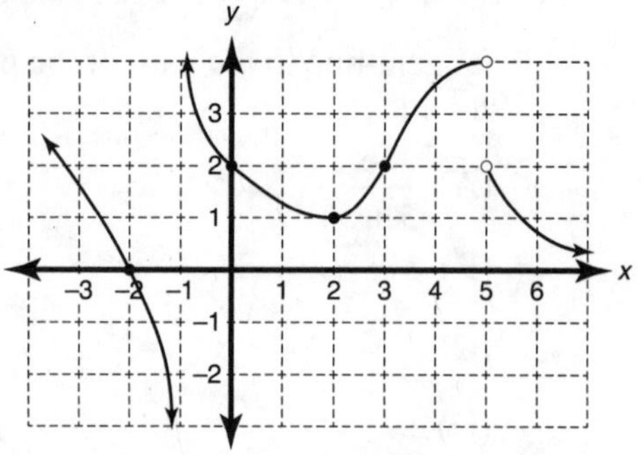

Let $F(x) = \int_0^{2x-1} f(t)\,dt$, where $f(t)$ is pictured above.

17. What is the domain of $F(x)$?
(A) All real numbers except -1 and 5
(B) $-1 < x < 5$
(C) $0 < x < 3$
(D) $x < -1$

18. What is the value of $F'(2)$?
(A) 0
(B) 1
(C) 2
(D) 4

19. The slope of the normal line to $f(x) = 3\sin^{-1} x$ at $x = 0$ is
(A) $-\dfrac{1}{3}$
(B) 0
(C) $\dfrac{1}{3}$
(D) 3

20. A particle moves in the xy-plane according to the parametric equations $x = \tan t$ and $y = e^{\frac{1}{2}t}$. An expression for the length of the path of the particle from $t = 0$ to $t = 1$ is

(A) $\int_0^1 \left[\sec^2 t + \frac{1}{2}e^{\frac{1}{2}t}\right] dt$

(B) $\int_0^1 \sqrt{\sec^4 t + \frac{1}{4}e^t}\, dt$

(C) $\int_0^1 \left[\sec^4 t + \frac{1}{4}e^t\right] dt$

(D) $\int_0^1 \sqrt{\sec^2 t + \frac{1}{2}e^{\frac{1}{2}t}}\, dt$

21. Which expression below represents the first four terms of the Maclaurin approximation to the area under the curve $f(x) = e^{x^2}$ from $x = 0$ to $x = 1$?

(A) $1 + \frac{1}{3} + \frac{1}{10} + \frac{1}{42}$

(B) $1 + 1 + \frac{1}{4} + \frac{1}{36}$

(C) $1 + 1 + \frac{1}{2} + \frac{1}{6}$

(D) $1 + \frac{1}{2} + \frac{1}{6} + \frac{1}{24}$

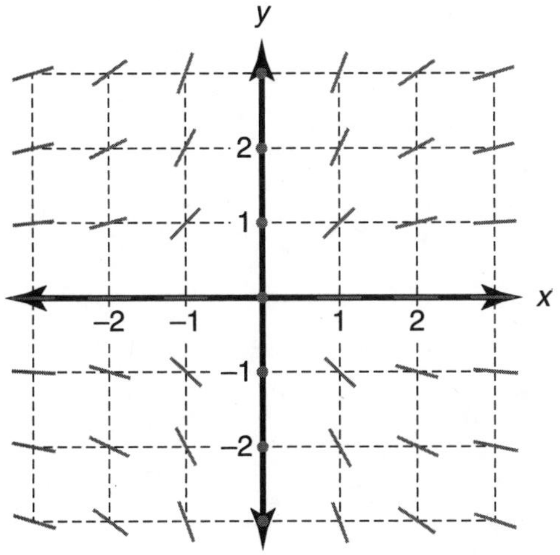

22. The slope field at the bottom of the previous column represents an approximation to the general solution to which differential equation?

(A) $\frac{dy}{dx} = \frac{y}{x}$

(B) $\frac{dy}{dx} = \frac{x}{y^2}$

(C) $\frac{dy}{dx} = \frac{y}{x^2}$

(D) $\frac{dy}{dx} = \frac{y^3}{x}$

23. Let $f(x) = x\sin(x)$. The first four nonzero terms of the Taylor approximation for $f'(x)$ about $x = 0$ are

(A) $1 - \frac{x^2}{2!} + \frac{x^4}{4!} - \frac{x^6}{6!}$

(B) $2x - \frac{4x^3}{3!} + \frac{6x^5}{5!} - \frac{8x^7}{7!}$

(C) $x^2 - \frac{x^4}{3!} + \frac{x^6}{5!} + \frac{x^8}{7!}$

(D) $x^2 - \frac{x^4}{3!} + \frac{x^6}{5!} - \frac{x^8}{7!}$

24. The area enclosed by the polar curve $r\cos\frac{1}{2}\theta = 1$ in the interval $0 \le \theta \le \frac{\pi}{2}$ is

(A) $\frac{1}{2}$

(B) $\frac{\sqrt{2}}{2}$

(C) $\frac{\pi}{4}$

(D) 1

GO ON TO NEXT PAGE

25. The volume of the solid generated by revolving the region enclosed between the graph of $y = 1 + x^2$ and the lines $y = 1$ and $x = 2$ about the x-axis is given by which integral expression?

(A) $\pi \int_0^2 x^4 dx$

(B) $\pi \int_0^2 (1+x^2)^2 dx$

(C) $\pi \int_1^5 (1-\sqrt{y-1})^2 dy$

(D) $\pi \int_0^2 \left[\left(1+x^2\right)^2 - 1^2\right] dx$

26. $\int \frac{2x-3}{x^2+9x+18} dx =$

(A) $\ln|(x+9)^3(x+2)| + C$

(B) $\ln\left|\frac{(x+6)^5}{(x+3)^3}\right| + C$

(C) $3 \ln |x+9| - \ln |x+2| + C$

(D) $5 \ln |x+6| + \ln |x+3| + C$

27. The acceleration vector of a particle moving in the xy-plane is $(-\pi \sin \pi t, 2t+1)$, for $t \geq 0$. If the velocity vector at $t = 0$ is $(1, 0)$, then how fast is the particle moving when $t = 2$?

(A) 5

(B) 6

(C) $\sqrt{37}$

(D) $\sqrt{40}$

28. What are all the values of a for which the series $\sum_{k=1}^{\infty} \frac{k^2}{k^{2a-3}+4}$ converges?

(A) $a > 2$

(B) $a \geq 3$

(C) $a < 3$

(D) $a > 1$

29. Evaluate the limit, if it exists: $\lim_{x \to 5^+} \frac{5-x}{|5-x|}$.

(A) 0

(B) 1

(C) -1

(D) The limit does not exist.

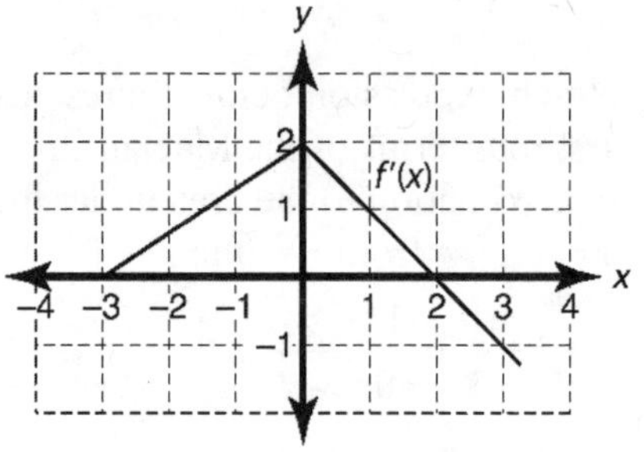

30. The graph of $f'(x)$, consisting of a pair of line segments, is pictured above. If $f(-3) = 0$, then $f(3) =$

(A) 3

(B) 4

(C) 4.5

(D) 5.5

Section I, Part B: Multiple-Choice Questions
Time: 45 minutes
Number of Questions: 15

A calculator may be used on this part of the examination.

31. If $f(x)=(x+1)\sin\left(\sqrt{x+1}\right)$, what is the average of f on the closed interval [0, 5]?
(A) 0.597
(B) 14.962
(C) 2.992
(D) −0.305

32. A particle moves in the xy-plane along the path of the curve $y=x\sin x$ for time $t\geq 0$. When the particle is at the point (3, 3 sin 3), $\frac{dy}{dt}=-2$. What is the value of $\frac{dx}{dt}$ at the same point?
(A) −2.829
(B) 0.423
(C) 0.707
(D) 2.020

33. Let $f(x)$ be a function defined for $1.6\leq x\leq 11.6$ such that $f'(x)=\ln x\sin x$. How many inflection points does the graph of $f(x)$ have on this interval?
(A) 2
(B) 3
(C) 4
(D) 5

34. Which of the following functions has the smallest average value on the given interval?
(A) $f(x)=\cos x$ on $0\leq x\leq\frac{3\pi}{4}$
(B) $f(x)=\cos 2x$ on $0\leq x\leq\pi$
(C) $f(x)=\sin x$ on $0\leq x\leq 2\pi$
(D) $f(x)=\cos 2x$ on $0\leq x\leq\frac{3\pi}{4}$

35. A particle moves along a line for time $t\geq 0$ such that its velocity is $v(t)=10e^{-t}\cos t$. What is the velocity of the particle when its acceleration is zero for the first time?
(A) −2.709
(B) −0.670
(C) 2.356
(D) 3.185

36. Which of the following series are conditionally convergent?
I. $\sum_{k=1}^{\infty}(-1)^{k+1}\frac{k^2}{k^3+1}$
II. $\sum_{k=1}^{\infty}(-1)^{k+1}\frac{k^2}{k^4+1}$
III. $\sum_{k=1}^{\infty}(-1)^{k+1}\frac{k^3}{k^3+1}$
(A) I only
(B) II only
(C) I and II
(D) I and III

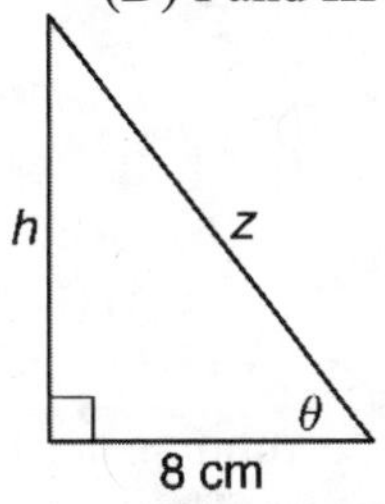

37. The base of the right triangle pictured above is 8 centimeters and the angle θ is increasing at the constant rate of 0.03 radians per second. How fast, in centimeters per second, is the altitude h of the triangle increasing when $h = 13$?
(A) 0.458 cm/sec
(B) 0.744 cm/sec
(C) 0.874 cm/sec
(D) 12.626 cm/sec

GO ON TO NEXT PAGE

38. Let $f'(x) = e^x + x$ and let $H(x)$ be the equation of the tangent line to $f(x)$ at $x = a$. If $H(x)$ is used to produce an estimate for $f(a + 0.1)$, then which of the following statements is true?
(A) $H(a + 0.1) > f(a + 0.1)$ for all values of a.
(B) $H(a + 0.1) < f(a + 0.1)$ for all values of a.
(C) $H(a + 0.1) > f(a + 0.1)$ for some values of a and $H(a + 0.1) < f(a + 0.1)$ for other values of a.
(D) $H(a + 0.1) = f(a + 0.1)$ for at least one value of a.

39. What are all values of x for which the series $\sum_{k=0}^{\infty} \frac{(2x)^k}{k+1}$ converges?
(A) $x = 0$
(B) $-\frac{1}{2} \le x \le \frac{1}{2}$
(C) $-2 < x < 2$
(D) $-\frac{1}{2} \le x < \frac{1}{2}$

40. What is the total area enclosed between the graphs of the functions $f(x) = \frac{1}{8}x^3 + \frac{1}{4}x^2 - \frac{5}{2}x + 1$ and $g(x) = \frac{1}{2}x + 1$?
(A) 10.667
(B) 31.500
(C) 35.333
(D) 42.167

41. A large auto dealer is running a special sales promotion. They expect to sell cars at the rate of $0.32x^2 - 0.01x^3$ cars per day for the first x days of the sale. According to the model, about how many cars will the dealer sell in the first 30 days of the sale?
(A) 18
(B) 29
(C) 722
(D) 855

x	$f(x)$	$f'(x)$
−1	4	3
−3	−2	7

42. The table above contains values of $f(x)$ and $f'(x)$ for certain values of x. If $g(x) = x^2 f(3x)$, then $g'(-1) =$
(A) −14
(B) 11
(C) 25
(D) 21

43. The base of a certain solid is the region in the first quadrant bounded by the x- and y-axes and the curve $y = 15 - e^x$. If each plane cross section of the solid perpendicular to the x-axis is a semicircle with diameter across the base, then the volume of the solid is
(A) 118.325
(B) 236.649
(C) 371.728
(D) 473.299

44. Let $f(x)$ be a continuous function with the properties that $\lim_{x\to\infty} f(x) = \infty$ and $\lim_{x\to\infty} f'(x) = 3$. What is the value of $\lim_{x\to\infty} [f(x)]^{\frac{1}{x}}$?
(A) 0
(B) 1
(C) 3
(D) ∞

45. Consider the differentiable function $f(x) = \ln x - x + 3$ on the closed interval $0.5 \le x \le 3.5$. What is the value of c in the interval $0.5 < x < 3.5$ that satisfies the Mean Value Theorem?
(A) 1
(B) 1.484
(C) 1.507
(D) 1.542

Section II
Free-Response Questions
Time: 1 hour and 30 minutes
Number of Problems: 6

Part A
Time: 30 minutes
Number of Problems: 2

You may use a calculator for any problem in this section.

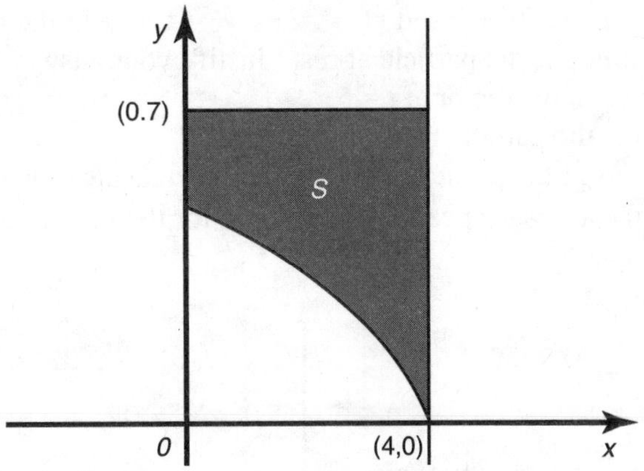

1. In the figure above, S is the shaded region in the first quadrant bounded by the graph of $y = 3\ln(5 - x)$ the horizontal line $y = 7$, and the vertical line $x = 4$.
   (a) Find the area of S.
   (b) Find the volume of the solid when S is revolved about the horizontal line $y = -1$.
   (c) The region S in the base of a solid. For this solid, each cross section perpendicular to the x-axis is a semicircle. Find the volume of the solid.

2. The Taylor expansion for a function $f(x)$ about $x = 4$ is given by
   $$f(x) = 1 + \frac{1}{2}(x-4) + \frac{1}{4}(x-4)^2 + \frac{1}{8}(x-4)^3 + \cdots = \sum_{k=0}^{\infty} \frac{(x-4)^k}{2^k}.$$
   (a) What are all values of x for which $f(x)$ converges?
   (b) Find the first three nonzero terms and the general term of $f'(x)$. Use the first three terms to estimate the value of $f'(3.9)$.
   (c) Let $g(x)$ be the second degree Taylor polynomial for $f(x)$, and let $h(x)$ be the function such that $h'(x) = g(x)$. If $h(5) = 0$, find $h(x)$.

Section II
Part B
Time: 60 minutes
Number of Problems: 4

You may not use a calculator for any problem in this section. During the timed portion for Section II, Part B, you may continue to work on the problems in Section II, Part A without the use of a calculator.

3. A particle moves in the *xy*-plane with position vector $\langle x(t), y(t)\rangle$ such that $x(t) = t^3 - 6t^2 + 9t + 1$ and $y(t) = -t^2 + 6t + 2$ in the time interval $0 \le t \le 5$.
   (a) At what time t is the particle at rest? Justify your answer.
   (b) Give the velocity vector at $t = 5$.
   (c) How fast is the particle moving when $t = 5$?
   (d) Is the speed of the particle increasing or decreasing when $t = 5$? Justify your answer.
   (e) What is the average speed of the particle for the time interval $0 \le t \le 5$?

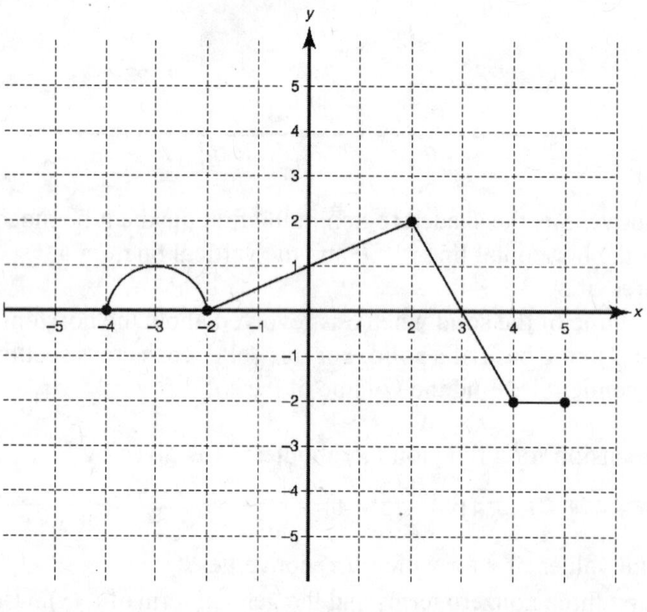

4. Let f be a continuous function defined on $[-4, 5]$ whose graph, consisting of three line segments and a semicircle centered on the *x*-axis at $x = -3$. Let h be the function given by

$$h(x) = \int_0^x f(t)\,dt.$$

   (a) Find the values of $h(-2)$ and $h(2)$.
   (b) For each value $h'(3)$ and $h''(3)$, find the value or state that it does not exist.
   (c) Find the x -coordinate of each point at which the graph of h has a horizontal tangent line. For each of these points, determine whether h has a relative minimum, maximum, or neither a minimum or maximum at the point. Justify your answers.
   (d) For $-4 < x < 5$, find all the values of x for which the graph of h has a point of inflection. Explain your reasoning.

5. A concrete reservoir in the shape of a triangular prism is being filled with water at the constant rate of 2 cubic feet per minute. The reservoir is 4 feet deep, measures 6 feet across the top, and is 20 feet long, as shown in the figure below. For any time $t \geq 0$, let h represent the depth of the water in the reservoir, and let w represent the width of the rectangular region of water at the top.
   (a) If the reservoir is initially empty, how long will it take to fill completely?
   (b) How fast is the depth of the water in the reservoir changing when the reservoir is half full? Indicate units of measure.
   (c) How fast is the rectangular area of the surface of the water changing when the reservoir is half full? Indicate units of measure.

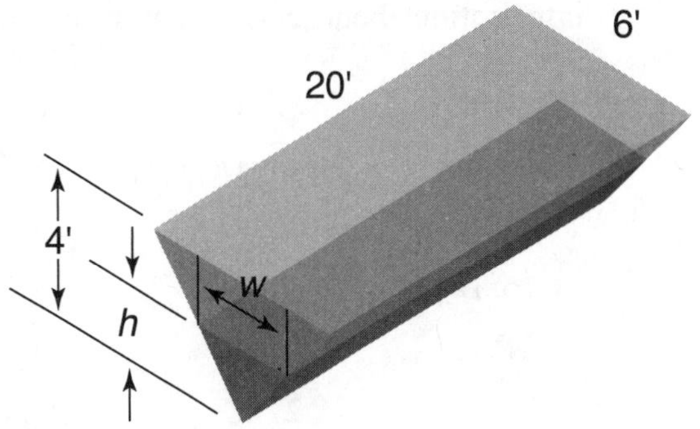

6. Consider the function $f(x)=\dfrac{10\ln x}{x^2}$, for $x \geq 1$. The graph of $f(x)$ is pictured below along with a table of values of $f(x)$.

x	$f(x)$
1	0
2	1.733
3	1.221
4	0.866
5	0.644
6	0.498
7	0.397

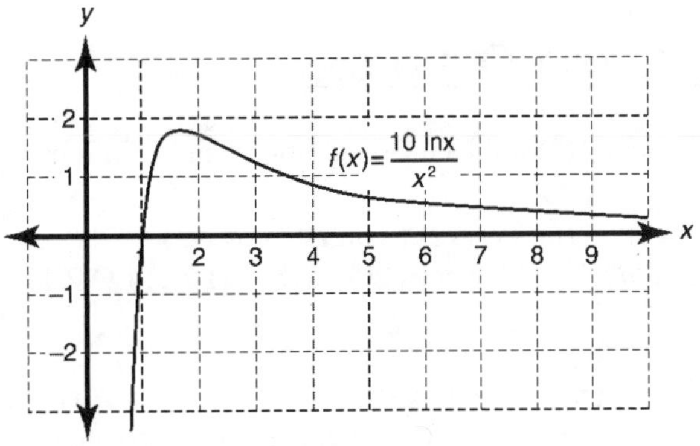

(a) Evaluate $\lim_{x\to\infty} f(x)$.

(b) Find the x-coordinate of the relative maximum of $f(x)$. Justify your answer.

(c) Use a midpoint Riemann sum with $n = 3$ to estimate the value of $\int_1^7 f(x)dx$.

(d) Evaluate $\int_1^\infty f(x)dx$.

Answers and Answer Explanations

Using the table below, score your test. Determine how many questions you answered correctly and how many you answered incorrectly. Additional information about scoring is at the end of the Practice Test.

1. D	2. B	3. C	4. D	5. B
6. D	7. D	8. B	9. B	10. B
11. A	12. A	13. A	14. A	15. A
16. D	17. C	18. D	19. A	20. B
21. A	22. C	23. B	24. D	25. D
26. B	27. C	28. C	29. C	30. C
31. C	32. C	33. C	34. D	35. B
36. A	37. C	38. B	39. D	40. D
41. D	42. C	43. A	44. B	45. D

MULTIPLE-CHOICE QUESTIONS

Note: Asterisks (*) indicate BC questions and solutions.

1. ANSWER: (D) $f'(x) = 2x(-\sin x) + \cos x(2) = -2x\sin x + 2\cos x$
(*Calculus for AP®*, pages 207–210; EU 2.1; LO 2.1C; EK 2.1C2,2.1C3; MPAC 2,3)

2. ANSWER: (B) $f'(x)$ increasing $\Rightarrow f''(x) > 0 \Rightarrow f(x)$ is concave up. $f'(x)$ decreasing $\Rightarrow f''(x) < 0 \Rightarrow f(x)$ is concave down. (B) is concave up for $x < 2$ and concave down for $x > 2$.
(*Calculus for AP®*, pages 316–331; EU 2.2; LO 2.2A; EK 2.2A1; MPAC 2,4)

3. ANSWER: (C) If the interval from 0 to 1 is partitioned into n subintervals, then each one has width $\Delta x = \frac{1}{n}$ and their x-coordinates are $\frac{0}{n}, \frac{1}{n}, \frac{2}{n}, \cdots, \frac{k}{n}, \cdots, \frac{n}{n}$. Thus, $x_k = \frac{k}{n}$. Recall that a definite integral is defined as the limit of a Riemann sum, $\lim_{n\to\infty} \sum_{k=1}^{n} f(x_k)\Delta x$. In this problem, $f(x) = \sqrt{x}$. Therefore,

$$\lim_{n\to\pi} \sum_{k=1}^{n} \sqrt{\frac{k}{n}} \cdot \frac{1}{n} = \lim_{n\to\infty} \sum_{k=1}^{n} \sqrt{x_k}\,\Delta x = \int_0^1 \sqrt{x}\,dx = \frac{2}{3}x^{\frac{3}{2}}\Big|_0^1 = \frac{2}{3}.$$

(*Calculus for AP®*, pages 395–410, 418–420; EU 3.2; LO 3.2A; EK 3.2A1,3.2A2; MPAC 2,3,5)

*4. ANSWER: (D) Using Euler's method, $y_{n+1} \approx y_n + \left.\frac{dy}{dx}\right|_{(x_n, y_n)} \cdot \Delta x$

$x_0 = 2$ $\quad y_0 = 5$ $\quad \left.\frac{dy}{dx}\right|_{(2,5)} = 5 - 4 + 3 = 4$

$x_1 = 2.5$ $\quad y_1 = 5 + 4(0.5) = 7$ $\quad \left.\frac{dy}{dx}\right|_{(2.5,\,7)} = 7 - 5 + 3 = 5$

$x_2 = 3$ $\quad y_2 = 7 + 5(0.5) = 9.5$ $\quad$ Therefore, $f(3) \approx 9.5$.

(*Calculus for AP*®, pages 611–615; EU 2.3; LO 2.3F; EK 2.3F2; MPAC 2,3,5)

5. ANSWER: (B) $y(5) = 8\sqrt{3 \cdot 5 + 1} = 32$

$$y' = \frac{8 \cdot 3}{2\sqrt{3x+1}} = \frac{12}{\sqrt{3x+1}} \Rightarrow y'(5) = \frac{12}{\sqrt{3 \cdot 5 + 1}} = 3$$

The equation of the tangent line is $y - 32 = 3(x - 5)$, or $y = 3x + 17$.
(*Calculus for AP*®, pages 165–167; EU 2.3; LO 2.3B; EK 2.3B1; MPAC 2,3)

*6. ANSWER: (D) $\frac{dy}{dx} = \frac{dy/dt}{dx/dt} = \frac{\frac{16}{2\sqrt{t}}}{\frac{10}{1+t}} = \frac{16(1+t)}{20\sqrt{t}}$. Therefore, $\left.\frac{dy}{dx}\right|_{t=4} = \frac{80}{40} = 2$.

(*Calculus for AP*®, pages 769–782; EU 2.1; LO 2.1C; EK 2.1C7; MPAC 2,3)

*7. ANSWER: (D)

$$\int_0^1 \frac{3}{x}\,dx = \lim_{b \to 0} \int_b^1 \frac{3}{x}\,dx = \lim_{b \to 0} 3\ln|x|\Big|_b^1 = 3\ln|1| - \lim_{b \to 0} 3\ln|b| = 0 - (-\infty) - \infty$$

(*Calculus for AP*®, pages 437–440; EU 3.3; LO 3.3B; EK 3.3B2; MPAC 1,2,3)

8. ANSWER: (B) Since $f(x)$ is strictly increasing, left end points produce inscribed rectangles and an underapproximation. Right end points produce circumscribed rectangles and an overapproximation. Since $f(x)$ is concave down, a trapezoidal approximation consists of line segments that are below $f(x)$, producing an underapproximation. So, I and II are false and III is true, making (B) correct.
(*Calculus for AP*®, pages 395–401; EU 3.2; LO 3.2B; EK 3.2B2; MPAC 4)

9. ANSWER: (B) Separating variables,

$$\int \frac{dy}{y} = \int \left(1 + \frac{1}{x^2}\right) dx \Rightarrow \ln|y| = x - \frac{1}{x} + C_1 \Rightarrow y = e^{x - \frac{1}{x} + C_1} \Rightarrow y = Ce^{x - \frac{1}{x}}$$

(*Calculus for AP*®, pages 618–624; EU 3.5; LO 3.5A; EK 3.5A2; MPAC 2,3)

10. ANSWER: (B) Differentiating both sides implicitly,

$2x \cdot 2y\frac{dy}{dx} + 2y^2 = 6x - 3y^2\frac{dy}{dx}.$

At point (1, 1), this equation is $4\frac{dy}{dx} + 2 = 6 - 3\frac{dy}{dx}$. Therefore,

$\left.\frac{dy}{dx}\right|_{(1,1)} = \frac{6-2}{4+3} = \frac{4}{7}.$

(*Calculus for AP®*, pages 240–245; EU 2.1; LO 2.1C; EK 2.1C5; MPAC 2,3)

11. ANSWER: (A) $f(x) = \int 12x^2 \sin(2x^3 - 16)dx$. Let
$u = 2x^3 - 16 \Rightarrow du = 6x^2dx.$
$f(x) = \int 2 \sin u\, du = -2 \cos u + C = -2 \cos(2x^3 - 16) + C.$
$5 = -2 \cos(2 \cdot 2^3 - 16) + C \Rightarrow 5 = -2 \cos(0) + C = -2 + C \Rightarrow C = 7.$
$f(x) = -2 \cos(2x^3 - 16) + 7.$
(*Calculus for AP®*, pages 457–461; EU 2.1; LO 2.1C; EK 2.1C2,2.1C3; MPAC 2,3,5)

*12. ANSWER: (A) The Taylor expansion for a function about $x = a$ is defined as $\sum_{k=0}^{\infty} \frac{f^{(k)}(a)(x-a)^k}{k!}$. Therefore, $\frac{f''(3)(x-3)^2}{2!} = -\frac{7(x-3)^2}{3}$. Solving,

$f''(3) = -\frac{7}{3} \cdot 2! = -\frac{14}{3}.$

Equivalently, differentiating the given polynomial twice and substituting $x = 3$ produces $f''(3) = -14/3$.
(*Calculus for AP®*, pages 728–737; EU 4.2; LO 4.2A; EK 4.2A1; MPAC 2,3,5)

13. ANSWER: (A) $f'(x) = 6x^5 - 20x^3 \Rightarrow f''(x) = 30x^4 - 60x^2 = 30x^2$
$(x^2 - 2)\ 30x^2(x^2 - 2) = 0 \Rightarrow x = 0, \pm\sqrt{2}$

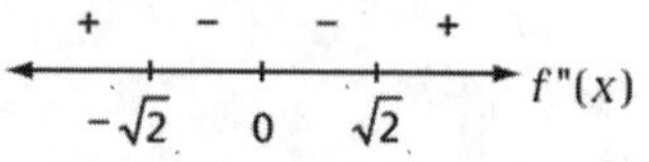

The sign of $f''(x)$ changes at $x = \pm\sqrt{2}$ only, so these are the locations of the inflection points.
(*Calculus for AP®*, pages 322–324; EU 2.2; LO 2.2A; EK 2.2A1; MPAC 2,3)

14. ANSWER: (A) $\frac{\cos(0) - e^0}{\ln(1+0)} = \frac{1-1}{0} = \frac{0}{0}$. This is a quotient indeterminate form, so L'Hôpital's Rule applies.

$\lim_{x\to 0}\frac{\cos x - e^x}{\ln(1+x)} = \lim_{x\to 0}\frac{-\sin x - e^x}{\frac{1}{1+x}} = \frac{-0-1}{\frac{1}{1+0}} = -1$

(*Calculus for AP®*, pages 337–343; EU 1.1; LO 1.1C; EK 1.1C3; MPAC 2,3,5)

*15. ANSWER: (A) I: The series is geometric with $r = 3/4$, so it converges.

II: $\lim_{k\to\infty}\frac{k^2}{(2k+1)^2} = \frac{1}{4} \neq 0$, so the series diverges by the nth-Term Test.

III: $|\sec k| \geq 1$, so $\frac{|\sec k|}{k} \geq \frac{1}{k}$. Since $\sum_{k=1}^{\infty}\frac{1}{k}$ is a divergent p-series (harmonic series, $p = 1$), the series $\sum_{k=1}^{\infty}\frac{|\sec k|}{k}$ diverges by the Direct Comparison Test. Therefore, (A) is correct.

(*Calculus for AP*®, pages 662–666, 692–695, 685–688; EU 4.1; LO 4.1A; EK 4.1A2,4.1A3,4.1A6; MPAC 2,3,5)

16. ANSWER: (D) Separating variables,

$$\int\frac{dy}{y-2} = \int k\,dt \Rightarrow \ln|y-2| = kt + C_1 \Rightarrow y = e^{kt+C_1} + 2 \Rightarrow y = Ce^{kt} + 2.$$

(*Calculus for AP*®, pages 618–624; EU 3.5; LO 3.5A; EK 3.5A2; MPAC 2,3)

17. ANSWER: (C) By the Second Fundamental Theorem, the domain is the largest continuous interval of $f(t)$ containing the lower limit of the integral. Since the upper limit is a function of x, solve the inequality $-1 < 2x - 1 < 5$. The solution is $0 < x < 3$.
(*Calculus for AP*®, pages 436–440; EU 3.3; LO 3.3A; EK 3.3A2; MPAC 1,2,4)

18. ANSWER: (D) $F'(x) = f(2x-1)\cdot 2 \Rightarrow F'(2) = 2f(2\cdot 2 - 1) = 2f(3) = 2\cdot 2 = 4$
(*Calculus for AP*®, pages 436–440; EU 2.1,3.4; LO 2.14C,3.3A; EK 2.1C4,3.3A2; MPAC 2,3,4)

19. ANSWER: (A) $f'(x) = \frac{3}{\sqrt{1-x^2}} \Rightarrow f'(0) = \frac{3}{1} = 3 \Rightarrow -\frac{1}{f'(0)} = -\frac{1}{3}$
(*Calculus for AP*®, pages 245–246; EU 2.1,2.3; LO 2.1C,2.3B; EK 2.1C2,2.3B1; MPAC 2,3)

*20. ANSWER: (B) $\frac{dx}{dt} = \sec^2 t$ and $\frac{dy}{dt} = \frac{1}{2}e^{\frac{1}{2}t}$

$$\text{Length} = \int_{t_1}^{t_2}\sqrt{\left(\frac{dx}{dt}\right)^2 + \left(\frac{dy}{dt}\right)^2}\,dt = \int_0^1\sqrt{\sec^4 t + \frac{1}{4}e^t}\,dt$$

(*Calculus for AP*®, page 778; EU 3.4; LO 3.4D; EK 3.4D3; MPAC 1,2)

*21. ANSWER: (A) The Maclaurin series for e^x is $\sum_{k=0}^{\infty}\frac{x^k}{k!}$. So, the series for e^{x^2} is

$$\sum_{k=0}^{\infty}\frac{(x^2)^k}{k!} = \sum_{k=0}^{\infty}\frac{x^{2k}}{k!}.$$

$$\text{Area} = \int_0^1 e^{x^2}\,dx = \int_0^1\left(\sum_{k=0}^{\infty}\frac{x^{2k}}{k!}\right)dx \approx \int_0^1\left(\frac{x^0}{0!}+\frac{x^2}{1!}+\frac{x^4}{2!}+\frac{x^6}{3!}\right)dx$$

$$= \frac{x^1}{1\cdot 0!}+\frac{x^3}{3\cdot 1!}+\frac{x^5}{5\cdot 2!}+\frac{x^7}{7\cdot 3!}\Bigg|_0^1 = 1+\frac{1}{3}+\frac{1}{10}+\frac{1}{42}$$

(*Calculus for AP*®, pages 728–737, 477–486; EU 4.2; LO 4.2B; EK 4.2B2; MPAC 2)

22. ANSWER: (C) The slopes are positive in quadrants I and II and negative in quadrants III and IV. This indicates no change in sign on opposite sides of the y-axis, thus x has an even power. There is a change in sign on opposite sides of the x-axis, thus y has an odd power. Therefore (C) is correct.
(*Calculus for AP*®, pages 606–611; EU 2.3; LO 2.3F; EK 2.3F1; MPAC 2,4)

*23. ANSWER: (B) The answer can be determined in two ways:

1. Find the series for $f(x) = x \sin x$ and differentiate. 2. Differentiate $f(x) = x \sin x$ and find its series.

$$1: f(x) = x\sin x = x\left(x-\frac{x^3}{3!}+\frac{x^5}{5!}-\frac{x^7}{7!}\right)$$

$$= x^2-\frac{x^4}{3!}+\frac{x^6}{5!}-\frac{x^8}{7!}.$$

$$f'(x) = 2x-\frac{4x^3}{3!}+\frac{6x^5}{5!}-\frac{8x^7}{7!}$$

$$2: f'(x) = x\cos x+\sin x \approx x\left(1-\frac{x^2}{2!}+\frac{x^4}{4!}-\frac{x^6}{6!}\right)+x-\frac{x^3}{3!}+\frac{x^5}{5!}-\frac{x^7}{7!}$$

(*Calculus for AP*®, pages 721–724; EU 4.2; LO 4.2B; EK 4.2B2,4.2B5; MPAC 1,2,3)

$$r = \frac{1}{\cos\left(\frac{1}{2}\theta\right)} = \sec\left(\frac{1}{2}\theta\right)$$

*24. ANSWER: (D)

$$\text{Polar area} = \frac{1}{2}\int_{\theta_1}^{\theta_2} r^2\,d\theta = \frac{1}{2}\int_0^{\frac{\pi}{2}} \sec^2\frac{1}{2}\theta\,d\theta$$

$$= 2\cdot\frac{1}{2}\tan\frac{1}{2}\theta\Bigg|_0^{\frac{\pi}{2}}$$

$$= \tan\frac{\pi}{4}-\tan 0$$

$$= 1-0 = 1$$

(*Calculus for AP*®, pages 803–810; EU 3.4; LO 3.4D; EK 3.4D1; MPAC 2,3)

25. ANSWER: (D) By the Washer Method,

$$\text{Volume} = \pi \int_0^2 \left[\left(1+x^2\right)^2 - 1^2\right] dx.$$

(*Calculus for AP®*, pages 525–528; EU 3.4; LO 3.4D; EK 3.4D2; MPAC 2)

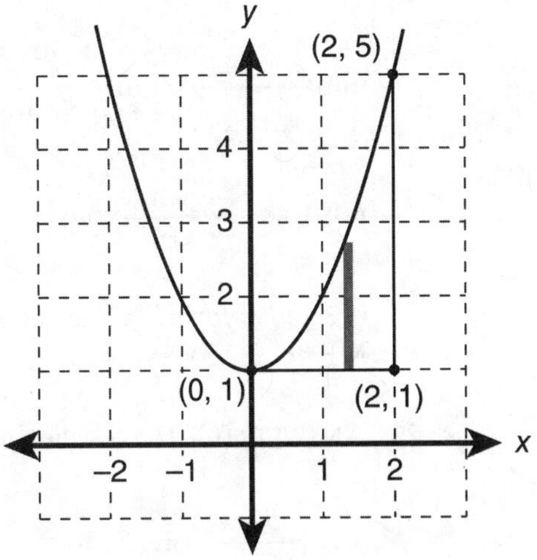

*26. ANSWER: (B) $\int \frac{2x-3}{x^2+9x+18}dx = \int \frac{2x-3}{(x+6)(x+3)}dx.$

Integrate by partial fractions.

$$\frac{2x-3}{(x+6)(x+3)} = \frac{A}{x+6} + \frac{B}{x+3} \Rightarrow 2x-3$$
$$= A(x+3) + B(x+6)$$

Let
$x = -6{:}2(-6) - 3 = A(-6+3) \Rightarrow -15 = 3A \Rightarrow A = 5$
Let $x = -3{:}2(-3) - 3 = B(-3+6) \Rightarrow -9 = 3B \Rightarrow B = -3$
Therefore,

$$\int \frac{2x-3}{(x+6)(x+3)}dx = \int \left(\frac{5}{x+6} - \frac{3}{x+3}\right)dx$$
$$= 5\ln|x+6| - 3\ln|x+3| + C$$
$$= \ln\left|\frac{(x+6)^5}{(x+3)^3}\right| + C.$$

(*Calculus for AP®*, pages 569–572; EU 3.3; LO 3.3B; EK 3.3B3,3.3B5; MPAC 2,3,5)

*27. ANSWER: (C) To get the velocity vector, integrate the coordinates of the acceleration vector.
$\int -\pi \sin \pi t dt = \cos \pi t + C_1 \cdot \cos(\pi \cdot 0) + C_1 = 1 \Rightarrow 1 + C_1 = 1 \Rightarrow C_1 = 0.$
$\int(2t+1)dt = t^2 + t + C_2\ 0^2 + 0 + C_2 = 0 \Rightarrow C_2 = 0.$ The velocity vector is $(\cos \pi t, t^2 + t)$. Therefore, the speed of the particle when $t = 2$ is
$\sqrt{\cos^2(\pi \cdot 2) + (2^2+2)^2} = \sqrt{1^2+6^2} = \sqrt{37}.$
(*Calculus for AP®*, pages 777–782; EU 2.3; LO 2.3C; EK 2.3C4; MPAC 2,3)

*28. ANSWER: (C) This is a variation on a p-series, $\sum_{k=1}^{\infty}\frac{1}{k^p}$, so the Limit Comparison Test should be used. If $\lim_{k\to\infty}\frac{u_k}{v_k}$ is finite and positive, then the original series and the comparison series will both converge or both diverge. A p-series converges if $p > 1$. Compare to $\sum_{k=1}^{\infty}\frac{1}{k^{2a-5}}$, because the difference in degree (denominator minus numerator) of the original series is $2a - 3 - 2 = 2a - 5$.

$$\lim_{k\to\infty}\frac{\dfrac{k^2}{k^{2a-3}+4}}{\dfrac{1}{k^{2a-5}}}=\lim_{k\to\infty}\frac{k^2\cdot k^{2a-5}}{k^{2a-3}+4}=\lim_{k\to\infty}\frac{k^{2a-3}}{k^{2a-3}+4}=1,$$ which is finite and

positive. $\sum_{k=1}^{\infty}\frac{1}{k^{2a-5}}$ converges if $2a-5>1\Rightarrow 2a>6\Rightarrow a>3$.

(*Calculus for AP*®, pages 688–689; 4.2; LO 4.2C; EK 4.2C2; MPAC 1,2,3)

29. ANSWER: (C) The function given by $y=\frac{5-x}{|5-x|}$, is a piecewise function given by

$$y=\begin{cases}\dfrac{5-x}{(5-x)}=1, & x\le 5\\[2ex] \dfrac{5-x}{-(5-x)}=-1, & x>5\end{cases}$$. As x approaches 5 from the left, $\frac{5-x}{|5-x|}$ approaches a value of 1.

As x approaches 5 from the right, $\frac{5-x}{|5-x|}$ approaches a value of -1, therefore the answer is -1.

(*Calculus for AP*®, pages 111–112; EU 1.1; LO 1.1A,1.1D; EK 1.1A1,1.1D1; MPAC 2,4)

30. ANSWER: (C) $f(3)=0+\int_{-3}^{3} f'(x)\,dx$ and represents the accumulated area under the curve from $x=-3$ to $x=3$. The net signed areas of the triangles are $\frac{1}{2}\cdot 3\cdot 2+\frac{1}{2}\cdot 2\cdot 2-\frac{1}{2}\cdot 1\cdot 1=3+2-\frac{1}{2}=4.5$.

(*Calculus for AP*®, pages 422–423; EU 2.2; LO 2.2A; EK 2.2A3; MPAC 2,4)

31. ANSWER: (C) The average value of a function, $f(x)$, on the closed interval $[a, b]$ is determined by $\frac{1}{b-a}\int_a^b f(x)\,dx$. Therefore, the solution is found by evaluating $\frac{1}{5-0}\int_0^5 (x+1)\sin\left(\sqrt{x+1}\right)dx=2.992$.

(*Calculus for AP*®, pages 490–494; EU 3.4; LO 3.4B; EK 3.4B1; MPAC 3)

*32. ANSWER: (C) $dy/dx=\frac{dy/dt}{dx/dt}\Rightarrow dx/dt=\frac{dy/dt}{dt\ dx}$. For the given function,

$\frac{dy}{dx}=x\cos x+\sin x\Rightarrow \left.\frac{dy}{dx}\right|_{x=3}=3\cos 3+\sin 3$. Therefore,

$$\left.\frac{dx}{dt}\right|_{x=3}=\frac{-2}{3\cos 3+\sin 3}\approx 0.707.$$

(*Calculus for AP*®, pages 754–764; EU 2.1; LO 2.1C; EK 2.1C4; MPAC 2,3)

33. ANSWER: (C) $1.6 \le x \le 11.6$. In looking at the graph of $f'(x)$ on the given window, there are four turning points. This represents four points at which $f''(x)$ (or the slope of $f'(x)$) is equal to 0 and changes sign from either positive to negative or negative to positive. So these represent four changes in concavity, hence four inflection points. (*Calculus for AP®*, pages 316–317; EU 2.2; LO 2.2A; EK 2.2A1; MPAC 2,4)

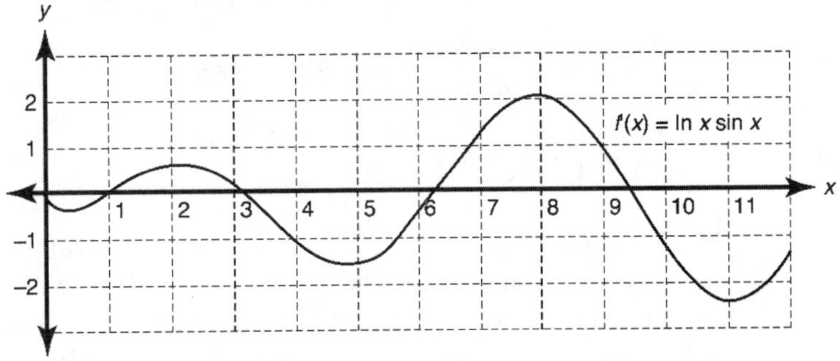

34. ANSWER: (D) The average value of a function in an interval is the value of the definite integral divided by its length, that is, $f_{\text{ave}} = \frac{1}{b-a}\int_a^b f(x)\,dx$. A look at the graphs of $y = \cos x$, $y = \cos 2x$, and $y = \sin x$ reveals that the areas under the curves can be easily compared without computation. (A) and (C) have positive areas, (B) is zero, and (D) is negative. Therefore, (D) is the only choice to have a negative average value, so it is the smallest. Alternatively, calculate the four average values on the calculator and see that (D) is the smallest.
(*Calculus for AP®*, pages 490–494; EU 3.4; LO 3.4B; EK 3.4B1; MPAC 1,2,3,4)

35. ANSWER: (B) Use the graphing calculator to graph $v(t)$. Use the derivative feature to graph $v'(t)$. Then, $v'(t) = a(t) = 0$ at $t = 2.35619$, $v(2.35619) = -0.670$.
(*Calculus for AP®*, pages 261–263; EU 2.3; LO 2.3C; EK 2.3C1; MPAC 2,3)

*36. ANSWER: (A) Series I and II are essentially p-series, so the convergence of the series of absolute values can be obtained by using the Limit Comparison test. Recall that $\sum_{k=1}^{\infty}\frac{1}{k^p}$ converges if $p > 1$ and diverges if $0 < p \le 1$. Compare I to $\sum_{k=1}^{\infty}\frac{1}{k}$, which is divergent. $\lim_{k\to\infty}\left|\frac{(1)^k \frac{k^2}{k^3+1}}{\frac{1}{k}}\right| = \lim_{k\to\infty}\left|\frac{k^3}{k^3+1}\right| = 1$, which is finite and positive, thus I does not converge absolutely. But the sequence of positive terms decreases to a limit of zero, so as an alternating series, I converges by the Alternating Series Test. Therefore, I is conditionally convergent. Compare II to $\sum_{k=1}^{\infty}\frac{1}{k^2}$. Using the same limit procedure, II converges absolutely. The sequence in III has limit 1, so it is divergent. In summary, I is the only series that converges conditionally.
(*Calculus for AP®*, pages 692–695; EU 4.1; LO 4.1A; EK 4.1A4; MPAC 1,2)

37. ANSWER: (C) $\tan\theta = \frac{h}{8} \Rightarrow 8\tan\theta \Rightarrow \frac{dh}{dt} = 8\sec^2\theta\frac{d\theta}{dt}$. When
$h=13, 8^2+13^2=z^2 \Rightarrow z=\sqrt{64+169}=\sqrt{233}.$
$\left.\frac{dh}{dt}\right|_{h=13} = 8\cdot\frac{233}{64}(0.03) = 0.874 \text{ cm/sec}.$
(*Calculus for AP®*, pages 274–279; EU 2.3; LO 2.3C; EK 2.3C2; MPAC 2,3)

38. ANSWER: (B) $f''(x) = e^x+1$, which is positive everywhere. Therefore, $f(x)$ is concave up everywhere, so any tangent line to $f(x)$ will be below the curve except at the point of tangency. Thus $H(a+0.1) < f(a+0.1)$ for all values of a. [Note: If, for example, $f''(x) = e^x - 1$, there would be a sign change in $f''(x)$, hence an inflection point on the graph of $f(x)$. In that case (C) would be the correct answer.]
(*Calculus for AP®*, page 323; EU 2.3; LO 2.3B; EK 2.3B2; MPAC 2,3)

*39. ANSWER: (D) Using the Ratio Test for Absolute Convergence,

$$\lim_{k\to\infty}\left|\frac{\frac{(2x)^{k+1}}{k+2}}{\frac{(2x)^k}{k+1}}\right| = \lim_{k\to\infty}\left|\frac{(2x)^{k+1}\cdot(k+1)}{(k+2)\cdot(2x)^k}\right| < 1$$

$$\Rightarrow \lim_{k\to\infty}|2x|<1 \Rightarrow |2x|<1 \Rightarrow -\frac{1}{2}<x<\frac{1}{2}$$

End points must be checked separately. $x=-\frac{1}{2}: \sum_{k=0}^{\infty}\frac{(-1)^k}{k+1}$ converges by the Alternating Series Test, since the series of positive terms is decreasing and $\lim_{k\to\infty}\frac{1}{k+1}=0$. $x=\frac{1}{2}: \sum_{k=0}^{\infty}\frac{1}{k+1}$ diverges, since it is a p-series (harmonic series, $p=1$) Therefore, the interval of convergence is $-\frac{1}{2}\le x<\frac{1}{2}$.
(*Calculus for AP®*, pages 715–717; EU 4.2; LO 4.2C; EK 4.2C2; MPAC 2,3,5)

40. ANSWER: (D) The functions intersect at $x = -6$, 0, and 4 and enclose two regions.

$$\text{Area} = \int_{-6}^{0}[f(x)-g(x)]\,dx + \int_{0}^{4}[g(x)-f(x)]\,dx = 31.5+10.667=42.167.$$

$$\text{Alternatively, Area} = \int_{-6}^{4}|f(x)-g(x)|\,dx = 42.167.$$

(*Calculus for AP®*, pages 477–486; EU 3.4; LO 3.4D; EK 3.4D1; MPAC 2,3)

41. ANSWER: (D) The total sales figure is represented by
$\int_0^{30} (0.32x^2 - 0.01x^3)\,dx = 855.$
(*Calculus for AP*®, pages 450–454; EU 3.4; LO 3.4A; EK 3.4A2; MPAC 2,3)

42. ANSWER: (C) By the Product and Chain Rules,
$g'(x) = x^2 \cdot -3f'(3x) + 2x \cdot f(3x)$. Therefore,
$g'(-1) = (-1)^2 \cdot 3f'(-3) - 2f(-3) = 3 \cdot 7 - 2(-2) = 25.$
(*Calculus for AP*®, pages 207–210, 227–233; EU 2.1; LO 2.1C; EK 2.1C3,2.1C4; MPAC 2,3,4)

43. ANSWER: (A) $15 - e^x = 0 \Rightarrow x = 2.70805$. The radius of each cross section is $\frac{15 - e^x}{2}$, so the area of each cross section is
$\frac{1}{2}\pi\left(\frac{15 - e^x}{2}\right)^2 = \frac{\pi}{8}(15 - e^x)^2$. Therefore,
$V = \int_0^{2.70805} \frac{\pi}{8}\left(15 - e^x\right)^2\,dx = 118.325.$
(*Calculus for AP*®, pages 518–522; EU 3.4; LO 3.4D; EK 3.4D2; MPAC 2,3)

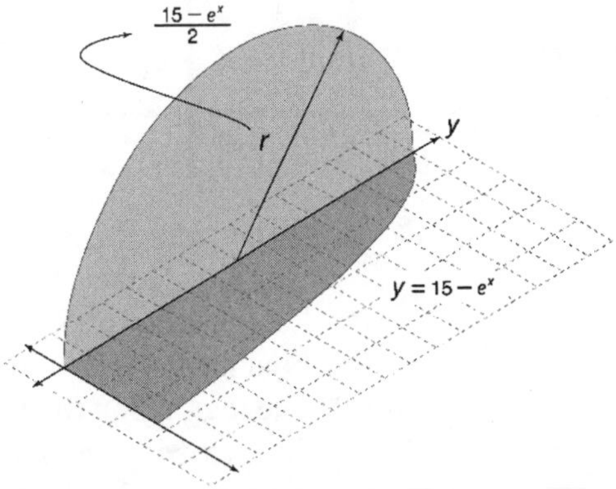

*44. ANSWER: (B) This is the indeterminate form ∞^0.
Let $y = [f(x)]^{\frac{1}{x}}$.
Then, $\ln y = \frac{1}{x}\ln[f(x)] = \frac{\ln[f(x)]}{x}$. Thus, $\lim_{x\to\infty} \ln y = \lim_{x\to\infty}\frac{\ln[f(x)]}{x}$.

This is the indeterminate form $\frac{\infty}{\infty}$, souse L'Hôpital's Rule.

$$\lim_{x\to\infty}\frac{\ln[f(x)]}{x} = \lim_{x\to\infty}\frac{\frac{f'(x)}{f(x)}}{1} = \frac{\frac{3}{\infty}}{1} = 0.$$ Therefore,
$\lim_{x\to\infty}\ln y = 0 \Rightarrow \lim_{x\to\infty} y = e^0 = 1.$
(*Calculus for AP*®, pages 337–343; EU 1.1; LO 1.1C; EK 1.1C3; MPAC 1,2,3)

45. ANSWER (D) The Mean Value Theorem guarantees at least one value c in the interval $0.5 < x < 3.5$ such that $f'(c) = \frac{f(3.5) - f(0.5)}{3.5 - 0.5}$. For the given function,

$f'(x) = -\frac{1}{x} - 1$. Therefore,

$f'(c) = \frac{1}{c} - 1 = \frac{0.75276 - 1.80685}{3.5 - 0.5} = -\frac{1.05409}{3} = -0.35136$. So,

$\frac{1}{c} - 1 = -0.35136 \Rightarrow c = 1.542.$
(*Calculus for AP*®, pages 308–311; EU 2.4; LO 2.4A; EK 2.4A1; MPAC 1,2,3)

FREE-RESPONSE QUESTIONS

1.

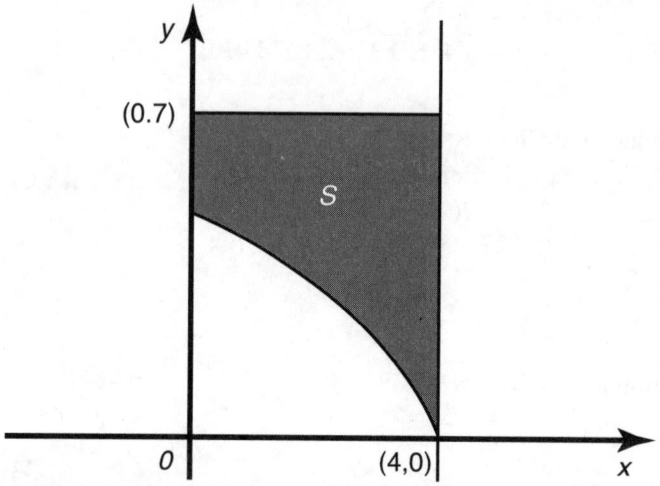

1. In the figure above, S, is the shaded region in the first quadrant bounded by the graph of $y = 3 \ln(5 - x)$, the horizontal line $y = 7$, and the vertical line $x = 4$.
   (a) Find the area of S.
   (b) Find the volume of the solid when S is revolved about the horizontal line $y = -1$.
   (c) The region S in the base of a solid. For this solid, each cross section perpendicular to the x-axis is a semicircle. Find the volume of the solid.

	Solution	Possible points
		1: Correct limits in an integral in (a), (b), or (c)
(a)	Integrate the function bounding region S above minus the function bounding region S below from $x = 0$ to $x = 4$. $\int_0^4 (7 - 3\ln(5 - x))\, cx = 15.858$	$2: \begin{cases} 1: \text{integrand} \\ 1: \text{answer} \end{cases}$
(b)	Since region S is not flush against the axis of rotation, the washer method can be used to determine the volume of the solid. $\pi \int_0^4 ((7-(-1))^2 - (3\ln(5-x)-(-1))^2)\, dx = 578.063$	$3: \begin{cases} 2: \text{integrand} \\ 1: \text{answer} \end{cases}$
(c)	To determine the volume of the solid, integrate the area of the cross-sectional shape, a semicircle. $\frac{1}{2}\pi \int_0^4 \left(\frac{1}{2}(7 - 3\ln(5-x))\right)^2 dx = 27.384$ or 27.383	$3: \begin{cases} 2: \text{integrand} \\ 1: \text{answer} \end{cases}$

1. (a) (*Calculus for AP*®, pages 477–486; EU 3.4; LO 3.4D; EK 3.4D1; MPAC 2,3,4)
1. (b) (*Calculus for AP*®, pages 525–528; EU 3.4; LO 3.4D; EK 3.4D2; MPAC 2,3,4,)
1. (c) (*Calculus for AP*®, pages 518–522; EU 3.4; LO 3.4D; EK 3.4D2; MPAC 2,3,4)

*2. The Taylor expansion for a function $f(x)$ about $x = 4$ is given by

$$f(x) = 1 + \frac{1}{2}(x-4) + \frac{1}{4}(x-4)^2 + \frac{1}{8}(x-4)^3 + \cdots = \sum_{k=0}^{\infty} \frac{(x-4)^k}{2^k}.$$

(a) What are all values of x for which $f(x)$ converges?
(b) Find the first three nonzero terms and the general term of $f'(x)$. Use the first three terms to estimate the value of $f'(3.9)$.
(c) Let $g(x)$ be the second degree Taylor polynomial for $f(x)$, and let $h(x)$ be the function such that $h'(x) = g(x)$. If $h(5) = 0$, find $h(x)$.

<table>
<tr><th></th><th>Solution</th><th>Possible points</th></tr>
<tr><td>(a)</td><td>Using the Ratio Test for Absolute Convergence,
$$\lim_{k\to\infty}\left|\frac{a_{k+1}}{a_k}\right| < 1 \Rightarrow \lim_{k\to\infty}\left|\frac{\frac{(x-4)^{k+1}}{2^{k+1}}}{\frac{(x-4)^k}{2^k}}\right| < 1 \Rightarrow$$
$$\lim_{k\to\infty}\left|\frac{(x-4)^{k+1}}{2^{k+1}}\cdot\frac{2^k}{(x-4)^k}\right| < 1 \Rightarrow \lim_{k\to\infty}\left|\frac{x-4}{2}\right| < 1.$$
Therefore, $\lvert x-4\rvert < 2 \Rightarrow 2 < x < 6$.
End points must be tested separately:
Let $x = 2: \sum_{k=0}^{\infty}\frac{(-2)^k}{2^k} = \sum_{k=0}^{\infty}(-1)^k$ which diverges by the nth-Term Test.
Let $x = 6: \sum_{k=0}^{\infty}\frac{(2)^k}{2^k} = \sum_{k=0}^{\infty}(1)^k$ which diverges by the nth-Term Test. The interval of convergence is $2 < x < 6$.</td><td>4: { 1: use of RTAC
1: open interval
1: test for $x = 2$
1: test for $x = 6$</td></tr>
<tr><td>(b)</td><td>$$f'(x) = \frac{1}{2} + \frac{2}{4}(x-4) + \frac{3}{8}(x-4)^2 + \cdots = \sum_{k=0}^{\infty}\frac{k(x-4)^{k-1}}{2^k}$$
$$f'(3.9) \approx \frac{1}{2} + \frac{2}{4}(3.9-4) + \frac{3}{8}(3.9-4)^3 =$$
$$\frac{1}{2} + \frac{1}{2}(-0.1) + \frac{3}{8}(-0.1)^2 = 0.454.$$</td><td>3: { 1: first 3 terms
<−1> first error
1: general term
1: $f'(3.9)$</td></tr>
</table>

	Solution	Possible points
(c)	$g(x)=1+\frac{1}{2}(x-4)+\frac{1}{4}(x-4)^2$ Therefore, $h(x)=\int g(x)\,dx \Rightarrow$ $h(x)=(x-4)+\frac{1}{4}(x-4)^2+\frac{1}{12}(x-4)^3+C$ $h(5)=(5-4)+\frac{1}{4}(5-4)^2+\frac{1}{12}(5-4)^3+C=0\Rightarrow$ $1+\frac{1}{4}+\frac{1}{12}+C=0\Rightarrow\frac{4}{3}+C=0\Rightarrow C=-\frac{4}{3}.$ $h(x)=(x-4)+\frac{1}{4}(x-4)^2+\frac{1}{12}(x-4)^3-\frac{4}{3}$	$2:\begin{cases}1\text{: antiderivative with constant}\\1\text{: solves for constant}\end{cases}$

2. (a) (*Calculus for AP*®, pages 715–717; EU 4.2; LO 4.2C; EK 4.2C2; MPAC 1,2,3,5)
2. (b) (*Calculus for AP*®, pages 721–724; EU 4.2; LO 4.2A; EK 4.2A2; MPAC 2,3,5)
2. (c) (*Calculus for AP*®, pages 721–724; EU 4.2; LO 4.2C; EK 4.2C4; MPAC 2,3)

*3. A particle moves in the *xy*-plane with position vector $(x(t),\ y(t))$ such that $x(t)=t^3-6t^2+9t+1$ and $y(t)=-t^2+6t+2$ in the time interval $0\le t\le 5$.

(a) At what time t is the particle at rest? Justify your answer.
(b) Give the velocity vector at $t=5$.
(c) How fast is the particle moving when $t=5$?
(d) Is the speed of the particle increasing or decreasing when $t=5$? Justify your answer.
(e) What is the average speed of the particle for the time interval $0\le t\le 5$?

	Solution	Possible points
(a)	$x'(t)=3t^2-12t+9=3(t-1)(t-3)=0$ $t=1$ or 3 $y'(t)=-2t+6=-2(t-3)=0$ $t=3$ The particle is at rest at $t=3$ because both $x'(3)=0$ and $y'(3)=0$.	$3:\begin{cases}1: x'(t)\text{ and }y'(t)\\1:\text{zeros of }x'(t)\text{ and }y'(t)\\1:\text{answer with reason}\end{cases}$
(b)	$x'(5)=3.25-12.5+9=24$ $y'(5)=-10+6=-4$ The velocity vector at $t=5$ is $(24,-4)$.	1: answer

	Solution	Possible points
(c)	The speed of the particle is $\sqrt{\left(\frac{dx}{dt}\right)^2+\left(\frac{dy}{dt}\right)^2}$ $=\sqrt{(3t^2-12t+9)^2+(-2t+6)^2}$. At $t=5$, the speed is $\sqrt{(24)^2+(-4)^2}=\sqrt{592}=24.331$.	$2:\begin{cases}1:\text{expression for speed}\\1:\text{answer}\end{cases}$
(d)	Using the calculator, $\frac{d}{dt}\left(\sqrt{(3t^2-12t+9)^2+(-2t+6)^2}\right)\Big\vert_{t=5}=18.084>0.$ Since the derivative of the speed function is positive when $t=5$, the speed is increasing at $t=5$.	$2:\begin{cases}1:\text{use of derivative of speed}\\1:\text{answer with reason}\end{cases}$
(e)	$\frac{1}{5-0}\int_0^5\sqrt{(3t^2-12t+9)^2+(-2t+6)^2}\ dt=6.609$	1: answer

3. (a), (b), (c) (*Calculus for AP*®, pages 777–782; EU 2.3; LO 2.3C; EK 2.3C4; MPAC 1,2,3)
3. (d) (*Calculus for AP*®, pages 316–331; EU 2.3; LO 2.3C; EK 2.3C4; MPAC 1,2,3,6)
3. (e) (*Calculus for AP*®, pages 490–494; EU 2.3; LO 2.3C; EK 2.3C4; MPAC 1,2,3)

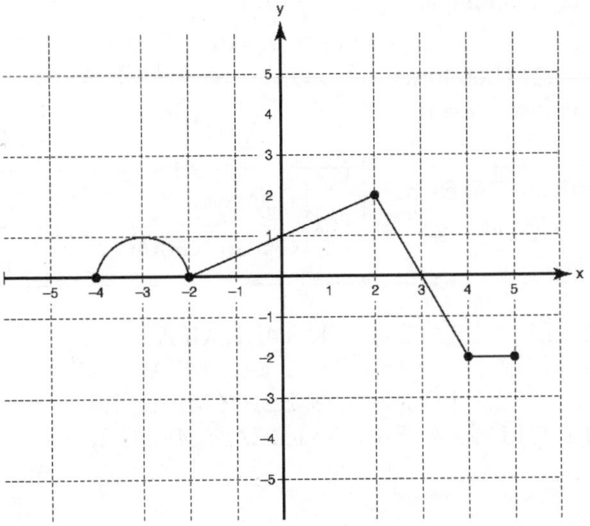

4. Let f be a continuous function defined on $[-4, 5]$ whose graph, consisting of three line segments and a semicircle centered on the x-axis at $x = -3$. Let h be the function given by

$$h(x)=\int_0^x f(t)\,dt.$$

(a) Find the values of $h(-2)$ and $h(2)$.
(b) For each value $h'(3)$ and $h''(3)$, find the value or state that it does not exist.

(c) Find the x-coordinate of each point at which the graph of h has a horizontal tangent line. For each of these points, determine whether h has a relative minimum, maximum, or neither a minimum or maximum at the point. Justify your answers.

(d) For $-4 < x < 5$, find all the values of x for which the graph of h has a point of inflection. Explain your reasoning.

	Solution	**Possible points**
(a)	$\int_0^{-2} f(t)\,dt = -\int_{-2}^{0} f(t)\,dt = -\left(\frac{1}{2}\right)(2)(1) = -1$ $\int_0^{2} f(t)\,dt = \left(\frac{1}{2}\right)(2)(1+2) = 3$	$2: \begin{cases} 1: h(-2) \\ 1: h(2) \end{cases}$
(b)	$h'(x) = f(x) \Rightarrow h'(3) = f(3) = 0$ $h''(x) = f'(x) \Rightarrow h''(3) = f'(3) = -2$	$2: \begin{cases} 1: h'(3) \\ 1: h''(3) \end{cases}$
(c)	The graph of h has a horizontal tangent line where $h'(x) = f(x) = 0$. This occurs at $x = -2$ and $x = 3$. $h'(x)$ changes from positive to negative at $x = 3$. Therefore, h has a relative maximum at $x = 3$. $h'(x)$ does not change sign at $x = -2$. Therefore, h has neither a relative maximum nor a relative minimum at $x = -2$.	$3: \begin{cases} 1: \text{considers } h'(x) = 0 \\ 1: x = -2 \text{ and } x = 3 \\ 1: \text{answers with justification} \end{cases}$
(d)	The graph of h has a point of inflection at each $x = -2$ and $x = 2$ because $h''(x) = f'(x)$ change sign at each of these values.	$2: \begin{cases} 1: \text{answer} \\ 1: \text{justification} \end{cases}$

4. (a) (*Calculus for AP*®, pages 422–423; EU 3.4; LO 3.4E; EK 3.4E1; MPAC 2,4)
4. (b) (*Calculus for AP*®, pages 436–440; EU 2.1; LO 2.1A; EK 2.1A5; MPAC 2,4)
4. (c) (*Calculus for AP*®, pages 199–200; EU 2.2; LO 2.2A; EK 2.2A1; MPAC 2,4,6)
4. (d) (*Calculus for AP*®, page 324; EU 2.2; LO 2.2A; EK 2.2A1,2.2A3; MPAC 2,4,6)

5. A concrete reservoir in the shape of a triangular prism is being filled with water at the constant rate of 2 cubic feet per minute. The reservoir is 4 feet deep, measures 6 feet across the top, and is 20 feet long, as shown in the figure to the right. For any time $t \geq 0$, let h represent the depth of the water in the reservoir, and let w represent the width of the rectangular region of water at the top.

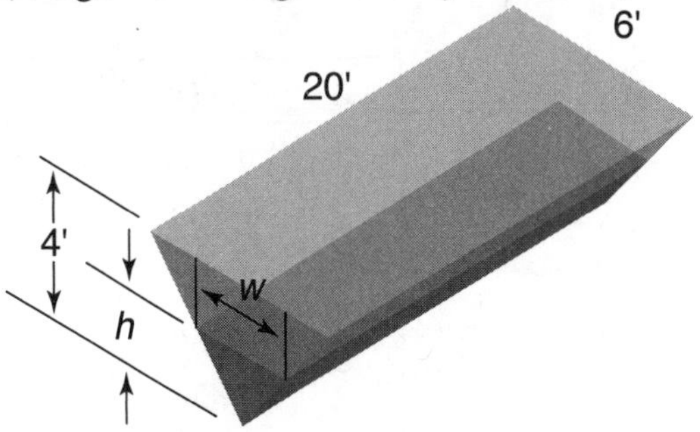

(a) If the reservoir is initially empty, how long will it take to fill completely?
(b) How fast is the depth of the water in the reservoir changing when the reservoir is half full? Indicate units of measure.
(c) How fast is the rectangular area of the surface of the water changing when the reservoir is half full? Indicate units of measure.

	Solution	Possible points
(a)	$V = \frac{1}{2} \cdot 6 \cdot 4 \cdot 20 = 240 \text{ ft}^3$ $\frac{240 \text{ ft}^3}{2 \text{ ft}^3/\text{min}} = 120$ min. The reservoir will be full in 120 minutes.	$2: \begin{cases} 1: \text{volume} \\ 1: \text{answer} \end{cases}$
(b)	Using similar triangles, $\frac{h}{w} = \frac{4}{6} \Rightarrow w = \frac{3}{2}h.$ Therefore, $V = \frac{1}{2} \cdot \frac{3}{2}h \cdot h \cdot 20 = 15h^2.$ $15h^2 = 120 \Rightarrow h^2 = 8 \Rightarrow h = 2\sqrt{2}$ $\frac{dV}{dt} = 30h\frac{dh}{dt} \Rightarrow \left.\frac{dh}{dt}\right\|_{\substack{V=120 \\ h=2\sqrt{2}}} = \frac{2}{30 \cdot 2\sqrt{2}} = \frac{1}{30\sqrt{2}}$ The depth of water in the reservoir is increasing at $\frac{1}{30\sqrt{2}}$ ft/min when the reservoir is half full.	$4: \begin{cases} 1: V \text{ vs. } h \text{ relationship} \\ 1: \text{depth when half full} \\ 1: \frac{dV}{dt} \\ 1: \text{answer} \end{cases}$
(c)	$A = w \cdot 20 = \frac{3}{2}h \cdot 20 = 30h$ Therefore, $\frac{dA}{dt} = 30\frac{dh}{dt}.$ $\left.\frac{dA}{dt}\right\|_{\substack{v=120 \\ h=2\sqrt{2}}} = 30 \cdot \frac{1}{30\sqrt{2}} = \frac{1}{\sqrt{2}}$ The area of the rectangular region of water is increasing at $\frac{1}{\sqrt{2}}$ ft²/min when the reservoir is half full.	$2: \begin{cases} 1: \frac{dA}{dt} \\ 1: \text{answer} \end{cases}$
	Units	1: correct units in both b and c

5. (a), (b), (c) (*Calculus for AP®*, pages 274–279; EU 2.3; LO 2.3C; EK 2.3C1,2.3C2; MPAC 2,3,4,6)

*6. Consider the function $f(x)=\dfrac{10\ln x}{x^2}$, for $x \geq 1$. The graph of $f(x)$ is pictured below along with a table of values of $f(x)$.

X	$f(x)$
1	0
2	1.733
3	1.221
4	0.866
5	0.644
6	0.498
7	0.397

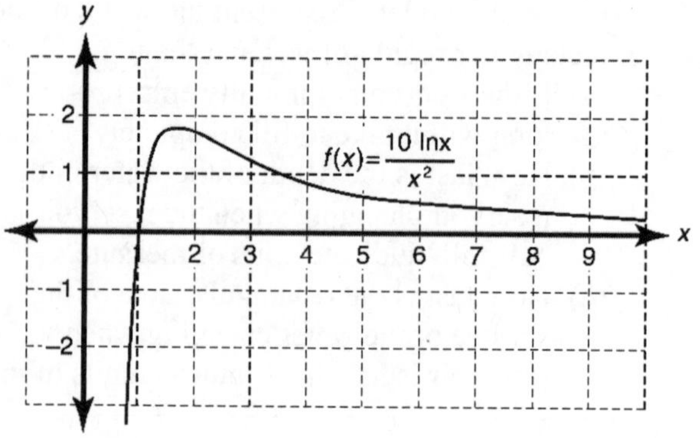

(a) Evaluate $\lim\limits_{x\to\infty} f(x)$.

(b) Find the x-coordinate of the relative maximum of $f(x)$. Justify your answer.

(c) Use a midpoint Riemann sum with $n = 3$ to estimate the value of $\int_1^7 f(x)\,dx$.

(d) Evaluate $\int_1^\infty f(x)\,dx$.

	Solution	Possible points
(a)	Indeterminate form $\dfrac{\infty}{\infty}$ $\lim\limits_{x\to\infty}\dfrac{10\ln x}{x^2}=\lim\limits_{x\to\infty}\dfrac{10/x}{2x}=\lim\limits_{x\to\infty}\dfrac{5}{x^2}=0$	1: answer
(b)	$f'(x)=\dfrac{x^2(10/x)-10\ln x(2x)}{x^4}=\dfrac{10x-20x\ln x}{x^4}$ $=\dfrac{10(1-2\ln x)}{x^3}=0$ $1-2\ln x=0 \Rightarrow \ln x=\dfrac{1}{2} \Rightarrow x=e^{\frac{1}{2}}=\sqrt{e}$ Using values less than and greater than $\sqrt{e}$ to test signs, $f'(1)=\dfrac{10(1-0)}{1^3}=10$ and $f'(e)=\dfrac{10(1-2)}{e^3}=-\dfrac{10}{e^3}$. 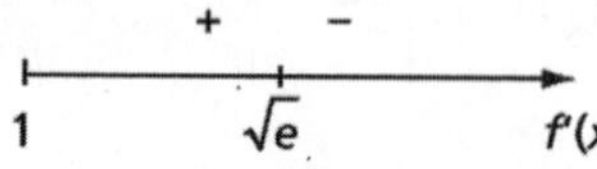 There is a relative maximum at $x=\sqrt{e}$ because $f'(x)$ changes from positive to negative at that point.	$3:\begin{cases}1:\text{derivative}\\1:\text{solution}\\1:\text{justification}\end{cases}$

	Solution	Possible points
(c)	$\int_1^7 \frac{10\ln x}{x^2} \approx \frac{7-1}{3}(1.733+0.866+0.498)=6.194$	$2:\begin{cases}1:\text{sum of correct midpoints}\\1:\text{answer including constant}\end{cases}$
(d)	Integration by parts $u=\ln x \quad v=-\frac{10}{x}$ $du=\frac{dx}{x} \quad dv=\frac{10}{x^2}dx$ $\int\frac{10\ln x}{x^2}dx=-\frac{10\ln x}{x}-\int-\frac{10}{x^2}dx$ Since this is an improper integral, $\int_1^\infty \frac{10\ln x}{x^2}=\lim_{b\to\infty}\left(-\frac{10\ln x}{x}-\frac{10}{x}\right)\Big\|_1^b$ $=\lim_{b\to\infty}\left[\left(-\frac{10\ln b}{b}-\frac{10}{b}\right)-\left(-\frac{10\ln 1}{1}-\frac{10}{1}\right)\right]$ $=\lim_{b\to\infty}\left(-\frac{10\ln b}{b}-0+0+10\right)$ $=\lim_{b\to\infty}-\frac{10\ln b}{b}+10.$ The limit is indeterminate of the form $\frac{\infty}{\infty}$. $\lim_{b\to\infty}-\frac{10\ln b}{b}+10=\lim_{b\to\infty}-\frac{10/b}{1}+10=\frac{0}{1}+10=10$	$3:\begin{cases}1:\text{integration by parts setup}\\1:\text{antiderivative}\\1:\text{answer}\end{cases}$

6. (a) (*Calculus for AP®*, pages 337–343; EU 1.1; LO 1.1C; EK 1.1C3; MPAC 2,3,4)
6. (b) (*Calculus for AP®*, pages 316–333; EU 2.2; LO 2.2A; EK 2.2A1; MPAC 2,3,4,6)
6. (c) (*Calculus for AP®*, pages 395–410, 418–420; EU 3.2; LO 3.2B; EK 3.2B2; MPAC 2,3,4)
6. (d) (*Calculus for AP®*, pages 586–594, 544–548; EU 3.2; LO 3.2D; EK 3.2D1,3.2D2; MPAC 2,3,4)

CALCULUS AB AND BC SCORING CHART

SECTION I: MULTIPLE-CHOICE QUESTIONS

______ × 1.2 = ______
correct (out of 45) — do not round (out of 54)

SECTION II: FREE-RESPONSE QUESTIONS

Question 1	Score out of 9 points =	______
Question 2	Score out of 9 points =	______
Question 3	Score out of 9 points =	______
Question 4	Score out of 9 points =	______
Question 5	Score out of 9 points =	______
Question 6	Score out of 9 points =	______
	Sum for Section II =	______ (out of 54)

Composite Score

Section I total	=
Section II total	=
Composite score	= ______ (out of 108)

Grade Conversion Chart*

Composite score range	AP® exam grade
68–108	5
52–67	4
39–51	3
27–38	2
0–26	1

***Note:** The ranges listed above are only approximate. Each year the ranges for the actual AP® exam are somewhat different. The cutoffs are established after the exams are given to over 200,000 students and are based on the difficulty level of the exam each year.

AP® CALCULUS BC PRACTICE TEST 2
Section I, Part A: Multiple-Choice Questions
Time: 60 minutes
Number of Questions: 30

A calculator may not be used on this part of the examination.

1. If $f(x) = e^{3x+7}$, then $f'(x) =$
   (A) e^{3x+7}
   (B) e^3
   (C) $3e^{3x+7}$
   (D) $(3x + 7)e^{3x+6}$

2. $\lim_{h \to 0} \dfrac{\sin\left(\dfrac{\pi}{6} + h\right) - \dfrac{1}{2}}{h} =$

   (A) -1

   (B) 0

   (C) $\dfrac{\pi}{6}$

   (D) $\dfrac{\sqrt{3}}{2}$

3. Let $f(x) = \dfrac{5 - 3x}{x^2 - 6x - 7}$. Which of the following integral expressions represents the area between $f(x)$ and the horizontal axis on the interval $2 \le x \le 4$?

   (A) $\displaystyle\int_2^4 \left[-\frac{2}{x-7} - \frac{1}{x+1}\right] dx$

   (B) $\displaystyle\frac{1}{4}\int_2^4 \left[-\frac{13}{x+7} + \frac{1}{x-1}\right] dx$

   (C) $\displaystyle\int_2^4 \left[-\frac{2}{x-7} + \frac{1}{x+1}\right] dx$

   (D) $\displaystyle\frac{1}{8}\int_2^4 \left[-\frac{1}{x-7} + \frac{1}{x+1}\right] dx$

4. If $f(x)$ is a function that is increasing and concave down on the interval $0 < x < 6$, then which of the following could be the graph of $f'(x)$?

(A)

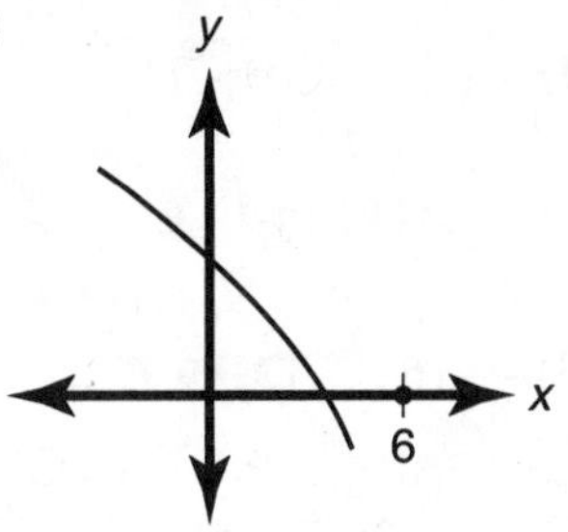

(B)

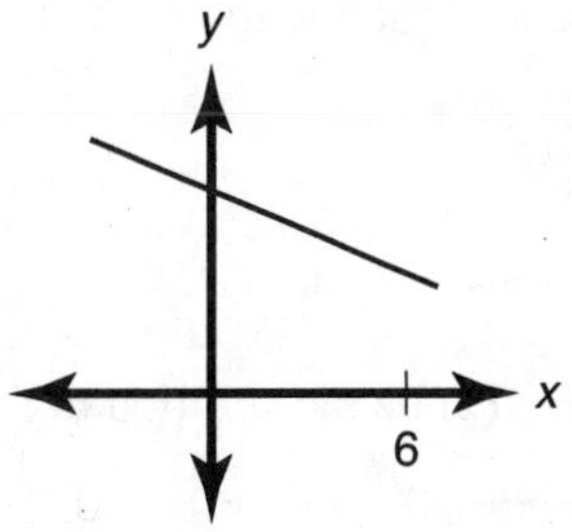

(C)

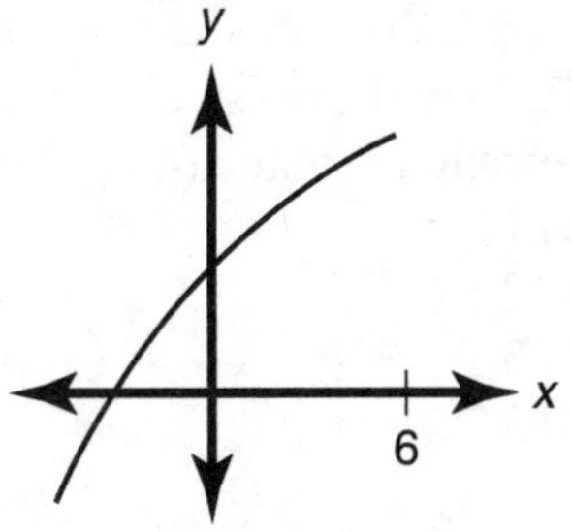

(D)

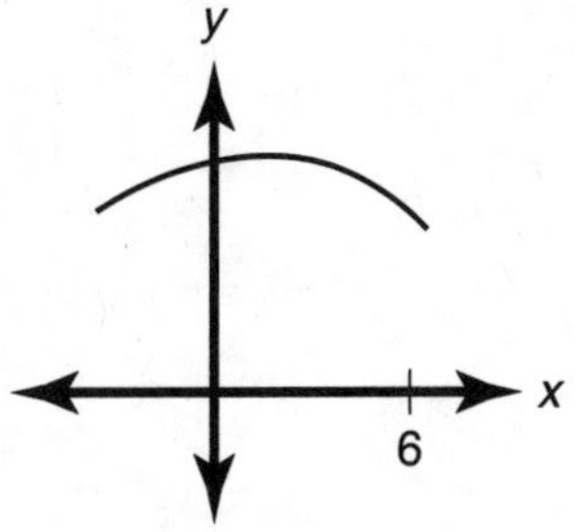

5. Let $f(x) = e^{2x^2}$. The first three terms of the Maclaurin series for $f'(x)$ are
(A) $1 + 2x^2 + 2x^4$.
(B) $2x^2 + 2x^3 + x^4$.
(C) $2x^2 + 2x^4 + \frac{4}{3}x^6$.
(D) $4x + 8x^3 + 8x^5$.

6. $\int x^2\sqrt{5x^3 - 13}\,dx =$
(A) $\frac{2}{9}x^3(5x^3 - 13)^{\frac{3}{2}} + C$
(B) $\frac{2}{3}(5x^3 - 13)^{\frac{1}{2}} + C$
(C) $\frac{1}{15}(5x^3 - 13)^{\frac{3}{2}} + C$
(D) $\frac{2}{45}(5x^3 - 13)^{\frac{3}{2}} + C$

7. If $f(x) = (2x + 1)\tan x$, then the slope of the tangent line to $f(x)$ at $x = 0$ is
(A) −1.
(B) 0.
(C) 1.
(D) undefined.

8. Let $y(x)$ be the solution to the differential equation $\frac{dy}{dx} = x + 2y$.
Using Euler's method, starting at the point (−3, 2) with step size $\Delta x = 0.5$, what is the approximate value of $y(-2)$?
(A) 1
(B) 2.5
(C) 3
(D) 3.75

9. A particle moves in the xy-plane such that its velocity vector for time $t \geq 0$ is $\left(\frac{1}{1+t^2}, 2^t\right)$. If the particle is at the point (3, 0) when $t = 0$, then what is the position vector of the particle when $t = 1$?
(A) $\left(\frac{\pi}{4}, \frac{1}{\ln 2}\right)$
(B) $\left(\frac{\pi}{4} + 3, 1\right)$
(C) $\left(\frac{\pi}{4} + 3, \frac{1}{\ln 2}\right)$
(D) $\left(\ln 2 + 3, \frac{1}{\ln 2}\right)$

10. Let $F(x) = \int_{13x+16}^{x^2+7x} 4\sqrt[3]{t+1}\,dt$. Which of the following values are x-intercepts of the graph of $F(x)$?
(A) $x = -2$ only
(B) $x = -1$ only
(C) $x = 8$ only
(D) $x = -2$ and 8

11. Let $f(x) = x^2e^x$ on the interval $-10 \leq x \leq 0$. The absolute maximum of $f(x)$ on this interval is
(A) $\frac{100}{e^{10}}$.
(B) $\frac{4}{e^2}$.
(C) 1.
(D) e.

12. The Maclaurin series $x^2 - x^5 + \frac{x^8}{2!} - \frac{x^{11}}{3!} + \cdots = \sum_{k=0}^{\infty}(-1)^k \frac{x^{3k+2}}{k!}$ represents the function $f(x) =$
(A) $x^2e^{-x^3}$
(B) $x^2\sin x^3$
(C) x^2e^{-3x}
(D) $\cos(3x + 2)$

13. $\int_3^{12} (x-3)^{-\frac{1}{2}}\, dx =$

(A) $\frac{1}{3}$
(B) 5
(C) 6
(D) ∞

14. Which one of the following statements is false?

(A) $\sum_{k=0}^{\infty} |\sin k|$ diverges

(B) $\sum_{k=0}^{\infty} \frac{7^k}{5^{k+2}}$ diverges

(C) $\sum_{k=0}^{\infty} \frac{2k^2+8k+3}{k^3+1}$ converges

(D) $\sum_{k=0}^{\infty} (-1)^k \frac{k+1}{k!}$ converges absolutely

15. The tangent line to the curve $y = x^3 + 7$ at $x = 1$ intersects the x-axis at $x =$

(A) $-\frac{11}{3}$.

(B) $-\frac{5}{3}$.

(C) -1.

(D) $\frac{1}{3}$.

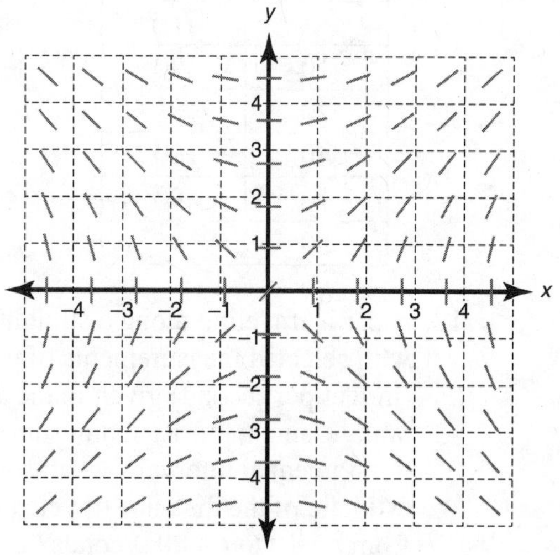

16. The slope field pictured above could be the slope field for which of the following differential equations?

(A) $\frac{dy}{dx} = x + y$

(B) $\frac{dy}{dx} = x - y$

(C) $\frac{dy}{dx} = \frac{x}{y}$

(D) $\frac{dy}{dx} = \frac{y}{x}$

17. Consider the curve defined by the parametric equations $x(t) = 3 + \sin t$ and $y(t) = 2t^2 + 5t + 1$. For any time t, $\frac{d^2y}{dx^2} =$

(A) $\frac{4t+5}{\cos t}$

(B) $\frac{4\cos t + (4t+5)\sin t}{\cos^2 t}$

(C) $-\frac{4}{\sin t}$

(D) $\frac{4\cos t + (4t+5)\sin t}{\cos^3 t}$

GO ON TO NEXT PAGE

t	$v(t)$
10	90
20	88
40	100
70	90
80	85

18. A car is traveling along a straight highway with selected measurements of its velocity (in feet per second) given in the above table. Using a left Riemann sum with $n = 4$ unequal intervals, what is the estimate of the distance traveled by the car from $t = 10$ to $t = 80$ seconds?
(A) 6560
(B) 6380
(C) 6430
(D) 6495

19. The first four terms of the Taylor expansion for $f(x)$ about $x = -3$ are $11 + \frac{x+3}{5} - \frac{7(x+3^2}{16} - \frac{5(x+3)^3}{48}$. What is value $f'''(-3)$?
(A) $-\frac{5}{48}$
(B) $-\frac{7}{48}$
(C) $-\frac{7}{16}$
(D) $-\frac{5}{8}$

20. What are all values of x for which the series $\sum_{k=0}^{\infty} \frac{\sqrt{k}x^{2k+1}}{k+3}$ converges?
(A) The series converges for $x = 0$ only.
(B) $-1 < x < 1$
(C) $-1 \le x < 1$
(D) $-1 \le x < 1$

21. If $f(x) = \ln x$ on the interval $1 \le x \le e$, then what is the value of c on the interval $1 < x < e$ that satisfies the Mean Value Theorem?
(A) $\frac{1}{e-1}$
(B) $\frac{e}{e-1}$
(C) $\frac{1+e}{2}$
(D) $e - 1$

22. If $\int_1^5 f(x)\,dx = 3a - 11$ and $\int_1^{12} f(x)\,dx = 7a + 15$, then find the value of a such that $\int_5^{12} 2f(x)\,dx = 82$.
(A) -27
(B) $\frac{37}{10}$
(C) $\frac{15}{4}$
(D) $\frac{32}{3}$

23. A particle moves in the xy-plane for time $t \ge 0$ according to the parametric equations $x(t) = e^t - t - 1$ and $y(t) = t^{\frac{3}{2}} - 2t$. Which of the following statements about the particle are true?
I. The particle is moving to the right when $t = 1$.
II. The particle is moving upward when $t = 4$.
III. The particle is at rest when $t = 0$.
(A) I only
(B) I and II only
(C) II and III only
(D) I, II, and III

24. If y is a function of x such that $y'\cos y = \sec^2 x$ and $y\left(\frac{\pi}{4}\right)=\frac{\pi}{6}$, then $y =$

(A) $\sin^{-1}(\tan x)-\frac{1}{2}$.

(B) $\sin^{-1}\left(\tan x-\frac{1}{2}\right)$.

(C) $-\sin^{-1}(\tan x)$.

(D) $\sin^{-1}\left(\tan x-\frac{3}{2}\right)$.

25. Let $f(x) = \sin^{-1}x$. The first two nonzero terms of the Taylor expansion for $f(x)$ about $x = 0$ are

(A) $x-\frac{1}{6}x^3$.

(B) $x+\frac{1}{2}x^2$.

(C) $x+\frac{1}{6}x^3$.

(D) $-x+\frac{1}{6}x^3$.

26. If $f'(x)=\frac{1}{3+x}$ and $f(0) = \ln 21$, then $f(x) =$

(A) $\ln|21 + 7x|$.
(B) $\ln|3 + x| + \ln 18$.
(C) $-\frac{1}{(3+x)^2}+\ln 21+\frac{1}{9}$.
(D) $\ln|3 + x| - \ln 7$.

27. What is the area enclosed by the lemniscate $r^2 = -25\cos 2\theta$?
(A) 50
(B) $\frac{25}{4}$
(C) $\frac{25}{2}$
(D) 25

28. What is the value of $\lim_{x\to 0}\frac{\int_0^x \cos t\,dt}{2x}$?

(A) 0
(B) $\frac{1}{2}$
(C) ∞
(D) Does not exist

29. Which of the following gives the length of the curve $y=4\sqrt{x}$ over the closed interval [2, 5]?

(A) $\int_2^5 \sqrt{\left(1+\frac{2}{\sqrt{x}}\right)}dx$

(B) $\int_2^5 \sqrt{\left(1+\frac{2}{x}\right)}dx$

(C) $\int_2^5 \sqrt{\left(1-\frac{4}{x}\right)}dx$

(D) $\int_2^5 \sqrt{\left(1+\frac{4}{x}\right)}dx$

30. Let $f(x) = \sin(3x)$.
If $f^{(n)}(x)$ represents the nth derivative of $f(x)$, then what is $f^{17}(x)$?
(A) $-3^{17}\cos(3x)$
(B) $3^{16}\sin(3x)$
(C) $3^{17}\sin(3x)$
(D) $3^{17}\cos(3x)$

END OF SECTION I PART A

GO ON TO NEXT PAGE

Section I, Part B: Multiple-Choice Questions
Time: 45 minutes
Number of Questions: 15

A calculator may be used on this part of the examination.

31. A particle moves along the x-axis so that its acceleration is $a(t) = 1 + \sin t$ for $t \geq 0$. If the initial velocity of the particle is 4, then what is the average velocity of the particle during the time interval $0 \leq t \leq 6$?
(A) 5.953
(B) 7.047
(C) 8.047
(D) 48.279

32. Oil is pumped continuously from a certain oil well at a rate modeled by the function $P(t) = 53t^2 - 2t^3$. Let t be the number of days for a 25-day period and let $P(t)$ be measured in barrels per day. To the nearest barrel, according to the model, how much oil will be pumped from the well from the 7th day to the 21st day?
(A) 2940
(B) 34,866
(C) 61,511
(D) 64,820

x	0	1	2	3	4
$f(x)$	10	30	46	58	66

33. Let $f(x)$ be a function which is continuous on the interval $0 \leq x \leq 4$ and differentiable on $0 < x < 4$, with selected values of $f(x)$ given in the above table. Which of the following statements is true?
(A) There is some value c between 0 and 4 such that $f'(c) = 0$.
(B) $f'(x) > 0$ for $0 < x < 4$
(C) There is some value c between 0 and 4 such that $f'(c) = 14$.
(D) $f''(x) < 0$ for $0 < x < 4$

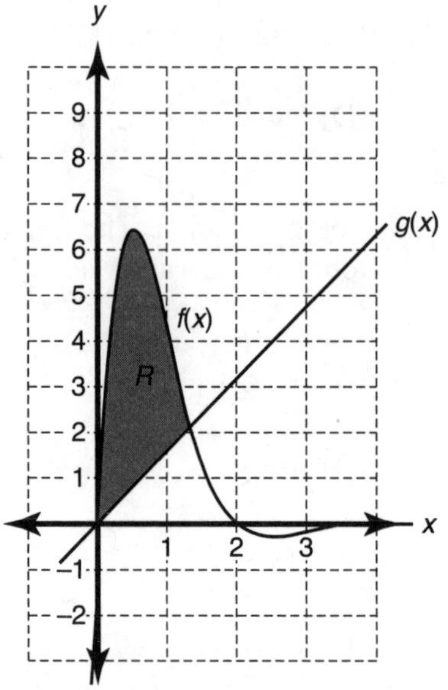

34. The graphs of $f(x) = 20e^{-x}\sin x$ and $g(x) = x$ are pictured above. R is the region in the first quadrant enclosed by the graphs of f and g. The volume of the solid generated by revolving R about the x-axis is
(A) 23.110.
(B) 45.699.
(C) 102.039.
(D) 143.569.

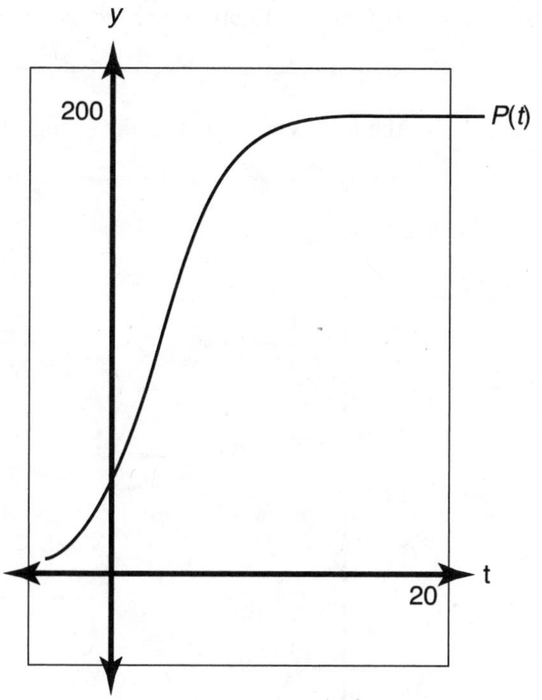

35. The spread of an infectious disease to workers on a large floor of an office building is modeled by the logistic equation $P(t)=\dfrac{200}{1+4e^{-\frac{1}{2}t}}$, where t is the number of days and $P(t)$ represents the number of infected people. The graph of $P(t)$ is shown above. What is the growth rate in infected people per day that this disease exhibits when it is spreading the fastest?
(A) 2.773
(B) 18.695
(C) 25
(D) 100

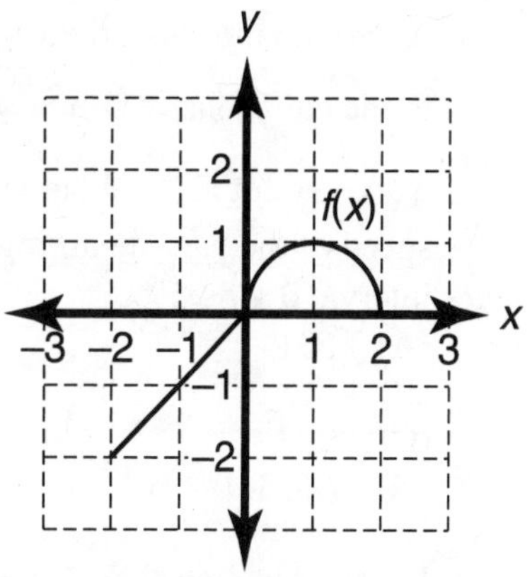

36. $f(x)$ is a function consisting of a line segment and a semicircle, as shown above. Let $g(x)$ be a function such that $g'(x) = f(x)$. If $g(-2) = 0$, then what is the value of $g(2)$?

(A) $-4+\dfrac{\pi}{2}$

(B) $-2+\dfrac{\pi}{2}$

(C) $2+\dfrac{\pi}{2}$

(D) $2+\pi$

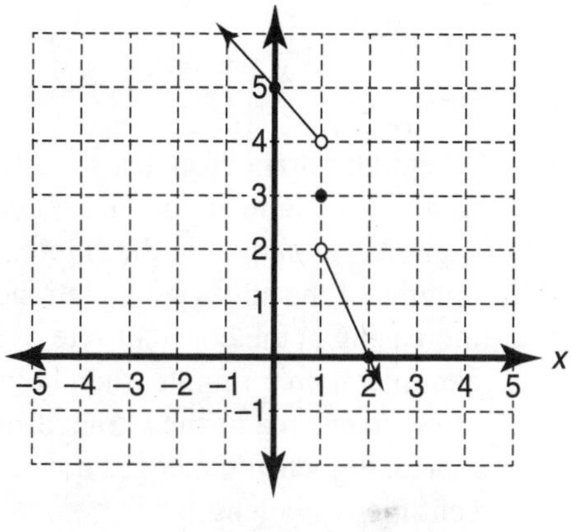

37. The graph of $f(x)$ is shown above. The value of $\lim_{x\to 1^-}\dfrac{d}{dx}[\ln f(x)]$ is
(A) −1
(B) −0.25
(C) 0
(D) 1.386

GO ON TO NEXT PAGE

38. A particle moves in the xy-plane according to the equations $x(t)=5\sqrt{2t+1}$ and $y(t)=e^{\frac{1}{2}t}$ for $t \geq 0$. What is the average speed of the particle during the time interval $0 \leq t \leq 5$?
(A) 3.531
(B) 4.788
(C) 7.293
(D) 17.653

39. For the function $f(x) = 2x^2 - x^3$, $f(1.2) = 1.152$. If $g(x)$ is the inverse of $f(x)$, what is the slope of the tangent to $g(x)$ at the point (1.152, 1.2)?
(A) −2.083
(B) −0.480
(C) 2.083
(D) 1.596

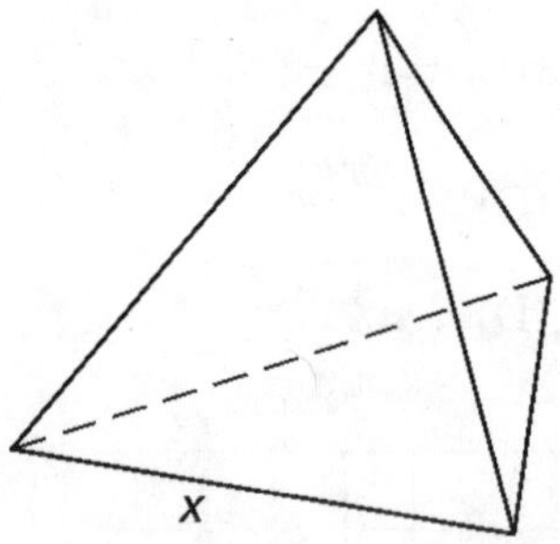

40. A regular tetrahedron is a solid figure with four faces which are congruent equilateral triangles, as shown in the figure. If the lengths of the edges of the tetrahedron are increasing at the constant rate of 2 centimeters per minute, then how fast is the surface area of the tetrahedron increasing when the edges are each 12 centimeters in length?
(A) 83.138 cm^2/min
(B) 20.785 cm^2/min
(C) 41.569 cm^2/min
(D) 48 cm^2/min

41. If $f(x)$ is a function defined on $0 \leq x \leq 4$ such that $\frac{1}{4-0}\int_0^4 f(x)dx = 2$, then which of the following could be the graph of $f(x)$?

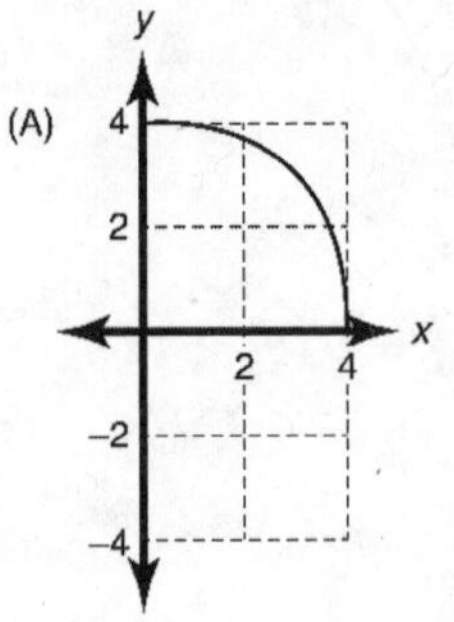

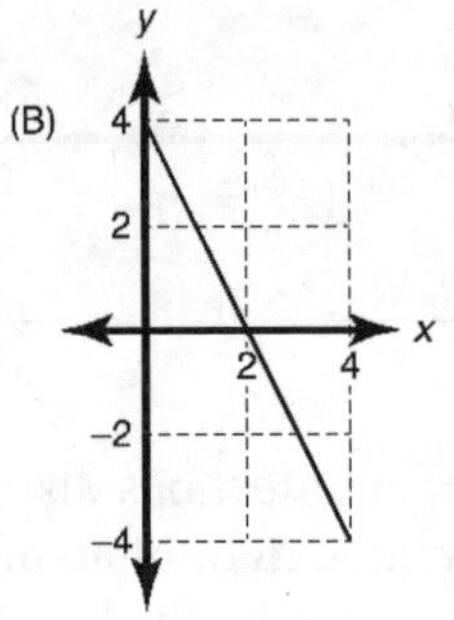

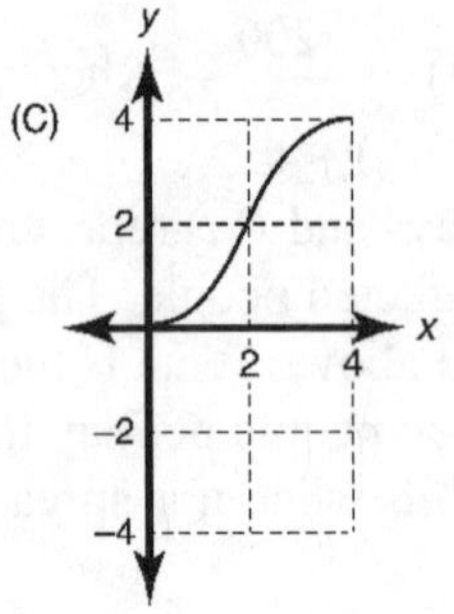

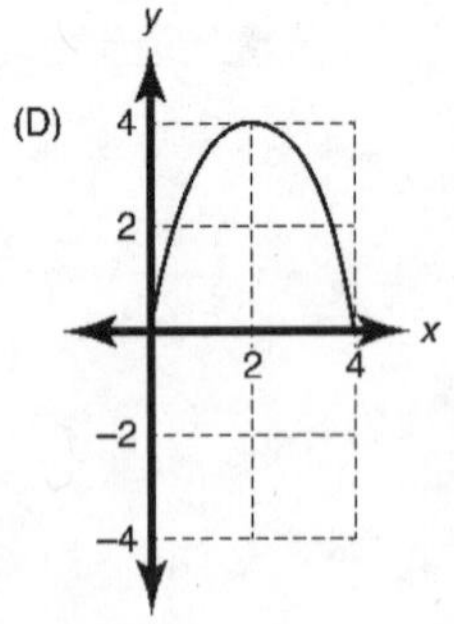

x	$f(x)$	$f'(x)$	$g(x)$	$g'(x)$
3	6	−3	5	−2
5	4	8	−9	7

42. The above table gives values of $f(x), f'(x)$, $g(x)$, and $g'(x)$ for selected values of x. If $h(x) = \dfrac{f(g(x))}{x^2}$, then $h'(3) =$

(A) $-\dfrac{56}{27}$

(B) $-\dfrac{16}{9}$

(C) $\dfrac{16}{27}$

(D) $\dfrac{92}{81}$

43. A particle moves along the x-axis such that its velocity is given by $v(t) = e^{\sin t} - 2$ for time $t \ge 0$. If the particle has position 5 when $t = 0$, then what is its position when it comes to rest for the first time?

(A) −0.406
(B) −0.332
(C) 0.766
(D) 4.594

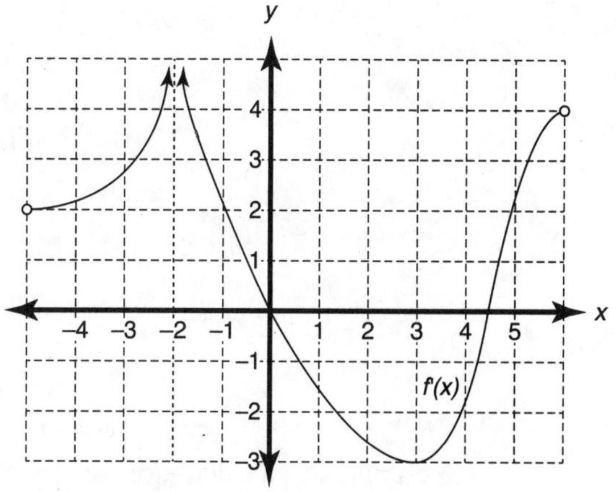

44. Let $f(x)$ be a continuous function in the interval $-5 \le x \le 5$, with the graph of $f'(x)$ pictured above. Which one of the following statements about $f(x)$ is false?

(A) The absolute maximum of $f(x)$ occurs at $x = 0$.
(B) $f(x)$ has a cusp at $x = -2$.
(C) The graph of $f(x)$ is concave down at $x = 1$.
(D) The graph of $f(x)$ has an inflection point at $x = 3$.

45. $f(x)$ is a continuous function defined on the interval $4 \le x \le 10$. A table of values of $f(x)$ is given below.

x	$f(x)$
4	24
5	29
6	37
7	40
8	47
9	51
10	58

What is the estimate of $\int_4^{10} f(x)dx$ produced by a midpoint Riemann sum with three subintervals of equal length?

(A) 216
(B) 234
(C) 240
(D) 284

END OF SECTION I PART B

GO ON TO NEXT PAGE

Section II
Free-Response Questions
Time: 1 hour and 30 minutes
Number of Problems: 6

Part A
Time: 30 minutes
Number of Problems: 2

You may use a calculator for any problem in this section.

1. The rate that water flows into two identical tanks during a 24-hour period is given by the models below. Both $P(t)$ and $Q(t)$ are measured in gallons per hour for $0 \le t \le 24$ hours, and both tanks are empty at time $t = 0$.
Tank 1: The graph of $P(t)$ consists of the line segments indicated in the figure.
Tank 2: $Q(t) = 18\cos(0.25t + 4.5)\sin(0.15t + 2.2) + 35$

(a) What is the value of $P'(7)$? What is the value of $Q'(7)$? Give units for both answers.

(b) How much water is in Tank 1 after 24 hours? Justify your answer.

(c) What is the average rate at which water flows into Tank 2 for the entire 24-hour period? Justify your answer.

(d) During the 24-hour period, is there ever a time other than $t = 0$ when the amount of water in the two tanks is the same? If yes, find all such values of t. If no, explain why not.

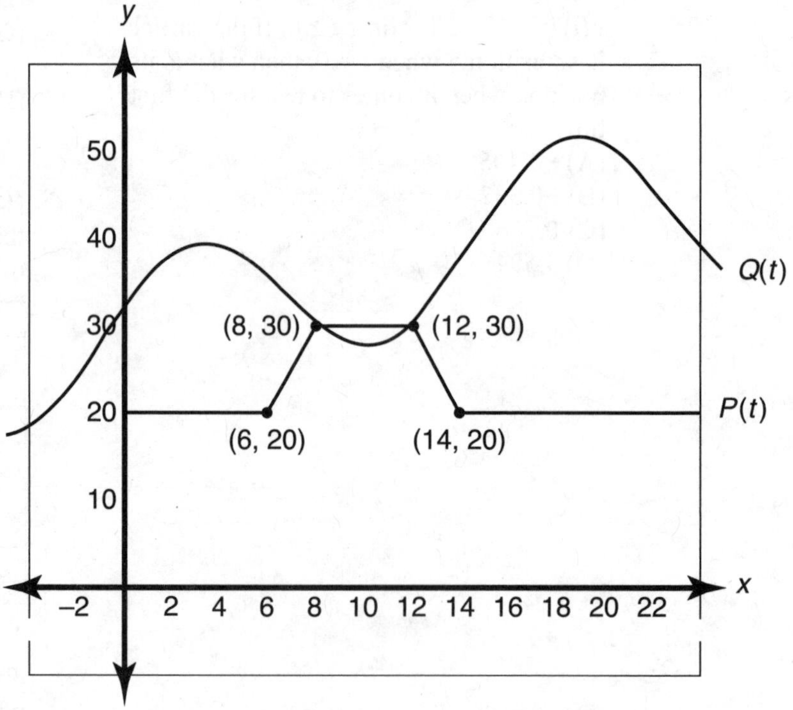

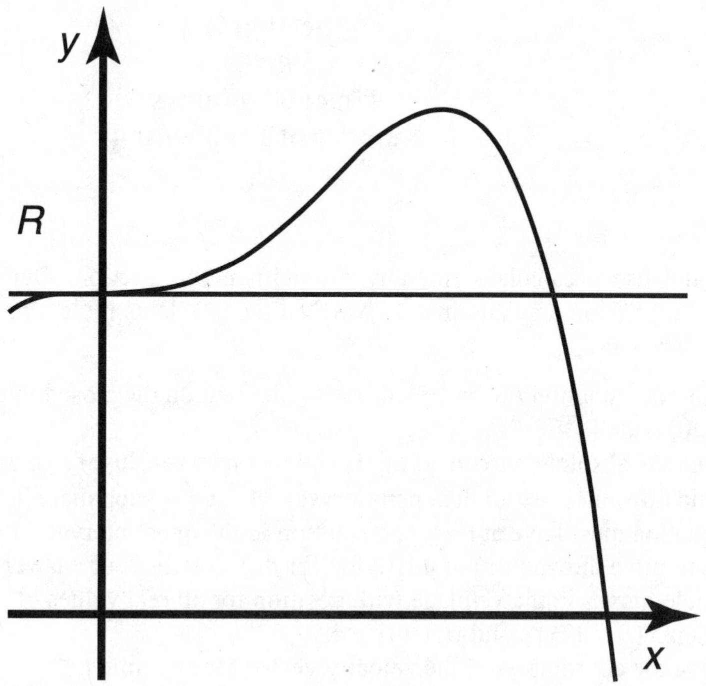

2. Let $\boldsymbol{R}$ be the region enclosed by the graph of $f(x) = -x^4 + 2.3x^3 + 5$ and the horizontal line $y = 5$, as shown in the figure above.
   (a) Find the volume of the solid generated when $\boldsymbol{R}$ is rotated about the line $y = -3$.
   (b) Region $\boldsymbol{R}$ is the base of a solid. For this solid, each cross section perpendicular to the x-axis is a rectangle whose height is twice as long as the length in $\boldsymbol{R}$. Find the volume of the solid.
   (c) The vertical line $x = h$ divides region $\boldsymbol{R}$ into two regions with equal areas. Write, but do not solve, an equation involving integral expressions whose solution gives the value h.

END OF SECTION II PART A

Section II
Part B
Time: 60 minutes
Number of Problems: 4

You may not use a calculator for any problem in this section. During the timed portion for Section II, Part B, you may continue to work on the problems in Section II, Part A without the use of a calculator.

3. Consider the function $f(x) = 4x^3 - 48x + 44$ defined on the closed interval whose endpoints are $(-4, -20)$ and $(4, 108)$.
   (a) Find the absolute maximum of $f(x)$ on this interval. Justify your answer.
   (b) Find all values of x in the open interval $-4 < x < 4$ such that $f'(x) = 16$. Explain why this equation must have at least one solution in the open interval $-4 < x < 4$.
   (c) Determine the point(s) of inflection for $f(x)$. Justify your answer.
4. A particle moves in the xy-plane with position for all real values of t given by the parametric equations $x(t) = 1 - t^3$ and $y(t) = t^2 - 4$.
   (a) Give the coordinates of the velocity vector for any time t.
   (b) Is the particle moving to the left or right when $t = -1$? Is the particle moving up or down when $t = -1$? Give a reason for each answer.
   (c) What is the slope of the path of the particle when $t = 0.5$?
   (d) How fast is the particle moving when its horizontal position is $x(t) = -7$?
   (e) Give the coordinates of the acceleration vector at a time when the particle is at rest.
5. Let $f(x)$ be the function that is the solution to the differential equation $\frac{dy}{dx} = \frac{y}{1+x^2}$, with initial condition $f(0) = 1$.
   (a) Fill in the table below with values of $\frac{dy}{dx}$ for the 15 ordered pairs (x, y) indicated and use the values to sketch a slope field for $\frac{dy}{dx}$ on the axes provided.

y \ x	−2	−1	0	1	2
2					
1					
0					

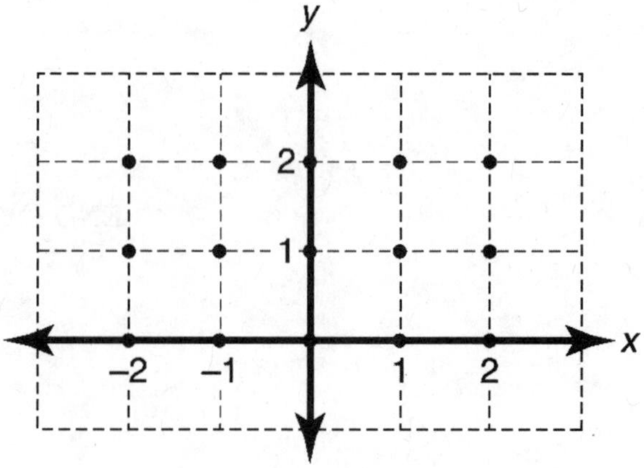

(b) Using Euler's method starting at $x_0 = 0$ with step size $\Delta x = \frac{1}{2}$, estimate the value of $f(1)$.

(c) Find the particular solution $f(x)$.

6. Let $y(x) = 3x + \frac{9}{4}x^2 + \frac{27}{18}x^3 + \cdots = \sum_{k=1}^{\infty} \frac{3^k x^k}{k \cdot k!}$.

(a) Find all values of x for which $y(x)$ converges.

(b) Use the first three terms of $y'(x)$ to estimate the value of $y'(0.01)$.

(c) Show that $y(x)$ is a solution to the differential equation $xy'(x) = e^{3x} - 1$.

END OF SECTION II PART B

Answers and Answer Explanations

Using the table below, score your test. Determine how many questions you answered correctly and how many you answered incorrectly. Additional information about scoring is at the end of the Practice Test.

1. C	2. D	3. A	4. B	5. D
6. D	7. C	8. D	9. C	10. D
11. B	12. C	13. C	14. C	15. B
16. C	17. D	18. A	19. D	20. B
21. D	22. C	23. B	24. B	25. C
26. A	27. D	28. B	29. D	30. D
31. C	32. C	33. C	34. D	35. C
36. B	37. B	38. A	39. C	40. A
41. C	42. A	43. D	44. B	45. C

MULTIPLE-CHOICE QUESTIONS

Note: Asterisks (*) indicate BC questions and solutions.

1. ANSWER: (C) By the Chain Rule, $f'(x) = e^{3x+7}\,3 = 3e^{3x+7}$.
(*Calculus for AP®*, page 202; EU 2.1; LO 2.1C; EK 2.1C2,2.1C4; MPAC 2,3)

2. ANSWER: (D) Recall that the definition of the derivative is $\lim_{h\to 0}\frac{f(x+h)-f(x)}{h}$. The given expression represents the definition of

$f'\left(\frac{\pi}{6}\right)$ for $f(x) = \sin x$ at $x = \frac{\pi}{6}$.

$f'(x) = \cos x \Rightarrow f'\left(\frac{\pi}{6}\right) = \cos\left(\frac{\pi}{6}\right) = \frac{\sqrt{3}}{2}$. Alternatively, this is the

quotient indeterminate form $\frac{0}{0}$. Using L'Hôpital's Rule,

$$\lim_{h\to 0}\frac{\sin\left(\frac{\pi}{6}+h\right)-\frac{1}{2}}{h} = \lim_{h\to 0}\frac{\cos\left(\frac{\pi}{6}+h\right)-0}{1} = \cos\frac{\pi}{6} = \frac{\sqrt{3}}{2}.$$

(*Calculus for AP®*, pages 169–171; EU 2.1; LO 2.1A; EK 2.1A3; MPAC 1,2,5)

*3. ANSWER: (A) Area $= \int_2^4 \left[\dfrac{5-3x}{(x-7)(x+1)} \right] dx$. Re-express using partial

fractions: $\dfrac{5-3x}{(x-7)(x+1)} = \dfrac{A}{x-7} + \dfrac{B}{x+1} \Rightarrow 5-3x = A(x+1)+B(x-7)$.

Let $x = 7: 5 - 3(7) = A(7 + 1) \Rightarrow 8A = -16 \Rightarrow A = -2$
Let $x = -1: 5 - 3(-1) = B(-1 - 7) \Rightarrow -8B = 8 \Rightarrow B = -1$

Therefore, area $= \int_2^4 \left[-\dfrac{2}{x-7} - \dfrac{1}{x+1} \right] dx$.

(*Calculus for AP®*, pages 477–486, 569–572; EU 3.4; LO 3.4D; EK 3.4D1; MPAC 2,5)

4. ANSWER: (B) $f(x)$ increasing $\Rightarrow f(x)$ positive
$f(x)$ concave down $\Rightarrow f''(x)$ negative $\Rightarrow f'(x)$ decreasing
(B) shows a graph that is both positive and decreasing.
(*Calculus for AP®*, pages 316–327; EU 2.2; LO 2.2A; EK 2.2A1,2.2A3; MPAC 2,4)

*5. ANSWER: (D) The Maclaurin series for e^x is $\sum_{k=0}^{\infty} \dfrac{x^k}{k!}$. By substitution,

$$f(x) = e^{2x^2} = \sum_{k=0}^{\infty} \frac{(2x^2)}{k!} = \sum_{k=0}^{\infty} \frac{2^k x^{2k}}{k!} = 1 + 2x^2 + \frac{4x^4}{2!} + \frac{8x^6}{3!} + \cdots$$

Therefore, $f'(x) = 4xe^{2x} = 4x + 8x^3 + 8x^5 + \cdots$

(Note: This last step can be viewed as differentiating the terms of $f(x)$ OR as multiplying the terms of $f(x)$ by $4x$.)
(*Calculus for AP®*, pages 728–737; EU 4.2; LO 4.2B; EK 4.2B2; MPAC 1,2)

6. ANSWER: (D) Integrate by u-substitution: Let $u = 5x^3 - 13$; then $du = 15x^2\, dx$.

$$\int x^2 \sqrt{5x^3 - 13}\, dx = \frac{1}{15} \int u^{\frac{1}{2}} du = \frac{1}{15} \cdot \frac{2}{3} u^{\frac{3}{2}} + C = \frac{2}{45}(5x^3 - 13)^{\frac{3}{2}} + C$$

(*Calculus for AP®*, pages 457–461; EU 3.3; LO 3.3B; EK 3.3B5; MPAC 2,3)

7. ANSWER: (C) Using the Product Rule,
$f'(x) = (2x + 1)\sec^2 x + \tan x \cdot 2 \Rightarrow f'(0) = 1 \cdot 1 + 0 \cdot 2 = 1$.
(*Calculus for AP®*, pages 207–210; EU 2.1,2.3; LO 2.1C,2.1B; EK 2.1C2,2.3B1; MPAC 2,3)

*8. ANSWER: (D) The formula for Euler's method is $y_{n+1} \approx y_n + \left.\frac{dy}{dx}\right|_{(x_n, y_n)} \cdot \Delta x$.

$x_0 = -3$ $\quad y_0 = 2$ $\quad \left.\frac{dy}{dx}\right|_{(-3,2)} = -3 + 4 = 1$

$x_1 = -2.5$ $\quad y_1 = 2 + 1(.5) = 2.5$ $\quad \left.\frac{dy}{dx}\right|_{(-2.5,2.5)} = -2.5 + 5 = 2.5$

$x_2 = -2$ $\quad y_2 = 2.5 + 2.5(.5) = 3.75$

Therefore, $y(-2) \approx 3.75$.
(*Calculus for AP®*, pages 611–615; EU 2.3; LO 2.3F; EK 2.3F2; MPAC 2,3,5)

*9. ANSWER: (C) Integrating the coordinates of the velocity vector,

$x(t) = \int \frac{1}{1+t^2} dt = \tan^{-1} t + C_1$.

$\tan^{-1}(0) + C_1 = 3 \Rightarrow x(t) = \tan^{-1} t + 3$

$y(t) = \int 2^t \, dt = \frac{2^t}{\ln 2} + C_2$

$\frac{2^0}{\ln 2} + C_2 = 0 \Rightarrow C_2 = -\frac{1}{\ln 2} \Rightarrow y(t) = \frac{2^t - 1}{\ln 2}$

$x(1) = \tan^{-1} 1 + 3 = \frac{\pi}{4} + 3$ and $y(1) = \frac{1}{\ln 2}$

The particle is at the point $\left(\frac{\pi}{4} + 3, \frac{1}{\ln 2}\right)$ when $t = 1$.
(*Calculus for AP®*, pages 777–782; EU 3.4; LO 3.4C; EK 3.4C2; MPAC 2,3)

*10. ANSWER: (D) Using the Second Fundamental Theorem for functions defined as definite integrals, the x-intercepts occur when $F(x) = 0$, which is when the upper and lower limits of the integral are equal.

Consequently, $x^2 + 7x = 13x + 16 \Rightarrow x^2 - 6x - 16 = 0 \Rightarrow (x+2)(x-8) = 0 \Rightarrow x = -2$ or 8.

(Note: There could possibly be other x-intercepts of $F(x)$.)
(*Calculus for AP®*, pages 436–440; EU 3.3; LO 3.3B; EK 3.3B5; MPAC 2,3,5)

11. ANSWER: (B) Absolute extremes in a closed interval occur at either critical points or end points.

$f'(x) = x^2 e^x + e^x \cdot 2x = x(x+2)e^x = 0 \Rightarrow x = 0$ or -2

Test all three values,

$f(-10) = 100e^{-10} = \frac{100}{e^{10}}, f(-2) = \frac{4}{e^2}$, and $f(0) = 0$.

The largest of these values is $\frac{4}{e^2}$, so the absolute maximum of $f(x)$ on the given interval is $\frac{4}{e^2}$.

(*Calculus for AP®*, pages 292–300; EU 2.3; LO 2.3C; EK 2.3C3; MPAC 2,3,5)

*12. ANSWER: (C) The given series can be re-expressed as

$$x^2\left(1-x^3+\frac{x^6}{2!}-\frac{x^9}{3!}+\cdots\right)=x^2\sum_{k=0}^{\infty}(-1)^k\frac{x^{3k}}{k!}.$$

Recall that the Maclaurin series for e^x is $1+x+\frac{x}{2!}+\frac{x^3}{3!}+\cdots=\sum_{k=0}^{\infty}\frac{x^k}{k!}$.

By substituting $-x^3$ for x, $e^{-x^3}=1-x^3+\frac{x^6}{2!}-\frac{x^9}{3!}+\cdots=\sum_{k=0}^{\infty}(-1)^k\frac{x^{3k}}{k!}$.

Consequently, $x^2\left(1-x^3+\frac{x^6}{2!}-\frac{x^9}{3!}+\cdots\right)=x^2\sum_{k=0}^{\infty}(-1)^k\frac{x^{3k}}{k!}=x^2e^{-3x}$.

(*Calculus for AP®*, pages 728–737; EU 4.2; LO 4.2B; EK 4.2B2; MPAC 1,2)

*13. ANSWER: (C) This is an improper integral. Therefore,

$$\int_3^{12}(x-3)^{-\frac{1}{2}}dx=\lim_{b\to 3^+}\int_b^{12}(x-3)^{-\frac{1}{2}}dx$$

$$=\lim_{b\to 3+}2(x-3)^{\frac{1}{2}}\Big|_b^{12}$$

$$=2\sqrt{9}-\lim_{b\to 3+}2(b-3)^{\frac{1}{2}}$$

$$=6-0=6.$$

(*Calculus for AP®*, pages 586–594; EU 3.3; LO 3.3B; EK 3.3B5; MPAC 2,3,5)

*14. ANSWER: (C) Consider each choice:

(A) The series diverges using the *n*th-Term Test (true).

(B) The series diverges because it is geometric and $|r|=\frac{7}{5}>1$ (true).

(C) The series, consisting of a ratio of expressions with degrees, is essentially a *p*-series, $\sum_{k=0}^{\infty}\frac{1}{k^p}$. A *p*-series converges for $p>1$.

Since the denominator has degree greater by 1 than the degree of the numerator, the series behaves the same as $\sum_{k=0}^{\infty}\frac{1}{k^1}$ by using the Limit Comparison Test. Since $p=1$ for the comparison series, both series diverge (false).

(D) The series converges using the Ratio Test (true).
The only false statement is (C).
(*Calculus for AP*®, pages 660–710; EU 4.1; LO 4.1A; EK 4.1A6; MPAC 2,3,5)

15. ANSWER: (B) $y'(x) = 3x^2 \Rightarrow y'(1) = 3$. Since $y(1) = 8$, the equation of the tangent line is $y - 8 = 3(x - 1) \Rightarrow y = 3x + 5$. The x-intercept occurs when $y = 0$. Solving for x, $2z + 5 = 0 \Rightarrow x = -\frac{5}{3}$.
(*Calculus for AP*®, pages 165–167; EU 2.3; LO 2.3B; EK 2.3B1; MPAC 2,3)

16. ANSWER: (C) Where $y = 0$ (along the x-axis) the line segments are essentially vertical, indicating a factor of y in the denominator of $\frac{dy}{dx}$.
Where $x = 0$ (along the y-axis), the segments are roughly horizontal, indicating a factor of x in the numerator of $\frac{dy}{dx}$.
Therefore, (C) is correct.
(*Calculus for AP*®, pages 606–611; EU 2.3; LO 2.3F; EK 2.3F1; MPAC 4,5)

*17. ANSWER: (D) $\frac{dy}{dx} = \frac{dy/dt}{dx/dt} = \frac{4t+5}{\cos t}$

$$\frac{d^2y}{dx^2} = \frac{\frac{d}{dt}\left(\frac{dy}{dx}\right)}{\frac{dx}{dt}} = \frac{\frac{\cos t \cdot 4 - (4t+5)(-\sin t)}{\cos^2 t}}{\cos t} = \frac{4\cos t + (4t+5)\sin t}{\cos^3 t}$$

(*Calculus for AP*®, pages 769–782; EU 2.1; LO 2.1C; EK 2.1C7; MPAC 2,3)

18. ANSWER: (A) Distance traveled

$$= \int_{10}^{80} v(t)\,dt \approx y_0\,\Delta x_1 + y_1\,\Delta x_2 + \cdots + y_{n-1}\,\Delta x_n$$

$= 90(20 - 10) + 88(40 - 20) + 100(70 - 40) + 90(80 - 70)$
$= 900 + 1760 + 3000 + 900$
$= 6560$ feet
(*Calculus for AP*®, pages 395–410, 418–420; EU 3.2; LO 3.2B; EK 3.2B2; MPAC 2,3,4)

*19. ANSWER: (D) The Taylor expansion for $f(x)$ about $x = -3$ is $f(-3) + f'(-3)(x+3) + \frac{f''(-3)(x+3)^2}{2!} + \frac{f'''(-3)(x+3)^3}{3!}$. Equating coefficients, $\frac{f'''(-3)}{3!} = -\frac{5}{48} \Rightarrow f'''(-3) = -\frac{5}{48} \cdot 6 = -\frac{5}{8}$.
(*Calculus for AP*®, pages 728–737; EU 4.2; LO 4.2A; EK 4.2A1; MPAC 2,3,5)

*20. ANSWER: (B) Using the Ratio Test for Absolute Convergence,

$$\lim_{k\to\infty}\left|\frac{\dfrac{\sqrt{k+1}x^{2k+3}}{k+4}}{\dfrac{\sqrt{k}x^{2k+1}}{k+3}}\right|<1 \Rightarrow \lim_{k\to\infty}\left|\frac{\sqrt{k+1}x^{2k+3}}{k+4}\cdot\frac{k+3}{\sqrt{k}x^{2k+1}}\right|<1$$

$$\Rightarrow \lim_{k\to\infty}\left|x^2\right|<1$$

$$\Rightarrow x^2<1$$

$$\Rightarrow -1<x<1.$$

End points must be tested separately.

Let $x=-1$: Noting that $(-1)^{2k+1}=-1$ for all k, the series is $\sum_{k=0}^{\infty}-\frac{\sqrt{k}}{k+3}$, which diverges ($p$-series, $p = 1/2$).

Let $x = 1$: Noting that $(1)^{2k+1} = 1$ for all k, the series is $\sum_{k=0}^{\infty}-\frac{\sqrt{k}}{k+3}$, which diverges ($p$-series, $p = 1/2$).

Therefore, the interval of convergence is $-1<x<1$.

(*Calculus for AP®*, pages 701–704; 4.2; LO 4.2C; EK 4.2C2; MPAC 2,3)

21. ANSWER: (D) The Mean Value Theorem guarantees at least one value c in the interval $-1<c<e$ such that $f'(c)=\frac{f(e)-f(1)}{e-1}$.

$f'(x)=\frac{1}{x}\Rightarrow f'(c)=\frac{1}{c}=\frac{\ln e-\ln 1}{e-1}\Rightarrow\frac{1}{c}=\frac{1-0}{e-1}=\frac{1}{e-1}$. Therefore, $c = e - 1$.

(*Calculus for AP®*, pages 308–311; EU 2.4; LO 2.4A; EK 2.4A1; MPAC 2,3)

22. ANSWER: (C) $\int_5^{12} 2f(x)\,dx=82\Rightarrow\int_5^{12} f(x)\,dx=41$. Using the additive property of definite integrals,

$$\int_1^5 f(x)\,dx+\int_5^{12} f(x)\,dx=\int_1^{12} f(x)\,dx\Rightarrow 3a-11+41$$

$$=7a+15\Rightarrow 15=4a\Rightarrow a=\frac{15}{4}.$$

(*Calculus for AP®*, page 425; EU 3.2; LO 3.2C; EK 3.2C2; MPAC 2,3,5)

*23. ANSWER: (B) $x'(t) = e^t - 1$ and $y'(t)=\frac{3}{2}t^{\frac{1}{2}}-2$

I. $x'(1) = e - 1 > 0 \Rightarrow$ moving right (true).

II. $y'(4)=\frac{3}{2}\sqrt{4}-2=3-2=1>0\Rightarrow$ moving up (true).

III. $x'(0) = e^0 - 1 = 0$; $y'(0) = 0 - 2 = -2 \Rightarrow$ the particle is not at rest since one of the coordinates of the velocity vector is not zero (false).

Therefore, (B) is correct.
(*Calculus for AP®*, pages 777–782; EU 2.3; LO 2.3C; EK 2.3C4; MPAC 2,5)

24. ANSWER: (B) Rewrite the equation as $\frac{dy}{dx}\cos y = \sec^2 x$. Separating variables and integrating, $\int \cos y dy = \int \sec^2 x dx \Rightarrow \sin y = \tan x + C$.
Using the initial condition,
$$\sin\frac{\pi}{6} = \tan\frac{\pi}{4} + C \Rightarrow \frac{1}{2} = 1 + C \Rightarrow C = -\frac{1}{2}$$
$$\Rightarrow \sin y = \tan x - \frac{1}{2} \Rightarrow y = \sin^{-1}\left(\tan x - \frac{1}{2}\right).$$
(*Calculus for AP®*, pages 618–624; EU 3.5; LO 3.5A; EK 3.5A2; MPAC 2,3)

*25. ANSWER: (C) The general Taylor expansion for $f(x)$ about $x = 0$ is
$$f(x) = f(0) + f'(0)x + \frac{f''(0)x^2}{2!} + \frac{f'''(0)x^3}{3!} + \cdots.\ f(0) = 0,$$
$$f'(x) = \frac{1}{\sqrt{1-x^2}} = \left(1-x^2\right)^{-\frac{1}{2}} \Rightarrow f'(0) = 1.$$
$$f''(x) = -\frac{1}{2}(1-x^2)^{-\frac{3}{2}} \cdot (-2x) = \frac{x}{(1-x^2)^{\frac{3}{2}}} \Rightarrow f''(0) = 0$$
$$f'''(x) = \frac{(1-x^2)\cdot 1 - x \cdot \frac{3}{2}(1-x^2)^{\frac{1}{2}} \cdot (-2x)}{\left(1-x^2\right)^3} \Rightarrow f'''(0) = 1.$$
The Taylor expansion for $f(x)$ about $x = 0$ is
$0 + \frac{1 \cdot x^1}{1!} + \frac{0 \cdot x^2}{2!} + \frac{1 \cdot x^3}{3!} + \cdots = x + \frac{1}{6}x^3 + \cdots$. Therefore (C) is correct.
(*Calculus for AP®*, pages 728–737; EU 4.2; LO 4.2A; EK 4.2A1; MPAC 1,2,3)

26. ANSWER: (A) $f(x) = \int \frac{dx}{3+x} = \ln|3+x| + C$. Using the initial condition,
$f(0) = \ln 3 + C = \ln 21 \Rightarrow C = \ln 21 - \ln 3 = \ln\frac{21}{3} = \ln 7$. Therefore,
$f(x) = \ln|3 + x| + \ln 7 = \ln|(3 + x)7| = \ln|21 + 7x|$.
(*Calculus for AP®*, pages 381–389; EU 3.3; LO 3.3B; EK 3.3B2; MPAC 2,3,5)

*27. ANSWER: (D) Polar area $=\frac{1}{2}\int_{\theta_1}^{\theta_2} r^2 d\theta$. Note from the graph that the limits of integration are $\theta=\frac{\pi}{4}$ to $\theta=\frac{3\pi}{4}$. Using symmetry, the area is

$$4\cdot\frac{1}{2}\int_{\frac{\pi}{4}}^{\frac{\pi}{2}} -25\cos 2\theta\, d\theta = -25\sin 2\theta\Big|_{\frac{\pi}{4}}^{\frac{\pi}{2}} = -25\left(\sin\pi-\sin\frac{\pi}{2}\right)$$

$$=-25(0-1)=25.$$

(*Calculus for AP*®, pages 803–810; EU 3.4; LO 3.4D; EK 3.4D1; MPAC 2,3)

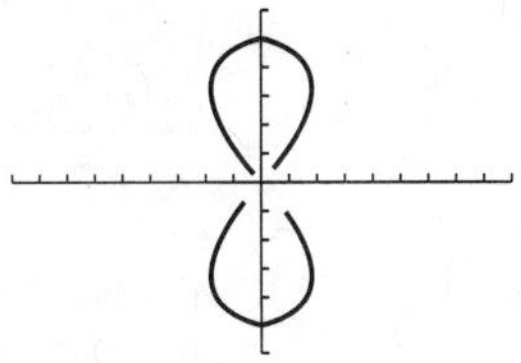

28. ANSWER: (B) This limit yields the indeterminate form $\frac{0}{0}$. Using L'Hôpital's Rule and the Fundamental Theorem of Calculus,

$$\lim_{x\to 0}\frac{\int_0^x \cos t\,dt}{2x} = \lim_{x\to 0}\frac{\frac{d}{dx}\left(\int_0^x \cos t\,dt\right)}{\frac{d}{dx}(2x)} = \lim_{x\to 0}\frac{\cos x}{2} = \frac{1}{2}.$$

(*Calculus for AP*®, pages 337–343; EU 1.1; LO 1.1C; EK 1.1C3; MPAC 2,3,5)

*29. ANSWER: (D) $f'(x)=\frac{2}{\sqrt{x}}$

Arc length $=\int_{x_1}^{x_2}\sqrt{1+\left(\frac{dy}{dx}\right)^2}\,dx = \int_2^5\sqrt{\left(1+\frac{4}{x}\right)}\,dx$

(*Calculus for AP*®, pages 532–537; EU 3.4; LO 3.4C; EK 3.4C2; MPAC 2,3,5)

30. ANSWER: (D)
$f(x)=\sin(3x) \Rightarrow f'(x)=3\cos(3x) \Rightarrow f''(x)=-3^2\sin(3x) \Rightarrow f'''(x)=-3^3\cos(3x)$
Continuing this cycle of four expressions, $f^{17}(x)=3^{17}\cos(3x)$.
(*Calculus for AP*®, pages 216–220; EU 2.1; LO 2.1C; EK 2.1C2,2.1C4; MPAC 2,3)

31. ANSWER: (C) $v(t)=\int(1+\sin t)dt = t-\cos t + C$. Using the initial condition, $v(0)=0-\cos 0 + C = 4 \Rightarrow C=5$.

$$v_{\text{ave}}=\frac{1}{6-0}\int_0^6 (t-\cos t+5)dt \approx 8.047$$

(*Calculus for AP*®, pages 490–494; EU 3.4; LO 3.4B; EK 3.4B1; MPAC 2,3)

32. ANSWER: (C) Total amount of oil $= \int_7^{21} P(t)dt$

$$= \int_7^{21} (53t^2 - 2t^3)dt \approx 61{,}511.$$

(*Calculus for AP*®, pages 450–454; EU 3.4; LO 3.4A; EK 3.4A2; MPAC 2,3)

33. ANSWER: (C) The statement in (C) illustrates the Mean Value Theorem, that there exists some value c between 0 and 4 such that $f'(c) = \dfrac{f(4) - f(0)}{4 - 0} = \dfrac{66 - 10}{4 - 0} = 14$. The conditions necessary for the Mean Value Theorem to be true are that the function must be continuous on a closed interval and differentiable on the corresponding open interval. [Note: Because there can be fluctuations in the function values between the selected points, neither of the statements in (B) or (D) is certain to be true.]
(*Calculus for AP*®, pages 308–311; EU 2.2,2.4; LO 2.2A,2.4A; EK 2.2A1,2.4A1; MPAC 2,4)

34. ANSWER: (D) The graphs of f and g intersect at $x = 0$ and $x = 2.10325$. Using the washer method,

$$\text{volume} = \pi \int_0^{2.10325} \left[f^2(x) - g^2(x) \right] dx \approx 143.569.$$

(*Calculus for AP*®, pages 525–528; EU 3.4; LO 3.4D; EK 3.4D2; MPAC 2,3,4)

*35. ANSWER: (C) The carrying capacity of a logistic model is the value of $\lim\limits_{t\to\infty} P(t) = \lim\limits_{t\to\infty} \dfrac{200}{1 + 4e^{-\frac{1}{2}t}} = \dfrac{200}{1+0} = 200$. The growth rate of a logistic equation is fastest when the population is half of the carrying capacity. Using calculator, $\dfrac{200}{1 + 4e^{-\frac{1}{2}t}} = 100 \Rightarrow t = 2.77259$.
(*Calculus for AP*®, pages 630–634; EU 3.5; LO 3.5B; EK 3.5B2; MPAC 1,2,3,4)

36. ANSWER: (B) $g(x)$ is the antiderivative of $f(x)$ and represents the net signed area between the graph of $f(x)$ and the horizontal axis, starting at $x = -2$. The triangle has area 2 and the semicircle has area $\dfrac{\pi}{2}$, so the net signed area is $-2 + \dfrac{\pi}{2}$.
(*Calculus for AP*®, pages 436–440; EU 3.2; LO 3.2C; EK 3.2C1,3.3B2; MPAC 2,3,4)

37. ANSWER: (B) Using properties of limits,

$$\lim_{x\to 1^-}\frac{d}{dx}[\ln(f(x))]=\lim_{x\to 1^-}\left[\frac{1}{f(x)}\cdot f'(x)\right]$$
$$=\frac{\lim_{x\to 1^-} f'(x)}{\lim_{x\to 1^-} f(x)}$$
$$=\frac{-1}{4}=-0.25.$$

(*Calculus for AP*®, pages 105–113; EU 1.1,2.1; LO 1.1A,2.1A; EK 1.1A1,2.1C4; MPAC 1,2,3,4)

*38. ANSWER: (A) $\frac{dx}{dt}=\frac{5\cdot 2}{2\sqrt{2t+1}}=\frac{5}{\sqrt{2t+1}}$ and $\frac{dy}{dt}=\frac{1}{2}e^{\frac{1}{2}t}$

$$\text{Average speed }=\frac{1}{t_2-t_1}\int_{t_1}^{t_2}\sqrt{\left(\frac{dx}{dt}\right)^2+\left(\frac{dy}{dt}\right)^2}\,dt$$
$$=\frac{1}{5}\int_0^5\sqrt{\left(\frac{5}{\sqrt{2t+1}}\right)^2+\left(\frac{1}{2}e^{\frac{1}{2}t}\right)^2}\,dt$$
$$=\frac{1}{5}\int_0^5\sqrt{\frac{25}{2t+1}+\frac{1}{4}e^t}\,dt=3.531.$$

(*Calculus for AP*®, pages 777–782, 490–494; EU 2.3; LO 2.3C; EK 2.3C4; MPAC 2,3)

39. ANSWER: (C) $f(x)$ contains (1.2, 1.152) ⇒ $g(x)$ contains (1.152, 1.2).

$$\frac{d}{dx}[g(x)]=\frac{1}{f'(g(x))}$$
$$=\frac{1}{4g(x)-3(g(x))^2}\Rightarrow\frac{d}{dx}[g(1.152)]$$
$$=\frac{1}{f'[g(1.152)]}$$
$$=\frac{1}{4(1.2)-3(1.2)^2}$$
$$=2.083$$

(*Calculus for AP*®, pages 247–248; 2.1; LO 2.1C; EK 2.1C6; MPAC 2,3)

40. ANSWER: (A) Let x equal the length of one edge. The area of one equilateral triangle with side x is

$A=x^2\frac{\sqrt{3}}{4}\Rightarrow$ surface area $S=4A=x^2\sqrt{3}$. Differentiating,

$$\frac{dS}{dt}=2\sqrt{3}x\frac{dx}{dt}\Rightarrow\left.\frac{dS}{dt}\right|_{x=12}=2\sqrt{3}\cdot 12\cdot 2=48\sqrt{3}\approx 83.138\text{ cm}^2/\text{min}.$$

(*Calculus for AP*®, pages 274–279; EU 2.3; LO 2.3C; EK 2.3C2; MPAC 2,3,4)

41. ANSWER: (C) The given expression represents the average value of $f(x)$ on $0 \le x \le 4$. The area under $f(x)$ is therefore $\int_0^4 f(x)dx = 4 \cdot 2 = 8$. The regions in (A) and (D) are all larger than 8, and the region in (B) has net signed area 0. The region in (C) could have area 8, with the apparent symmetry of the curve to the point (2, 2).
(*Calculus for AP*®, pages 490–494; EU 3.4; LO 3.4B; EK 3.4B1; MPAC 2,4,5)

42. ANSWER: (A) Using the Quotient Rule and Chain Rule,
$h'(x) = \dfrac{x^2 \cdot f'[g(x)] \cdot g'(x) - f[g(x)] \cdot 2x}{x^4}$. Therefore,

$$h'(3) = \frac{3^2 \cdot f'[g(3)] \cdot g'(3) - f[g(3)] \cdot 2 \cdot 3}{3^4}$$

$$= \frac{9 \cdot 8 \cdot (-2) - 4 \cdot 2 \cdot 3}{81} = -\frac{168}{81} = -\frac{56}{27}.$$

(*Calculus for AP*®, pages 207–210, 227–233; EU 2.1; LO 2.1C; EK 2.1C3,2.1C4; MPAC 2,3,4)

43. ANSWER: (D) The particle comes to rest when $v(t) = e^{\sin t} - 2 = 0 \Rightarrow t = 0.76585$. The position of the particle is

$$s(t) = 5 + \int_0^t v(t)dt \Rightarrow s(0.76585) = 5 + \int_0^{0.76585} (e^{\sin t} - 2)dt = 4.594.$$

(*Calculus for AP*®, pages 436–440; EU 2.3; LO 2.3C; EK 2.3C1; MPAC 2,3)

44. ANSWER: (B) Consider each choice:
(A) Since $f'(x)$ changes from positive to negative at $x = 0$, $f(x)$ has a relative maximum at $x = 0$. But the area from 0 to 4 is a larger negative number than the positive region from 4 to 5, so $x = 0$ is the location of the absolute maximum (true).
(B) $f(x)$ is continuous and $\lim_{x \to -2^-} f'(x) = \lim_{x \to -2^+} f'(x) = \infty$. Since these limits have the same sign and are infinitely large, $f(x)$ has a vertical tangent at $x = -2$ (false).
(C) $f'(x)$ is decreasing at $x = 1$, so $f''(1) < 0 \Rightarrow f(x)$ is concave down at $x = 1$ (true).
(D) $f(x)$ changes from decreasing to increasing at $x = 3$, so $f''(x)$ changes from negative to positive at $x = 3$. Hence $f(x)$ has an inflection point at $x = 3$ (true).
Choice (B) is the only false statement.
(*Calculus for AP*®, pages 316–327; EU 2.2; LO 2.2A; EK 2.2A1; MPAC 2,4)

45. ANSWER: (C) Using the midpoint Riemann sum,

$$\int_a^b f(x)\,dx \approx \frac{b-a}{n}\left(y_{m_1} + y_{m_2} + \cdots + y_{m_n}\right) = \frac{10-4}{3}(29+40+51)$$
$$= 2(120) = 240.$$

(*Calculus for AP*®, pages 395–410, 418–420; EU 3.2; LO 3.2B; EK 3.2B2; MPAC 2,3,4)

FREE-RESPONSE QUESTIONS

1. Water flows into two identical tanks during a 24-hour period at rates given by the models below. Both $P(t)$ and $Q(t)$ are measured in gallons per hour for $0 \le t \le 24$ hours, and both tanks are empty at time $t = 0$.
   Tank 1: The graph of $P(t)$ consists of the line segments indicated in the figure.
   Tank 2: $Q(t) = 18\cos(0.25t + 4.5) \cdot \sin(0.15t + 2.2) + 35$
   (a) What is the value of $P'(7)$? What is the value of $Q'(7)$? Give units for both answers.
   (b) How much water is in Tank 1 after 24 hours? Justify your answer.
   (c) What is the average rate at which water flows into Tank 2 for the entire 24-hour period? Justify your answer.
   (d) During the 24-hour period, is there ever a time other than $t = 0$ when the amount of water in the two tanks is the same? If yes, find all such values of t. If no, explain why not.

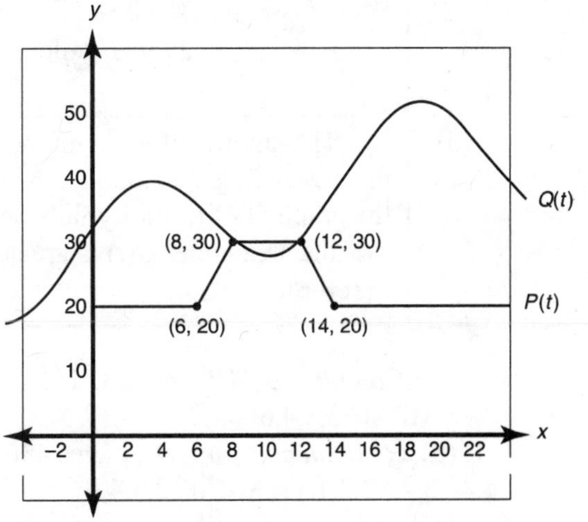

	Solution	Possible points
(a)	$P'(7)=\frac{30-20}{8-6}=5; Q'(7)=-2.699$, using the derivative feature of the calculator. Both are measured in gallons per hour^2.	$3:\begin{cases}1: P'(7)\\1: Q'(7)\\1: \text{units}\end{cases}$
(b)	The amount of water is represented by the accumulated area under $P(t)$. The region consists of a rectangle and a trapezoid. $V_1=20\cdot 24+\frac{1}{2}\cdot 10(8+4)=480+60=540$ gallons	$2:\begin{cases}1: \text{area interpretation}\\1: \text{answer}\end{cases}$
(c)	Average rate $=\frac{1}{24-0}\int_0^{24} Q(t)dt$ $=$ 39.087 gallons per hour	$3:\begin{cases}1: \text{constant and limits}\\1: \text{integrand}\\1: \text{answer}\end{cases}$
(d)	No. The amount of water in the tanks is represented by the accumulated area under each graph. Even though the graph of $Q(t)$ briefly falls below the graph of $P(t)$,the area under $Q(t)$ is greater than the area under $P(t)$ for $0<t\le 24$.	1: answer with reason

1. (a) (*Calculus for AP*®, page 171; EU 2.1,2.2; LO2.1A,2.1B,2.2A; EK 2.1A5,2.1B1,2.2A2; MPAC 2,3,4,6)
1. (b), (c) (*Calculus for AP*®, pages 436–440, 490–494; EU 3.4,2.1; LO3.4A,2.1A; EK 3.4A2,2.1A1; MPAC 2,3,4,6)
1. (d) (*Calculus for AP*®, pages 450–454; EU 3.4; LO 3.4A; EK3.4A2; MPAC 2,3,4,6)

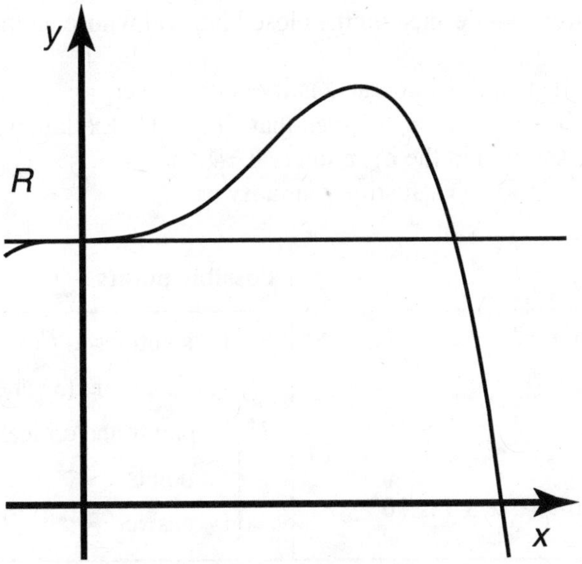

2. Let ***R*** be the region enclosed by the graph of $f(x) = -x^4 + 2.3x^3 + 5$ and the horizontal line $y = 5$, as shown in the figure above.
   (a) Find the volume of the solid generated when ***R*** is rotated about the line $y = -3$.
   (b) Region ***R*** is the base of a solid. For this solid, each cross section perpendicular to the x-axis is a rectangle whose height is twice as long as the length in ***R***. Find the volume of the solid.
   (c) The vertical line $x = h$ divides region ***R*** into two regions with equal areas. Write, but do not solve, an equation involving integral expressions whose solution gives the value h.

	Solution	**Possible points**
(a)	Intersection: $f(x) = 5 \Rightarrow x = 0, 2.3$ $\text{Volume} = \pi \int_0^{2.3} \left[(f(x)+3)^2 - (5+3)^2 \right] dx = 184.271$	$4: \begin{cases} 2: \text{integrand} \\ 1: \text{limits} \\ 1: \text{answer} \end{cases}$
(b)	$\text{Volume} = \int_0^{2.3} 2(f(x)-5)^2 dx = 14.295$ (or 14.294)	$3: \begin{cases} 2: \text{integrand} \\ 1: \text{answer} \end{cases}$
(c)	$\int_0^h (f(x)-5)\,dx = \int_h^{2.3} (f(x)-5)\,dx$	$2: \begin{cases} 1: \text{area of one region} \\ 1: \text{equation} \end{cases}$

2. (a) (*Calculus for AP®*, pages 525–528; EU 3.4; LO 3.4D; EK3.4D1; MPAC 2,3,4)
2. (b) (*Calculus for AP®*, pages 518–522; EU 3.4; LO 3.4D; EK3.4D2; MPAC 2,3,4)
2. (c) (*Calculus for AP®*, pages 477–486; EU 3.4; LO 3.4D; EK3.4D1; MPAC 2,3,4)

3. Consider the function $f(x) = 4x^3 - 48x + 44$ defined on the closed interval whose endpoints are $(-4, -20)$ and $(4, 108)$.
   (a) Find the absolute maximum of $f(x)$ on this interval. Justify your answer.
   (b) Find all values of x in the open interval $-4 < x < 4$ such that $f'(x) = 16$. Explain why this equation must have at least one solution in the open interval $-4 < x < 4$.
   (c) Determine the point(s) of inflection for $f(x)$. Justify your answer.

	Solution	Possible points
(a	$f'(x) = 12x^2 - 48 = 0 \Rightarrow x^2 = 4 \Rightarrow x = \pm 2$ $f(-4) = -20$ $f(-2) = -32 + 96 + 44 = 108$ $f(2) = 32 - 96 + 44 = -20$ $f(4) = 108$ The absolute maximum of $f(x)$ on $-4 \le x \le 4$ is 108	$3: \begin{cases} 1: \text{ solutions to } f'(x) = 0 \\ 1: \text{ values of } f(x) \text{ at end points and critical points} \\ 1: \text{ answer} \end{cases}$
(b	$12x^2 - 48 = 16 \Rightarrow 12x^2 = 64 \Rightarrow x^2 = \frac{64}{12} \Rightarrow x = \pm\frac{4}{\sqrt{3}}$ $m_{sec} = \frac{108 + 20}{4 + 4} = \frac{128}{8} = 16$ using $(-4, -20)$ and $(4, 108)$ The Mean Value Theorem guarantees that there is at least one value of x in the open interval $-4 < x < 4$ for which the tangent line to $f(x)$ is parallel to the secant line through $(-4, -20)$ and $(4, 108)$.	$3: \begin{cases} 1: \text{ solutions to } f'(x) = 16 \\ 1: m_{sec} = 16 \\ 1: \text{ explanation with MVT} \end{cases}$
(c	$f(x) = 12x^2 - 48$ $f''(x) = 24x = 0$ $x = 0$ 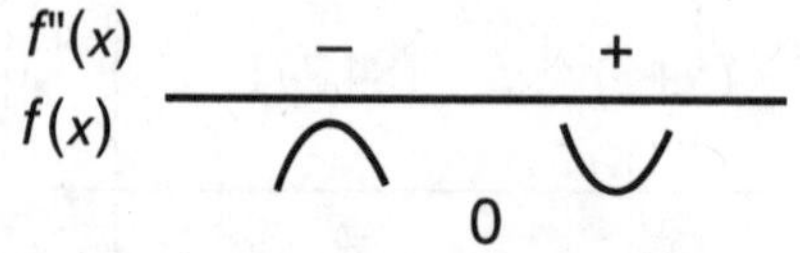 Since $f''(x)$ changes signs at $x = 0$, and $f(0) = 44$, then $f(x)$ has a point of inflection of $(0, 44)$. (Note: While sign charts can be used to assist with determining the solution, they are not sufficient for justifications. Students are required to write a justification explaining the information found in the sign chart.)	$3: \begin{cases} 1: \text{ Considers } f''(x) = 0 \\ 2: \text{ Answer with justification} \end{cases}$

3. (a) (*Calculus for AP*®, pages 292–293; EU 2.2,2.3; LO 2.2A,2.3C; EK 2.2A1,2.3C3; MPAC 2,3)
3. (b) (*Calculus for AP*®, pages 308–311; EU 2.4; LO 2.4A; EK2.4A1; MPAC 2,3,6)
3. (c) (*Calculus for AP*®, page 324; EU 2.2; LO 2.2A; EK2.2A1; MPAC 2,3)

*4. A particle moves in the xy-plane with position for all real values of t given by the parametric equations $x(t) = 1 - t^3$ and $y(t) = t^2 - 4$.
(a) Give the coordinates of the velocity vector for any time t.
(b) Is the particle moving to the left or right when $t = -1$? Is the particle moving up or down when $t = -1$? Give a reason for each answer.
(c) What is the slope of the path of the particle when $t = 0.5$?
(d) How fast is the particle moving when its horizontal position is $x(t) = -7$?
(e) Give the coordinates of the acceleration vector when the particle is at rest.

	Solution	Possible points
(a)	$x'(t) = -3t^2$ and $y'(t) = 2t$ The velocity vector is $(-3t^2, 2t)$.	1: both coordinates
(b)	The particle is moving left because $x'(-1) = -3 < 0$. The particle is moving down because $y'(-1) = -2 < 0$.	$2: \begin{cases} 1: \text{answer with reason for right/left} \\ 1: \text{answer with reason for up/down} \end{cases}$
(c)	$\text{Slope} = \frac{dy}{dx} = \frac{y'(t)}{x'(t)} \Rightarrow \left.\frac{dy}{dx}\right\|_{t=0.5} = \frac{2(0.5)}{-3(0.5)^2} = \frac{1}{-0.75} = -\frac{4}{3}$ When $t = 0.5$, the slope of the path of the particle is $-\frac{4}{3}$.	$2: \begin{cases} 1: \frac{dy}{dx} \\ 1: \text{answer} \end{cases}$
(d)	$x(t) = -7 \Rightarrow 1 - t^3 = -7 \Rightarrow t^3 = 8 \Rightarrow t = 2$ Speed $= \sqrt{(x'(t))^2 + (y'(t))^2}$, so the speed at $t = 2$ is $\sqrt{(-12)^2 + (4)^2} = \sqrt{144 + 16} = \sqrt{160} = 4\sqrt{10}$. When $x(t) = -7$, the speed of the particle is $=4\sqrt{10}$.	$2: \begin{cases} 1: t \text{ when } x = -7 \\ 1: \text{answer} \end{cases}$
(e)	The particle is at rest when both coordinates of the velocity vector are zero. $t = 0$ is the only solution to both $-3t^2 = 0$ and $2t = 0$. The acceleration vector is $(x''(0), y''(0)) = (-6(0), 2) = (0, 2)$.	$2: \begin{cases} 1: t \text{ when at rest} \\ 1: \text{answer} \end{cases}$

4. (a), (b), (c), (d), (e) (*Calculus for AP*®, pages 769–782; EU 2.1,2.3; LO 2.1C,2.3C; EK 2.1C7,2.3C4; MPAC 2,3)

5. Let $f(x)$ be the function which is the solution to the differential equation $\frac{dy}{dx} = \frac{y}{1+x^2}$, with initial condition $f(0) = 1$.

(a) Fill in the table below with values $\frac{dy}{dx}$ for the 15 ordered pairs (x, y) indicated and use the values to sketch a slope field for $\frac{dy}{dx}$ on the axes provided.

*(b). Using Euler's method starting at $x_0 = 0$ with step size $\Delta x = \frac{1}{2}$, estimate the value of $f(1)$.

(c) Find the particular solution $f(x)$.

	Solution	Possible points
(a)	(see table and slope field below)	$2: \begin{cases} 1: \text{values of } \frac{dy}{dx} \\ 1: \text{slopefield sketch} \end{cases}$

y \ x	−2	−1	0	1	2
2	$\frac{2}{5}$	1	2	1	$\frac{2}{5}$
1	$\frac{1}{5}$	$\frac{1}{2}$	1	$\frac{2}{5}$	$\frac{1}{5}$
0	0	0	0	0	0

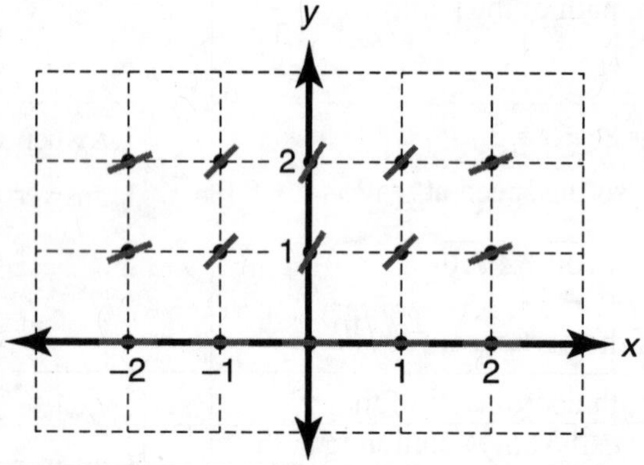

	Solution	Possible points
(b)	The formula for Euler's method is $y_{n+1} \approx y_n + \left.\frac{dy}{dx}\right\|_{(x_n, y_n)} \cdot \Delta x$ $x_0 = 0 \qquad y_0 = 1$ $\left.\frac{dy}{dx}\right\|_{(0,1)} = \frac{1}{1+0} = 1$ $x_1 = \frac{1}{2} \qquad y_1 = 1 + 1 \cdot \frac{1}{2} = \frac{3}{2}$ $\left.\frac{dy}{dx}\right\|_{\left(\frac{1}{2},\frac{3}{2}\right)} = \frac{\frac{3}{2}}{1+\left(\frac{1}{2}\right)^2} = \frac{\frac{3}{2}}{\frac{5}{4}} = \frac{3}{2} \cdot \frac{4}{5} = \frac{6}{5}$ $x_2 = 1 \qquad y_2 = \frac{3}{2} + \frac{6}{5} \cdot \frac{1}{2} = \frac{3}{2} + \frac{3}{5} = \frac{21}{10} = 2.1$ Therefore, $f(1) \approx 2.1$	$2: \begin{cases} 1: \text{Euler's method or table} \\ 1: \text{answer} \end{cases}$
(c)	Separating variables, $\int \frac{dy}{y} = \int \frac{dx}{1+x^2} \Rightarrow$ $\ln\|y\| = \tan^{-1} x + C_1 \Rightarrow y = e^{\tan^{-1} x + C_1} \Rightarrow y = Ce^{\tan^{-1} x}$. Using (0, 1), $1 = Ce^{\tan^{-1}(0)} \Rightarrow 1 = Ce^0 \Rightarrow C = 1.$ Therefore $f(x) = e^{\tan^{-1} x}$.	$5: \begin{cases} 1: \text{separates variables} \\ 1: \text{antiderivative with respect to } y \\ 1: \text{antiderivative with respect to } x \\ 1: \text{includes constant of integration} \\ 1: \text{solves for } f(x) \text{ using initial condition} \end{cases}$

5. (a), (b) (*Calculus for AP*®, pages 606–615; EU 2.3; LO 2.3F; EK2.3F1,2.3F2; MPAC 2,3)
5. (c) (*Calculus for AP*®, pages 618–624; EU 3.5; LO 3.5A; EK3.5A2; MPAC 2,3)

*6. Let $y(x)=3x+\frac{9}{4}x^2+\frac{27}{18}x^3+\cdots=\sum_{k=1}^{\infty}\frac{3^k x^k}{k\cdot k!}$.

(a) Find all values of x for which $y(x)$ converges.

(b) Use the first three terms of $y'(x)$ to estimate the value of $y'(0.01)$.

(c) Show that $y(x)$ is a solution to the differential equation $x \cdot y'(x) = e^{3x} - 1$.

	Solution	Possible points
(a)	Using the Ratio Test for Absolute Convergence, $\lim_{k\to\infty}\left\lvert\frac{\frac{3^{k+1}x^{k+1}}{(k+1)(k+1)!}}{\frac{3^k x^k}{k\cdot k!}}\right\rvert<1\Rightarrow$ $\lim_{k\to\infty}\left\lvert\frac{3^{k+1}x^{k+1}}{(k+1)(k+1)!}\cdot\frac{k\cdot k!}{3^k x^k}\right\rvert<1\Rightarrow$ $\lim_{k\to\infty}\left\lvert\frac{3x}{k+1}\right\rvert<1\Rightarrow 0<1$ which is true for all x. Therefore, the series converges for all real numbers.	$2:\begin{cases}1:\text{ use of RTAC}\\1:\text{ answer}\end{cases}$
(b)	$y'(x)=3+\frac{9}{2}x+\frac{27}{6}x^2+\cdots$ $y'(0.01)\approx 3+\frac{9}{2}(0.01)+\frac{9}{2}(0.0001)$ $=3+0.045+0.00045=3.04545$ $y'(0.01)\approx 3.045$	$2:\begin{cases}1: y'(x)\\1:\text{ answer}\end{cases}$
(c)	$y(x)=3x+\frac{9}{4}x^2+\frac{27}{18}x^3+\cdots=\sum_{k=1}^{\infty}\frac{3^k x^k}{k\cdot k!}\Rightarrow$ $y'(x)=3+\frac{9}{2}x+\frac{27}{6}x^2+\cdots=\sum_{k=1}^{\infty}\frac{k\cdot 3^k x^{k-1}}{k\cdot k!}\Rightarrow$ $x\cdot y'(x)=3x+\frac{9}{2}x^2+\frac{27}{6}x^3+\cdots=\sum_{k=1}^{\infty}\frac{3^k x^k}{k!}$ use of series for e^x series for $e^x=\sum_{k=0}^{\infty}\frac{x^k}{k!}$, $e^{3x}=\sum_{k=0}^{\infty}\frac{(3x)^k}{k!}=1+3x+\frac{(3x)^2}{2!}+\frac{(3x)^3}{3!}+\cdots$ Therefore, $e^{3x}-1=3x+\frac{9}{2!}x^2+\frac{27}{3!}x^3+\cdots=\sum_{k=1}^{\infty}\frac{3^k x^k}{k!}$ Hence $x - y'(x) = e^{3x} - 1$, so $y(x)$ is a solution to the given differential equation.	$5:\begin{cases}1:\text{series for } y'(x)\\1:\text{series for } x\cdot y'(x)\\1:\text{use of series for } e^x\\1:\text{series for } e^{3x}-1\\1:\text{conclusion}\end{cases}$

6. (a) (*Calculus for AP®*, pages 715–717; EU 4.2; LO 4.2C; EK4.2C1,4.2C2; MPAC 2,3,5)
6. (b) (*Calculus for AP®*, pages 721–724; EU 4.2; LO 4.2A; EK4.2A2; MPAC 2,3)
6. (c) (*Calculus for AP®*, pages 728–737; EU 4.2;LO 4.2B; EK 4.2B2; MPAC 2,3)

CALCULUS AB AND BC SCORING CHART

SECTION I: MULTIPLE-CHOICE QUESTIONS

______ × 1.2 = ______
correct (out of 45)   do not round (out of 54)

SECTION II: FREE-RESPONSE QUESTIONS

Question 1	Score out of 9 points	=	______
Question 2	Score out of 9 points	=	______
Question 3	Score out of 9 points	=	______
Question 4	Score out of 9 points	=	______
Question 5	Score out of 9 points	=	______
Question 6	Score out of 9 points	=	______
	Sum for Section II	=	(out of 54)

Composite Score

Section I total	=
Section II total	=
Composite score	= ______ (out of 108)

Grade Conversion Chart*

Composite score range	AP® exam grade
68–108	5
52–67	4
39–51	3
27–38	2
0–26	1

***Note:** The ranges listed above are only approximate. Each year the ranges for the actual AP® exam are somewhat different. The cutoffs are established after the exams are given to over 200,000 students and are based on the difficulty level of the exam each year.